AMERICAN PAINTINGS *in the Museum of Fine Arts, Boston*

Distributed by New York Graphic Society · Greenwich, Connecticut

American Paintings

in the

Museum of Fine Arts, Boston

Volume I · Text

Museum of Fine Arts : Boston, Massachusetts

INTRODUCTION

For the development of the Museum of Fine Arts, the first acquisition was prophetic. A few months after the charter of the Museum was granted, February 4, 1870, Mrs. Samuel Hooper and Miss Alice Hooper of Boston offered to the trustees the gift of *Elijah in the Desert* by Washington Allston. Not only was this first possession a painting from the hand of an American artist, it was also a superb work. The collection of American paintings rising from this cornerstone has become great and in some respects is unsurpassed. It abounds in major works, and this first gift has been multiplied many hundred fold by other generous donors, most of them Bostonians, dedicated like their prototypes to building what has become a testimony to American genius and a mirror of American life.

Six years later, on July 4, 1876 when the infant Boston Museum opened the doors of its first permanent home in Copley Square, the American paintings on view were conspicuous, thanks to enviable circumstances. The Boston Athenaeum, forerunner and "godparent" of the Museum of Fine Arts, and the City of Boston placed on deposit their most cherished works of art—important paintings by Trumbull, West and Neagle, and portraits of statesmen, patriots and soldiers, founders of the Republic prominent in Boston's past, by Copley, Stuart and William Page. This galaxy of American classics which included the best known of all American paintings, the Athenaeum portraits by Stuart of George and Martha Washington, joined the Allston gift and became the nucleus of the future collection.

Like the nucleus itself, it was inevitable that the Boston collection should come to reflect with lustre the activity of those artists who for one hundred and fifty years made Boston one of the principal centers of painting in the colonies and the young Republic. So the Boston Museum possesses notable groups of paintings by most of the early artists active in the city and known by name—Smibert, Badger, Greenwood, Blackburn, and Feke, an unexampled series of portraits by Copley, Stuart, and Harding, and a unique assemblage of paintings by Allston.

Catalogued here are some sixty works by Copley, including pastels and oil studies of both his American and English periods, and about fifty portraits from the hand of Stuart. Such an array by our two most famous portrait painters is not to be found elsewhere. There are nine paintings by Smibert, eight by Blackburn, fourteen by Harding who alone in Boston rivaled Stuart in popularity, and fifteen works by Allston. One cannot claim that this extraordinary treasure of early American paintings has come about through love of art alone. As in the case of the Museum's unparalleled collections of New England furniture, embroideries and silver, family pride, a long-established regard for local history and culture and a belief in tradition have stirred the inheritors of these artistic manifestations to insure their preservation. The practice has continued for nearly a hundred years, so that the Museum of Fine Arts has become a pantheon of early American art—with an unmistakable New England accent.

Nor with few exceptions have Bostonians overlooked the achievement of New England artists of later generations. From the beginning, the trustees and staff were determined to build a museum of universal significance, a museum of world art. Nevertheless, pride in American accomplishment and especially that of New England is conspicuous among many thousands of acquisitions. Thus the Museum commenced early to collect the works of Winslow Homer: *The Fog Warning* was purchased in 1894; *All's Well* in 1899. Today there are eight paintings by Homer in the Museum in addition to a brilliant collection of forty-one watercolors and fifteen drawings. William Morris Hunt, who aside from achieving wide acclaim as a painter in his lifetime, opened American eyes to the values of contemporary French art, is represented by no less than sixty-five studies and completed paintings, as well as numerous drawings. John La Farge, the New Yorker, was thrust upon the Boston scene by the artistic drive of H. H. Richardson who engaged him to enrich his Trinity Church with murals. Local enthusiasts responded to La Farge's complex, spiritual art, so that the eleven examples in the Museum are all gifts of Boston collectors. John Singer Sargent was an international figure from the start. Yet he could claim Boston as his "spiritual home," and he held the trustees enthralled. In addition to a dazzling array of forty-five watercolors bought in one package in 1912, the trustees over the years acquired by gift or purchase twenty-one paintings, portraits, landscapes, and studies. Their total devotion was demonstrated by the commission to decorate with murals the Rotunda in 1916, and the Huntington Avenue staircase in 1921.

This is not to say that leading artists from "west of Coolidge Corner" were ignored. Trumbull had his early admirers; Sully found favor in Boston before the middle of the 19th century and is represented by a masterpiece, *The Passage of the Delaware*. The popularity of Inness (who was not without his brief New England period) is proven by the bequests of fifteen paintings, and Vedder was a favorite in influential circles.

Some less famous New England artists of the previous generation began to find representation while the Museum was still young. Thus, among those who have attracted particular attention in recent years are others who have long figured in the collection; for example, the genre painter, Henry Sargent; the anatomist, Dr. William Rimmer; and the marine painter, Robert Salmon. Other artists like Fitz Hugh Lane, the poet of harbor and quiet inlet, had to await the enthusiastic pursuit of Maxim Karolik.

French impressionism early found favor in Boston, so it was a natural consequence that the Boston practitioners of the style, Edmund Tarbell and Frank W. Benson, should have been welcomed to the collection. Moreover, with their contemporary, James Paxton, the follower of Gérôme, they were the prestigious members of the Museum School faculty for many years, and with the addition of Joseph DeCamp, constituted the "Boston School." Eighteen works represent the group.

Preoccupied with local lights, Boston showed its provincial side, its complacency, by ignoring some of America's foremost artists of the turn of the century whose activity was centered elsewhere. To be sure, both Whistler and Cassatt were represented by 1910, but it was not until 1935 that the first important Eakins was acquired and a decade later that Ryder was adequately represented. Likewise, The Eight found no response in Boston during their years of rebellion against the academy. Only in 1932 did the trustees purchase the first work of the group, a Henri, and then began to make up for lost time by acquiring paintings by all of its members.

Many lovers of painting have left their imprint upon this old collection. But the only benefactor of the Museum who was also a serious and systematic collector of American painting was not an American by birth, but a naturalized Russian, Maxim Karolik. The effect of his activity was prodigious; his gift in 1949 of the M. & M. Karolik collection of 233 pictures, his subsequent gifts and ultimate bequest of 101 pictures, a total of 334 works, enriched the collection immensely, and added new facets of American painting impossible for the department to have acquired unaided and brought balance to a collection overweighted by the eighteenth century. Animated by his conviction that American painting from the time of Stuart to the advent of Winslow Homer was neglected, if not virtually unknown, he set about to discover and celebrate this "barren" period of the nineteenth century. Both obscure and once famous artists fell within his ken. The Hudson River School and related minor landscape painters of New England came into focus; portrait, still life and genre painters, forgotten artists of the West, as well as those whose names, like Bierstadt, were at that time better known than their works. Above all, he was proud of contributing materially to restoring the reputation of Martin Johnson Heade, painter of salt marsh and sunset, and of Fitz Hugh Lane whose vision of the coastal scene from Maine to Boston has deepened our pride in American poetic capacity. The former is represented by thirty paintings, the latter by thirteen. Maxim Karolik's feeling for folk painting provided the Museum with its first works of this genre, including some notable examples. The completion of the original collection did not quiet his zeal. He broke out of the framework of 1815–1865 and bought paintings of the last quarter of the century, notably a fine group of still lifes by John Frederick Peto. To the original representation of folk paintings, he added by adroit purchase directly from the New England heirs, two marvelous group portraits of the 1840's, "as American as apple pie," *The Moore Family* by Erastus Salisbury Field and *The Atwood Family* by Henry Darby.

This phenomenal activity, this "rediscovery" of the middle decades of the nineteenth century, continued for some twenty years. Maxim Karolik's pursuit was unremitting. It demanded much time and effort from the Department of Paintings, as well as from the Director, for from the beginning the Karolik acquisitions were made in close collaboration with the Museum. The will to develop a broad representation of the manifold styles and new directions of painting in the twentieth century, to bring the collection up to date was never relaxed during this time. The program to strengthen the representation of The Eight, for example, has continued to the present with special emphasis on Maurice Prendergast, the only Boston member of the group. Fine examples of the realists and expressionists of the succeeding generation have also been acquired. To a distinguished group of works by George Bellows, including the well-known *Emma and her Children*, there have been added in more recent years brilliant paintings by Hopper, Sheeler, Avery, Knaths, Marin, Feininger and a collage by Arthur Dove. It is well to remember that this collecting program has been pursued with constant reference to the concomitant acquisition of drawings and watercolors by the same artists and others, such as Charles Burchfield, Mark Tobey and Andrew Wyeth, works that are the responsibility of the Department of Prints and Drawings.

In most recent years, the collection has been enriched with works by artists of fantasy such as Lee Gatch, Loren MacIver, and Jan Cox, and some of the leading masters of pure abstraction: Kline, Okada, Albers and Morris Louis. Conspicuous among these are the gifts of a certain few trustees and local collectors. Thus, the admirable example of the first friends of the Museum finds followers today. But one should hope that there will be a widening and an acceleration of the practice, that Boston collectors in the Museum's second century will wish to match in numbers, in generosity, and in devotion those who in the past have made the American collection great by sharing their love of painting with the public.

PERRY TOWNSEND RATHBONE
Director,
Museum of Fine Arts

ACKNOWLEDGMENTS

The publication of this catalogue would never have been possible without the years of work devoted to its preparation by Barbara Neville Parker who was Assistant Curator in charge of American Paintings from 1927 to 1956. At the time of her retirement, the manuscript of the catalogue was in an almost completed form. It was then a matter of deep regret that while the great importance of her contribution was recognized, the Museum did not have the funds for its publication. Only since the Ford Foundation seven years ago recognized the egregious lack of definitive scholarly catalogues of American public collections and made funds available to museums on a matching basis to help supply a long-standing need, was it possible to take up this project again and contemplate its publication.

In the intervening years, the collection has been enormously expanded with approximately three hundred paintings being added by gift, purchase and bequest. The cataloguing of these additional works was undertaken by Miss Arianwen Howard, who also brought Mrs. Parker's catalogue entries up to date, including new references and information that had come to light in the ten years since her retirement. Miss Howard was assisted by Miss Sarah Bullock, Miss Elizabeth Gwin, and Miss Laura Luckey. Thomas N. Maytham, formerly Assistant Curator of the Department of Paintings, supervised and gave guidance throughout the two years during which the catalogue was prepared. He read and corrected the entire manuscript and took responsibility in many questions of presentation, attribution and dating. Mrs. Angelica Rudenstine, formerly Editor of Publications, helped to establish the format for the catalogue, edited the entire text, prepared the manuscript for the printer and saw it through all the stages of proof.

Innumerable people have, over the years, given valuable help in the preparation of this catalogue, and it is almost impossible to thank all of them individually. Within the Museum itself, special thanks are due to Adolph Cavallo, Curator of Textiles, and his staff for help in identification and dating of costumes; to Miss Marjorie Childs and her staff in the Museum Library for help with bibliographical problems; to Francis Dolloff, Conservator of Prints and Drawings, who helped in the identification of media. The late Maxim Karolik gave tirelessly of his time, searching for new material, helping with research, and giving both of his knowledge and enthusiasm.

Outside the Museum a special word of thanks is due to Professor Jules Prown, Curator of the Garvan and Related Collections, Yale University Art Gallery. Prior to the publication of his definitive work on John Singleton Copley, Professor Prown made available to us his extensive specialized knowledge of his sixty-one Copleys in the Museum's collection. Robert and Morton Vose of the Vose Galleries, and Charles D. Childs of Boston have, over a period of many years, given invaluable assistance to the authors of this catalogue. They have put all of the records of their firms at our disposal, investigated the histories of paintings which passed through their hands, and made untold contributions to the documentation of many of the paintings published here.

Innumerable colleagues in other institutions, independent scholars, collectors, dealers, and librarians, have helped to make this catalogue what it is. The list of individuals and institutions who have answered enquiries of all kinds is so long that it would be impractical to publish it here. One can only say that without the patient and generous cooperation of these people, the catalogue would have been impossible to produce.

Finally, we wish to express our gratitude to the Ford Foundation and specifically to its Program in the Arts and Humanities for the offer of financial aid that has reanimated this project and which has helped materially to bring it to fruition.

PERRY TOWNSEND RATHBONE

EXPLANATIONS

THE M. AND M. KAROLIK COLLECTION: Reference to the two hundred and thirty-three paintings which were published in the *M. and M. Karolik Collection of American Paintings, 1815–1865*, Cambridge, Mass., 1949, has been limited to an abbreviated entry form. This includes the name of the artist and his dates, the title of the picture, its medium and measurements, a signature, date or inscription (if any), the Museum Accession number, and the reference in the 1949 catalogue. No biography or other discussion has been included in these entries, except in the case of a change of attribution or title. In this case, the reasons for such a change are given in full. The 1949 catalogue is referred to as: *Karolik Catalogue, 1949*.

LOANS: Paintings on long term loan to the Museum have been included with the agreement of the lenders. In most cases, the information contained in the loan entries is of a basic nature.

ARRANGEMENT: The catalogue is arranged alphabetically by artist. The paintings within an artist's *oeuvre* are arranged chronologically, with undatable works at the end, followed by attributed works. Copies after, of any date, come last. The volume of plates has been arranged chronologically with necessary departures from a strict sequence of years in order to gather together without interruption the illustrations of one artist's work. Thus, the volume presents an historical and harmonious stylistic panorama of American painting from the late 17th century to the middle of the 20th century.

RIGHT AND LEFT: These terms indicate the spectator's right and left, unless the context clearly implies the contrary.

COSTUME: Owing to the problems involved in the precise dating of costume the evidence provided by the dress of the sitters has not been used as conclusive in the dating of pictures. It is true to say, however, that the general evidence provided by dress has been taken into consideration in the approximate dating of many of the otherwise undated works. In instances where costumes have provided more specifically datable information, this is indicated in the entry.

MEASUREMENTS: Height precedes width in all cases. Measurements are given to the nearest quarter inch.

ABBREVIATIONS: The Museum of Fine Arts, Boston has been abbreviated in all instances to: Boston, MFA. Names of museums have in many instances been abbreviated, e.g.,

Metropolitan Museum for Metropolitan Museum of Art; Springfield Museum, for Springfield Museum of Fine Arts, etc. Names of cities are given only where the title of the museum does not include it, e.g., New York, Metropolitan Museum, but Chicago Art Institute. States are added in cases where confusion is possible. State names are abbreviated throughout. Cities are cited in full.

1.   **Robert Gibbs**
fig. 1

Full-length and turned three-quarters right, the child stands with his right arm akimbo, holding a pair of gloves in his left hand. He wears a brown dress with slashed sleeves trimmed with strips of gold, over a white shirt. His pinafore and wide collar are white, as are his shoes, which have red soles. The tiled floor is brown and white, the background and drapery brown.

Oil on canvas. 40 × 33 in. (101.6 × 83.8 cm.)

Dated upper right: *AE. 4 1/2. A⁰. 1670.*

Collections: Anne Hagar Damon, great-great-great-granddaughter of the sitter; Theron J. Damon, her son, Worcester, Mass., about 1926.

Lent by Theron J. Damon. 249.35

Robert Gibbs (1665–1702) was the son of Robert and Elizabeth Sheafe Gibbs of Boston. A wealthy Boston merchant like his father, he became a freeman of Salem village in 1690 and in 1692 married Mary Shrimpton of Boston. This painting and the pendant portraits of his brother Henry and sister Margaret (Mrs. David M. Giltinan, West Virginia) are among the finest of the relatively few extant seventeenth-century American portraits. The three are almost certainly by the Freake Limner who is identified by his portraits, painted five years later, of the Boston attorney and merchant *John Freake* and his wife and child (Worcester, Mass., Art Museum).

References: J.W. Gibbs, *Memoir of the Gibbs Family*, Philadelphia, 1879, pp. 13, 36–38./ W.H. Downes, "Boston Painters and Paintings," *Atlantic Monthly*, 1888, LXII, no. 369, p. 90./ A.M. Earle, *Child Life in Colonial Days*, New York, 1899, pp. 43–44 (repr. opp. p. 36)./ —, *Two Centuries of Costume in America*, New York, 1903, I, pp. 274–276 (repr. opp. p. 316)./ "Early New England Art in Worcester," *Art News*, 1934, XXXII, no. 38, p. 10./ A. Burroughs, *Limners and Likenesses*, Cambridge, Mass., 1936, pp. 9–11 (repr. p. 5)./ "300 Years of Life in America," *Art Digest*, 1939, XIII, no. 17, p. 42./ H.W. Williams, Jr., "Life in America for 300 Years," *Metropolitan Museum Bulletin*, 1939, XXXIV, no. 4, p. 79./ H. Saint-Gaudens, "Survey of American Painting," *Carnegie Magazine*, 1940, XIV, no. 5, p. 132 (repr. p. 132)./ J.T. Flexner, *First Flowers of Our Wilderness*, Boston, 1947, p. 349 (repr. p. 246)./ V. Barker, *American Painting*, New York, 1950, pp. 40–44./ S.P. Feld, "Loan Collection, 1965," *Metropolitan Museum Bulletin*, 1965, XXIII, no. 8, p. 276 (repr.).

Exhibitions: Worcester, Mass., Art Museum, *XVIIth Century Painting in New England*, 1934, p. 89 (repr. p. 88)./ Paris, Musée du Jeu de Paume, *Trois Siècles d'Art aux Etats-Unis*, 1938, no. 2./ New York, Metropolitan Museum, *Life in America*, 1939, no. 3 (repr. p. 3)./ Pittsburgh, Pa., Carnegie Institute, *Survey of American Painting*, 1940, no. 8./ New York, Wildenstein and Co., *The Child Through Four Centuries*, 1945, no. 9./ New York, Metropolitan Museum, *Three Centuries of American Painting*, 1965, no catalogue (see *Bulletin* above).

2.   **Katherine Winthrop (Mrs. Samuel Browne, later Mrs. Epes Sargent)**
fig. 3

Three-quarter length, seated on a brown rock before a wooded landscape, she faces front holding flowers in each hand. She wears a blue dress with a red scarf.

Oil on canvas. 50½ × 40¾ in. (128.2 × 103.5 cm.)

Painted about 1730.

Collections: J.D. Sargent, great-grandson of the sitter, Boston; George Nixon Black, Boston.

Bequest of George Nixon Black. 29.784

Katherine Winthrop (1711–1781), daughter of John Winthrop, married Samuel Browne, a wealthy merchant of Salem, Mass., in 1732, and after his death she married Colonel Epes Sargent of Gloucester in 1744. By her first husband she had two children, William and Abigail. By her second husband she had five. Her age, pose, and costume suggest a date of about 1730. Although attributed to Smibert when acquired, cleaning and further study led to the rejection of this attribution. Despite similarities to the work of John Greenwood, no positive attribution can be made. The composition is probably derived from the 1692 mezzotint by John Smith after Kneller's portrait of Princess Anne. An almost identical portrait, perhaps a source for our painting or an early copy of it, owned by the Rhode Island Historical Society, is identified as a Smibert portrait of Katherine Winthrop's sister, Mrs. Joseph Wanton.

References: F.W. Bayley, *Copley*, Boston, 1915, p. 215./—, *Five Colonial Artists*, Boston, 1929 (repr. p. 423)./ J.H. Morgan and H.W. Foote, *Blackburn*, Worcester, Mass., 1937, p. 34./ H.W. Foote, *Smibert*, Cambridge, Mass., 1950, pp. 213–14 (doubts Smibert attribution)./ C.C. Sellers, "Mezzotint Prototypes of Colonial Portraiture," *Art Quarterly*, 1957, xx, no. 4, p. 431 (fig. 18B).

3.

fig. 2

Lady in a Blue Dress

Three-quarter length, she stands facing three-quarters right with her head turned left, wearing a dark blue satin dress with a white underblouse and a gold satin stole. In her left hand, resting on a window ledge, she holds a branch of apple blossoms. Through the window appears a landscape with evergreens against a blue sky.
Oil on canvas. 49¾ × 40 in. (126.3 × 101.6 cm.)
Painted about 1735–1740.
Bequest of Maxim Karolik. 64.448

4.

fig. 94

Quaker Meeting

A painted oval with gray spandrels. A soft green and brown paneled interior with two ranks of figures on benches: the men wear brown, blue, red, and gray with black hats; the women wear gray, yellow, white, and green.
Oil on canvas. Painted oval. 25 × 30 in. (63.5 × 76.2 cm.)
Painted about 1790.
Collections: Otto H. Kahn, New York; Maxim Karolik, Newport, R.I., 1961.
Bequest of Maxim Karolik. 64.456

Essentials of composition and even details of pose were probably derived either from a watercolor (9 × 12 in.) of Quakers attending a *Gracechurch Street Meeting*, London (described in London Friends' Institute, *Biographical Catalogue . . . of the Series of Friends . . . whose Portraits are in the London Friends' Institute*, London, 1888, p. 767–770; the watercolor dates from about 1760) or more likely from its source, a painting (ca. 3 × 4 ft.) then owned by William Lucas of Hitchen. A *Quaker Meeting* (Quaker Collection of Haverford College Library) by the Dutch painter Egbert van Heemskerck (1634/5–1704), probably painted in London about 1690, also includes numerous similarities of composition and detail: hats on the wall, the man leaning on his cane. A nearly identical version of the Boston picture is owned by Mr. T.E. Letchworth, Sway, Hants. Its existence suggests the possibility of a British origin for ours, and because of internal evidence a date possibly in the 1760's. While the Boston picture may have been painted in London, the lengthy tradition for the subject and the provincial primitive American style leave open an equal possibility of an origin in this country late in the eighteenth century.

5.

Portrait of a Woman in a White Bonnet

Bust-length and facing front against a brown background, she wears a low-cut black dress, a white gimp, and a white lace bonnet tied with a black ribbon.
Oil on panel. 26¾ × 21¾ in. (67.9 × 55.2 cm.)
Painted about 1810–1815.
Gift of Miss Sarah Jane Colburn. 10.233

Painted in the early nineteenth century, the style is similar to that of Henry Williams (1787–1830), a Boston portrait painter.

6.

fig. 159

Phoebe Drake

Full-length and turned three-quarters left, the young girl stands on a red and green patterned carpet, before a brown wall and a green curtain. She wears a white Empire dress with a gold clasp on the pink satin sash and matching pink shoes. She holds a brown book in her left hand; her right rests on a table draped with gold and on which stands a blue and white basket of peaches.

Oil on canvas. 48 × 36 in. (121.9 × 91.4 cm.)
Painted about 1815–1820.
Collections: Mrs. Fannie A. Currier; Nancy L. Currier, her granddaughter, Chestnut Hill, Mass., about 1959; Maxim Karolik, Newport, R.I., 1961.
Bequest of Maxim Karolik. 64.462

7.　　　　**Old Lady with a Plaid Shawl**
Oil on canvas. 30 × 25 in. (76.2 × 63.5 cm.)
Painted about 1815–1825.
M. and M. Karolik Collection. 47.1230
Reference: Karolik Catalogue, 1949, no. 4 (repr.).

8.　　　　**Miss Smith of Poughkeepsie**
Half-length, seated and turned three-quarters left, the young girl wears a pink dress with a white lace collar, a red necklace, and gold earrings. Green background.
Oil on panel. 10¼ × 8¼ in. (26 × 21 cm.)
Painted about 1815–1825.
Bequest of Maxim Karolik. 64.415
The girl's name is traditional and a precise identification is impossible.

9.　　　　**Portrait of a Man**
A young man, bust-length, turned three-quarters right, wears a black coat with a white neckcloth. The background is green.
Oil on canvas. 27 × 23 in. (68.5 × 58.4 cm.)
Painted about 1820.
Gift of William Brewster. 29.892
Closely related to the work of James Frothingham (1786–1864).

10.　　　　**Portrait of an Artist**
Oil on canvas. 11¾ × 10½ in. (29.7 × 26.6 cm.)
Painted about 1825–1830.
M. and M. Karolik Collection. 48.408
Reference: Karolik Catalogue, 1949, no. 9 (repr.).

11.　　　　**Commodore David Porter**
Oil on canvas. 30 × 25 in. (76.2 × 63.5 cm.)
Painted about 1825–1835.
M. and M. Karolik Collection. 47.1229
Reference: Karolik Catalogue, 1949, no. 11 (repr.).

12.
fig. 158　　　**Pennsylvania Dutch Lady**
Oil on canvas. 33¾ × 23¾ in. (85.7 × 60.3 cm.)
Painted in 1826.
M. and M. Karolik Collection. 47.1225
Reference: Karolik Catalogue, 1949, no. 3 (repr.).

13.
fig. 245　　　**Girl in Red**
Oil on canvas. 53¼ × 39 in. (135.2 × 99 cm.)
Painted about 1830–1840.
M. and M. Karolik Collection. 47.1215
Reference: Karolik Catalogue, 1949, no. 7 (repr.).

14.　　　　**New England Hillside**
Oil on canvas. 24 × 31 in. (61 × 78.7 cm.)
Painted about 1830–1840.
M. and M. Karolik Collection. 47.1248
Reference: Karolik Catalogue, 1949, no. 27 (repr.).

15.
fig. 246　　　**Mrs. Catherine Arnold Hummel (formerly Old Lady with a Bible)**
Oil on canvas. 36 × 29 in. (91.4 × 73.6 cm.)
Painted about 1835–1840.
M. and M. Karolik Collection. 47.1213

The subject was identified by Mrs. Guilford Jones of Denver, her great-great-granddaughter. Catherine Hummel was the wife of Jacob Hummel, a Pennsylvania German leather manufacturer. They lived near Torresville, Pa.

Reference: Karolik Catalogue, 1949, no. 5 (repr.).

16.

Portrait of a Gentleman
Half-length, he faces three-quarters left, wearing a black coat and vest with a white shirt. Brown background.
Oil on cardboard. 14½ × 11¼ in. (36.8 × 28.5 cm.)
Painted about 1835–1840.
Bequest of Maxim Karolik. 64.604

17.

Portrait of a Lady
Half-length, she faces three-quarters right and wears a black dress with a white lace fichu fastened by a gold brooch. The background is gray.
Oil on cardboard. 14¼ × 10 in. (36.2 × 25.4 cm.)
Painted about 1835–1840.
Bequest of Maxim Karolik. 64.605
Pendant to the preceding.

18.

Woman with a Yellow Necklace
Half-length, she is seated facing front and wears a black dress with a white lace collar. The background is brown.
Oil on canvas. 21 × 17 in. (53.3 × 43.2 cm.)
Painted about 1835–1840.
Collection: Maxim Karolik, Newport, R.I., 1948.
Bequest of Maxim Karolik. 64.416

19.

Egg Salad
Oil on canvas. 8½ × 11 in. (21.6 × 27.9 cm.)
Painted about 1840.
M. and M. Karolik Collection. 47.1220
Reference: Karolik Catalogue, 1949, no. 30 (repr.).

20.
fig. 247

Girl with a Gray Cat
Oil on canvas. 44¼ × 35 in. (112.3 × 88.9 cm.)
Painted about 1840.
M. and M. Karolik Collection. 47.1251
Reference: Karolik Catalogue, 1949, no. 6 (repr.).

21.

Daniel Webster at His Farm
Oil on canvas. 26 × 20 in. (66 × 50.8 cm.)
Painted about 1840–1845.
M. and M. Karolik Collection. 47.1211
Reference: Karolik Catalogue, 1949, no. 10 (repr.).

22.
fig. 275

Tomatoes, Fruit, and Flowers
Oil on canvas. 20 × 31½ in. (50.8 × 80 cm.)
Painted about 1840–1850.
M. and M. Karolik Collection. 47.1265
Reference: Karolik Catalogue, 1949, no. 31 (repr.).

23.

Lock Haven, Pennsylvania
Oil on canvas. 14½ × 25¾ in. (36.8 × 65.4 cm.)
Dated on back: *July 7th. 1849.*
M. and M. Karolik Collection. 47.1199
Reference: Karolik Catalogue, 1949, no. 23 (repr.).

24.
fig. 281

Flowers, Butterfly, and Book
Oil on panel. 10½ × 14¼ in. (26.6 × 36.2 cm.)
Painted before 1850.

M. and M. Karolik Collection. 47.1252

Reference: *Karolik Catalogue*, 1949, no. 33 (repr.).

25.   **Judd's House, Southold, Long Island**
Oil on canvas. 25 × 29¾ in. (63.5 × 75.5 cm.)
Painted about 1850.
M. and M. Karolik Collection. 47.1260
Reference: *Karolik Catalogue*, 1949, no. 20 (repr.).

26.   **Buckland, Massachusetts (formerly New England Village)**
Oil on canvas. 24¼ × 31 in. (61.6 × 78.7 cm.)
Painted between 1850 and 1868.
M. and M. Karolik Collection. 47.1195

The village was recognized as Buckland, Mass. by Clifford R. Monahon of the Rhode Island Historical Society. The house with four chimneys to the right of the painting was the Griswold Homestead, his wife's family home. The Methodist Church in the village center was built in 1850 and the little Baptist Church at the corner of the graveyard was built in 1828 and removed to Ashfield, Mass. in 1868. The painting must have been done between 1850 and 1868.

Reference: *Karolik Catalogue*, 1949, no. 28 (repr.).

27.   **Meditation by the Sea**
fig. 270   Oil on canvas. 13½ × 19½ in. (34.3 × 49.5 cm.)
Painted about 1850–1860.
M. and M. Karolik Collection. 45.892
Reference: *Karolik Catalogue*, 1949, no. 25 (repr.).

28.   **View of West Point from Above Washington Valley**
Oil on oval canvas. 14½ × 20 in. (36.8 × 50.8 cm.)
Painted about 1850–1860.
M. and M. Karolik Collection. 47.1192
Reference: *Karolik Catalogue*, 1949, no. 22 (repr.).

29.   **Woodcutting in Winter**
Oil on canvas. 26¼ × 36¼ in. (66.7 × 91.2 cm.)
Painted about 1850–1860.
M. and M. Karolik Collection. 48.409
Reference: *Karolik Catalogue*, 1949, no. 18 (repr.).

30.   **Woodshed Interior**
Oil on canvas. 14 × 20 in. (35.5 × 50.8 cm.)
Painted about 1850–1860.
M. and M. Karolik Collection. 47.1191
Reference: *Karolik Catalogue*, 1949, no. 14 (repr.).

31.   **Portrait of a Baby**
Oil on canvas. 27¼ × 22¼ in. (69.2 × 56.5 cm.)
Painted about 1850–1870.
M. and M. Karolik Collection. 48.1025
Reference: *Karolik Catalogue*, 1949, no. 8 (repr.).

32.   **A River Landing**
Oil on canvas. 18 × 24 in. (45.7 × 61 cm.)
Signed and dated lower right: . . . . *1855*. (Signature illegible).
M. and M. Karolik Collection. 47.1177
Reference: *Karolik Catalogue*, 1949, no. 22 (repr.).

33.   **Watermelon**
Oil on canvas. 22 × 27½ in. (55.9 × 69.8 cm.)
Dated on the stretcher: *1855*.
M. and M. Karolik Collection. 48.410
Reference: *Karolik Catalogue*, 1949, no. 32 (repr.).

34.

fig. 280

A Street in Winter: Evening
Oil on canvas. 15 × 18 in. (38.1 × 45.7 cm.)
Painted about 1855.
M. and M. Karolik Collection. 47.1216
Reference: Karolik Catalogue, 1949, no. 15 (repr.).

35.

fig. 271

The Railroad Suspension Bridge near Niagara Falls
Against a blue and pink sunset sky with yellow clouds, the bridge and vehicles are silhouetted in brown. Brown cliffs and rows of green trees frame the blue Niagara river and distant falls.
Oil on canvas. 30¼ × 39 in. (76.8 × 99 cm.)
Painted after 1855.
Collection: Maxim Karolik, Newport, R.I., 1952.
M. and M. Karolik Collection. 62.259

The first of its kind, this long-span wire suspension bridge, with a double roadway for railway and vehicular use, was designed and built by John Augustus Roebling, a Prussian immigrant, and was completed in 1855. A lithograph engraved by Charles Parsons for N. Currier (published 1856) was the source for this painting, a replica with the Vose Galleries, Boston, and probably the version by Thomas Doughty (Hirschl and Adler Galleries, N.Y.) signed and dated 1855. Despite a date prior to the lithograph, Doughty's painting must derive from it (or possibly another print); he was too ill to travel to Niagara. His painting called *Lewiston Bridge* is actually of Roebling's bridge, which was halfway between Lewiston, N.Y. and the Falls.

Reference: J.I.H. Baur, *American Painting in the Nineteenth Century,* New York, 1953, p. 22 (repr. p. 44).

Exhibitions: New York, American Federation of Arts, circulated in Germany and Italy, and Whitney Museum, *American Painting in the Nineteenth Century,* 1953–1954, no. 65./ Washington, D.C., Smithsonian Institution and circulated in the U.S., *19th Century American Paintings,* 1954–1956, no. 8 (repr.)./ Boston, MFA and circulated in the U.S., *The M. and M. Karolik Collection,* 1957–1959, no. 151./ Buffalo, Albright-Knox Art Gallery, *Three Centuries of Niagara Falls,* 1964, no. 4 (repr. p. 24).

36.

Haydee, Robert, and Lillian Long
In a green, woody landscape, three children are seated around a gray fountain: Haydee, on the left, wears a blue dress; Lillian, center, is in white, holding a rose; Robert wears blue and white.
Oil on canvas. 44 × 34¾ in. (111.7 × 88.2 cm.)
Painted about 1858.
Collections: Mrs. Lillian Long Hersome; Frank B. Hersome, Pepperell, Mass.
Gift of Frank B. Hersome. 59.423

Portrayed are the three eldest children of Stephen and Maria Long of Minneapolis. The date for the painting is based on the apparent age of Lillian, born in 1855.

37.

Littleton, New Hampshire
Oil on canvas. 24 × 40¼ in. (61 × 102.2 cm.)
Painted about 1858–1869.
M. and M. Karolik Collection. 47.1210
Reference: Karolik Catalogue, 1949, no. 19 (repr.).

38.

fig. 296

Four Wine Tasters in a Cellar
In a brown, dimly lit cellar, four men in gray suits sit or stand among the casks and bottle racks. An attendant in brown stands at the left holding a candle.
Oil on canvas. 28 × 36 in. (71.1 × 91.4 cm.)
Painted in 1859 (?).
Collection: Maxim Karolik, Newport, R.I., 1959.
Gift of Maxim Karolik. 62.258

Perhaps painted in 1859; that date and the initials T.C. are carved into two of the left-hand barrels.

39. **Shrewsbury River near Seabright, New Jersey**
Oil on canvas. 19×29 in. (48.2×73.6 cm.)
Painted about 1860–1865.
M. and M. Karolik Collection. 47.1224
Reference: *Karolik Catalogue,* 1949, no. 21 (repr.).

40. **Camp Butler, Maryland, 1861**
Oil on panel. 8½×11 in. (21.6×27.9 cm.)
Inscribed on back: *Camp Butler/ Annapolis Junction, MD./ May 2d–11th 1861./ The First Camp in Active Service,/ of the Fifth Regiment N.Y.S.N.G.*
M. and M. Karolik Collection. 47.1218
Reference: *Karolik Catalogue,* 1949, no. 29 (repr.).

41. **Summer Landscape: Haymaking**
Oil on canvas. 27½×36¼ in. (69.8×92.1 cm.)
Painted about 1875.
M. and M. Karolik Collection. 47.1235
Reference: *Karolik Catalogue,* 1949, no. 16 (repr.).

42.
fig. 276 **Musicians in the Snow**
Oil on canvas. 30×40 in. (76.2×101.6 cm.)
Painted in 1876 (?).
M. and M. Karolik Collection. 47.1219
Reference: *Karolik Catalogue,* 1949, no. 24 (repr.).

43. **Running Before the Storm**
Oil on canvas. 24×36¼ in. (61×92.1 cm.)
Painted after 1877.
M. and M. Karolik Collection. 46.851

The painting is probably a copy with minor variations after the engraving by John Sartain, itself taken from a painting or design (location unknown) by Joseph John. The engraving is included in H.W. Morris' book, *Work Days of God, or, Science and the Bible,* Philadelphia, 1877, p. 234 which would seem to provide a date *post quem* for the painting. Joseph John was active during the second half of the last century as a landscape, genre, and animal painter.
Reference: *Karolik Catalogue,* 1949, no. 26 (repr.).

Christmas Party
See Robert D. Wilkie, Cat. no. 1039

New England Family Group
See George Hollingsworth, Cat. no. 557

JOSEF ALBERS was born in 1888 in Bottrop in the Ruhr district of Germany. He studied in the Royal Art School of Berlin in 1913–15, at the School of Applied Arts in Essen from 1916–19, at the Art Academy of Munich in 1919–20, and at the Bauhaus in Weimar from 1920–23. He then taught at the Bauhaus in Weimar and Dessau and in Berlin from then until 1933, when he moved to the United States to teach at Black Mountain College, North Carolina, where he was head of the Art Department until 1949. He was then Chairman of the Department of Design at Yale University from 1950–58 and Visiting Critic there from 1958–60. He presently lives near New Haven. His work has stressed an analytical approach to the nature of the interaction of pure color when precisely measured and organized in basic geometric designs.

44.

fig. 612

Variant: Three Reds Around Blue

A composition of rectangular shapes of Turquoise Blue, Indian Red, Terra Rosa, and Cadmium Red Deep (artist's identification) organized to imply space or depth through apparent overlapping of pigments, but in fact utilizing only pure color from the tube.

Oil on masonite. 22½ × 29¾ in. (57.2 × 75.5 cm.)

Signed (with initial) and dated lower right: *JA 48* (initials in monogram).

Collections: With the artist until 1956; Mr. and Mrs. Herbert M. Agoos, Cambridge, Mass.

Gift of Mr. and Mrs. Herbert M. Agoos. 66.23

Variant themes "came into existence about 1945 through a need to study color in related quantities, that is, color in measurable amounts ... To this end all variants are built on an underlying checkerboard-like structure, or graph." Colors are "never mixed with each other, nor with any additional painting media. They are applied directly from the tube in one primary coat, without any under or over painting." (Letter from the artist, 1966.)

FRANCIS ALEXANDER (1800–1880), born in Killingly, Conn., studied briefly in New York with Alexander Robertson at the Academy of Fine Arts and copied portraits by John Trumbull and Samuel Waldo. From 1821 to 1825, he painted portraits in Killingly and Providence, R.I. It was probably in 1825 that he received some encouraging advice from Gilbert Stuart in Boston, and by 1828 he was an established and prominent portraitist and lithographer of that city. He visited Italy from 1831 to 1833, settled in Florence in 1853, and lived there until his death.

45.

Madam Powel (Elizabeth Willing)

Half-length, seated and turned three-quarters left, the elderly lady wears a black dress with a figured blue shawl, a white collar and cap. The background is dark red.

Oil on panel. 30 × 23¾ in. (76.2 × 60.3 cm.)

Painted about 1825–1830.

Bequest of Pauline L. Dolliver. 22.7

The subject has been identified by comparison with the Stuart portrait of Mrs. Powel (formerly owned by Mr. T.I. Hare Powel, R.I.). Born in 1742/43, Elizabeth Willing was the daughter of Thomas Willing and married Samuel Powel, both prominent Philadelphians. There are many contemporary references to the hospitality of the Samuel Powels. Madam Powel died in 1830. Her apparent age and the style of the work indicate a date of about 1825–1830.

Reference: C.W. Pierce, "Alexander," *Old Time New England*, 1953, XLIV, no. 2, p. 44 (repr. p. 28).

46.

fig. 203

Self-portrait

Bust-length, in profile to the right, he faces three-quarters front, wearing a green coat, white shirt, and black stock. The background is brown.

Oil on canvas. 24 × 18 in. (61 × 45.7 cm.)

Painted about 1830. Inscribed on back of canvas: *Presented to W. Willard/ by/ his friend Francis Alexander/ Mar. 12th 1870.*

Collections: W. Willard, Boston, 1870; Marion Waterman and Helen A. Cook, Boston; G.H. Waterman, Mt. Vernon, N.H.; Maxim Karolik, 1960.

M. and M. Karolik Collection. 62.257

The painting is identified by tradition alone as a self-portrait. The W. Willard to whom the picture was given was probably William Willard, portrait painter, active in Boston during the 1850's.

47.

Charlotte Mackay (?)

Half-length, turned three-quarters left, she wears a red shawl over a white dress. The background is brown.

Oil on canvas. 30×25 in. (76.2×63.5 cm.)
Painted about 1840.
Gift of Mrs. Edith Mackay Floyd. 34.179
The sitter has been identified by family tradition alone as Charlotte Mackay, born in 1845, daughter of Robert Caldwell and Charlotte Lodge Mackay. She died at twenty-one during a European voyage. Her apparent age in the portrait indicates it must have been painted about 1860–1865. The costume and hairstyle, however, are those of the 1840's and would have been considered extremely provincial by 1860. It seems unlikely that a young lady who was able to embark on a European voyage would have been portrayed in the fashions of a previous generation. The identification must, therefore, be seriously questioned.

Reference: C.W. Pierce, "Alexander," *Old Time New England*, 1953, XLIV, no. 2, p. 44.

48.
fig. 204

Charles Dickens

Seated at a table writing, turned three-quarters left, he wears a black coat and shirt and a red waistcoat. The tablecloth is green, and the curtain to the left is red.
Oil on canvas. 44×35½ in. (111.7×90.2 cm.)
Painted in 1842.
Gift of the Estate of Mrs. James T. Fields. 24.18
When it became known, late in 1841, that Charles Dickens (1812–1870) was coming to Boston, Alexander wrote to him asking for a sitting. The portrait was painted the week after his arrival on January 22, 1842.

References: F.G. Kitton, "Charles Dickens and His Less Familiar Portraits" (London) *Magazine of Art*, 1888, XI, p. 287./ M.A.DeW. Howe, "The Story of the Dickens Portrait," *Brentano's Book Chat*, Midwinter 1923, pp. 22–25 (repr.)./ E.F. Payne, *Dickens' Days in Boston*, Boston, 1927, pp. 4, 13./ F.F. Sherman, *Early American Painting*, New York, 1932, p. 147./ A. Burroughs, *Limners and Likenesses*, Cambridge, Mass., 1936, p. 127./ E.P. Richardson, *American Romantic Painting*, New York, 1945, no. 83 (repr.)./ C.W. Pierce, "Alexander," *Old Time New England*, 1953, XLIV, no. 2, pp. 41, 44 (repr. p. 40).

Exhibitions: Boston Athenaeum, *Exhibitions*, 1843, no. 77./ —, 1871, no. 239 (for sale)./ —, 1871–1872, no. 215 (for sale)./ Boston, Copley Hall, *Portraits*, 1896, no. 6./ New London, Conn., Lyman Allyn Museum, *Eighty Eminent Painters of New England*, 1947, no. 55 (repr.).

49.

Mrs. Beale Thayer and Miss Sarah Blanchard

Two young women, close together, bust-length. One turns three-quarters right in a black dress with a white lace collar; the other faces front and wears a red hairband. In the background is a red and brown wall before blue sky with pink clouds.
Oil on canvas. Painted oval. 24×18½ in. (61×47 cm.)
Signed lower right: *Alexander*. Inscribed on back, lower left: *Alexander/ Boston.*
Bequest of Maxim Karolik. 64.413
A label on the back is hand written: *Mrs. Beale Thayer/ "Aunt Abbey"/ Miss Sarah Blanchard.*

JOHN WHITE ALEXANDER (1856–1915), born in Allegheny, Pa., worked for some years in New York as an illustrator for *Harper's Weekly*. In 1877 he studied in Munich, Venice, and Florence, where he knew Duveneck and Whistler. He returned to New York in 1881 and became a prominent portraitist. He was President of the National Academy of Design from 1909 until his death in New York.

50.
fig. 426

Mrs. Samuel Tilton (Helen Reed)

Three-quarter length, seated in profile to the right, her head facing front, she wears a brown dress trimmed with fur and a white cap. The background is brown.
Oil on canvas. 46×34 in. (116.8×86.3 cm.)
Painted about 1880.

Gift of Mrs. William Rodman Fay, granddaughter of the sitter. 54.598

The portrait was painted in Florence about 1880. (Letter from Mrs. Fay, April 21, 1954.)

Exhibition: Toronto Art Gallery and circulated in Canada, and New York, Whitney Museum, *American Painting from 1865–1905*, 1961, no. 1.

51.
fig. 424

Isabella and the Pot of Basil

Isabella stands full-length against a lavender curtain on the left, wearing a black and white robe and holding the pot of basil, which is resting on a gray ledge.
Oil on canvas. 75½ × 35¾ in. (191.8 × 90.8 cm.)
Signed and dated lower left: *John Alexander '97.*
Gift of Ernest Wadsworth Longfellow. 98.181

The story, from Boccaccio's *Decameron*, was used by Keats in his poem *Isabella; or, The Pot of Basil*. Isabella's lover was murdered by her two brothers in a wood near Florence; she then kept his head in a pot planted with sweet basil.

Exhibitions: Pittsburgh, Pa., Carnegie Institute, *2nd Annual*, 1897, no. 3 (fig. 60)./ —, and circulated in the U.S., *Alexander Memorial*, 1916–1917, p. 29, no. 6 (repr.)./ Indianapolis, Herron Museum of Art, *Inaugural Exhibition*, 1906, no. 8./ New York, National Academy of Design, Washington, D.C., Corcoran Gallery, and New York, Grand Central Art Galleries, *National Academy of Design Centennial*, 1925–1926, no. 309 (repr. p. 47).

WASHINGTON ALLSTON (1779–1843), born in Georgetown, S.C., at the age of eight moved to Newport, R.I. Graduating from Harvard in 1800, in 1801, with the miniaturist Edward G. Malbone, he left for London, where he worked under Benjamin West at the Royal Academy until 1803, when he moved to Paris. In 1804 he traveled slowly through Italy to Rome, where he remained until 1808 and developed a use of color based on Venetian and Roman sources of the sixteenth and seventeenth centuries. In 1808 he returned to Boston and married Ann Channing but was again in London with his pupil Samuel F.B. Morse by 1811. He settled in Boston in 1818, then lived in Cambridge from 1830 until his death. His importance lies not only in his position as the first American Romantic painter, but as a strong influence on his younger contemporaries.

52.
fig. 172

Landscape with a Lake

Oil on canvas. 38 × 51¼ in. (96.5 × 130 cm.)
Signed and dated on back: *W. Allston pinxt 1804.*
M. and M. Karolik Collection. 47.1241
Reference: *Karolik Catalogue*, 1949, no. 1 (repr.).

53.
fig. 175

Rising of a Thunderstorm at Sea

A pilot boat struggles toward a distant ship on a dark, gray-green sea; a blue sky with dark storm clouds at left.
Oil on canvas. 38½ × 51 in. (97.8 × 129.5 cm.)
Painted in 1804.
Collections: J. Mason, Boston, by 1827; Samuel D. Parker, Boston, by 1839; Eliza Parker, about 1869; heirs of Eliza Parker.
Everett Fund. 78.46

While Richardson (*Allston*, 1948) cites the influence of Joseph Vernet on Allston in Paris in terms of subject and dramatic mood, the early work of J.M.W. Turner served as an equally strong inspiration, in particular *The Egremont Seapiece* (Lord Egremont, Petworth House, Sussex). That picture, exhibited in 1802 at the Royal Academy, where Allston was studying at the time, appears to have been a direct model for the composition as well as the handling of the sky and waves. Described in the 1839 exhibition at Harding's Gallery as *Rising of a thunderstorm at Sea; pilotboat going off to a ship*, and given the date, 1804, when Allston was working in Paris.

References: E.P. Richardson, *Way of Western Art*, Cambridge, Mass., 1939, p. 63./ —, "Allston and the Development of Romantic Color," *Art Quarterly*, 1944, VII, no. 1, pp. 33, 41 (fig. 1)./ —, *American Romantic Painting*, New York, 1945, no. 12 (repr.)./ —, *Allston*, Chicago, 1948, pp. 64–66, 188 (pl. VI)./ V. Barker, *American Painting*, New York, 1950, p. 341./ J.T. Flexner, *Light of Distant Skies*, New York, 1954, p. 132./ E.P. Richardson, *Painting in America*, New York, 1956, pp. 145, 147, 316 (fig. 61)./ V. Young, "Changing Landscape in American Art," *Arts Yearbook 2*, 1958, p. 93 (repr. p. 110).

Exhibitions: Bristol, England, *Allston*, 1814, no. 4./ Boston Athenaeum, *Exhibition*, 1827, no. 29 (lent J. Mason)./ Boston, Harding's Gallery, *Allston*, 1839, no. 32 (lent S.D. Parker)./ Boston Athenaeum, *Exhibition*, 1850, no. 105 (lent S.D. Parker)./ Boston, MFA, *Contemporary Art*, 1879, no. 110./ —, *Allston*, 1881, no. 233./ New York, Whitney Museum, *A Century of American Landscape Painting*, 1938, no. 7./ Pittsburgh, Pa., Carnegie Institute, *A Century of American Landscape Painting*, 1939, no. 51./ Baltimore Museum, *Souvenir of Romanticism in America*, 1940 (under "Paintings")./ Detroit Institute of Arts, *Five Centuries of Marine Painting*, 1942, no. 72 (pl. 12)./ New York, Museum of Modern Art, *Romantic Painting in America*, 1943, pp. 11, 12, no. 2./ Chicago Art Institute and New York, Whitney Museum, *Hudson River School*, 1945, no. 7 (repr. p. 19)./ Detroit Institute of Arts and Boston, MFA, *Allston*, 1947, no. 4 (repr. p. 15)./ Brooklyn Museum, *The Coast and The Sea*, 1948–1949, no. 2./ Chicago Art Institute, *From Colony to Nation*, 1949, no. 1./ Detroit Institute of Arts and San Francisco, M.H. de Young Memorial Museum, *Painting in America, the Story of 450 Years*, 1957, no. 66./ Boston, MFA and Wellesley College, Jewett Arts Center, *Four Boston Masters*, 1959, no. 17./ New York, World's Fair, Gallery of Better Living Center, *Four Centuries of American Masterpieces*, 1964, no. 7 (repr.).

54.
fig. 173

Self-Portrait

Standing, half-length against a brown wall, the young man turns three-quarters right. He wears a black coat, green waistcoat, and brown stock.

Oil on canvas. $31\frac{1}{2} \times 26\frac{1}{2}$ in. (80×67.3 cm.)

Signed and dated center left: *W. Allston/ Romae 1805.*

Collections: Given by the artist to Mrs. Nathaniel Amory, Boston, by 1839; inherited by her sister, Mrs. Wormely, 1865; *John T. Johnson Sale*, Chickering Hall, New York, Dec. 19–22, 1876, no. 140; Miss Alice Hooper, Boston, 1876.

Bequest of Miss Alice Hooper. 84.301

Painted while Allston was studying in Rome. The influence of Titian, whose pictures Allston had seen in the Louvre, is clearly evident.

References: M.F. Sweetser, *Allston*, Boston, 1879, pp. 51, 187./ A. Burroughs, *Limners and Likenesses*, Cambridge, Mass., 1936, p. 129./ E.P. Richardson, *Allston*, Chicago, 1948, pp. 77, 190 (pl. XI)./ J.T. Flexner, *Light of Distant Skies*, New York, 1954, p. 135 (pl. 66).

Exhibitions: Boston, Harding's Gallery, *Allston*, 1839, no. 23./ Boston, MFA, *Allston*, 1881, no. 229./ San Francisco, M.H. de Young Memorial Museum and California Palace of the Legion of Honor, *American Painting*, 1935, no. 49 (repr.)./ Harvard University, *Tercentenary*, 1936, no. 4./ Richmond, Virginia Museum of Fine Arts, *American Painting—Inaugural Exhibition*, 1936, no. 16./ Detroit Institute of Arts and Boston, MFA, *Allston*, 1947, no. 1 (repr. p. 13)./ Boston, MFA, *Great Americans*, 1954, no. 25 (repr.)./ Brooklyn Museum, *The Face of America*, 1957–1958, no. 36 (fig. 19)./ Washington, D.C., Corcoran Gallery, *American Painters of the South*, 1960, no. 57.

55.
fig. 174

William Ellery Channing

Unfinished. Half-length and facing front, he wears a black coat and white stock. The background is red and brown.

Oil on canvas. $31 \times 27\frac{1}{2}$ in. (78.7×69.8 cm.)

Painted between 1809 and 1811.

Collection: William Francis Channing, the sitter's son, Pasadena, Calif.

Gift of William Francis Channing. 97.65

William Ellery Channing (1780–1842) was born in Newport, R.I., the son of William and Lucy Ellery Channing, and graduated from Harvard in

1798. In 1803 he was ordained pastor of the Federal Street Church in Boston. He was known as "The Apostle of Unitarianism," and as a clergyman, educator, and writer, deeply concerned about the problems of temperance and peace, his influence was considerable. He died in Bennington, Vt. Allston and Channing were lifelong friends, and this portrait was painted during Allston's Boston period of 1808–1811, about the time of his marriage to Channing's sister, Ann, in 1809. The lower portion of the picture is considerably repainted. A more finished version is owned by the Channing Memorial and hangs in the Colonial Society, Boston. John Cheney's engraving of our portrait is reproduced as frontispiece in *Memoir of William Ellery Channing*, Boston, 1848, I.

References: M.F. Sweetser, *Allston*, Boston, 1879, p. 188./ J.B. Flagg, *Allston*, New York, 1892, p. 82./ E.P. Richardson, *American Romantic Painting*, New York, 1945, no. 16 (repr.)./ —, *Allston*, Chicago, 1948, pp. 90, 91, 195 (pl. xxiii)./ —, "Realism and Idealism in American Painting," *Art Quarterly*, 1949, xii, no. 1, p. 11 (repr.).

Exhibitions: Detroit Institute of Arts and Boston, MFA, *Allston*, 1947, no. 12 (repr. p. 20)./ Cambridge, Mass., Fogg Art Museum, *American Spirit in Portraiture*, 1951, no. 17.

56.

fig. 179

The Poor Author and the Rich Bookseller

In an office interior of gray and brown, the rich bookseller, seated on the left beside a table, interviews the author; a boy sweeps from under the latter's feet. All wear brown, red, and white.

Oil on canvas. 31 × 28 in. (78.7 × 71.1 cm.)

Painted in 1811.

Collections: T.H. Perkins, Jr., Boston, by 1839; Ignatius Sargent, Boston, by 1850; Charles Sprague Sargent, Boston.

Bequest of Charles Sprague Sargent. 27.220

The style would suggest a date of about 1811, which is the date given by Harding's Gallery catalogue of 1839. It is one of Allston's occasional essays into anecdote, an interest which originated with the eighteenth-century humorous satire of Hogarth and Rowlandson.

References: M.F. Sweetser, *Allston*, Boston, 1879, p. 188./ J.B. Flagg, *Allston*, New York, 1892, p. 83./ E.P. Richardson, *Allston*, Chicago, 1948, pp. 89, 93, 195 (pl. xx)./ V. Barker, *American Painting*, New York, 1950, p. 342.

Exhibitions: Boston, Harding's Gallery, *Allston*, 1839, no. 30 (lent T.H. Perkins, Jr.)./ Boston Athenaeum, *Exhibition*, 1850, no. 95 (lent I. Sargent)./ Boston, MFA, *Allston*, 1881, no. 216./ Brookline, Mass., Town Hall, *Loan Collection*, 1897, no. 2./ Detroit Institute of Arts and Boston, MFA, *Allston*, 1947, no. 5./ Chicago Art Institute, *From Colony to Nation*, 1949, no. 2.

57.

fig. 182

The Angel Releasing St. Peter from Prison

To the left of the dark and brown dungeon stands the angel in brilliant white. Peter, robed in purple, crouches in awe while in the background two soldiers sleep.

Oil on canvas. 124½ × 108½ in. (316.2 × 275.6 cm.)

Painted in 1812.

Collections: Commissioned by Sir George Howland Beaumont in 1812, and given by him to the Parish Church of Cole Orton, Leicestershire, England; returned to the Beaumonts in 1853; purchased by Robert William Hooper in 1859 and given by him to the Chapel of the Worcester (Mass.) Lunatic Hospital, with a contingent remainder to the Museum of Fine Arts, Boston.

Gift of Robert William Hooper through the Worcester State Hospital. 21.1379

The subject is from *Acts of the Apostles*, 12: "The same night Peter was sleeping between two soldiers, bound with two chains . . . and behold, the angel of the Lord came upon him, and a light shined in the prison. . . ." Allston, answering Sir George Beaumont's commission, began work on the painting in 1812. A study for the head of St. Peter is owned by Mrs. E.A. Bliss, Bryn Mawr, Pa.; a sketch for the whole composition is owned by the Countess Béla Hadik, New Hampshire.

References: *Crayon*, 1855, I, no. 13, p. 194./ H.T. Tuckerman, *Book of the Artists*, New York, 1870, p. 142./ M.F. Sweetser, *Allston*, Boston, 1879, pp. 61–62./ J.B. Flagg, *Allston*, New York, 1892, pp. 91–95./ W. Dunlap, *History of the Arts of Design*, Boston, 1918, II, p. 331./ E.P. Richardson, *Allston*, Chicago, 1948, pp. 108, 123, 196 (pl. XXVIII).

Exhibitions: London, British Institution, 1816, no. 206./ Manchester, England, *Art Treasures Exhibition*, 1856./ Boston Athenaeum, *Exhibitions*, 1862, no. 50./ —, 1864, no. 131./ Detroit Institute of Arts and Boston, MFA, *Allston*, 1947, no. 21 (repr. p. 28).

58.

Donna Mencia in the Robber's Cavern

Oil on canvas. 56 × 43½ in. (142.3 × 110.5 cm.)

Signed and dated lower right: *W. Allston. 1815.*

M. and M. Karolik Collection. 47.1239

Reference: *Karolik Catalogue*, 1949, no. 2 (repr.).

59.

Head of a Jew

Unfinished. Bust-length and turned three-quarters right, his bearded face raised, he wears a brown robe and skullcap. The background is green.

Oil on canvas. 30¼ × 25¼ in. (76.8 × 64.1 cm.)

Painted in 1817.

Collections: J.S. Copley Greene, Boston; Mary Amory Greene, Cambridge, Mass.; Henry Copley Greene, her nephew, Cambridge.

Gift of Henry Copley Greene. 41.291

This painting and the two following ones (Cat. nos. 60 and 61) are part of a series of heads of Polish Jews, done in London in 1817.

References: M.F. Sweetser, *Allston*, Boston, 1879, p. 188./ E.P. Richardson, *Allston*, Chicago, 1948, pp. 102, 116 (pl. XXXVI).

Exhibitions: Boston Athenaeum, *Exhibition*, 1828, no. 171 (or 146 or 148)./ Boston, Harding's Gallery, *Allston*, 1839, no. 28./ Boston Athenaeum, *Exhibition*, 1850, no. 89./ Detroit Institute of Arts and Boston, MFA, *Allston*, 1947, no. 15./ Charleston, S.C., Gibbes Art Gallery, *American Jewish Art and History in the South*, 1964, no. A-2.

60.

Head of a Jew

Half-length, turned three-quarters right, and with his left hand on a staff, he wears black with a red skullcap. Brown background.

Oil on canvas. 29¾ × 25 in. (75.5 × 63.3 cm.)

Painted in 1817.

Collections: Purchased from the artist by the Boston Athenaeum, 1829.

Deposited by the Boston Athenaeum, 1876. Ath. 13

References: M.F. Sweetser, *Allston*, Boston, 1879, p. 187./ E.P. Richardson, *Allston*, Chicago, 1948, pp. 116, 201 (pl. XCV).

Exhibitions: Boston Athenaeum, *Exhibition*, 1828, no. 148 (or 146 or 171)./ Boston, Harding's Gallery, *Allston*, 1839, no. 20./ Boston Athenaeum, *Exhibition*, 1850, no. 75./ Boston, MFA, *Allston*, 1881, no. 221.

61.

fig. 181

Isaac of York

Unfinished. Bust-length study of a gray-bearded man, turned three-quarters left, wearing a brown skullcap and robe. The background is brown; the foreground, green.

Oil on canvas. 30 × 25 in. (76.2 × 63.5 cm.)

Painted in 1817.

Collection: Purchased from the artist by the Boston Athenaeum, 1833.

Deposited by the Boston Athenaeum, 1876. Ath. 15

The artist named this sketch *Isaac of York*, from Walter Scott's *Ivanhoe*.

References: S. Clarke, "Our First Great Painter and His Works," *Atlantic Monthly*, 1865, XV, p. 136./ J.B. Flagg, *Allston*, New York, 1892, p. 272./ E.P. Richardson, *Allston*, Chicago, 1948, pp. 116, 200 (pl. XXXV).

Exhibitions: Boston Athenaeum, *Exhibitions*, 1828, no. 146 (or 148 or 171); 1833, no. 38./ Boston, Harding's Gallery, *Allston*, 1839, no. 19./ Albany, N.Y., Albany Gallery, *4th Exhibition*, 1849, no. 75./ Boston Athenaeum, *Exhibition*, 1850, no. 102./

Boston, MFA, *Allston*, 1881, no. 220./ Detroit Institute of Arts and Boston, MFA, *Allston*, 1947, no. 14.

62.
fig. 178

Study for Belshazzar's Feast

Painted primarily in brown. Daniel, in the center, dominates the crowded banquet hall by pointing to the writing on the wall. On the left Belshazzar, seated on a white throne, and his Queen, both in gold, recoil in fear.

Oil on cardboard. 25½ × 34¼ in. (64.8 × 87 cm.)
Painted in 1817.
Bequest of Ruth Charlotte Dana, the artist's niece. 06.1875

The subject is from *Daniel*, V. Because the astrologers, Chaldeans, and soothsayers had failed to read the writing on the wall, Belshazzar called the prophet Daniel, who read and interpreted the words before the frightened king. This study and another in sepia (Cambridge, Mass., Fogg Art Museum) were both done in 1817 before Allston's return to Boston from England. His large unfinished painting of *Belshazzar's Feast* is in the Detroit Institute of Arts.

References: J.B. Flagg, *Allston*, New York, 1892, p. 71./ E.P. Richardson, *Allston*, Chicago, 1948, pp. 123, 202 (pl. XXXIX).

Exhibitions: Boston Athenaeum, *Exhibitions*, 1847, no. 2; 1857, no. 290./ Boston, MFA, *Allston*, 1881, no. 267./ Detroit Institute of Arts and Boston, MFA, *Allston*, 1947, no. 25./ Buffalo, Albright Art Gallery, *Expressionism in American Painting*, 1952, no. 2 (repr. p. 11).

63.
fig. 177

Elijah in the Desert

A predominantly brown landscape of mountains, stumpy trees, and dark clouds appears against a blue sky. In the foreground Elijah, wearing a blue tunic, receives food from the ravens.

Oil on canvas. 48¾ × 72½ in. (123.8 × 184.2 cm.)
Signed twice on back, upper left: *W. Allston 1818* and *W. Allston A.R.A.*
Collections: Henry Labouchere (later Lord Taunton), London, before 1828; Mrs. Samuel Hooper and Miss Alice Hooper, Boston, 1870.
Gift of Mrs. Samuel Hooper and Miss Alice Hooper. 70.1

The subject is from *Kings*, I, 17: Elijah at the word of the Lord "went and dwelt by the brook Charith, that is before Jordan. And the ravens brought him bread and flesh in the evening, and he drank of the brook." Allston painted *Elijah* and *Uriel in the Sun* in London for the British Institution Exhibition of that year. He described his technique for painting *Elijah*, saying that he had mixed his colors with skim milk and had painted rapidly, finishing it in about three weeks. In a letter of July (?) 1833, James Fenimore Cooper wrote to Henry Labouchere, ". . . I will come all the way to Hamilton Place to see you, if you have Alston's [sic] *Elijah* yet in your possession . . . I take it for granted that you will be willing to sell, for I remember when I went to see the picture, five years since, it was in the garret. . . ." (James F. Beard, ed., *Letters and Journals of James Fenimore Cooper*, II, Cambridge, Mass., 1960, p. 397.) The painting was the MFA's first registered acquisition.

References: J.B. Flagg, *Allston*, New York, 1892, pp. 72, 129, 131, 196./ W. Dunlap, *History of the Arts of Design*, Boston, 1918, II, pp. 329, 331./ A. Burroughs, *Limners and Likenesses*, Cambridge, Mass., 1936, p. 130./ J.T. Soby and D. Miller, *Romantic Painting in America*, Museum of Modern Art, New York, 1943, pp. 11, 12./ E.P. Richardson, "Allston and the Development of Romantic Color," *Art Quarterly*, 1944, VII, no. 1, pp. 33, 52 (repr. p. 7)./ —, *American Romantic Painting*, New York, 1945, no. 19 (repr.)./ —, *Allston*, Chicago, 1948, pp. 117, 119–120, 204 (pl. XLII)./ V. Barker, *American Painting*, New York, 1950, p. 344./ J.T. Flexner, *Light of Distant Skies*, New York, 1954, p. 141 (pl. 58)./ E.P. Richardson, *Painting in America*, New York, 1956, p. 147.

Exhibitions: London, British Institution, 1818, no. 242./ London, Royal Academy, *Taunton Collection*, 1870, no. 129./ Boston Athenaeum, *Exhibition for the Benefit of the French*, 1871, no. 151./ Boston, MFA, *Contemporary Art*, 1879, no. 55./ —, *Allston*, 1881, no. 224./ New York, Whitney Museum, *A Century of American Landscape Painting*, 1938, no. 6. (repr.)./ Paris, Musée du Jeu de Paume, *Trois Siècles d'Art aux Etats-Unis*, 1938, no. 3./ New London, Conn., Lyman Allyn Museum, *Trumbull and His Contemporaries*, 1944, no. 39./ Detroit Institute of Arts, *World of the Romantic Artist*, 1944–1945, no. 35./ Chicago Art Institute and New York, Whitney Museum, *Hudson River School*, 1945, no. 4 (repr. p. 16)./ Detroit Institute of Arts and Boston, MFA, *Allston*, 1947, no. 20 (repr. p. 26)./ Columbus, O., Columbus Gallery, *Romantic America*, 1948, no. 1./ New York, American Federation of Arts, circulated in Germany and Italy, and Whitney Museum, *American Painting in the Nineteenth Century*, 1953–1954, no. 47./ Boston, MFA and Wellesley College, Jewett Arts Center, *Four Boston Masters*, 1959, no. 21 (repr. p. 35, not shown at Wellesley)./ Washington, D.C., Corcoran Gallery, *The American Muse*, 1959, no. 60 (repr.)./ Utica, N.Y., Munson-Williams-Proctor Institute, *19th Century American Painting*, 1960, no. 1.

64.

fig. 180

Beatrice

Half-length and facing front, she wears a green dress with white, slashed sleeves and clasps a gold cross held by a chain about her neck. Brown background.

Oil on canvas. 31¼ × 25¼ in. (76.8 × 64.1 cm.)

Painted in 1819.

Collections: Theodore Lyman, Boston, 1819; Samuel A. Eliot, Boston, by 1839; Mrs. Samuel A. Eliot, Boston, 1879; heirs of Mrs. Eliot, by 1881; Miss Ellen T. Bullard, Boston.

Anonymous gift. 59.778

Henry Francis Cary's translation of Dante's *Divina Commedia* (1805–1812) aroused considerable interest in the poet and was probably the source of Allston's inspiration. Beatrice, of the noble Portinari family of Florence, was born in 1265 and died in 1290 as the wife of Simone de' Bardi. Dante is said to have loved her since he was nine years old. After her death he idealized this love in the *Vita Nova* and made her the central figure, as a spiritual and mystical symbol of divine knowledge, in the *Divina Commedia*. On November 15, 1819, Allston wrote to C.R. Leslie, "I have painted a small picture from Spenser and a head of Beatrice, both just sold" (J.B. Flagg, *see below*). The work was engraved by John Cheney in 1836.

References: A. Jameson, *Athenaeum*, London, 1844, p. 41./ M.F. Sweetser, *Allston*, Boston, 1879, pp. 111, 187./ E.P. Peabody, *Last Evening with Allston and Other Papers*, Boston, 1886, pp. 46–49./ J.B. Flagg, *Allston*, New York, 1892, p. 161./ E.P. Richardson, "Allston and the Development of Romantic Color," *Art Quarterly*, 1944, VII, no. 1, pp. 33, 54 (fig. 9)./ —, *Allston*, Chicago, 1948, pp. 139, 141, 148, 207 (pl. XLVII).

Exhibitions: Boston Athenaeum, *Exhibition*, 1827, no. 37./ Boston, Harding's Gallery, *Allston*, 1839, no. 10./ Boston, MFA, *Allston*, 1881, no. 232./ Detroit Institute of Arts and Boston, MFA, *Allston*, 1947, no. 28.

65.

fig. 176

Moonlit Landscape

The light of the moon, which breaks through the gray and white clouds in the blue sky, makes the river landscape brown and blue. The horseman, figures, and beached boats are silhouetted in brown.

Oil on canvas. 24 × 35 in. (61 × 88.9 cm.)

Painted in 1819.

Collections: H.J. Bigelow, Boston, by 1839; Mrs. Jacob Bigelow, Boston, by 1881; William Sturgis Bigelow, Boston.

Gift of William Sturgis Bigelow. 21.1429

In addition to the evidence of style, the date of the painting is derived from a letter written by Allston in May, 1821. In it he describes his activities after his return to Boston in October, 1818 and records the paintings done in the beginning of 1819, one of which is *Moonlit Landscape* (Allston to William Collins, *Dana Papers*, Massachusetts Historical Society, Boston).

References: M.F. Sweetser, *Allston*, Boston, 1879, pp. 115, 188./ J.T. Soby and D. Miller, *Romantic Painting in America*, Museum of Modern Art, New York, 1943, p. 13 (repr. p. 52)./ E.P. Richardson, "Allston and the Development of Romantic Color," *Art Quarterly*, 1944, VII, no. 1, p. 43 (repr. p. 50)./ —, *American Romantic Painting*, New

York, 1945, no. 20 (repr.)./ —, *Allston*, Chicago, 1948, pp. 144–145, 206 (pl. XLVI)./ V. Barker, *American Painting*, New York, 1950, p. 349 (pl. 48)./ J.T. Flexner *American Painting*, New York, 1950, pp. 24, 112 (pl. 12)./ —, *Light of Distant Skies*, New York, 1954, p. 174 (pl. 71)./ E.P. Richardson, *Painting in America*, 1956, pp. 145–147 (fig. 65)./ A. Eliot, *300 Years of American Painting*, New York, 1957, p. 42 (repr. p. 41)./ V. Young, "Changing Landscape in American Art," *Arts Yearbook 2*, 1958, p. 93 (repr. p. 88).

Exhibitions: Boston Athenaeum, *Exhibition*, 1829, no. 130./ Boston, Harding's Gallery, *Allston*, 1839, no. 24./ Boston Athenaeum, *Exhibitions*, 1850, no. 91; 1857, no. 222./ Boston, MFA, *Allston*, 1881, no. 215./ Hartford, Conn., Wadsworth Atheneum, *Night Scenes*, 1940, no. 52./ Detroit Institute of Arts and Boston, MFA, *Allston*, 1947, no. 26 (repr. p. 30)./ Detroit Institute of Arts and San Francisco, M.H. de Young Memorial Museum, *Painting in America, the Story of 450 Years*, 1957, no. 67 (repr. p. 23)./ New York, Wildenstein and Co., *The American Vision*, 1957, no. 7 (repr.)./ Boston, MFA and Wellesley College, Jewett Arts Center, *Four Boston Masters*, 1959, no. 22 (repr. p. 32)./ St. Louis City Art Museum, *200 Years of American Painting*, 1964, p. 9 (repr.).

66.   **American Scenery. Time: Afternoon with a Southwest Haze**
A hazy, wooded landscape with distant blue hills under soft pink clouds. A horseman crosses a brown pool in the foreground.
Oil on canvas. 18½ × 24½ in. (47 × 62.2 cm.)
Painted in 1835.
Collections: Edmund Dwight, Boston, before 1839; Edmund Dwight, his son, Boston, 1849.
Bequest of Edmund Dwight. 00.505
Richardson (*see below*) suggests a late date, about 1835.
References: M.F. Sweetser, *Allston*, Boston, 1879, p. 115./ E.P. Richardson, *Allston*, Chicago, 1948, pp. 148, 212 (pl. LV).
Exhibitions: Boston, Harding's Gallery, *Allston*, 1839, no. 14./ Boston Athenaeum, *Exhibition*, 1850, no. 82./ Boston, MFA, *Allston*, 1881, no. 218.

VICTOR GIFFORD AUDUBON (1809–1860) (attributed)

67.   **Hudson River View**
Oil on canvas. 20 × 30 in. (50.8 × 76.2 cm.)
Painted about 1840–1850.
M. and M. Karolik Collection. 47.1206
Reference: *Karolik Catalogue*, 1949, no. 34 (repr.).

MILTON AVERY   (1893–1965), born in Altmar, N.Y., was the son of Russell and Esther Avery. When he was twelve, they moved to Hartford, Conn., where he attended the Connecticut League of Art Students, his only formal art training. The year 1925, when he moved to New York City, and his marriage in 1926 were pivotal points in his life. His subjects are landscapes, sometimes inspired by his summer visits to New England, and his family. His atmospheric style has its roots in French painting, especially the Impressionists and Matisse, which he first saw in New York. He worked in New York and Massachusetts until his death.

68.   **Marsden Hartley**
fig. 588
Half-length, facing front, he leans with his elbow on a brown table right. He wears a mauve suit, pink shirt, and a red bow tie with a blue and white flower in his lapel. Intense blue eyes dominate the greenish yellow hue of his face. Thin wispy hair falls over reddish ears. The background is green.
Oil on canvas. 36 × 28 in. (91.4 × 71.1 cm.)
Signed and dated lower right: *Milton Avery 1943*.
Collection: Estate of the artist, New York.
Charles Henry Hayden Fund. 65.1293
Although Hartley and Avery were friends, the portrait was not from life but, as customary with Avery, was from a preliminary sketch. It was painted in the year of Hartley's death.

Reference: H. Kramer, *Milton Avery: Paintings 1930–1960*, New York, 1962, p. 73 (repr.).

WILLIAM BABCOCK (1826–1899), born in Boston, received artistic training there before leaving for Paris in 1847 to study with Thomas Couture. Deeply influenced by Millet, he continued to work in France until his death in Bois d'Arcy.

69.
fig. 340

Girl with a Pink Bonnet

Bust-length, facing half right, she wears a pink kerchief, red roses at her throat, and a brown smock over blue. The background is green.
Oil on canvas. 13¾ × 10½ in. (34.9 × 26.6 cm.)
Signed and dated lower left: *WP Babcock '65* (initials in monogram).
Gift of Miss Emma E. Hicks. 29.48

70.

Classical Scene

In a green landscape with yellow sky beyond, Cupid holds blue drapery over the kneeling Venus. Another putto plays lower right.
Oil on panel. 9¼ × 12¾ in. (23.5 × 32.3 cm.)
Gift of the Estate of Mrs. James T. Fields. 35.1980
Exhibition: Cambridge, Mass., Busch-Reisinger Museum, *Babcock*, 1954.

71.

Landscape with Figures

A lady, in yellow and white, plays with three children beneath a tree; they are dressed in red, blue, and brown. In the background is a brown landscape under blue sky.
Oil on canvas. 10 × 13¾ in. (25.4 × 34.9 cm.)
Signed lower right: *Wm. Babcock.*
Gift of John Richardson Hall. 17.1621
Exhibition: Cambridge, Mass., Busch-Reisinger Museum, *Babcock*, 1954.

72.

The Quartet

Two men in profile to the right, and two girls in white, all bust-length, gather about an open book. The background is dark.
Oil on panel. 6 × 10 in. (15.2 × 25.4 cm.)
Signed lower left: *W.P. Babcock* (initials in monogram).
Bequest of the artist. 00.508

73.

The Red Hat

In a blue and green landscape, the figure of a girl, half-length, turns right to look over her shoulder. From under the red hat, her yellow hair falls on bare shoulders; she wears a white blouse and carries a red scarf over one arm.
Oil on panel. 12½ × 10¼ in. (31.7 × 26 cm.)
Signed upper right: *Wm. Babcock.*
Bequest of the artist. 00.506
Exhibition: Cambridge, Mass., Busch-Reisinger Museum, *Babcock*, 1954.

74.

Still Life with Fish

A mackerel before a red pitcher, with some leeks, lemon slices, and a knife. The table and background are brown.
Oil on canvas. 12½ × 15¾ in. (31.7 × 40 cm.)
Signed upper left: *WP Babcock.*
Collection: Professor A.R. Marston, Lawrence, Kan.
Anonymous gift in memory of John W. Bigelow. 08.443
Painted in Barbizon, France, as inscribed on the back.

75.

Susanna and the Elders

Susanna lies on a white coverlet on the ground, while the elders, robed in red, stand above her. A cupid kneels right, before a dark and obscure landscape.
Oil on panel. 11¾ × 10 in. (29.7 × 25.4 cm.)
Signed upper right: *W.P. Babcock* (initials in monogram).
Bequest of the artist. 00.509
Exhibition: Cambridge, Mass., Busch-Reisinger Museum, *Babcock*, 1954.

HENRY BACON (1837–1912), born in Haverhill, Mass., was a field artist for *Leslie's Weekly* during the Civil War. In 1864 he left for study at the École des Beaux Arts in Paris and settled there, traveling extensively until his death in Cairo, Egypt.

76.
fig. 410

On Shipboard
The deck of an ocean liner, with passengers dressed in brown or gray who are sitting, resting, or playing quoits. The sea below is blue under cloudy sky.
Oil on canvas. 19¼ × 28½ in. (48.9 × 72.3 cm.)
Signed and dated lower left: *Henry Bacon 1877.*
Gift of Mrs. Edward Livingston Davis. 13.1692

Exhibitions: New York, Whitney Museum, *The Social Scene in Paintings and Prints from 1800–1935*, 1935, no. 4./ Hartford, Conn., Wadsworth Atheneum, *Off for the Holidays*, 1955, no. 7 (repr.).

JOSEPH BADGER (1708–1765), born in Charlestown, Mass., moved about 1733 to Boston, where his trade was house painting and glazing. Self-taught, he probably did not start painting portraits until after 1740. The death of Smibert in 1751 made him one of the principal resident portraitists in Boston until his death.

77.
fig. 14

Elizabeth Storer (Mrs. Isaac Smith)
Three-quarter length, she stands facing front before a brown background, wearing a blue dress with white bodice and cuffs.
Oil on canvas. 36 × 29 in. (91.4 × 73.6 cm.)
Painted about 1746.
Collections: William Smith, son of the sitter; Elizabeth Storer Smith (Mrs. Edward Cruft), his daughter; Frances Cordis Cruft, her granddaughter.
Bequest of Frances Cordis Cruft. 42.376

Elizabeth Storer (1726–1786) was born in Boston, the daughter of Ebenezer and Mary Storer. She married Isaac Smith, a prosperous Boston merchant, in 1746 and had six children by him. She died in Boston. The portrait was probably done at the time of her marriage. The Yale Gallery of Fine Arts owns the portraits of Mr. and Mrs. Isaac Smith, painted by Copley in 1769.

78.

Mrs. William Foye (Elizabeth Campbell)
Seated, three-quarter length, she faces three-quarters right in a gray dress with white bodice and cuffs. A brown wall is in the left background, and a green landscape may be seen through a window, right.
Oil on canvas. 36 × 29 in. (91.4 × 73.6 cm.)
Painted about 1750.
Collections: Descended in the donor's family to Mrs. William Perkins (Catherine Callender Amory), grandmother of the donors; Mrs. John Homans, Canton, Mass., 1918.
Gift of Miss Katharine Amory Homans and Miss Marian Jackson Homans. 48.1162

Elizabeth Campbell (1695–1782), daughter of John and Elizabeth Campbell of Boston, in 1716 married William Foye, the Treasurer of Massachusetts from 1736 to 1753. She probably died in Milton, Mass. Park dates the painting about 1750, which agrees with the sitter's apparent age. Badger's portrait of her son William (Cat. no. 79) is also in the MFA collection.
Reference: L. Park, *Badger*, Boston, 1918, p. 16.

79.
fig. 15

William Foye
Half-length, turned three-quarters right, he stands wearing a blue coat and red waistcoat, both trimmed in gold. His right arm is akimbo, his left hand thrust into the waistcoat. A brown background is to the left, a green wooded landscape, right.
Oil on canvas. 36 × 29 in. (91.4 × 73.6 cm.)
Painted about 1750.
Collections: Same as Cat. no. 78.

Gift of Miss Katharine Amory Homans and Miss Marian Jackson Homans.
48.1163

William Foye, Jr. (1716–1771), son of William and Elizabeth Campbell Foye of Boston and Milton, graduated from Harvard in 1735. He later took part in the expedition against Cartagena under Admiral Vernon in 1740–1741. He settled in Halifax, Nova Scotia and was, for twenty-two years until his death, its Provost Marshal. The portrait probably was painted in Boston at approximately the same time as his mother's, about 1750.

References: L. Park, *Badger*, Boston, 1918, p. 17./ C.B. Fergusson, *The Origin of Representative Government in Canada*, Halifax, Nova Scotia, 1958 (repr. p. 45).

80.
fig. 13

Mrs. John Edwards (Abigail Fowle)

Seated in a high-backed chair, three-quarter length, she faces three-quarters right, holding a book. Her dress is brown, her shawl, sleeves, and cap are white. A landscape is in the right background.

Oil on canvas. 47 × 36 in. (119.4 × 91.4 cm.)
Painted about 1750–1760.
Collections: Thomas Carter Smith, the sitter's great-grandson; Frances Barnard Townsend, his daughter; Dr. Charles Wendell Townsend, her son, Boston.
Gift of Dr. Charles Wendell Townsend. 24.421

Abigail Fowle (1679–1760), daughter of Isaac and Beriah Bright Fowle of Charlestown, Mass., first married William Smith, a wealthy shipmaster. Ten years after his death, in 1730, she married John Edwards, a Boston goldsmith, whose son had married one of her daughters. From her apparent age, the portrait was probably painted about 1750–1760.

References: F.W. Bayley, *Five Colonial Artists*, Boston, 1929 (repr. p. 21, misidentified as Mrs. Jonathan Edwards, née Sarah Pierepont [sic])./ J.T. Flexner, *First Flowers of Our Wilderness*, Boston, 1947, p. 344 (repr. p. 196)./ V. Barker, *American Painting*, New York, 1950, p. 124./ E.P. Richardson, *Painting in America*, New York, 1956, p. 44 (fig. 17).

Exhibitions: Rhode Island School of Design Museum, *Old and New England*, 1945, no. 8 (repr. p. 15)./ Chicago Art Institute, *From Colony to Nation*, 1949, no. 19./ Colorado Springs Fine Arts Center, *Likeness of America 1680–1820*, 1949, no. 4 (repr. no. 11)./ Detroit Institute of Arts and San Francisco, M.H. de Young Memorial Museum, *Painting in America, the Story of 450 Years*, 1957, no. 21.

81.

Reverend Ellis Gray

Half-length, facing front, he wears white ecclesiastical bands with a black suit. The background is brown, with painted spandrels below.

Oil on canvas. 30 × 25 in. (76.2 × 63.5 cm.)
Painted about 1758.
Collections: Mrs. Robert S. Russell, Boston; Richard Cary Curtis, her nephew, Cambridge, Mass., 1924.
Gift of Mrs. Richard Cary Curtis. 58.334

Son of Edward and Hannah Ellis Gray, the Rev. Gray (1716–1753) was born in Boston and graduated from Harvard in 1734. Ordained in 1738, he was, with the Rev. William Welsteed, pastor of the Congregational Second Church in Boston. He died of apoplexy in 1753. Five portraits of the Rev. Gray by Badger are known. Park cites the one in the Massachusetts Historical Society, Boston, painted about 1750, as being the original from which the other four were taken about 1758.

Reference: L. Park, *Badger*, Boston, 1918, p. 19.

82.
fig. 12

Thomas Dawes

Full-length, turned three-quarters right, the child stands holding a black hat under his left arm and an orange in his right hand. His coat and breeches are red, his stockings and ruffles white, his waistcoat brown. An indistinct landscape in the background is brown and black.

Oil on canvas. 50¼ × 40½ in. (127.6 × 102.8 cm.)
Painted about 1764.
Collections: Thomas Dawes, Boston; the Rev. Thomas Dawes, his grandson, Brewster, Mass., 1823; Elizabeth Dawes (Mrs. George Minot), his sister, Cambridge, Mass., 1878; Ellen Minot Fuller, her daughter, Exeter, N.H., about 1907; Arthur Ossoli Fuller, her husband, Exeter, about 1930.
Lent by the Heirs of Ellen Minot Fuller. 256.42

Thomas Dawes (1757–1825), born in Boston the son of Col. Thomas and Hannah Blake Dawes, graduated from Harvard in 1777. In 1780 and in 1788 he was a member of the State Convention. From 1792 to 1802 he sat on the bench of the Massachusetts Supreme Court and was then Judge of Probate until his death. Inscribed on the back of the painting is: *Thomas Dawes/ Taken in the year 1750, et.7 years/ Given to his grandson, T. Dawes 3rd 1823.* The date given is erroneous, for Thomas was not born until 1757; his father, Col. Dawes (1731–1809), would have been twelve years old in 1750. On the basis of the sitter's age, this portrait may be dated about 1764.
References: H.W. Holland, *William Dawes and His Ride with Paul Revere*, Boston, 1878, p. 68 (pl. XI, attrib. Copley)./ F.W. Bayley, *Copley*, Boston, 1915, pp. 91–92 (attrib. Copley)./ L. Park, *Badger*, Boston, 1918, pp. 13–14 (repr. opp. p. 22)./ —, "Badger and His Portraits of Children," *Old Time New England*, 1923, XIII, no. 3, p. 105 (repr. p. 98).

THOMAS BALL   (1819–1911), born in Charlestown, Mass., worked first in Boston from 1837 to 1853 as a musician, and as a miniature and portrait painter. He studied sculpture in Italy from 1854 to 1857, returned to Boston as a sculptor, and in 1864 settled again in Italy. He worked there until 1897, frequently visiting the U.S., and on his return lived in Montclair, N.J., where he died.

83.
fig. 244

Cornelia M. Walter (Mrs. William B. Richards)
Three-quarter length, seated facing front in a red armchair, she wears a blue satin dress with lace cuffs on its short sleeves and holds a closed fan. Green drapery and a brown damask screen are behind her.
Oil on canvas. 50¼ × 40¼ in. (127.6 × 102.2 cm.)
Painted about 1840–1850.
Collections: William B. Richards, Boston; Elise Bordman Richards, Boston.
Gift of Elise Bordman Richards. 12.424

Cornelia Walter (1814–1898), born in Boston the daughter of Lynde and Ann Mansfield Walter, succeeded her brother Lynde M. Walter as editor of the *Boston Transcript*. Her portrait was painted about 1840–1850, before her marriage to William Richards of Boston (Ball, *see below*).
Reference: T. Ball, *My Threescore Years and Ten*, Boston, 1891, pp. 94–98.

JAMES BARD   (1815–1897)

84.
fig. 274

The Hudson River Steamboat "Rip Van Winkle"
Oil on canvas. 31¼ × 53 in. (79.4 × 134.6 cm.)
Signed and dated lower right: *Drawn & Painted by James Bard/ 162 Perry St. N.Y. 1854.*
M. and M. Karolik Collection. 47.1212
Reference: *Karolik Catalogue*, 1949, no. 35 (repr.).

WALTER BARKER   born in 1921 in Coblenz, Germany, graduated from the University of Indiana and Washington University in St. Louis, and studied painting with Max Beckmann, Philip Guston, and Fred Conway. In 1949 he taught art history at Salem College, Winston-Salem, N.C., and from 1950 to 1962 he taught painting at the Washington University School, St. Louis. He has traveled extensively in Europe, Egypt, the Near East, and in Mexico. He now lives in New York as instructor at the Brooklyn Museum School.

85.

fig. 603

Stormy Sky, Venice

The yellow sky is obscured from below by blue storm clouds streaked with black. Santa Maria della Salute and surroundings are indistinctly visible beyond the blue and green lagoon.

Oil on canvas. 64 × 84 in. (162.6 × 213.4 cm.)
Signed and dated upper left: *Barker 58.*
Anonymous gift. 59.324

Exhibition: New York, Fine Arts Associates, *Barker*, 1959, no. 3.

JAMES HENRY BEARD (1812–1893) was born in Buffalo, N.Y. Having learned portrait painting from an unknown itinerant artist in Painesville, O., he painted in Pittsburgh, Cincinnati, and in the South. He settled and worked in Cincinnati until 1870, except for a brief residence in New York City (1846–1847) and his service in the Civil War. He then lived in New York and was elected to the National Academy in 1872. He died in Flushing, N.Y.

86.

fig. 239

Lyman Beecher

Bust-length, the elderly gentleman faces front, wearing a black coat with a white shirt and tie. The background is brown.

Oil on chipboard. 14 × 11¾ in. (35.5 × 29.7 cm.)
Painted about 1840.

Collections: Given by the sitter to Timothy Batelle Mason, Cincinnati, by 1860; Abigail Hall Mason, his wife, 1861; Edward Beecher Mason, her son, 1875; Almira Campbell Mason, his wife, 1907; Maud Mason, her daughter, Boston, 1916.

Gift of Maud Mason. 42.190

Lyman Beecher (1775–1863), son of David and Esther Lyman Beecher of New Haven, Conn., was deeply influenced by Timothy Dwight, Professor of Theology at Yale. Ordained into the Presbyterian Church in 1799, he became famous for his evangelical preaching in Boston. He was President of the Lane Theological Seminary, Cincinnati, from 1832 until 1850 and died in Brooklyn, N.Y. The portrait is dated according to his apparent age.

CECILIA BEAUX (1863–1942) was born in Philadelphia and studied there with William Sartain. In 1889 she attended the Académies Julian and Colarossi in Paris and traveled in England and Italy. A prominent portraitist in Philadelphia, Boston, and New York, she was elected to the National Academy in 1902 and died in Gloucester, Mass.

87.

A Lady In Black

Full-length, seated on a green sofa beside a large gold cushion, she looks up from a book. To the left of the gray wall behind, the open window is partly screened by a gold curtain.

Oil on canvas. 78¼ × 47½ in. (198.7 × 120.6 cm.)
Signed lower left: *Cecilia Beaux.* Painted in 1916.

Gift of Alfred I. du Pont. 21.1841

The date was given by the donor.

Exhibition: Philadelphia, Pennsylvania Academy of the Fine Arts, *Paintings and Drawings of Cecilia Beaux*, 1955, no. 55 (as Mrs. Alfred du Pont).

HANNES BECKMANN was born in Stuttgart, Germany in 1909. After attending school in Hamburg he studied at the Bauhaus, Dessau in 1928 with Paul Klee, Vassily Kandinsky, and Joseph Albers. In 1932 he went to Vienna, where he studied for two years at the Graphische Lehr und Versuchsanstalt, Photographic Department. From 1938 to 1944 he was in Prague working as acting director of a prominent photographic studio. From 1944 until the end of the war he was interned in a concentration camp. He came to the United States in 1948 and settled in New York, where he is head of the Photographic Department at the Guggenheim Museum. After 1952 he taught Color and Design at the Cooper Union Art School in New York.

88.

fig. 613

Neither-Nor

Alternating vertical bands of light blue, brown, gray, white, and tan with interlocking and overlying rectangles against a blue field.
Oil on celotex. 29¼ × 29¼ in. (74.3 × 74.3 cm.)
Signed and dated lower left: *h.b.61.*
Abraham Shuman Fund. 65.503

GEORGE WESLEY BELLOWS (1882–1925), born in Columbus, O., in 1904, began study at the New York School of Art. He taught at the Art Students League in 1910 and 1911, and at the School of the Chicago Art Institute in 1919; in 1913 he helped organize the Armory Show. He began work in lithography in 1916. His summers were spent principally in Maine, but also in Carmel, Calif., Santa Fé, N.M., Woodstock, N.Y., and Newport, R.I. He died in New York City.

89.

fig. 552

Rainy Night

Green grass and trees are dominant in a view of a street, gray with rain. To the left a figure muffled in black descends the steps from a white house.
Oil on canvas. 22¼ × 28 in. (56.5 × 71.1 cm.)
Inscribed on back, center: *Wet Night/ Geo. Bellows/ 146 E. 19th St./ N.Y.*
Painted in 1916.
Collections: With Frank K.M. Rehn, New York; Duncan Phillips, Washington, D.C.; John F. Braun, Philadelphia.
Charles Henry Hayden Fund. 32.420

The date is given by the artist's wife.

Reference: *MFA Bulletin*, 1932, xxx, no. 182, pp. 80–81 (repr. p. 82).

Exhibitions: Washington, D.C., Corcoran Gallery, *Paintings from the Collection of Mrs. D.C. Phillips and Mr. Duncan Phillips*, 1920, no. 12 (as *Wet Night*)./ New York, American Academy of Arts and Letters, *Impressionist Mood in American Painting*, 1959, no. 44./ Boston, Vose Galleries, *Exhibition in Honor of Robert C. Vose*, 1961, no. 3.

90.

fig. 555

Study of Emma and the Children

Painted in simplified planes of russet and orange, accented with purple, Emma reclines on a chaise longue, holding her two daughters. Behind, an abstract landscape in purple.
Oil on canvas. 58¼ × 67 in. (147.9 × 170.2 cm.)
Painted in 1917.
Collections: Given by the artist to John Carroll, Woodstock, N.Y., 1922; Mrs. John Carroll, East Chatham, N.Y.
Abraham Shuman Fund. 63.261

An almost identical lithograph, *Mother and Children*, 1916, is reproduced in Emma Bellows' *George Bellows—His Lithographs*, 1927, no. 164. Represented in this study are Bellows' wife Emma and their daughters Anne and Jean. The apparent age of the younger girl, Jean (born April, 1915), suggests that the picture dates from 1917, before Bellows' summer trip to California. The painting, one of several compositions of the artist's family, is a study in which he experimented with the Cubist technique which he had encountered at the Armory Show in New York in 1913. A later, finished version is Cat. no. 92. A nearly identical version, *My Family* (1916, 60 × 66 in.), until recently in the artist's estate, is painted in summer greens.

91.

fig. 554

Emma in Black Print

Three-quarter length, she faces front wearing a black print dress and holding a black straw hat in her right hand. The background is black.
Oil on canvas. 40 × 32 in. (101.6 × 81.2 cm.)
Signed lower right: *geo Bellows*. Painted in 1919.
Collections: With Frank K.M. Rehn, New York; John T. Spaulding, Boston, 1923.
Bequest of John T. Spaulding. 48.518

"I have always regarded this portrait of my wife as one of the very few best things which I have done. There are only three or four quite good enough to hang with it." (Letter from the artist, Feb. 5, 1923.) Painted in Newport, R.I. the summer of 1919.

Reference: E.S. Bellows, *Paintings of Bellows*, New York, 1929, no. 88 (repr.).

Exhibition: New York, Metropolitan Museum, *Bellows Memorial*, 1925, no. 34 (repr. p. 75).

92.
fig. 553

Emma and Her Children

Mrs. Bellows and her two daughters are seated full-length on a black sofa. She wears a long black dress. Jean, eight years old, wears white muslin; Anne, twelve, has a green shawl over a pink dress. The room is gray with red curtains.

Oil on canvas. 59 × 65 in. (149.8 × 165.1 cm.)

Painted in 1923.

Collections: Mrs. George Bellows, New York; with the Boston Art Club.

Gift of Subscribers and the John Lowell Gardner Fund. 25.105

"Painted in Bellows' studio at Woodstock, N.Y., September of 1923." (Letter from Mrs. Emma Story Bellows, May 28, 1943.)

References: "A Recent Portrait by Bellows," *MFA Bulletin*, 1925, XXIII, no. 138, p. 33 (repr.)./ E.S. Bellows, *Paintings of Bellows*, New York, 1929, no. 129 (repr.)./ G.W. Eggers, *Bellows*, New York, 1931 (repr. p. 34)./ W.F. Paris, *Hall of American Artists*, New York, 1952, VII, pp. 88, 97.

Exhibitions: Washington, D.C., Corcoran Gallery, *Contemporary Oils*, 1923, no. 212 (repr. frontispiece)./ New York, Metropolitan Museum, *Bellows Memorial*, 1925, no. 50 (repr. p. 100)./ New York, Century Club, *Bellows*, 1939, no. 9 (repr.)./ Chicago Art Institute, *Bellows*, 1946, no. 52 (repr. p. 54)./ New York, Metropolitan Museum, *Art Students League*, 1951, no. 46 (repr.)./ Washington, D.C., Corcoran Gallery and Toledo Museum, *25th Biennial Exhibit of Contemporary American Paintings*, 1957, no. 9 (repr. p. 14)./ Rhode Island School of Design Museum, Manchester, N.H., Currier Gallery, and Dartmouth College, Carpenter Art Galleries, *Dynamic Symmetry* 1961, no. 8 (repr.).

FRANK WESTON BENSON (1862–1951), born in Salem, Mass., studied at the Boston Museum School and at the Académie Julian in Paris under Boulanger and Lefebvre. He was elected to the National Academy in 1905. From 1889 to 1917 he was an instructor at the Museum School and lived in Boston until his death. Famous for his paintings and etchings of water fowl and fishing scenes, he was, with his Boston colleague, Tarbell, a member of the Ten American Painters.

93.
fig. 503

Girl in a Red Shawl

Three-quarter length, she is seated in profile to the left before a gray background. She wears a white dress with a red shawl and a black hat.

Oil on canvas. 32¼ × 32¼ in. (81.9 × 81.9 cm.)

Signed and dated lower right: *Frank W. Benson/ 1890.*

Collection: Mrs. David P. Kimball, Boston, 1896.

Bequest of David P. Kimball in memory of his wife Clara Bertram Kimball. 23.519

Exhibitions: Boston, Chase's Gallery, *Benson and Tarbell*, 1891, no. 2./ Chicago, *World's Columbian Exposition*, 1893, no. 177./ Boston, Copley Hall, *Portraits*, 1896, no. 22./ Boston, *South End Free Art Exhibition*, 1899, no. 75./Boston, St. Botolph Club, *Benson*, 1900, no. 9./ New York, American Federation of Arts, circulated in the U.S., *American Traditional Painters*, 1962–1963.

94.

Decorative Head

Bust-length, her head turned three-quarters left, a girl with red hair, wearing a green robe, is posed before a green circular design.

Oil on canvas. 20 × 24 in. (50.8 × 61 cm.)

Signed and dated upper left: *F.W. Benson. 1894.*

Bequest of Dr. Arthur C. Cabot. 13.2907

Exhibitions: Philadelphia, Pennsylvania Academy of the Fine Arts, *64th Annual*, 1894–1895, no. 11./ Boston, St. Botolph Club, *Benson*, 1900, no. 6.

95.
fig. 502

Gertrude

Full-length, turned three-quarters left, the girl is seated in a white rocking chair, in a room with buff and brown walls. She wears a pink and white dress with brown shoes and wool stockings.
Oil on canvas. 50 × 40 in. (127 × 101.6 cm.)
Signed and dated lower right: *F.W. Benson 1899.*
Gift of Mrs. William Rodman Fay. 54.596
The portrait is of the donor (née Gertrude Schirmer) and was painted at West Manchester, Mass.

96.
fig. 505

Eleanor

Full-length, the girl sits on a white fence in left profile; she wears a pink dress and holds a straw hat. Behind her, green trees screen a blue landscape.
Oil on canvas. 25 × 30 in. (63.5 × 76.2 cm.)
Signed and dated lower left: *F.W. Benson/1907.*
Charles Henry Hayden Fund. 08.326
Exhibitions: Boston, Doll and Richards, *20th Annual*, 1907 (as *Lady in Pink*)./ Philadelphia, Pennsylvania Academy of the Fine Arts, *Ten American Painters*, 1908, no. 4 (repr.)./ Boston, St. Botolph Club, *Benson*, 1910, no. 14./ Washington, D.C., Corcoran Gallery, *Benson*, 1921, no. 13./ Akron Art Institute, *Benson*, 1924, no. 15./ Pittsburgh, Pa., Carnegie Institute, *Benson*, 1924, no. 8./ Salem, Mass., Essex Institute, *Benson*, 1956, no. 7 (repr. p. 18).

97.
fig. 500

Pintails Decoyed

Against a cloudy mauve and white sky, a hunter in a gray and brown marsh blind waits for the birds to settle into his decoys in the foreground.
Oil on canvas. 36 × 44 in. (91.4 × 111.7 cm.)
Signed and dated lower left: *F.W. Benson '21.*
Collection: Dr. Frederick L. Jack, Boston, 1923.
Gift of Dr. Freedrick L. Jack. 35.1230
Exhibition: Boston, MFA, *Benson and Tarbell*, 1938, no. 28.

98.
fig. 501

Salmon Fishing

A guide in black trousers and hat with a white shirt stands in the blue river. He holds a gaff in readiness for the leaping salmon. Steep, wooded banks are on the distant shore.
Oil on canvas. 36¼ × 44¼ in. (92.1 × 112.3 cm.)
Signed and dated lower left: *F.W. Benson '27.*
Gift of Friends of the Museum. 27.574
Exhibitions: Boston, Guild of Boston Artists, 1928./ Milwaukee Art Center, *Sports and Adventure in American Art*, 1947, no. 5.

99.
fig. 504

Lower Camp Pool

A blue river flows past its brown bank, left, into the foreground pool. One man unloads tackle from a gray canoe, another fishes from the water's edge. Trees bordering the river are green; the wooded hills beyond are blue under blue, cloudy sky.
Oil on canvas. 32 × 40¼ in. (81.2 × 102.2 cm.)
Signed and dated lower left: *F.W. Benson/ '28.*
Collections: Moreau Delano, West Orange, N.J.; Susan A. Delano McKelvey, his sister, New York and Boston, 1937.
Bequest of Susan A.D. McKelvey. 64.1917

100.

Early Morning

Five blue-winged teal fly over gray water. Purple sky.
Oil on canvas. 24 × 60¼ in. (61 × 153 cm.)
Signed lower left: *F.W. Benson.*
Bequest of Dr. Arthur C. Cabot. 13.2908
Exhibition: Boston, St. Botolph Club, *Benson*, 1900, no. 14.

THOMAS HART BENTON, born in Neosho, Mo. in 1889, studied at the Art Institute of Chicago in 1906–1907 and at the Académie Julian in Paris from 1908 to 1911. He returned to work in New York between 1913 and 1935 and during this period traveled throughout the country. He became well known for his mural paintings. From 1935 to 1941 he was Director of the Paintings Department at the Art Institute of Kansas City, Mo., where he now lives.

101.
fig. 585

New England Editor

Three-quarter length, an old man in right profile sits writing at an orange table; he wears a white shirt and blue trousers with suspenders. A brown-toned painting of the whaleship Catalpa *hangs above a bookcase on the green-blue wall.*
Oil and tempera on gesso panel. 30 × 37 in. (76.2 × 94 cm.)
Signed and dated lower right: *Benton '46.*
Charles Henry Hayden Fund. 46.1456
The sitter, George Anthony Hough (1868–1955), was born in New Bedford, Mass. He was editor of the *New Bedford Standard* at twenty-three, became its managing editor, and was known for the many leading newspapermen whom he trained. Politically, he was independent and aggressive, devoted to the minority, to the rights of individuals, and to fighting corruption in government. He died on Martha's Vineyard, Mass., where he had been Vice-President of the *Vineyard Gazette.* The whaleship *Catalpa* of New Bedford, commanded by Capt. George Anthony, accomplished a great feat at sea by rescuing some of the Fenian prisoners from the coast of Australia in 1876.
Exhibition: New Britain, Conn., Art Museum, *Benton*, 1954, no. 11 (repr.).

EUGENE BERMAN was born in St. Petersburg, Russia in 1899. He traveled as a child in western Europe (1908–1913) but returned to St. Petersburg in 1914 to study painting. In 1918 he fled the Russian Revolution to Paris, where he studied with Vuillard and Denis at the Académie Ranson. He achieved a considerable reputation while living in Paris, then moved to Italy early in the 1920's before coming to America about 1935. A considerable part of his fame has derived from his activity as a designer of sets for the ballet and opera. He now lives primarily in Rome.

102.
fig. 561

Vue Urbaine Nocturne

People and horses on a street corner at night are lighted by the yellow glow from an open door, right. Houses behind and a factory chimney are brown against the red sky.
Oil on canvas. 31½ × 39¼ in. (80 × 99.7 cm.)
Signed and dated lower right: *E. Berman, 1930.* Inscribed on back, left: *E. Berman/ Paris 1930/ Nocturne.*
Gift by contribution. 32.20
Exhibition: Phoenix Museum of Art, *Berman*, 1963, no. 8.

103.
fig. 562

Jeune Homme Couché

Before a green wall, a young man sleeps face down under a white sheet on a pink and red couch. The mat on the brown floor is green.
Oil on canvas. 35 × 58 in. (88.9 × 147.3 cm.)
Signed and dated lower right: *E. Berman 1931.* Inscribed on back, upper center: *E Berman/ Paris 1931/ Jeune Homme Couché.*
Maria Antoinette Evans Fund. 32.4
The model is said to be the poet Georges Huymet.
References: "Art in Paris," *Formes*, 1931, no. 11 (repr. opp. p. 89)./ F. Neugass, "Berman," *Die Kunst*, 1932, LXV, no. 12 (repr. p. 352)./ J.T. Soby, *After Picasso*, New York, 1935, p. 39 (pl. 19).
Exhibitions: New York, John Levy Galleries, *Berman*, 1932, no. 8./ Chicago Art Institute, *Paintings by Berman*, 1933./ Springfield, Mass., Museum of Fine Arts, *Cézanne to the Present*, 1935, no. 2./ Buffalo, Albright Art Gallery, *The Art of Today*, 1936, no. 6./ Boston, Institute of Modern Art, *Berman*, 1942, no. 7 (repr.)./ Phoenix Museum of Art, *Berman*, 1963, no. 7.

ALBERT BIERSTADT (1830–1902), born in Solingen, Germany, was brought to New Bedford, Mass. about 1831–1832 and raised there. In 1853 he returned to study at the Düsseldorf Academy, and until 1857 traveled in Germany and Switzerland, spending a winter in Rome. In 1858 he accompanied General F.W. Lander's expedition to the West Coast, and in 1860 settled in New York and was elected to the National Academy. From 1866 to 1882 he lived in Irvington-on-the-Hudson, then lived until his death in New York, but traveled regularly in the United States, Canada, and Europe.

104.

Fishing Boats at Capri
Oil on paper mounted on canvas. 13½ × 19½ in. (34.3 × 49.5 cm.)
Signed and dated lower right: *Capri/ june 14 1857/ A Bierstadt* (A and B in monogram).
M. and M. Karolik Collection. 47.1264
Reference: Karolik Catalogue, 1949, no. 36 (repr.).

105.
fig. 385

The Portico of Octavia, Rome
Beneath the old archway of red brick and yellow plaster, peasants in costumes of white, blue, red, and green sell their wares about a gray stone table. The cobbles and the houses seen through the arch are brown.
Oil on canvas. 28½ × 37 in. (72.3 × 94 cm.)
Signed and dated lower right: *A Bierstadt/ 1858* (A and B in monogram).
Collection: Bought by the Boston Athenaeum, 1858.
Deposited by the Boston Athenaeum, 1876. Ath. 27

"This painting shows only a small part of the remaining ruins of the portico built by Augustus in honor of his sister, but reconstructed after a fire in the reign of Septimius Severus (A.D. 193–211). A medieval brick arch replaces two of the portico's Corinthian columns. The artist painted the view inside the portico, then used as a fish market." (Scherer, *see below*.)

References: E.P. Richardson, American Romantic Painting, New York, 1945, no. 201 (repr.)./ M.R. Scherer, Marvels of Ancient Rome, New York, 1955, no. 47 (repr.).

Exhibitions: Boston, MFA, Contemporary Art, 1879, no. 156./ Detroit Institute of Arts, World of the Romantic Artist, 1944–1945, no. 88 (repr. p. 30)./ — and Toledo Museum, Travelers in Arcadia, 1951, no. 4 (repr. p. 17)./ New York, American Academy of Arts and Letters, The Great Decade in American Writing, 1850–1860, 1954, no. 102./ New York, Grolier Club, The Italian Influence on American Literature, 1961, no. 240 (repr.)./ Wilmington Society of Fine Arts, American Painting, 1857–1869, 1962, no. 5 (repr. p. 28)./ Santa Barbara Museum, Bierstadt, 1964, no. 8.

106.

The Black Horse
Oil on paper mounted on cardboard. 13½ × 19¼ in. (34.3 × 48.9 cm.)
Signed lower left: *A Bierstadt* (A and B in monogram). Painted about 1858.
M. and M. Karolik Collection. 48.412
Reference: Karolik Catalogue, 1949, no. 38 (repr.).

107.
fig. 384

Indians near Fort Laramie
Oil and paper mounted on cardboard. 13½ × 19½ in. (34.3 × 49.5 cm.)
Signed lower left: *A Bierstadt* (A and B in monogram). Inscribed on back before mounting: *Indians near Fort Laramie.* Painted about 1858.
M. and M. Karolik Collection. 48.411
Reference: Karolik Catalogue, 1949, no. 37 (repr.).

108.
fig. 386

Study of a Brown Horse
The horse rears against a gray background.
Oil on panel. 14½ × 19¾ in. (36.8 × 50.1 cm.)
Signed lower right: *A Bierstadt* (A and B in monogram). Painted about 1858.
Collection: Maxim Karolik, Newport, R.I., about 1946.
Bequest of Maxim Karolik. 64.420

In style and subject the study closely resembles *The Black Horse* in the M. and M. Karolik Collection (Cat. no. 106). Both were probably painted in 1857 or 1858, while Bierstadt was on the Lander expedition.

109.

Grove of Trees
Oil and paper mounted on cardboard. 13½ × 19 in. (34.3 × 48.2 cm.)

Signed lower right: *A Bierstadt* (A and B in monogram). Painted in 1858–1859 or 1863.
M. and M. Karolik Collection. 47.1197
Reference: Karolik Catalogue, 1949, no. 43 (repr.).

110. **Indian Camp**
Oil on paper mounted on canvas. 13¼ × 17¾ in. (33 × 45.1 cm.)
Signed lower right: *A Bierstadt* (A and B in monogram). Painted in 1858–1859 or 1863.
M. and M. Karolik Collection. 47.1205
Reference: Karolik Catalogue, 1949, no. 42 (repr.).

111. **Thunderstorm in the Rocky Mountains**
fig. 388

Above a dull, green, rocky landscape, gray storm clouds gather. Deer drink from a blue lake in the right foreground.
Oil on canvas. 19 × 29 in. (48.2 × 73.6 cm.)
Signed and dated lower left: *A B 59* (initials in monogram).
Collections: Elias T. Milliken, Boston, 1863; Mrs. E.T. Milliken, Boston; Mrs. Edward Hale and Mrs. J.C. Perkins, Boston.
Given in memory of Elias T. Milliken by his daughters, Mrs. Edward Hale and Mrs. John Carroll Perkins. 43.134

Thunderstorm in the Rocky Mountains was probably painted from sketches done by Bierstadt while with the Lander expedition to the West Coast.
References: E.P. Richardson, *American Romantic Painting*, New York, 1945, no. 202 (repr.)./ —, *Painting in America*, New York, 1956, p. 230 (fig. 104).
Exhibitions: Detroit Institute of Arts, *World of the Romantic Artist*, 1944–1945, no. 44 (repr. p. 19)./ New York, American Federation of Arts, circulated in Germany and Italy, and Whitney Museum, *American Painting in the Nineteenth Century*, 1953–1954, no. 15./ St. Louis City Art Museum and Minneapolis, Walker Art Center, *Westward America*, 1954, no. 157./ Detroit Institute of Arts and San Francisco, M.H. de Young Memorial Museum, *Painting in America, the Story of 450 Years*, 1957, no. 112 (repr. p. 25)./ New Bedford, Mass., Swain School of Design, W. Crapo Gallery, *Ryder-Bierstadt*, 1960, no. 25 (repr.)./ Wilmington Society of Fine Arts, *American Painting, 1857–1869*, 1962, no. 4 (repr. p. 28).

112. **View from the Wind River Mountains, Wyoming**
fig. 387

Oil on canvas. 30¼ × 48¼ in. (76.8 × 122.5 cm.)
Signed and dated lower left: *A Bierstadt 1860* (A and B monogram).
M. and M. Karolik Collection. 47.1202
Reference: Karolik Catalogue, 1949, no. 39 (repr.).

113. **Yosemite**
fig. 391

A corner of the valley where the wooded land is green and brown and snow covers the gray and green mountains behind. Gray clouds are in the blue sky.
Oil on canvas. 13½ × 19 in. (34.3 × 48.2 cm.)
Signed lower left: *A Bierstadt* (A and B in monogram). Painted about 1863.
Bequest of Maxim Karolik. 64.421

Probably painted during Bierstadt's trip to the West in 1863.

114. **Valley of the Yosemite**
Oil on chipboard. 11¾ × 19¼ in. (29.7 × 48.9 cm.)
Signed and dated lower right: *A Bierstadt 64* (A and B in monogram).
M. and M. Karolik Collection. 47.1236
Reference: Karolik Catalogue, 1949, no. 40 (repr.).

115. **Lake Tahoe, California**
fig. 389

Oil on canvas. 22 × 30 in. (55.9 × 76.2 cm.)
Signed and dated lower left: *A Bierstadt 67* (A and B in monogram).
M. and M. Karolik Collection. 47.1243
Reference: Karolik Catalogue, 1949, no. 41 (repr.).

116.
fig. 390

The Buffalo Trail
Oil on canvas. 32 × 48 in. (81.2 × 121.9 cm.)
Signed lower right: *A Bierstadt* (A and B in monogram). Painted in 1867–1868.
M. and M. Karolik Collection. 47.1268
Reference: Karolik Catalogue, 1949, no. 44 (repr.).

117.

Snow Scene with Buffaloes
Oil on panel. 18 × 24 in. (45.7 × 61 cm.)
Signed lower left: *A Bierstadt* (A and B in monogram). Painted in 1867–1868.
M. and M. Karolik Collection. 47.1245
Reference: Karolik Catalogue, 1949, no. 45 (repr.).

118.
fig. 393

Niagara from the American Side
A close-up view of the falls, from a brown and green bank touched with red. The gray, blue, and green water creates a gray mist touching the distant trees and sky with gray and yellow.
Oil on paper, mounted on canvas. 14 × 19½ in. (35.5 × 49.5 cm.)
Signed lower left: *A Bierstadt* (A and B in monogram). Painted in 1869.
Bequest of Maxim Karolik. 64.418
Dated on the basis of style; Bierstadt did visit Niagara in 1869.

119.
fig. 392

The Ambush
Oil on canvas. 30 × 50½ in. (76.2 × 128.2 cm.)
Signed lower left: *A Bierstadt* (A and B in monogram). Painted about 1870–1875.
M. and M. Karolik Collection. 47.1226
Reference: Karolik Catalogue, 1949, no. 47 (repr.).

120.
fig. 396

Storm in the Mountains
Oil on canvas. 38 × 60 in. (96.5 × 152.4 cm.)
Signed lower right: *A Bierstadt* (A and B in monogram). Painted about 1870–1880.
M. and M. Karolik Collection. 47.1257
Reference: Karolik Catalogue, 1949, no. 50 (repr.).

121.

Seal Rocks, Farallones
Oil on paper mounted on cardboard. 13½ × 19 in. (34.3 × 48.2 cm.)
Signed lower left: *A Bierstadt* (A and B in monogram). Inscribed on back before rebacking: *Seal Farralone Is Pacific 1872.*
M. and M. Karolik Collection. 47.1254
Reference: Karolik Catalogue, 1949, no. 46 (repr.).

122.

Geyser, Yellowstone Park
Oil on paper mounted on cardboard. 14 × 19½ in. (35.5 × 49.5 cm.)
Signed lower right: *A Bierstadt* (A and B in monogram). Painted about 1872–1873.
M. and M. Karolik Collection. 47.1253
Reference: Karolik Catalogue, 1949, no. 48 (repr.).

123.

Rocky Mountains, Colorado
Oil and paper mounted on masonite. 13¾ × 19½ in. (34.9 × 49.5 cm.)
Signed lower right: *A Bierstadt* (A and B in monogram). Inscribed on back: *Rocky Mts. Colo.* Painted in 1873.
M. and M. Karolik Collection. 47.1255
Reference: Karolik Catalogue, 1949, no. 49 (repr.).

124.

Moose Hunters' Camp, Nova Scotia
Oil on canvas. 26½ × 36½ in. (67.3 × 92.7 cm.)
Signed lower right: *A Bierstadt* (A and B in monogram). Painted about 1875–1878.

M. and M. Karolik Collection. 47.1256
Reference: Karolik Catalogue, 1949, no. 51 (repr.).

125.   **Banana Trees**

A study of two banana trees, with huge, bright green leaves and brown trunks against a blue sky.
Oil on canvas. Mounted on masonite. 19¼ × 13½ in. (48.9 × 34.3 cm.)
Signed lower left: *A Bierstadt* (A and B in monogram). Painted in 1877 or 1881.
Collection: Maxim Karolik, Newport, R.I., 1952.
Bequest of Maxim Karolik. 64.417

The subject matter and style would indicate that this was painted while Bierstadt was on a visit either to Nassau (1877) or to the Bahamas (1881).

126.   **Sailboats**
fig. 394

A schooner-rigged steamer, with dressed ship, lies at anchor with other schooners; a catboat sails among them. The distant shore is green.
Oil on cardboard. 13¾ × 19 in. (34.9 × 48.2 cm.)
Signed lower left: *A Bierstadt* (A and B in monogram). Painted in 1877 or 1881.
Collection: Norman Hirschl, New York.
Bequest of Maxim Karolik. 64.419

Probably painted on Bierstadt's visits to Nassau or the Bahamas; the sponging boats and the white ensign of the Royal Navy suggest these places and the style supports such a date. A variant, surely of the same area, is in the California Palace of the Legion of Honor.

127.   **Palm Trees with a Domed Church**

Oil on paper mounted on canvas. 14 × 19½ in. (35.5 × 49.5 cm.)
Signed lower left: *A Bierstadt* (A and B in monogram). Painted about 1880–1890.
M. and M. Karolik Collection. 47.1232
Reference: Karolik Catalogue, 1949, no. 53 (repr.).

128.   **The St. Lawrence River from the Citadel, Quebec**

Oil on paper mounted on canvas. 22 × 30½ in. (55.9 × 77.5 cm.)
Signed lower left: *A Bierstadt* (A and B in monogram). Inscribed on back before relining: *View from the Citadel, Quebec.* Painted after 1880.
M. and M. Karolik Collection. 47.1258
Reference: Karolik Catalogue, 1949, no. 52 (repr.).

129.   **Interior of a Library**
fig. 395

In a darkened Victorian interior, a woman looks up from reading. To the right of a window looking on sunlit trees, a boy sits reading beside a lectern; a green curtain, right, partly hides a cast of a classical statue.
Oil on canvas. 19¾ × 14½ in. (50.1 × 36.8 cm.)
Signed lower left: *A Bierstadt.* Painted in 1886.
Collections: Edward Bierstadt; sold Anderson Galleries, New York, April 27, 1905, no. 29 (as *Interior of Library, Minneapolis*), bought in; Edward Bierstadt, sold, American Art Galleries, New York, January 22, 1908, no. 60; Mrs. H. Busch; Maxim Karolik, Newport, R.I., 1961.
M. and M. Karolik Collection. 62.260

Presumably painted when Bierstadt visited the Lake Superior area in the summer of 1886.

130.   **Wreck of the "Ancon" in Loring Bay, Alaska**
fig. 397

Oil on paper mounted on panel. 14 × 19¾ in. (35.5 × 50.1 cm.)
Signed lower right: *A Bierstadt* (A and B in monogram). Painted in 1889.
M. and M. Karolik Collection. 47.1250
Reference: Karolik Catalogue, 1949, no. 54 (repr.).

GEORGE CALEB BINGHAM (1811–1879) was born in Augusta County, Va., but moved, in 1819, with his family to Missouri, where he spent most of his life. He studied at the Pennsylvania Academy in Philadelphia in 1837, lived in Washington, D.C. from 1840 to 1844, then studied in Düsseldorf, Germany from 1856 to 1858 and again in 1859. Also a politician, he was an active painter of portraits and especially of genre scenes of midcentury life on the Mississippi and in the towns on its banks: river men, political subjects, and so on. He died in St. Louis, Mo.

131.
fig. 285

The Squatters

An old man, smoking, leans on his staff center left in front of a log cabin left. A young man seated on a log in the foreground left regards the viewer. A lady bends over a wash-tub, hanging wash on the line which disappears left. The Missouri River is in the distance right.

Oil on canvas. 25 × 30 (63.5 × 76 cm.)
Signed and dated lower left: *G.C. Bingham 1850.*
Collections: Sold American Art Union, Dec. 16, 1852, no. 162; N.P. Hood, 1852; Henry L. Shattuck, Brookline, Mass., 1937.
Future Donation.

"The Squatters as a class, are not fond of the toil of agriculture, but erect their rude Cabins upon those remote portions of the National domain, where the abundant game supplies their phisical wants. When this source of subsistance becomes diminished, in consequence of increasing settlements around, they usually sell out their slight improvement, with their 'pre-emption title' to the land, and again follow the receding footsteps of Savage." (Letter from the artist to the American Art-Union, Nov. 18, 1850.) The sketches of the old man and of the young man are nos. 96 and 44 respectively in Bingham's *Sketchbook* (St. Louis Mercantile Library).

References: American Art Union, *Supplementary Bulletin*, New York, 1851, no. 10, p. 4./ A. Christ-Janer, *George Caleb Bingham of Missouri*, New York, 1940, pp. 55, 57./ J.B. Cowdrey, *American Art Union*, New York, 1953, p. 23./ J.F. McDermott, "Another Bingham Found: 'The Squatters,'" *The Art Quarterly*, 1956, vol. XIX, pp. 68–71 (repr. p. 69)./ —, *George Caleb Bingham*, Norman, Oklahoma, 1959, pp. 75–76, 178, 415 (repr. pl. 29).
Exhibition: Jones's Store in St. Louis, October, 1850 (as "The Squatter's Settlement").

132.
fig. 284

Wood-Boatmen on a River

Oil on canvas. 29 × 36 in. (73.6 × 91.4 cm.)
Signed and dated lower left: *G.C. Bingham/ 1854.*
M. and M. Karolik Collection. 46.848
Reference: *Karolik Catalogue*, 1949, no. 55 (repr.).

THOMAS BIRCH (1779–1851), born in Warwickshire, England, came to Philadelphia in 1794 with his father and they worked together as designers and engravers. Thomas began painting portraits sometime before 1807. He later became well known for his marine and winter subjects and for his naval paintings of the War of 1812. He traveled extensively in the South and East of the U.S., but Philadelphia remained his permanent home until his death.

133.
fig. 190

The "Wasp" and the "Frolic"

Oil on canvas. 20 × 30 in. (50.8 × 76.2 cm.)
Signed and dated lower right: *Thos. Birch 1820.*
M. and M. Karolik Collection. 47.1186
Reference: *Karolik Catalogue*, 1949, no. 56 (repr.).

134.

Philadelphia from Petty Island

Oil on canvas. 20 × 32 in. (50.8 × 81.2 cm.)
Painted about 1825.
M. and M. Karolik Collection. 47.1267
Reference: *Karolik Catalogue*, 1949, no. 48 (repr.).

135. **New York Harbor**
Oil on canvas. 20¼ × 30¼ in. (51.4 × 76.8 cm.)
Inscribed on back before relining: *New York/ T. Birch/ Phila.* Painted about
1827–1835.
M. and M. Karolik Collection. 47.1181
Reference: *Karolik Catalogue*, 1949, no. 57 (repr.).

136.
fig. 191
Skating
Oil on canvas. 20 × 30 in. (50.8 × 76.2 cm.)
Signed lower right: *T. Birch.* Painted about 1830.
M. and M. Karolik Collection. 47.1185
Reference: *Karolik Catalogue*, 1949, no. 61 (repr.).

137.
fig. 193
Seascape
Oil on canvas. 17¼ × 27½ in. (43.8 × 69.8 cm.)
Signed and dated lower left: *Birch 1831.*
M. and M. Karolik Collection. 47.1183
Reference: *Karolik Catalogue*, 1949, no. 59 (repr.).

138.
fig. 192
Stranded Ship by a Lighthouse
*To the left, a red-hulled ship lies grounded on the beach before a lighthouse on a point.
Other three-masted ships, silhouetted against the blue sky, sail on the choppy green sea.*
Oil on canvas. 20 × 30 in. (50.8 × 76.2 cm.)
Signed and dated lower left: *Thos Birch 1832.*
Collections: Copley Amory, Sr., Boston; Maxim Karolik, Newport, R.I.,
1961.
M. and M. Karolik Collection. 62.261

139. **Milford, North Wales, Pennsylvania**
Oil on canvas. 22½ × 28½ in. (57.1 × 72.3 cm.)
Signed and dated lower right: *T. Birch 1833.*
M. and M. Karolik Collection. 47.1207
Reference: *Karolik Catalogue*, 1949, no. 60 (repr.).

140. **Sleigh Ride in the Country**
Oil on canvas. 20 × 30 in. (50.8 × 76.2 cm.)
Signed and dated lower right: *T. Birch 1841.*
M. and M. Karolik Collection. 47.1182
Reference: *Karolik Catalogue*, 1949, no. 62 (repr.).

141.
fig. 189
The Rescue
*An open lifeboat crowded with crew members flees a badly damaged ship about to be
tossed onto gray coastal rocks in a rough green sea. The sky behind is stormy.*
Oil on canvas. 22 × 30 in. (55.9 × 76.2 cm.)
Signed and dated on a rock, center: *Thos. Birch/ 1843.*
Bequest of Maxim Karolik. 64.447
Two nearly identical versions are *The Rescue*, 1877, with Harry Shaw New-
man in 1948 and *A Shipwreck*, 1824, in the Brooklyn Museum.
Exhibitions: Minneapolis Institute of Arts and circulated in the U.S., *19th Century
American Paintings from the Collection of Maxim Karolik*, 1953–1954./ Washington, D.C.,
Smithsonian Institution, circulated in the U.S., *19th Century American Paintings*,
1954–1956, no. 7 (repr.)./ Ogunquit Museum, *8th Annual—Luminist and Trompe l'Oeil
Painters*, 1960, no. 1.

142. **The Landing of William Penn**
Oil on canvas. 34 × 48 in. (86.3 × 121.9 cm.)
Painted about 1850.
M. and M. Karolik Collection. 47.1179
Reference: *Karolik Catalogue*, 1949, no. 63 (repr.).

ISABEL BISHOP (Mrs. Harold G. Wolff), born in Cincinnati, O. in 1902, first studied in New York at the School of Applied Design. She twice attended the Art Students League, from 1920 to 1922 and from 1927 to 1930, and taught there from 1936 to 1937. In 1941 she was elected to the National Academy and in 1957 taught and lectured at the Skowhegan School in Maine. She now lives and works in New York.

143. **Ice Cream Cones**
fig. 577
Painted in gray, browns, and yellow, two office girls stand by a building eating ice cream cones.
Tempera and oil on masonite. 34 × 20 in. (86.3 × 50.8 cm.)
Painted in 1942.
Charles Henry Hayden Fund. 42.298
"Painted in New York in 1942." (Letter from the artist, July 9, 1942.)
Exhibitions: New York, Midtown Galleries, *Bishop*, 1949, no. 8 (repr. cover)./ Smith College Museum, *Ten Women Who Paint*, 1949, no. 1 (repr.).

JOSEPH BLACKBURN (active 1752–1774) was probably born in England. In 1753 he came to Boston from Bermuda, where he had arrived the year before, and by 1754 had worked in Newport, R.I. He visited Salem and from 1761 to 1763 was in Portsmouth, N.H. Perhaps because his popularity as a portrait painter was eclipsed by Copley's successes, Blackburn left for London in 1764. The last portraits recorded are of *Sir Richard Acton* and *Lady Anne Acton*, signed and dated 1774.

144. **Isaac Winslow and His Family**
fig. 24
A family of four, in three-quarter length. To the left Isaac, turned three-quarters right, stands in a brown suit, lined with white; Mrs. Winslow, seated center and facing front in a pink dress with white lace, holds baby Hannah, who wears white over a yellow petticoat; their daughter Lucy, standing in left profile, holds branches of apples in the skirt of her white and blue dress. The background left is draped in green; at the right is a walled garden below pink clouds.
Oil on canvas. 54½ × 79½ in. (138.4 × 201.9 cm.)
Signed and dated lower left: *I. Blackburn Pinx 1755.*
Collections: Samuel Winslow, great-grandson of the sitters, Roxbury, Mass., in 1878; Edward M. Winslow, Boston, 1902; George Scott Winslow, Boston, 1911; Miss Anna W. Winslow, Newcastle, Me., 1942.
Abraham Shuman Fund. 42.684
Isaac Winslow (1709–1777), born in Boston, was the son of Col. Edward and Hannah Moody Winslow. A graduate of Harvard in 1727, he was a partner with his brother Joshua in a profitable shipping business. A Loyalist, he moved to Halifax, N.S. in 1776, where he died. The MFA also owns portraits of him by Feke (Cat. no. 398) and one, with his second wife, by Copley (Cat. no. 296). Lucy Waldo, born in Boston in 1724, was the daughter of Samuel and Lucy Wainwright Waldo. She married Winslow in 1747; five of her eleven children died in infancy, and she died in Roxbury in 1768. Lucy Winslow, born in Boston in 1749, married George Irving, a Boston merchant, in 1768. Two years later she died and he married Mary MacIntosh Royall (see *Mary and Elizabeth Royall*, J.S. Copley, Cat. no. 254). Hannah Winslow (1755–1819) was married to John Wall, Captain in the British Army, in 1778. They lived in Nottinghamshire, England and later in Ireland.
References: F.S. Drake, *34th Report of the Boston Records, the Town of Roxbury*, Boston, 1878, p. 257./ A.T. Perkins, "Blackburn and Smibert," *Massachusetts Historical Society Proceedings*, 1878, XVI, p. 392./ W. Lincoln, *Genealogy of the Waldo Family*, Worcester, Mass., 1902, I, p. 188./ L. Park, *Blackburn*, Worcester, Mass., 1923, no. 88./ T. Bolton and H.L. Binsse, "Blackburn," *The Antiquarian*, 1930, XV, no. 5, p. 92./ J.T. Flexner, *First Flowers of Our Wilderness*, Boston, 1947, p. 344 (repr. pp. 208–209)./ O.W. Larkin, *Art and Life in America*, New York, 1949, p. 52 (repr.)./

V. Robie, "Waldo Portraits by Smibert and Blackburn," *The American Society Legion of Honor Magazine*, New York, Spring 1949, pp. 51–52./ V. Barker, *American Painting*, New York, 1950, p. 110 (fig. 16).

Exhibitions: Boston Athenaeum, *Exhibition*, 1871, no. 204./ Boston, MFA, *One Hundred Colonial Portraits*, 1930, p. 99 (repr.)./ New York, Metropolitan Museum, *Life in America*, 1939, no. 12 (repr. p. 9)./ Worcester, Mass., Art Museum, *New England Painting, 1700–75*, 1943, no. 28./ Chicago Art Institute, *From Colony to Nation*, 1949, no. 23 (repr.).

145.

fig. 25

Thomas Bulfinch

Half-length and turned three-quarters left with startlingly black eyebrows, he wears a black suit, the coat lined in green. The background is brown.

Oil on oval canvas. 30 × 26 in. (76.2 × 66 cm.)
Painted about 1756.
Collection: J. Templeman Coolidge, Jr., Boston, by 1895.
Gift of Mr. and Mrs. J. Templeman Coolidge. 45.516

Thomas Bulfinch (1728–1802) was the son of Thomas and Judith Colman Bulfinch. A graduate of Harvard in 1749, he studied medicine in London from 1754 to 1757 and returned to Boston to become a wealthy, eminent, and cultivated doctor. His son by his marriage to Susan Apthorp was Charles Bulfinch (1763–1844), Boston architect. Park (*see below*) and Frank W. Bayley (letter of May 1930) provide the date supported by Bulfinch's apparent age.

References: F.W. Bayley, "Blackburn," *Little Known Early American Portrait Painters*, Boston, 1916–1919, no. 1./ L. Park, *Blackburn*, Worcester, Mass., 1923, no. 23./ F.W. Bayley, *Five Colonial Artists*, Boston, 1929 (repr. p. 83)./ T. Bolton and H.L. Binsse, "Blackburn," *The Antiquarian*, 1930, xv, no. 5, p. 90.

Exhibitions: Boston, Copley Society, *Portraits by American Painters Before the Revolution*, 1922, no. 32 (attrib. Smibert)./ Boston, MFA, *One Hundred Colonial Portraits*, 1930, p. 16 (repr.).

146.

fig. 26

Susan Apthorp (Mrs. Thomas Bulfinch)

Three-quarter length, facing front, she is seated resting her right arm on a low pedestal. She wears a blue dress embellished with lace and a green stole. The background right is a green and blue wooded landscape with a river.

Oil on canvas. 50 × 40 in. (127 × 101.6 cm.)
Signed and dated center left: *I. Blackburn Pinxit 1757.*
Collection: J. Templeman Coolidge, Jr., Boston, by 1895.
Gift of Mr. and Mrs. J. Templeman Coolidge. 45.517

Susan Apthorp (1734–1815) was the daughter of Charles and Grizell Eastwick Apthorp of Boston. She married Thomas Bulfinch in 1759 and spent her wedded life in the Bulfinch mansion in Bowdoin Square. She was, apparently, "a woman of marked intelligence and cultivation, and throughout her long life commanded more than ordinary regard from her children and associates" (Park, *see below*).

References: A.T. Perkins, "Blackburn and Smibert," *Massachusetts Historical Society Proceedings*, 1878, xvi, p. 387./ L. Park, *Blackburn*, Worcester, Mass., 1923, no. 5./ C.A. Place, *Charles Bulfinch*, Boston and New York, 1923, p. 2 (repr. p. 3)./ F.W. Bayley, *Five Colonial Artists*, Boston, 1929 (repr. p. 61)./ F.W. Coburn, "Blackburn," *Dictionary of American Biography*, 1929, ii, p. 316./ T. Bolton and H.L. Binsse, "Blackburn," *The Antiquarian*, 1930, xv, no. 5, p. 88./ K. Roberts, "Elizabeth Browne, Joseph Blackburn and 'Northwest Passage,'" *Art in America*, 1953, xli, no. 1, p. 19 (fig. 4).

Exhibitions: Boston, Copley Hall, *Portraits of Women*, 1895, no. 25./ Boston, Art Club, *Early American Portraits*, 1911, no. 5./ Boston, Copley Society, *Portraits by American Painters Before the Revolution*, 1922, no. 18./ Boston, MFA, *One Hundred Colonial Portraits*, 1930, p. 7 (repr.)./ Colorado Springs Fine Arts Center, *Likeness of America 1680–1820*, 1949, no. 8 (repr. no. 6).

147.

fig. 27

Jonathan Simpson

Nearly full-length, turned three-quarters right, and wearing a brown suit with white stockings, he is seated at a green covered table, on which lie papers and a pewter inkpot; in his right hand he holds a quill pen.

Oil on canvas. 50¾ × 40¼ in. (128.9 × 102.2 cm.)

Painted about 1758.

Collections: Miss Simpson, the sitter's granddaughter, Boston; Mr. and Mrs. Robert C. Winthrop, Jr., Boston.

Gift of the children of Mr. and Mrs. Robert C. Winthrop, Jr. 24.340

Jonathan Simpson (1712–1795) was born in Boston the son of Jonathan and Mary Baker Simpson. Although a prosperous Boston merchant, his Loyalist sympathies during the Revolution forced him to withdraw to England, and he died in Bristol. Another portrait of Simpson, also by Blackburn (G.E. Dow, ed., *The Holyoke Diaries*, Salem, Mass., 1911, repr. opp. p. 95, attributed to Copley), now owned by Edward H. Osgood, Hamilton, Mass., is signed and dated *I. Blackburn pinxit 1758*. A comparison of Simpson's age in both portraits suggests that this one was painted at the same time.

References: L. Park, *Blackburn*, Worcester, Mass., 1923, no. 66./ F.W. Bayley, *Five Colonial Artists*, Boston, 1929 (repr. p. 121)./ T. Bolton and H.L. Binsse, "Blackburn," *The Antiquarian*, 1930, XV, no. 5, p. 92./ E.A. Jones, *Loyalists of Massachusetts*, London, 1930 (pl. XLIX)./ F.W. Coburn, "Blackburn," *Connoisseur*, 1937, XCIX, p. 75 (repr. p. 71)./ J.H. Morgan and H.W. Foote, *Extension of L. Park's List of the Work of Blackburn*, Worcester, Mass., 1937, p. 69./ C.H. Collins Baker, "Notes on Blackburn," *Huntington Library Quarterly*, 1945, IX, p. 41.

Exhibitions: Boston, Copley Hall, *Portraits*, 1896, no. 25./ Boston, Copley Society, *Portraits by American Painters Before the Revolution*, 1922, no. 14./ San Francisco, M.H. de Young Memorial Museum and California Palace of the Legion of Honor, *American Painting*, 1935, no. 2.

148.
fig. 28

Mrs. Jonathan Simpson (Margaret Lechmere)

Three-quarter length, seated and turned three-quarters left, with her left hand she holds a book on a red pedestal. Her brown brocade dress has white Brussels lace and part of her white stole rests on the pedestal before green drapery. Through a window in the brown background, left, trees are against a blue and pink sky.

Oil on canvas. 50¾ × 40¼ in. (128.9 × 102.2 cm.)

Painted about 1758.

Collections: Same as Cat. no. 147.

Gift of the children of Mr. and Mrs. Robert C. Winthrop, Jr. 24.341

Margaret Lechmere, born in Boston in 1719, was the daughter of Thomas and Anne Winthrop Lechmere. Her father owned the land now known as Lechmere Point in Cambridge. In 1754 she married the Hon. Jonathan Simpson and went with him to England during the Revolution. She died in London some time after 1776. Her portrait was probably painted at the same time as its pendant (Cat. no. 147).

References: L. Park, *Blackburn*, Worcester, Mass., 1923, no. 67./ F.W. Bayley, *Five Colonial Artists*, Boston, 1929 (repr. p. 123)./ T. Bolton and H.L. Binsse, "Blackburn," *The Antiquarian*, 1930, XV, no. 5, p. 92./ A. Burroughs, *Limners and Likenesses*, Cambridge, Mass., 1936, p. 56./ F.W. Coburn, "Blackburn," *Connoisseur*, 1937, XCIX, p. 75 (repr. p. 71)./ J.H. Morgan and H.W. Foote, *Extension of L. Park's List of the Work of Blackburn*, Worcester, Mass., 1937, p. 69.

Exhibitions: Boston, Copley Hall, *Portraits*, 1896, no. 25./ Boston, Copley Society, *Portraits by American Painters Before the Revolution*, 1922, no. 12./ San Francisco, M.H. de Young Memorial Museum and California Palace of the Legion of Honor, *American Painting*, 1935, no. 3 (repr.)./ University of Minnesota Gallery, *Survey of Colonial and Provincial Painting*, 1939, no. 5 (pl. 5).

149.
fig. 29

Jonathan Warner

Three-quarter length and turned three-quarters right, he stands before a brown and green background wearing a gray suit with ornate buttons. One hand is thrust into his waistcoat, the other holds a black tricorn hat.

Oil on canvas. 50 × 40 in. (127 × 101.6 cm.)

Signed and dated lower left: *I. Blackburn Pinxit 1761.*

Collections: Elizabeth Warner Cazeaux, niece of the sitter; Lendall Pitts Cazeaux, her son, Roxbury, Mass.
General Funds. 83.29

Born in Portsmouth, N.H., Jonathan Warner (1726–1814) was the son of Daniel and Sarah Hill Warner. He was married three times: to Mary Nelson in 1748, to Mary MacPhedris in 1754, and to Elizabeth Pitts in 1781. A rich Tory merchant and member of the King's Council, he refused to sign the "association" of March 1776 to defend the United Colonies by force of arms. Nevertheless he continued to live in Portsmouth until his death.

References: A.M. Earle, *Two Centuries of Costume*, New York, 1903, I (repr. opp. p. 378)./ S. Isham, *American Painting*, New York, 1905 (fig. 5)./ L. Park, *Blackburn*, Worcester, Mass., 1923, no. 78./ T. Bolton and H.L. Binsse, "Blackburn," *The Antiquarian*, 1930, XV, no. 5, p. 92./ A. Burroughs, *Limners and Likenesses*, Cambridge, Mass., 1936, p. 56./ J.H. Morgan and H.W. Foote, *Extension of L. Park's List of the Work of Blackburn*, Worcester, Mass., 1937, p. 10./ C.H. Collins Baker, "Notes on Blackburn," *Huntington Library Quarterly*, 1945, IX, p. 42.

Exhibitions: Chicago, *World's Columbian Exposition*, 1893, no. 2807./ Colorado Springs Fine Arts Center, *Likeness of America, 1680–1820*, 1949, no. 9./ Vancouver Art Gallery, *Two Hundred Years of American Painting*, 1955, no. 4.

150.
fig. 30

Dr. Joshua Babcock

Three-quarter length and seated turned three-quarters right, he wears a black suit with white shirt ruffles and neckcloth. He holds a book in his right hand and rests that arm on two books lying on a brown table. The background is blue-gray.
Oil on canvas. 45 × 36¾ in. (114.3 × 93.3 cm.)
Painted about 1761.
Collections: Rev. Samuel S. Mathews, the sitter's great-grandson, Danielson, Conn., by 1903; Mrs. Ernest W. Bowditch, Milton, Mass., by 1930; Elizabeth Bowditch Eustis, her daughter, Milton; Augustus H. Eustis, her husband, Milton.
Gift of Augustus Eustis. 64.1010

Dr. Joshua Babcock (1707–1783) was born in Westerly, R.I., son of James and Elizabeth Babcock. A graduate of Yale University in 1724, a wealthy physician and lawyer, he married twice: in 1735 Hannah Stanton of Stonington, Conn.; and in 1780 Ann Maxson of Newport, R.I. He was a member of the Council of War from 1776 to 1779, an incorporator of Brown University, Providence, R.I., and twice Chief Justice of the Supreme Court. He died in Westerly. A portrait of Hannah Stanton Babcock, owned in 1941 by Henry A. Murray of New York City, is signed and dated *I. Blackburn Pinxit 1761*. This, the pendant portrait, was probably painted at the same time. A portrait of his son Adam by Gilbert Stuart (Cat. no. 918) is also in the MFA collection.

References: S. Babcock, *The Babcock Genealogy*, New York, 1903 (repr. opp. p. 36)./ W. Updike, *History of the Episcopal Church in Narragansett, R.I.*, Boston, 1907, I (repr. opp. p. 528)./ F.W. Bayley, "Blackburn," *Little Known Early American Portrait Painters*, Boston, 1916–1919, no. 1./ L. Park, *Blackburn*, Worcester, Mass., 1923, no. 11./ T. Bolton and H.L. Binsse, "Blackburn," *The Antiquarian*, 1930, XV, no. 5, p. 88.

Exhibition: Boston, MFA, *One Hundred Colonial Portraits*, 1930, p. 9 (repr.).

151.
fig. 31

Mrs. Joseph Blaney (Abigail Browne) (attributed to Blackburn)

Standing three-quarter length, leaning on a pedestal, she turns three-quarters right and rests her right arm on the column's base. She wears a white dress, shaded in gray, and a brown stole. In the right background, green trees are seen through a window in the brown wall.
Oil on canvas. 49½ × 39½ in. (125.7 × 100.3 cm.)
Painted about 1757.
Collections: J.D. Sargent, the sitter's great-nephew, Boston; George Nixon Black, Boston.

Bequest of George Nixon Black. 29.785

Born in Salem, Abigail Browne (1735–1776) was the third child of Samuel and Katherine Winthrop Browne, one of the wealthiest merchants of Essex County (*see* portrait of *Katherine Winthrop*, Anonymous, Cat. no. 2). In 1757 she married Joseph Blaney (1729/30–1786?), a merchant of Marblehead. She died childless. Judging from the style, she was probably portrayed about the time of her marriage.

References: F.W. Bayley, *Copley*, Boston, 1915, p. 60 (attrib. Copley)./ A. Burroughs, *Limners and Likenesses*, Cambridge, Mass., 1936, pp. 37, 70 (attrib. Winthrop Chandler)./ J.H. Morgan and H.W. Foote, *Extension of L. Park's List of the Work of Blackburn*, Worcester, Mass., 1937, no. 108.

RALPH ALBERT BLAKELOCK (1847–1919), born in New York, traveled and sketched in the West from 1869 to 1872. Self-taught, he worked in and around New York but with little financial success. In 1899, impoverished, he became insane and was confined to an asylum until 1916, the year of his election to the National Academy. He died in the Adirondacks. He was one of the most important American Romantic painters of the late nineteenth century.

152.
fig. 429

Rockaway Beach, Long Island, N.Y.
People dressed in red, brown, and blue stroll on the yellow beach between the distant brown, gray, and white pavilions and the dark green sea. The sky is pale blue with gray clouds.
Oil on panel. 11¾ × 20 in. (29.7 × 50.8 cm.)
Signed lower right: *R.A. Blakelock*. Signed and dated over this in red: *R.A. Blakelock, 1870*. Painted about 1869–1870.
Collections: Purchased from the artist by Col. William P. Roome, sold *Roome Collection*, American Art Association, New York, March 31–April 1, 1926, no. 12 (bought in [repr. as *On the Beach*])./ *H. A. Hammond Smith, E. H. van Ingen and other properties sale*, Anderson Galleries, New York, Jan. 24, 1928, no. 71./ Mrs. J.G. Roome?; Mrs. Pierce Trowbridge Wetter, New York, sold, *Mrs. C. H. Parmly, Mrs. B.N. Carter, Mrs. P.T. Wetter and other owners*, Parke-Bernet, New York, April 6, 1946, no. 57./ Sydney A. Levyne, Baltimore, 1947./ Maxim Karolik, Newport, R.I.
M. and M. Karolik Collection. 62.262

Written in ink on the back of the panel, possibly in Blakelock's hand: *On the Beach at Rockaway. R.A. Blakelock/ Price of picture $200 with copyright*. Of the two superimposed signatures on the face of the painting, it is probable that the first is by Blakelock himself; the second and dated signature, apparently surrounded by the characteristic arrowhead, may be by the artist himself, or a later hand. If it is Blakelock's own, it can be taken as evidence that the artist did not stay in the West for the entire period 1869 to 1872 but that he interrupted his journey for some time. Although the upper signature, which cannot be conclusively authenticated, may be later and erroneously dated, the style of the painting is consistent with that of the years around 1870.

References: L. Goodrich, "The Blakelock Archives" (unpublished), Frick Art Reference Library, New York./ T.N. Maytham, "Some Recent Accessions," *MFA Bulletin*, 1962, LX, no. 332, p. 142 (repr.).

Exhibition: Boston, MFA, *New Paintings in the M. and M. Karolik Collection*, 1962–1963.

153.
fig. 430

Moonlight Sonata
Yellow light from a full moon in a pale green sky is reflected in a lake surrounded by a dark woody landscape below. The foreground trees are silhouetted in black.
Oil on canvas. 30 × 22 in. (76.2 × 55.9 cm.)
Signed lower right, in arrowhead: *R.A. Blakelock*. Painted before or during 1892.
Collections: Purchased from the artist by Lew Bloom, New York, between 1889 and 1892; Ralph Cudney, Chicago, until about 1936.

Charles Henry Hayden Fund. 45.201
Probably painted shortly before its purchase by the artist's actor friend Lew Bloom.

Reference: V. Young, "The Art of Blakelock," *Arts*, 1957, XXXII, no. 1, p. 26 (repr.).

Exhibitions: San Francisco Museum, *Survey of Landscape Painting*, 1936, no. 4 (repr.)./ Montana State University, *American Paintings*, 1937, no. 1 (repr.)./ New York, Babcock Galleries, *Blakelock*, 1942, no. 10./ New York, Whitney Museum, *Blakelock*, 1947, no. 14 (repr. p. 33).

HYMAN BLOOM was born in Brunoviski, Latvia in 1913 and emigrated to Boston in 1920. He studied painting with Harold Zimmerman for several years during the twenties and later with Denman Ross in Cambridge. In 1942 he started work for the Federal Arts Project. From 1949 to 1951 he taught painting at Wellesley College and from 1951 to 1953 at Harvard. He lives in Boston.

154.

The Christmas Tree
Very broadly painted, the green tree with a red and blue trunk is decorated with red, white, blue, and yellow ornaments. The background is blue.
Oil on canvas. 50 × 28 in. (127 × 71.1 cm.)
Signed lower right: *Bloom*. Inscribed on back, top center: *Bloom/1939*.
Collections: Federal Arts Project, Massachusetts; given to the Division of Education, Boston MFA.
Gift of the Division of Education. 52.474
One of three versions of this subject all painted in 1939. This picture was lent to the exhibition *Americans 1942* at the Museum of Modern Art, New York and listed on page 123 of the catalogue, but was not exhibited.
Exhibition: Cincinnati Art Museum, *The Critics' Choice*, 1945, no. 6.

PETER BLUME was born in Russia in 1906 and brought to Brooklyn, N.Y. in 1911. From 1921 to 1924 he studied in New York at the Art Educational Alliance and briefly attended classes at the Art Students League and the Beaux Arts Institute. He worked in Massachusetts and Exeter, N.H. in 1926–1927 and in Charleston, S.C. in 1930, when he settled in Sherman, Conn. In 1932 he visited Italy, France, and England, returning to Sherman, where he lived until 1956. He later traveled to Key West and Mexico, where he did some mural painting; he revisited Europe and in 1954 made a trip around the world. From 1956 to 1960 he was artist-in-residence at the American Academy in Rome, to which he returned in 1962.

155.
fig. 560

Winter, New Hampshire
Black, red, and gray farm buildings are grouped in deep snow. The sky is gray, tinged with pink.
Oil on canvas. 20¼ × 25 in. (51.4 × 63.5 cm.)
Signed and dated lower left: *Peter Blume/ 1927*.
Collection: John T. Spaulding, Boston, by 1930.
Bequest of John T. Spaulding. 48.519
Exhibitions: New York, Daniel Gallery, *Blume*, 1930, no. 3./ Boston, MFA, *The Spaulding Collections*, 1948, no. 3./ Manchester, N.H., Currier Gallery and Hartford, Conn., Wadsworth Atheneum, *Blume Retrospective*, 1964, p. 12, no. 4 (pl. 3).

JOHN S. BLUNT (1798–1835)

156.

Winter Scene
Oil on canvas mounted on masonite. 23¾ × 27½ in. (60.3 × 69.8 cm.)
Signed and illegibly dated lower right: *J.S. Blunt*. Painted about 1831.(?)
M. and M. Karolik Collection. 47.1242
Reference: *Karolik Catalogue*, 1949, no. 65 (repr.).

157.
fig. 398

Boston Harbor
Oil on panel. 20½ × 28 in. (52.1 × 71.1 cm.)
Inscribed on back of panel: *Boston Harbour Jany 12th 1835 1 mile below the*

Castle looking to the East J S Blunt.
M. and M. Karolik Collection. 47.1240
Reference: *Karolik Catalogue*, 1949, no. 64 (repr.).

DAVID GILMOUR BLYTHE (1815–1865) was born near East Liverpool, O., and was apprenticed to a Pittsburgh wood-carver from 1832 to 1835. He then worked for a year in Pittsburgh as a carpenter and house painter, and from 1837 to 1840 he served in the U.S. Navy. He was an itinerant portrait painter in Pennsylvania and Ohio from 1841 to 1855, interrupted by a sojourn in Uniontown, Pa., 1846 to 1851. Best known for his genre paintings, he lived and worked in Pittsburgh from 1855 until his death.

158. **In the Pittsburgh Post Office**
fig. 317   Oil on canvas. 25 × 30 in. (63.5 × 76.2 cm.)
Signed center left: *Blythe*. Painted between 1856 and 1861.
M. and M. Karolik Collection. 46.849
References: *Karolik Catalogue*, 1949, no. 66 (repr.)./ D. Miller, *Blythe*, Pittsburgh, 1950, pp. 74, 130.

159. **Lincoln Crushing the Dragon of Rebellion**
Oil on canvas. 18 × 22 in. (45.7 × 55.9 cm.)
Signed lower left: *Blythe*. Dated on building to right: *1862*.
M. and M. Karolik Collection. 48.413
References: *Karolik Catalogue*, 1949, no. 67 (repr.)./ D. Miller, *Blythe*, Pittsburgh, 1950, pp. 88, 129.

160. **Libby Prison**
fig. 318   Oil on canvas. 24 × 36 in. (61 × 91.4 cm.)
Signed lower right: *Blythe*. Painted in 1863.
M. and M. Karolik Collection. 48.414
References: *Karolik Catalogue*, 1949, no. 68 (repr.)./ D. Miller, *Blythe*, Pittsburgh, 1950, pp. 84, 129 (repr. opp. p. 96).

161. **Battle of Gettysburg**
fig. 319   *Three gray horses, one of them ridden by a man in orange, pull a gray cannon into the midst of the raging battle. To their left, horses and a soldier are silhouetted against an exploding cannon; to the right, a man is being carried on a stretcher under the smoke-filled sky. Browns, grays, and yellows predominate.*
Oil on canvas. 26 × 34½ in. (66 × 87.7 cm.)
Inscribed lower right: *study . . . the . . . the/ Battle of Gettysburg Presented to the Keystone Battery/ through Capt. Poulterer By D G Blythe*. Painted between 1863 and 1865.
Bequest of Maxim Karolik. 64.450

The Battle of Gettysburg was fought on July 1, 2, and 3, 1863. The Keystone Battery, to whom the painting was presented, was an artillery unit of the Pennsylvania Militia, commanded by Capt. Matthew Hastings. Stephen B. Poulterer, a Philadelphian, was commissioned First Lieutenant in the Battery in 1862 and was still serving as such in 1864. It is possible that he was promoted to the rank of Captain early in 1865, since at the end of 1864 the Battery was commanded by Capt. Edward Fitski.

Exhibition: Washington, D.C., Corcoran Gallery and Boston, MFA, *The Civil War: The Artists' Record*, 1961–1962, p. 19, no. 117 (repr. p. 142).

EDWARD DARLEY BOIT (1840–1915) was born in Boston and in 1863 graduated from Harvard. He lived in Newport, R.I. until 1871, when he left to study painting in Rome with Frederic Crowninshield and in Paris with Thomas Couture. It was probably in Paris that he met John Singer Sargent, who was to become his lifelong friend. He lived in Paris and Biarritz, frequently returning to his home in Boston, and worked throughout Europe until his death in Paris.

162. **Rocky Hillside**
Beneath blue sky with white clouds, two rock-strewn brown paths lead uphill through a grove of evergreens.
Oil on canvas. 21½ × 23¾ in. (54.6 × 60.3 cm.)
Signed and dated lower left: *Boit. 1907–8–*
Gift of Mrs. Horatio Greenough Curtis in memory of Horatio Greenough Curtis. 27.1326
Exhibition: Boston, Doll and Richards, *Boit*, 1910, no. 14.

163. **Afternoon in the Apennines**
Beyond green fields in the foreground a view of distant hills of brown, gray, and blue under gray sky.
Oil on canvas. 22 × 26 in. (55.9 × 66 cm.)
Signed and dated lower left: *Boit–1909–*
Gift of Mrs. Horatio Greenough Curtis in memory of Horatio Greenough Curtis. 27.1327
Exhibition: Boston, Doll and Richards, *Boit*, 1910, no. 11.

DE WITT CLINTON BOUTELLE (1820–1884)

164. **Indian Surveying a Landscape**
Oil on canvas. 40 × 54 in. (101.6 × 137.2 cm.)
Signed and dated on rock, lower left: *Boutelle/1855.*
M. and M. Karolik Collection. 47.1223
Reference: Karolik Catalogue, 1949, no. 69 (repr.).

EDWARD BOWERS (about 1822—after 1870)

165. **Fruit and Wine**
Oil on canvas. 20 × 16 in. (50.8 × 40.6 cm.)
Signed and dated lower right on table edge: *E. Bowers, Detroit, 1865.*
M. and M. Karolik Collection. 47.1266
Reference: Karolik Catalogue, 1949, no. 70 (repr.).

JOHN BREWSTER, JR. (1766–after 1846)

166. **Child with a Peach**
fig. 160
Oil on canvas. 25 × 21 in. (63.5 × 53.3 cm.)
Painted about 1810–1820.
M. and M. Karolik Collection. 45.893
Reference: Karolik Catalogue, 1949, no. 71 (repr.).

ALEXANDER BROOK was born in Brooklyn, N.Y. in 1898 and studied there at the Pratt Institute and then at the Art Students League with Kenneth Hayes Miller from 1915 to 1919. He was Assistant Director of the Whitney Studio Club from 1922 to 1927 and in 1943 went to Panama and the Caribbean as an artist-correspondent. He now lives in Sag Harbor, N.Y.

167. **A Number of Things**
fig. 574
A still-life of a vase, string and cardboard, books, leaves, and a gray and black striped cloth, on a table. A cane and bells against the gray, brown, and black wall.
Oil on canvas. 32 × 48 in. (81.2 × 121.9 cm.)
Signed and dated lower right: *A. Brook '35.*
Abraham Shuman Fund. 36.137
Reference: E.P. Richardson, *Painting in America*, New York, 1956, p. 390.
Exhibitions: New York, Downtown Gallery, *Brook*, 1936./ New York, Museum of Modern Art, *Art in Our Time*, 1939, no. 113 (repr.)./ San Francisco, California Palace of the Legion of Honor, *Seven Centuries of Painting*, 1940, no. L-235 (repr.)./ Pittsfield, Mass., Berkshire Museum, *Brook*, 1941, no. 10./ Dayton Art Institute, *Brook*, 1955, no. 8 (repr.)./ Ogunquit Museum, *Brook*, 1962, no. 8.

GEORGE LORING BROWN (1814–1889), born in Boston, illustrated children's books until G.P.A. Healy encouraged him to turn to painting. In 1831 he went to work in London, then to study in Paris with Isabey and at the Louvre, becoming a great admirer of Claude Lorrain. He worked in Boston and New York from 1834 to 1839, then lived principally in Rome until 1859, frequently traveling in Italy and Switzerland. He returned to work in and around Boston until his death in Malden, Mass.

168.

Leatherstocking Kills the Panther
Oil on panel. 14 × 20 in. (35.5 × 50.8 cm.)
Inscribed on back: *G.L. Brown. Pinxt./ Boston/ 1834/ from Cooper's Pioneers.*
M. and M. Karolik Collection. 47.1221
Reference: Karolik Catalogue, 1949, no. 72 (repr.).

169.

Castello Dell'Ovo, Bay of Naples
Oil on canvas. 30¾ × 38¾ in. (78.1 × 98.4 cm.)
Signed and dated lower right: *G.L. Brown/ Naples 1844.* Inscribed on back before relining: *View of the Castello d'Ovo. Bay of Naples./ G.L. Brown Naples/ 1844 Ital/ Painted for Geo. Tiffany Esq. Baltimore.*
M. and M. Karolik Collection. 47.1196
Reference: Karolik Catalogue, 1949, no. 73 (repr.).

170.
fig. 315

Monte Pellegrino at Palermo, Sicily
The brown rocks of Monte Pellegrino stand against the blue sky, seen across the calm blue waters of the bay. In the foreground brown houses and walled terraces with trees line the broad quay.
Oil on canvas. 19¼ × 32 in. (48.9 × 81.2 cm.)
Signed lower right: *Palermo/ GL Brown.* Written on back, upper left: *Monte Pelegrino* [sic] *at Palermo painted from Nature, by G.L. Brown, Sep.1856.*
Collection: Maxim Karolik, Newport, R.I., 1961.
M. and M. Karolik Collection. 62.263
Monte Pellegrino (Mount of the Pilgrim), once described by Goethe as the most beautiful headland in the world, holds the Sanctuary of St. Rosalia, patron saint of Palermo.
Exhibition: Boston, MFA, New Paintings in the M. and M. Karolik Collection, 1962–1963.

171.

Medford Marshes
Oil on canvas. 21¼ × 43 in. (54 × 109.2 cm.)
Signed and dated lower right: *Geo. L. Brown/ 1862.* Inscribed on back of original canvas: *"Dog Days"/ View of the Medford Salt Marshes and Mystic River/ Boston Charlestown & Bunker Hill in the distance/ from Nature by Geo. L. Brown/ Medford 1863.*
M. and M. Karolik Collection. 47.1228
Reference: Karolik Catalogue, 1949, no. 74 (repr.).

172.

View on the Italian Coast near Naples
On a brown rocky beach, sheltered on the right by trees and green and yellow bushes behind gray crags, figures unload their brightly colored fishing boats, center. Other boats are moored on the green water, left, before distant blue mountains. The sky is blue.
Oil on canvas. 34 × 60 in. (86.3 × 152.4 cm.)
Signed and dated lower left: *Geo. L. Brown/ 1866.*
Bequest of Maxim Karolik. 64.455

173.
fig. 316

The Public Garden, Boston
Oil on canvas. 18 × 30 in. (45.7 × 76.2 cm.)
Signed lower left: *George L. Brown.* Painted in or after 1869.
M. and M. Karolik Collection. 47.1259
Reference: Karolik Catalogue, 1949, no. 75 (repr.).

JOHN APPLETON BROWN (1844–1902), born in Newburyport, Mass., studied painting in Boston until he opened his own studio there in 1864. In 1866 he went to Paris and in 1867 was a pupil of Emile Lambinet there; in 1868 he returned to Boston. In the 1880's he worked in England, Italy, and southern France, and after returning to America in 1886, he worked principally in New England until his death. The Impressionists as well as the Barbizon painters exerted a strong influence on him.

174. **On the Coast of France**
Dull green trees and grassland are in the foreground, before yellow sand dunes and the sea in the right distance, under gray sky.
Oil on canvas. 20½ × 30 in. (52 × 76.2 cm.)
Signed and dated lower left: J. Appleton Brown, '75.
Bequest of Ernest Wadsworth Longfellow. 23.470

175. **The Month of May**
Apple trees in blossom stand on a green hillside before blue sky.
Oil on canvas. 17 × 21¼ in. (43.2 × 54 cm.)
Signed lower right: J. Appleton Brown. Painted about 1890–1900.
Gift of Alexander Cochrane. 13.553
The broad style and bright palette suggest the relatively late date.

176. **Brook in Summer**
A brook shaded by brown willows meanders through green fields, in which cows graze.
Oil on canvas. 20 × 27 in. (50.8 × 68.6 cm.)
Signed lower right: Appleton Brown.
Bequest of Arthur Tracy Cabot. 13.2906

177. **Early Summer**
Beyond a bright green meadow filled with white and mauve flowers, green trees stand against a cloudy blue sky.
Oil on canvas. 29 × 36¼ in. (73.6 × 92.1 cm.)
Signed lower left: Appleton Brown.
Gift of the Estate of Mrs. G.H. Champlin. 11.1279

178. **Hillside in Summer**
Yellow and gray houses are seen beyond a yellow-green meadow, dotted with trees beneath cloudy blue sky.
Oil on canvas. 17 × 21 in. (43.2 × 53.3 cm.)
Signed lower left: J. Appleton Brown.
The John Pickering Lyman Collection, Gift of Theodora Lyman. 19.1323

179. **New England Landscape**
A blue pond reflects its grassy banks, white birches, and other trees beyond. The blue sky is cloudy.
Pastel on paper. 18 × 22 in. (45.7 × 55.9 cm.)
Signed lower left: J. Appleton Brown.
The William R. Wilson Donation. 15.880

180. **A Showery May Morning**
Apple trees are in blossom on the far bank of a blue pond; other trees and an open green meadow lie beyond under a cloudy gray and blue sky.
Oil on canvas. 31 × 42 in. (78.7 × 106.7 cm.)
Signed lower right: J. Appleton Brown.
Bequest of Charles T. and Susan P. Baker. 21.1254

JOHN GEORGE BROWN (1831–1913) was probably born in Durham, England. He was apprenticed to a glass-maker in Newcastle before studying at the Royal Scottish Academy, Edinburgh and at the Royal Academy in London. He came to New York in 1853 as a portrait painter. In 1863 he was elected to the National Academy of Design and later became its Vice-President. He worked as a popular genre painter in New York until his death.

181.

fig. 409

Tuckered Out—The Shoeshine Boy

A child in tattered gray knickers and white shirt, with black boots and stockings, sleeps on his upturned shoeshine kit, slumped in the corner of a green room. His brushes and brown jacket lie about him.
Oil on canvas. 24 × 16 in. (61 × 40.6 cm.)
Signed lower left: *J.G. Brown N.A./ Copyright*. Painted about 1875–1900.
Bequest of Maxim Karolik. 64.467

MATHER BROWN (1761–1831), born in Boston, was taught drawing at an early age by Gilbert Stuart and had become a proficient miniaturist by 1777. He was a pupil of West in London in 1781; the next year he started to exhibit regularly at the Royal Academy and received frequent commissions from the Royal Family. From 1809 to 1824 he worked in Manchester and Liverpool and then in London until his death.

182.

fig. 149

Admiral Peter Rainier

Half-length, turned three-quarters right before a blue sky with gray clouds, he wears a blue uniform coat, braided and buttoned in gold, white lapels and waistcoat, and black stock. He has a full ruddy face and wears spectacles.
Oil on canvas. 30 × 25 in. (76.2 × 63.5 cm.)
Painted about 1783–1787.
Collections: Peter Rainier, nephew of the sitter, England; Hughes Stanton, England.
Mary Little Pierce Residuary Fund. 04.1757

Peter Rainier (about 1741–1808) was born the son of Peter and Sarah Spratt Rainier in Sandwich, England. In 1756 he began a distinguished career in the Royal Navy, achieving the rank of Admiral in 1805. Two years later he became a Member of Parliament for Sandwich, a post he held until his death in Westminster. His uniform is that worn by Captains of the Royal Navy between 1774 and 1787. He was portrayed, perhaps in 1778, when promoted to the rank of Captain, or possibly, from his apparent age, between 1783 and 1787, when he was again in England. Purchased by the MFA as a Copley, Park (*see below*) attributed the portrait to Stuart and it is probably the one listed by Mason as such (*see below*). However, comparison with portraits signed by Brown, and discovered later, supports the present attribution.
References: G.C. Mason, *Stuart*, New York, 1879, p. 247 (probably refers to this portrait)./ L. Park, *Stuart*, New York, 1926, II, no. 688 (repr. IV, p. 421).
Exhibitions: San Francisco, M.H. de Young Memorial Museum and California Palace of the Legion of Honor, *American Painting*, 1935, no. 8 (repr. as by Copley)./ San Francisco, California Palace of the Legion of Honor, *Seven Centuries of Painting*, 1940, no. L-100 (as by Copley).

183.

fig. 148

A Commander in the East India Company

Half-length and facing three-quarters right, he leans on a balustrade overlooking a bay with a three-masted ship at anchor. His blue uniform coat, with its white waistcoat, is buttoned and embroidered in gold.
Oil on canvas. 36 × 28 in. (91.4 × 71.1 cm.)
Signed and dated lower right: *M. Brown pinx/ 1786*.
Abraham Shuman Fund. 54.147

The uniform identifies the subject's rank in the East India Company. A Charles Lindergreen, appointed to this rank in 1786, was painted by Brown (see *Exhibition of 1789*, Royal Academy, London, no. 203); however, his age in 1786 (thirty-two years) does not agree with the apparent age of the sitter in this portrait.

GEORGE DE FOREST BRUSH (1855–1941), born in Shelbyville, Tenn., studied at the National Academy of Design, New York and with Gérôme in Paris. Painter of idealized figure pieces, Indian subjects, and portraits, he was elected to the National Academy in 1910 and worked in New York and Dublin, N.H. until his death in Hanover, N.H.

184.
fig. 422

Mother and Child

Three-quarter length, wearing brown and black, a woman stands turned three-quarters right holding a naked child. Behind her is the base of a column and beyond, a dark distant landscape.
Oil on circular panel. 38½ × 38½ in. (97.8 × 97.8 cm.)
Signed and dated lower left: *Geo. de Forest Brush/ 1895.*
William Wilkins Warren Fund. 95.1375

References: W.H. Downes, "American Paintings in the Boston Art Museum," *Brush and Pencil*, 1900, VI, no. 5, pp. 205–206./ S. Hartmann, *American Painting*, Boston, 1901, I (repr. frontispiece).

Exhibitions: Buffalo, *Pan American Exposition*, 1901, no. 631./ Indianapolis, Herron Museum of Art, *Inaugural Exhibition*, 1906, no. 18./ Berlin, Königliche Akademie der Künste, *Ausstellung Amerikanischer Kunst*, 1910, p. 46 (repr.)./ New York, Grand Central Art Galleries, *Brush*, 1930, no. 34.

DENNIS MILLER BUNKER (1861–1890), born in New York, was first a pupil at the National Academy and then at the Art Students League, New York. From 1881 to 1884 he studied in Paris under Hébert at the Académie Julian and under Gérôme at the École des Beaux Arts. On his return to the United States in 1885, he became an instructor at the Cowles Art School in Boston, revisiting Europe in 1888. He worked in Boston and Medfield, Mass. until his death in Boston.

185.
fig. 485

Samuel Torrey Morse

Three-quarter length, he is seated turned three-quarters left and wears a brown suit with a red bow tie. The background is black.
Oil on canvas. 43½ × 36 in. (110.5 × 91.4 cm.)
Signed and dated lower right: *D.M. Bunker/ 1887.*

Gift of Miss Jessie Gwendolen Morse, granddaughter of the sitter. 45.232

Samuel Torrey Morse (1816–1890) traveled to the East as supercargo on ships before settling in Boston as a merchant and shipper of jute. Although the picture was painted and signed in 1887, Bunker repainted the hands in 1888 (Gammell, *see below*).

Reference: R.H.I. Gammell, *Dennis Miller Bunker*, New York, 1953, p. 50.
Exhibition: Boston, MFA, *Bunker*, 1945, no. 2.

186.
fig. 484

George Augustus Gardner

Seated three-quarter length and facing three-quarters right, he wears a black coat and waistcoat with gray trousers, a white tie, and wing collar. The background is black.
Oil on canvas. 44 × 36 in. (111.7 × 91.4 cm.)
Painted in 1888.
Gift of G. Gardner Monks, John P. Monks, and Mrs. Constantin Pertzoff, grandchildren of the sitter. 44.622

George Augustus Gardner (1829–1916), born in Boston, graduated from Harvard in 1849. Owner of many merchant ships, with the post–Civil War decline in trade he became involved in railroads, banking, and real estate and was a noted Boston philanthropist. The picture is dated by Gammell (*see below*).

Reference: R.H.I. Gammell, *Dennis Miller Bunker*, New York, 1953, p. 29.
Exhibition: Boston, MFA, *Bunker*, 1943, no. 3 (pl. 2)./ —, *Bunker*, 1945, no. 3.

187.
fig. 487

The Pool, Medfield

A small blue stream with grassy banks winds through a green meadow. Beyond are a row of trees and a yellow house.
Oil on canvas. 18 × 24 in. (45.7 × 61 cm.)
Signed and dated lower left: *D.M. Bunker/ 1889.*

Collections: Arthur T. Cabot, Boston; Estate of Arthur T. Cabot, Boston, 1912.
Emily L. Ainsley Fund. 45.475
Exhibitions: Boston, MFA, *Bunker*, 1943, no. 15 (pl. 4)./ Toronto Art Gallery and circulated in Canada, and New York, Whitney Museum, *American Painting from 1865–1905*, 1961, no. 8 (pl. XIV)./ New York, American Federation of Arts, circulated in the U.S., *American Traditional Painters*, 1962–1963.

188.
fig. 486

Jessica
Half-length and in right profile, a redheaded girl in black stands against a black background.
Oil on canvas. 26 × 24 in. (66 × 61 cm.)
Signed and dated lower left: *D.M. Bunker. 1890.*
Gift by contribution. 91.130
References: W.H. Downes, "American Paintings in the Boston Art Museum," *Brush and Pencil*, 1900, VI, no. 5, p. 210 (repr. p. 208)./ R.H.I. Gammell, *Twilight in Painting*, New York, 1946 (pl. 47).
Exhibitions: Boston, St. Botolph Club, *Bunker*, 1891, no. 18./ Boston, MFA, *Bunker*, 1943, no. 8 (pl. 3)./ —, *Bunker*, 1945, no. 4.

189.

Meadow Lands
Beneath a gray sky, a green meadow stretches toward distant blue woods.
Oil on canvas. 25 × 30 in. (63.5 × 76.2 cm.)
Signed and dated lower right: *D.M. Bunker, 1890.*
Gift of Miss Susan Upham. 91.43
Painted at Medfield, Mass.
Exhibitions: Boston, MFA, *Bunker*, 1943, no. 17./ —, *Bunker*, 1945, no. 5.

J. D. BUNTING

Otherwise unknown, J.D. Bunting was postmaster at Darby, Pa. between 1840 and 1850.

190.
fig. 269

View of Darby, Pennsylvania, After the Burning of Lord's Mill
In the middle distance the white shell of the mill stands before a green wooded hill under yellow sky. In the foreground is the brown shop and wood-filled yard of G.B. Founders, blacksmith and wagon builder.
Oil on canvas. 42 × 51¼ in. (106.7 × 130.8 cm.)
Signed lower right: *J.D. Bunting.* Painted about 1840–1850.
Collections: The artist's family, Darby, Pa.; Maxim Karolik, Newport, R.I., 1951.
M. and M. Karolik Collection. 62.264
Exhibitions: Worcester, Mass., Art Museum, *The Private Collection of Maxim Karolik*, 1952, no. 12. New York, American Federation of Arts, circulated in Germany and Italy, and Whitney Museum, *American Painting in the Nineteenth Century*, 1953–1954, no. 62./ Washington, D.C., Smithsonian Institution, circulated in the U.S., *19th Century American Paintings*, 1954–1956, no. 14./ Boston, MFA and circulated in the U.S., *The M. and M. Karolik Collection*, 1957–1959, no. 155./ Boston, MFA, *New Paintings in the M. and M. Karolik Collection*, 1962–1963.

K. CALHOUN

Nothing is known of the artist beyond his signature on the pastel.

191.
fig. 423

Copley Square with Trinity Church and the Old Museum
Looking from Boylston Street toward the red brick Museum with Trinity Church on the left and the Westminster Hotel beyond. Black and brown vehicles and figures fill the gray square.
Pastel on paper. 5 × 10½ in. (12.7 × 26.6 cm.)
Signed and dated lower right: *K Calhoun—1911* (K and C in monogram).
Gift of George H. Edgell. 39.803
The MFA collection was moved from Copley Square to Huntington Avenue in 1908.

MRS. ROBERT CARTER Nothing is known of the artist.

192. **Napoleon's Army Crossing the Alps**
Oil on canvas. 21½ × 28¾ in. (54.6 × 73 cm.)
Inscribed lower right: *Painted by Mrs. Robert Carter, and presented to her/ husband, as an expression of her love and duty to him. / Troy. February 17/ 1833.*
M. and M. Karolik Collection. *47.1249*
Reference: Karolik Catalogue, 1949, no. 76 (repr.).

JOHN WILLIAM CASILEAR (1811–1893), born in New York, was apprenticed to the engraver Peter Maverick in 1826 and entered Asher B. Durand's studio in 1831. After working principally in New York as a prominent engraver, especially of bank notes, he studied in Europe from 1840 to 1843 and again in 1857–1858. He began landscape painting during the latter year and continued working in Vermont and New York until his death in Saratoga, N.Y., a lesser known but important member of the Hudson River School.

193.   **A Mountain Brook**
fig. 313   *The brown brook froths white over gray rocks in the background; on the banks are green trees and brown and gray rocks. Gray clouds fill the blue sky.*
Oil on composition board. 12 × 10 in. (30.5 × 25.4 cm.)
Signed and dated lower right: *JWC '77/* (initials in monogram).
Collections: Sturges family, New York (purchased from the artist); H.C. Sturges, New York; Mrs. H.C. Sturges, Fairfield, Conn.; LeRoy Ireland, Philadelphia, 1944; Maxim Karolik, Newport, 1944.
Bequest of Maxim Karolik. 64.422

MARY STEVENSON CASSATT (1844–1926) was born in Allegheny City, Pa., and studied at the Pennsylvania Academy of the Fine Arts in 1864–1865. After brief studies at the Academy of Parma with Carlo Raimondi, and in Spain, Belgium, and Holland in 1872, she moved to Paris, where she came under the influence of Degas and of Japanese prints. She soon became a close associate of the Impressionist group and first exhibited with them in 1877. She actively supported their cause in American circles and helped to form the collection of Mrs. H.D. Havemeyer. In 1914 she became blind, and she died twelve years later at the Château de Beaufresne, Oise, France.

194.   **Young Woman Reading**
fig. 472   *Three-quarter length, turned three-quarters right, she sits on an orange-striped sofa holding her book in her right hand and resting her left elbow on a cushion. She wears a blue dress and red-striped robe. The background is gray.*
Oil on panel. 13¾ × 10½ in. (34.9 × 26.6 cm.)
Signed and dated upper left: *M.S. Cassatt/ Paris/ 1876.*
Collections: Mary E.G. Duffee; Frances Harold Duffee, her daughter, 1894; E.D. Levinson, Cedarhurst, N.Y.; John T. Spaulding, Boston, 1934.
Bequest of John T. Spaulding. 48.523
Reference: J. Rewald, *History of Impressionism,* New York, 1946 (repr. p. 319).
Exhibitions: Boston, MFA, *The Spaulding Collections,* 1948, no. 7./ Utica, N.Y., Munson-Williams-Proctor Institute, *Expatriates,* 1953, no. 17./ Chicago Art Institute and New York, Metropolitan Museum, *Sargent, Whistler and Mary Cassatt,* 1954, no. 3 (repr. p. 14)./ Mt. Holyoke College Gallery, *French and American Impressionism,* 1956, no. 28.

195.   **Head of a Young Girl**
fig. 471   *Facing three-quarters right, she wears a bright multicolored robe. The background is brown.*
Oil on panel. 12¾ × 9 in. (32.3 × 22.9 cm.)
Painted before 1878.
Collections: Given by the artist to Alfred Q. Collins, Paris, 1878; Walter Gay, Paris.
Gift of Walter Gay. 27.497

An old label on the back reads: *Mary Cassatt/ given to Alfred Q. Collins by Miss Cassatt in 1878 and by him to Walter Gay.* Alfred Collins (1855/56–1903) and Walter Gay (1856–1937) were both artists.

196.
fig. 473

At the Opera

Half-length, seated and in left profile, a woman in black leans forward, looking through black opera glasses. In the left background members of the audience sit in gilt-faced balconies before a brown wall.

Oil on canvas. 31½ × 25½ in. (80 × 64.8 cm.)
Signed lower left: *Mary Cassatt.* Painted in 1879.
Collections: J. Gardner Cassatt, the artist's brother, 1880; with Martin and Camentron, Paris, by 1893; F.W. Bayley, Boston.
Charles Henry Hayden Fund. 10.35

Although mentioned in a review by Brownell (*see below*) of the second exhibition of the Society of American Artists at New York in 1879, the picture is not listed in the catalogue. Circumstantial evidence suggests that use of the illustration in the review was purely coincidental.

References: W.C. Brownell, "The Younger Painters of America, III," *Scribners' Monthly,* 1881, XXII, no. 3, p. 333 (engraved by A.F.P. Davis, 1880, repr.)./ F. Watson, *Cassatt,* New York, 1932 (repr. p. 29)./ M. Breuning, *Cassatt,* New York, 1944 (repr. p. 37)./ J. Leymarie, *Impressionism,* Geneva, 1955, II (repr. p. 69)./ J. Rewald, *History of Impressionism,* New York, 1961, p. 423 (repr. p. 425).

Exhibitions: Paris, Durand-Ruel, *Cassatt,* 1893, no. 13 (as *La Loge*)./ Chicago Art Institute, *Cassatt,* 1926–1927, no. 1./ Pittsburgh, Pa., Carnegie Institute, *Cassatt,* 1928, no. 2./ Chicago Art Institute, *Century of Progress,* 1933, no. 437./ Hartford, Conn., Wadsworth Atheneum, *American Painting and Sculpture of the 18th, 19th and 20th Centuries,* 1935, no. 13 (repr.)./ Brooklyn Museum, *Leaders of American Impressionism,* 1937, no. 31 (pl. III)./ New York, Seligmann & Co., *The Stage,* 1939, no. 23 (pl. 23)./ Baltimore Museum, *Cassatt,* 1941–1942, no. 7./ New York, Wildenstein and Co., *Cassatt,* 1947, no. 5 (repr. p. 19)./ Philadelphia, Pennsylvania Academy of the Fine Arts, *150th Anniversary,* 1955, no. 121./ Pittsburgh, Pa., Carnegie Institute, *American Classics of the 19th Century,* 1957, no. 76./ Baltimore Museum, *Manet, Degas, Cassatt, Morisot,* 1962, no. 101 (repr. p. 15)./ New York World's Fair, Gallery of Better Living Center, *Four Centuries of American Masterpieces,* 1964, no. 10 (repr.).

197.
fig. 476

A Cup of Tea

Two young ladies, sitting on a pink and gray chintz sofa, drink tea at a red-covered table. One wears black with yellow gloves, the other wears brown. The striped wall covering is pink and gray; the ornate mantel to the right is white.

Oil on canvas. 25½ × 36½ in. (64.8 × 92.7 cm.)
Signed lower left: *Mary Cassatt.* Painted about 1880.
Collections: Henri Rouart, Paris; sold, Galerie Manzi-Joyant, Paris, Dec. 9–11, 1912, no. 91; Dikran G. Kelekian, Paris.
Maria Hopkins Fund. 42.178

Painted about 1880 and exhibited at the Impressionist exhibition of that year, the painting represents the artist's sister Lydia, on the left, with a young visitor at their summer villa in Marly-le-Roi. The silver service, characteristic of the Philadelphia silversmiths, and a wedding present to the artist's grandmother, is marked *M.S. 1813.* In a soft-ground and aquatint version of the composition of 1883, the figure of the visitor is replaced by that of the artist's mother. Breeskin, p. 69, no. 60, is also a version.

References: A. Ségard, *Cassatt,* Paris, 1913, pp. 124–126 (repr.)./ B.N. Parker, "A Philadelphian in Paris," *MFA Bulletin,* 1942, XL, no. 240, p. 63 (repr.)./ M. Breuning, *Cassatt,* New York, 1944 (repr. p. 17)./ A.D. Breeskin, *The Graphic Work of Mary Cassatt,* New York, 1948, p. 21.

Exhibitions: Paris, *5th Impressionist Exhibition,* 1880./ Paris, Durand-Ruel, *Cassatt,* 1893, no. 5 (as *Five O'Clock*)./ Baltimore Museum, *Cassatt,* 1941–1942, no. 6 (repr.)./ New York, Wildenstein and Co., *Cassatt,* 1947, no. 4 (repr. p. 16)./ Milwaukee Art Institute, *Masters of Impressionism,* 1948, no. 4./ Chicago Art Institute and New York, Metropolitan Museum, *Sargent, Whistler and Mary Cassatt,* 1954, no. 9 (repr.

p. 23)./ Palm Beach, Fla., Society of the Four Arts, *Sargent-Cassatt*, 1959, no. 40 (repr. p. 13)./ New York, American Academy of Arts and Letters, *A Change of Sky*, 1960, no. 14./ Baltimore Museum, *Manet, Degas, Cassatt, Morisot*, 1962, no. 102 (repr. p. 40).

198. **Head of a Baby**

A sketch on a brown background. The baby faces front in a white dress touched with green.
Pastel on paper, mounted on canvas. 14 × 12 in. (35.5 × 30.5 cm.)
Drawn before 1891.
Collections: Given by the artist to Mrs. George Agassiz (Mabel Simkins) about 1891; Mrs. Richard Storey, her niece, South Hamilton, Mass., about 1958.
Gift of Mrs. Richard Storey in memory of her mother, Mrs. Bayard Thayer. 62.340

199. **Two Sisters (Study for The Banjo Lesson)**
fig. 474

Two girls, half-length, face right: one in pink leans over the shoulder of the other, who wears blue with a yellow scarf. The background is green.
Pastel on paper. 17 × 17 in. (43.2 × 43.2 cm.)
Signed lower right: *MC*. Drawn about 1894.
Collections: With Durand-Ruel, Paris; Payson T. Thompson; sold, American Art Association, New York, Jan. 12, 1928, no. 80 (as *Mother and Daughter*, repr.); with Durand-Ruel, New York.
Charles Henry Hayden Fund. 32.98

The same subjects appear in full length in *The Banjo Lesson*, a drypoint and aquatint dated 1894. The sitters are identified by A.D. Breeskin as "Mlle. Margot and her sister" (*The Graphic Work of Mary Cassatt*, New York, 1948, no. 156, repr.). A pastel of the sisters, also showing the banjo, is owned by The Virginia Museum of Fine Arts.
References: P. Henry, "Four Established Painters," *MFA Bulletin*, 1932, xxx, no. 182, p. 81 (repr.)./ M. Breuning, *Cassatt*, New York, 1944 (repr. p. 36).
Exhibitions: New York, Durand-Ruel, *Cassatt*, 1917, no. 6./ —, *Cassatt*, 1923, no. 3./ —, *Cassatt*, 1924, no. 22./ —, *Cassatt*, 1926, no. 7.

200. **Mother and Child**
fig. 475

A woman, three-quarter length and facing three-quarters left in a gray dress, is seated on a mahogany sofa which is covered in yellow. She holds a child in a red dress and white smock who kneels in her lap. Beyond are a gray-green wall and a bright green landscape right.
Oil on canvas. 36½ × 29 in. (92.8 × 73.8 cm.)
Signed lower right: *Mary Cassatt*. Painted about 1902.
Collections: with Durand-Ruel; John M. Longyear, Boston; Mrs. John M. Longyear, by 1915.
Anonymous loan. 96.42

Exhibitions: Manchester, England, Art Gallery, *Modern French Paintings*, 1907–1908, no. 68 (lent Durand-Ruel)./ Berlin, Königliche Akademie der Künste, *Ausstellung Amerikanischer Kunst*, 1910, p. 48 (repr.)./ Boston, MFA, *Art in New England*, 1939, no. 8 (pl. VIII).

THOMAS CHAMBERS, possibly an Englishman from Yorkshire, came to America in 1832. A landscape and marine painter, he lived and worked in New York City from 1834 to 1841, and in Boston from 1843 to 1851. He was in Albany, N.Y. from 1852 to 1857 and again in New York in 1858–1859, 1861, and 1866.

201. **Summer: Fishermen Netting**

Fishermen net from their boat in a blue and brown lake. Purple and green hills rise behind green fields. The clouds are pink in the blue sky.
Oil on canvas. 18 × 24¼ in. (45.7 × 61.6 cm.)
Collection: Maxim Karolik, Newport, R.I., 1948.

M. and M. Karolik Collection. 62.266

Exhibitions: Minneapolis Institute of Arts and circulated in the U.S., *19th Century American Paintings from the Collection of Maxim Karolik*, 1953–1954 (as *Mountain and Lake*)./ Boston, MFA, *New Paintings in the M. and M. Karolik Collection*, 1962–1963.

BENJAMIN CHAMPNEY (1817–1907), born in New Ipswich, N.H., was apprenticed to a lithographer in Boston and about 1834 studied drawing with the portraitist Robert Cooke. From 1841 to 1846 he studied in France and traveled in Germany, Switzerland, and Italy. After his return to Boston in 1846, he settled in Woburn, Mass., and except for a visit to Italy in 1865, spent every summer in North Conway, N.H. He died in Woburn.

202.
fig. 302

Mount Chocorua, New Hampshire
The gray and green mist-covered mountain, touched with yellow, rises above the tree-lined river in the foreground. The sky is yellow, becoming blue above.
Oil on canvas. 12 × 18 in. (30.5 × 45.7 cm.)
Signed and dated lower left: *B. Champney 1858.*
Collection: Maxim Karolik, Newport, R.I., 1944.
Bequest of Maxim Karolik. 64.423

JOSEPH GOODHUE CHANDLER (1813–after 1880), was born in South Hadley, Mass. First trained as a cabinetmaker, he later studied painting with William Collins of Albany, N.Y. and turned to itinerant portrait painting. From 1852 to 1860 he was a successful portraitist in Boston. His wife, Lucretia Ann Waite, was also a painter. He died in Hubbardstown, Mass.

203.

Still Life with Fruits
Various brightly colored fruits on two marble shelves placed one above the other contrast sharply with the brown background.
Oil on canvas. 25 × 30 in. (63.5 × 76.2 cm.)
Signed lower right: *J.G. Chandler.* Painted about 1866.
Collection: Maxim Karolik, Newport, R.I., 1959.
M. and M. Karolik Collection. 62.267

A characteristic composition by Chandler; a closely related version (Shelburne, Vt., Shelburne Museum), possibly painted at the same time, is signed and dated 1866.

Exhibition: Boston, MFA, *New Paintings in the M. and M. Karolik Collection*, 1962–1963.

WINTHROP CHANDLER (1747–1790) was born at Chandler Hill near Thompson, Conn. In 1762 he probably was apprenticed to an artisan in Boston and later is said to have received professional training in portrait painting. By 1770 he was receiving important commissions. He then worked principally in and around Woodstock, Conn. and Thompson. He lived in Worcester, Mass. from 1785 until his death at Chandler Hill.

204.
fig. 92

Levi Willard
Half-length and facing front within a brown painted oval, he wears a blue coat and waistcoat embellished with ornate gold buttons and buttonholes. The background is brown with brown spandrels.
Oil on canvas. 26¾ × 23½ in. (67.9 × 59.7 cm.)
Painted about 1770–1775.
Collections: Levi Willard, Lancaster, Mass.; Martha Codman Karolik, his great-great-granddaughter, Newport, R.I.
M. and M. Karolik Collection. 37.42

Col. Levi Willard, born in Lancaster, Mass. in 1727 was the son of Samuel and Elizabeth Phelps Willard. He married Catherine Chandler and was partner of the merchant firm of Willard and Ward, Lancaster, Mass. A Grantee of Walpole, N.H., a Collector of Excise for Worcester County in 1766, and a Justice of the Peace, he was Ensign of the Louisburg Garrison in 1745 and took part in the Canadian Campaign of 1760; he was thought to be a British sympathizer. He died in Lancaster in 1775.

References: F.W. Bayley, *Little Known Early American Portrait Painters*, Boston, 1916–1919, no. 2./ E.J. Hipkiss, *M. and M. Karolik Collection of Eighteenth Century American Arts*, Boston, 1941, no. 11 (repr. p. 23)./ N.F. Little, "Chandler," *Art in America*, 1947, xxxv, no. 2, pp. 84, 117 (fig. 15).

Exhibition: Worcester, Mass., Art Museum, *Chandler*, 1947, no. 15.

205.
fig. 93

Mrs. Levi Willard (Catherine Chandler)

Half-length and facing front within a brown painted oval, she wears a white bonnet and shawl over a brown dress. The background is brown.
Oil on canvas. 26¾ × 23½ in. (67.9 × 59.7 cm.)
Painted about 1770–1775.
Collections: Same as Cat. no. 204.
M. and M. Karolik Collection. 37.43

Catherine Chandler (1735–1791), born in Worcester, Mass., was the daughter of the Hon. John and Hannah Gardiner Chandler and a first cousin of the artist. She had five children by Levi Willard, one of whom, Catherine, married John Amory, Jr., whose portraits by Gilbert Stuart (Cat. nos. 916, 917) are in the MFA's collection. Mrs. Willard died in Lancaster, Mass. Pendant to the preceding.

References: F.W. Bayley, *Little Known Early American Portrait Painters*, Boston, 1916–1919, no. 2./ E.J. Hipkiss, *M. and M. Karolik Collection of Eighteenth Century American Arts*, Boston, 1941, no. 12 (repr. p. 23)./ N.F. Little, "Chandler," *Art in America*, 1947, xxxv, no. 2, pp. 84, 117 (fig. 16).

Exhibition: Worcester, Mass., Art Museum, *Chandler*, 1947, no. 16.

JOHN GADSBY CHAPMAN (1808–1889)

206.
fig. 305

Pines of the Villa Barberini

Oil on canvas. 27 × 21 in. (68.6 × 53.3 cm.)
Signed and dated lower left: *J.B.C. Roma 1856* (initials in monogram).
Inscribed on back: *Pines of the Villa Barberini near Albano.*
M. and M. Karolik Collection. 47.1427
Reference: *Karolik Catalogue*, 1949, no. 77 (repr.).

RONALD CHASE

was born in Seminole, Okla. in 1934. He graduated from Bard College in 1956 with a degree in theater. Largly self-taught, he turned to painting in 1958 and between 1959 and 1964 received four resident fellowships at the McDowell Colony, Peterborough, N.H. He has recently worked in the production of films.

207.
fig. 602

Portrait Collage with Lavender

A composition of old banking notes and receipts thinly overpainted with dark brown, lighter toward the center. In the upper center, a copy of a youthful self-portrait by Rembrandt in light and dark brown. Above it are four scraps of lavender paper.
Collage. Oil on paper mounted on cardboard. 19½ × 12¾ in. (49.5 × 32.4 cm.)
Signed and dated across bottom: *Portrait Collage No. 3 Ronald Chase/ Sept. 1963.*
Charles Henry Hayden Fund. 65.11

WILLIAM MERRITT CHASE (1849–1916) was born in Williamsburg, Ind. He first studied in Indianapolis and at the National Academy, New York. In 1872 he was at the Munich Academy with von Piloty and Wilhelm Leibl, then in Venice with Duveneck and Twachtman. In 1878 he settled in New York and taught at the Art Students League and in his own 10th St. studio. In 1890 he was elected a member of the National Academy; in 1902 he was one of the Ten American Painters. He lived in New York until his death. He was one of the most influential teachers of his time.

208.
fig. 479

Gray Day on the Lagoon

Black steamships and smaller boats crowd the green water of the lagoon. The Giudecca in the distance appears brown under dark gray sky.

Oil on panel. 13 × 19 in. (33 × 48.2 cm.)

Signed lower right: *Wm. M. Chase.* Painted about 1877.

Bequest of Ernest Wadsworth Longfellow. 37.597

The style would indicate a date of about 1877; it was probably painted on Chase's first visit to Venice.

Exhibitions: New York, American-British Art Center, *Chase*, 1948, no. 5./ Indianapolis, Herron Museum of Art, *Chase*, 1949, no. 9./ Southampton, N.Y., Parrish Art Museum, *Chase*, 1957, no. 22 (repr.)./ Santa Barbara, University of California Art Gallery and circulated in the U.S., *Retrospective Exhibition of Paintings by William Merritt Chase*, 1964–1965, no. 2 (repr.).

209.
fig. 480

Summertime

A girl in white rows an olive green boat on gray water. Beyond are green trees against blue sky.

Oil on panel. 10¼ × 16 in. (26 × 40.6 cm.)

Signed lower left: *Wm. M. Chase.* Painted in the 1880's.

Collection: James Maurice Prendergast, Boston, 1891.

Bequest of Julia C. Prendergast in memory of her brother, James Maurice Prendergast. 44.41

Dated in the 1880's according to style.

Exhibition: New London, Conn., Lyman Allyn Museum, *Men of the Tile Club*, 1945, no. 41.

210.
fig. 481

Park Bench

A lady in blue sits at the far end of a long rustic cedar bench. The path in front is brown, and the trees behind are green.

Oil on canvas. 12 × 16 in. (30.5 × 40.6 cm.)

Signed lower left: *Wm. M. Chase.* Painted about 1890.

Gift of Arthur Weisenberger. 49.1790

Exhibition: Southampton, N.Y., Parrish Art Museum, *Chase*, 1957, no. 38 (repr.).

211.
fig. 482

Still Life—Fish

Silver-gray fish lie scattered on a brown table, some of them piled in dishes. Behind, left, are two brown jars against the brown wall.

Oil on canvas. 44½ × 56 in. (113 × 142.2 cm.)

Signed lower left: *Wm. M. Chase.* Painted between 1890 and 1910.

Charles Henry Hayden Fund. 08.453

Most of his still lifes of fish were done between 1890 and 1910 at Shinnecock, L.I., N.Y., where he spent many summers.

Reference: K.M. Roof, *Chase*, New York, 1917, p. 326.

Exhibition: Southampton, N.Y., Parrish Art Museum, *Chase*, 1957, no. 101 (repr.).

212.
fig. 483

A Lady in Evening Dress

Half-length and facing front before a brown background, she wears a yellow dress with a pink-lined white fur wrap and a black choker.

Oil on canvas. 24 × 19¾ in. (61 × 50.1 cm.)

Signed upper right: *Wm. M. Chase.* Painted about 1893.

Collection: Mrs. Frederick P. Vinton, Boston.

Ellen Kelleran Gardner Fund. 22.680

The sitter appears to be the same as that in *Woman with the White Shawl*, in the Pennsylvania Academy of the Fine Arts, Philadelphia (K.M. Roof, *Chase*, New York, 1917, repr. p. 232), which was painted in 1893.

WILLIAM CHRISTOPHER was born in Columbus, Ga. in 1924. He studied in Paris at the Académie Julian, the École des Beaux Arts, and in Fontainebleau; then in New York under the painter Amédée Ozenfant. He has worked as a painter, teacher, and cabinetmaker. Since 1960 he has lived in Hartland, Vt.

213. *fig. 607*	**The Great Golden Cloud**

On a white background, a collage composed of three layers: above, the cloud of gold leaf; then the block of printed strips from magazines; below, a crowd a gray heads. Pieces of the gold fall at random.

Casein, tempera, and collage of gold leaf and magazine print on gessoed masonite panel. 34¾ × 36¾ in. (88.2 × 93.3 cm.)

Signed and dated on back, upper left: *Christopher/ The Golden Cloud/ 1961.* Lower left beneath the magazine print, the name *Christopher* is pasted.

Collection: Mr. and Mrs. Irving R. Shapiro, Boston, 1961.

Gift of Mr. and Mrs. Irving R. Shapiro. 63.279

Symbolized in the picture is the dilemma of modern life; the forces of commercial promotion, political power, and materialistic values that manipulate man's basic emotions of desire and fear. "... The printed 90's [represent] the fall-out of Strontium 90 from above the cloud and the omnipresence of the great cloud of gold that is always being held out as our ultimate happiness. I feel we are living in an age of the worship of Mammon and the holy spirit of man is being neglected. ..." (Letter from the artist, April 6, 1963.)

Exhibitions: Boston, Joan Peterson Gallery, *Christopher*, 1961, no. 10./ New York, Amel Gallery, *Christopher*, 1961.

FREDERICK EDWIN CHURCH (1826–1900)

214. **The Harp of the Winds**

Oil on canvas. 14 × 12 in. (35.5 × 30.5 cm.)
Painted about 1850.
M. and M. Karolik Collection. 48.415
Reference: Karolik Catalogue, 1949, no. 78 (repr.).

215. **Cayambe**

Oil on canvas. 12 × 18 in. (30.5 × 45.7 cm.)
Painted after 1853.
M. and M. Karolik Collection. 47.1237
Reference: Karolik Catalogue, 1949, no. 79 (repr.).

216. **The Finding of Moses**
fig. 310

Oil on canvas. 29½ × 47¾ in. (74.9 × 121.2 cm.)
Painted about 1860.
M. and M. Karolik Collection. 47.1231
Reference: Karolik Catalogue, 1949, no. 80 (repr.).

ALVAN CLARK (1804–1887), astronomer and painter, was born in Ashfield, Mass. He taught himself to engrave and to paint in 1824–1825 and then worked in Boston, Providence, R.I., New York City, and Fall River, Mass. In 1844 he developed an interest in optics and with his son established the firm of Alvan Clark & Sons, renowned makers of telescopes and lenses. He died in Cambridge, Mass.

217. **Self-Portrait**
fig. 236

Half-length and turned three-quarters right against a brown background, he wears a black coat and stock with a green and brown plaid waistcoat.

Oil on panel. 27 × 21½ in. (68.6 × 54.6 cm.)
Painted about 1840–1845.
Lent by Mrs. Alvan C. Eastman. 21.60
The date is based on his apparent age.

218. **Gilman Low**

Half-length and turned three-quarters left, dressed in black, he is seated with his right

arm resting on a red covered table. Behind, right, is a red curtain; the background is
brown.
Oil on canvas. 36 × 29 in. (91.4 × 73.6 cm.)
Painted about 1840–1850.
Gift of Mrs. Walter R. Eaton. 33.666

Gilman Low was a Boston leather merchant. The portrait's date is estimated
from its style.

219.
fig. 237

Henry Codman

*Half-length, turned three-quarters left before a brown background, he wears a black
coat and stock. The spandrels are dark brown.*
Oil on panel. 12¼ × 10 in. (31.1 × 25.4 cm.)
Painted in 1850.
Collections: Martha Codman Karolik, the sitter's granddaughter, Newport,
R.I.; Maxim Karolik, 1948.
Bequest of Maxim Karolik. 64.607

Henry Codman, son of Stephen and Hannah Robinson Codman, was born
in Portland, Me. in 1789. A realtor, he lived and worked in Boston, where
he died in 1853. The receipt for the portraits of Codman and his wife (Cat.
no. 220) reads: "Received Boston Sept. 30 1850 from/ Henry Codman
Esqr. seventy five dollars for/ painting two portraits/ Alvan Clark." He is
the father of John Amory Codman (*see* p. 53).

220.

Mrs. Henry Codman (Catherine Willard Amory)

*Bust-length, facing front, she wears a dress with a gray collar. The background is
brown with dark brown spandrels.*
Oil on panel. 9½ × 8½ in. (24.1 × 21.6 cm.)
Painted in 1850.
Collections: Same as Cat. no. 219.
Bequest of Maxim Karolik. 64.608

Catherine Amory (1796–1850) was the daughter of John and Catherine
Willard Amory, Jr. (portraits by Gilbert Stuart, Cat. nos. 916 and 917),
and the granddaughter of John and Katharine Greene Amory, portraits
by Copley, Cat. nos. 278, 258). She married Henry Codman in 1821 and
died in Roxbury, Mass.

221.

Charles Henry Cummings

*Bust-length in an oval setting and turned three-quarters left, he wears a black suit and
stock and steel-rimmed spectacles. The background is brown.*
Oil on oval canvas. 27 × 22 in. (68.6 × 55.9 cm.)
Painted about 1851.
Gift of Mabel H. Cummings, in memory of her sister, Emma G. Cummings. 41.705

Charles Henry Cummings was born in Boston in 1828. A flour commission
merchant for the dealers S. Robinson, Co., he married Harriet Elizabeth
Whiting in 1851. They lived in Cambridge until 1886 and then in Brookline,
where he died in 1910. He and his wife (Cat. no. 222) were portrayed probably at the time of their marriage.

222.
fig. 235

Mrs. Charles Henry Cummings (Harriet Elizabeth Whiting)

*Half-length, she faces front, wearing a black dress and a black velvet pendant. The
background is brown.*
Oil on oval canvas. 27 × 22 in. (68.6 × 55.9 cm.)
Painted about 1851.
Gift of Miss Mabel Cummings, in memory of her sister, Emma G. Cummings. 41.706

Harriet Elizabeth Whiting (1828–1890) was born in Boston. She had nine
children, the youngest of whom was the donor of the painting. She died in
Brookline. Pendant to the preceding.

JAMES GOODWYN CLONNEY (1812–1867)

223.   **In the Woodshed**
Oil on canvas. 17¼ × 14 in. (43.8 × 35.5 cm.)
Signed and dated lower right on barrel head: *1838/ J.G. Clonney.*
M. and M. Karolik Collection. 47.1193
Reference: Karolik Catalogue, 1949, no. 81 (repr.).

224.   **In the Cornfield**
fig. 255
Oil on canvas. 14 × 17 in. (35.5 × 43.2 cm.)
Signed and dated lower left: *J.G. Clonney 1844.*
M. and M. Karolik Collection. 47.1263
Reference: Karolik Catalogue, 1949, no. 82 (repr.).

225.   **The Sleigh Ride**
Oil on canvas. 25 × 34 in. (61 × 86.3 cm.)
Painted about 1845.
M. and. M. Karolik Collection. 48.417
Reference: Karolik Catalogue, 1949, no. 83 (repr.).

226.   **The Happy Moment**
Oil on canvas. 27 × 22 in. (68.6 × 55.9 cm.)
Signed and dated lower right: *Clonney 1847.*
M. and M. Karolik Collection. 47.1222
Reference: Karolik Catalogue, 1949, no. 84 (repr.).

227.   **Waking Up**
Oil on canvas. 27 × 22 in. (68.6 × 55.9 cm.)
Signed and dated lower right: *Clonney 1851.*
M. and M. Karolik Collection. 47.1189
Reference: Karolik Catalogue, 1949, no. 85 (repr.).

228.   **What a Catch!**
Oil on canvas. 24 × 34 in. (61 × 86.3 cm.)
Signed and dated lower right center: *Clonney 1855.*
M. and M. Karolik Collection. 47.1217
Reference: Karolik Catalogue, 1949, no. 86 (repr.).

CHARLES CODMAN (1800–1842)

229.   **The Bathing Pool**
Oil on canvas. 17 × 19 in. (43.2 × 48.2 cm.)
Signed lower right: *C. Codman/ Portland.* Painted about 1830.
M. and M. Karolik Collection. 47.1262
Reference: Karolik Catalogue, 1949, no. 87 (repr.).

JOHN AMORY CODMAN (1824–1886), son of Henry and Catherine Willard Amory Codman (portraits by Alvan Clark, Cat. nos. 219, 220) and father of Martha Codman Karolik, was born in Roxbury, Mass. He was painting by 1839 and worked in Boston as a portrait and landscape painter.

230.   **Harbor Overlooked by a Mansion**
In the foreground, right, the black and brown stern of a moored sailing ship on blue, gray, and green water; across the grassy shore is a white mansion on a wooded hill. The cloudy sky is yellow and gray.
Oil on cardboard. 9 × 11¾ in. (22.9 × 29.7 cm.)
Collections: The artist, Boston; Martha Codman (Mrs. Maxim Karolik), his daughter, Washington, D.C.; Maxim Karolik, Newport, R.I., 1948.
Bequest of Maxim Karolik. 64.593

231.   **Horses and Hunters by the Sea**
fig. 339
Three boys and a girl, dressed in brown, gray, and yellow, are on a beach with chestnut and black horses. Beyond is a blue sea under gray cloudy sky.

Oil on cardboard. 9 × 12¼ in. (22.9 × 31.1 cm.)
Collections: Same as Cat. no. 230.
Bequest of Maxim Karolik. 64.595

232.　　　　**Rocky Coast with Lighthouse**
Beyond the shore of green grass and shrubs, and gray and brown rocks, the sea is blue and the distant lighthouse white. Blue sky with white clouds.
Oil on canvas. 12 × 20 in. (30.5 × 50.8 cm.)
Collections: Same as Cat. no. 230.
Bequest of Maxim Karolik. 64.590

233.　　　　**Rocky Shore with Coast Guard Station**
The station is gray beyond the brown and gray rocks; both sea and sky are blue.
Oil on canvas. 12 × 20 in. (30.5 × 50.8 cm.)
Collections: Same as Cat. no. 230.
Bequest of Maxim Karolik. 64.592
Same locale as Cat. no. 230.

234.　　　　**Shore of Marblehead Neck and Tinker's Island**
fig. 338
The sea is blue and green beyond the brown and green coast; the buildings are gray and the ships' sails white. Blue sky with white clouds.
Oil on canvas. 11¾ × 20 in. (29.7 × 50.8 cm.)
Collections: Same as Cat. no. 230.
Bequest of Maxim Karolik. 64.591

235.　　　　**View of a Bay**
The rocky foreground is green, brown, and gray, and to the right people stand and sit about a fire. White and gray boats sail on the blue sea beneath a cloudy sky.
Oil on panel. 5½ × 14¾ in. (14 × 37.5 cm.)
Collections: Same as Cat. no. 230.
Bequest of Maxim Karolik. 64.594

JOSEPH FOXCROFT COLE (1837–1892), born in Jay, Me., was apprenticed with Winslow Homer at Bufford's lithograph shop in Boston until 1860; that year he studied in Paris with Lambinet. From 1865 to 1867 and from 1873 to 1877 he worked in France and Belgium with Jacques and other members of the Barbizon School. He returned to live in Winchester, Mass. and in Boston, where he died. With William Morris Hunt he was one of the first American enthusiasts of Barbizon art.

236.　　　　**Valley of the Rombouillet, France**
A brown-roofed cottage is in the foreground, with green hills and fields beyond it. The sky is blue.
Oil on canvas. 22½ × 36 in. (57.1 × 91.4 cm.)
Signed lower left: *J. Foxcroft Cole*. Painted between 1860 and 1877.
Gift of the Misses Louisa W. and Marian R. Case. 20.597

237.　　　　**View of Moret, France**
The church and gray buildings of Moret and the poplars on green banks are reflected in the river.
Oil on canvas. 18¼ × 26 in. (46.3 × 66 cm.)
Signed and dated lower left: *J. Foxcroft Cole 1872.*
Gift from the Isaac Fenno Collection. 18.397

238.　　　　**Landscape**
A pool reflects the willows and sedges. In the distance are thick woods beneath a pale golden sky.
Oil on canvas. 18¼ × 26¼ in. (46.3 × 66.7 cm.)
Signed and dated lower left: *J. Foxcroft Cole, 1873.*
Gift of Alexander Cochrane. 13.550

239.

fig. 371

Normandy Pastoral: Near Honfleur

Cows graze or rest in the green fields about a brook. A peasant girl, right, wears blue and white; the sky is blue and cloudy.

Oil on canvas. 38 × 52¾ in. (96.5 × 134 cm.)

Signed and dated lower left: *J. Foxcroft Cole 1875.*

Gift by subscription and Everett Fund. 93.97

Reference: W.H. Downes, "American Paintings in the Boston Art Museum," *Brush and Pencil*, 1900, VI, no. 5, p. 210.

Exhibitions: Boston, MFA, *Contemporary Art*, 1879, no. 207./ —, *Cole Memorial*, 1893, no. 42 or no. 75.

240.

The Aberjona River, Winchester

The river is bordered with green marshes and woods; the dark silhouette of horses and a wagon cross a bridge; the sky is yellow with pink clouds.

Oil on canvas. 18¼ × 26 in. (46.3 × 66 cm.)

Signed lower right: *J. Foxcroft Cole.* Painted after 1877.

Gift of Alexander Cochrane. 13.551

Judging from the style, it was probably painted after his return from France in 1877.

Exhibition: Boston, MFA, *Cole Memorial*, 1893, no. 64.

THOMAS COLE

(1801–1848) was born in Bolton-le-Moor, Lancashire, England. He came to America with his family in 1819 and until 1822 worked as a block engraver in Steubenville, O. In that year he took up portrait painting in Philadelphia, but by 1825 he had turned to landscape painting. He moved to New York in 1823, was a founder of the National Academy in 1826, and from 1829 to 1832 traveled throughout England, France, and Italy. On his return, he settled in Catskill, N.Y. and worked extensively in New England and the surrounding mountains. In 1841–1842 he was again in Europe, and he died in Catskill. He was a founder and leader of the Hudson River School of landscape painters.

241.

Sunny Morning on the Hudson River

Oil on panel. 18¾ × 25¼ in. (47.6 × 64.1 cm.)

Signed lower center: *Cole.* Painted about 1827.

M. and M. Karolik Collection. 47.1200

Reference: Karolik Catalogue, 1949, no. 88 (repr.).

242.

fig. 231

Expulsion from the Garden of Eden

Oil on canvas. 39 × 54 in. (99 × 137.2 cm.)

Signed lower left: *T Cole.* Painted about 1827–1828.

M. and M. Karolik Collection. 47.1188

Reference: Karolik Catalogue, 1949, no. 89 (repr.).

243.

fig. 228

Salvator Rosa Sketching Banditti

The mountainous landscape is brown, shaded with green and black; a castle, above, is silhouetted against gray sky. Under twisted trees in the foreground, Salvator, in red, sketches the banditti in their cave.

Oil on panel. 7 × 9½ in. (17.8 × 24.1 cm.)

Painted about 1831–1832 or 1841–1842.

Collections: John M. Falconer, New York, in 1897; *John M. Falconer Sale*, Anderson Galleries, New York, April 28–29, 1904, no. 410 (measurements, 17½ × 14½ in., probably refer to framed size); Maxim Karolik, Newport, R.I., 1944.

M. and M. Karolik Collection. 62.268

In his youth Salvator Rosa (1615–1673) was known to have spent much time sketching the banditti in their caves amid the wild scenery of the Abruzzi Mountains. This study was probably done in Italy when Cole traveled there in 1831–1832 or in 1841–1842.

Exhibitions: Brooklyn Museum, *Opening Exhibition*, 1897, no. 494./ Hartford, Conn., Wadsworth Atheneum and New York, Whitney Museum, *Thomas Cole—One Hundred Years Later*, 1948–1949, no. 15 (pl. VI).

244.
fig. 229

Sunset in the Catskills

A lake, reflecting yellow light from the blue sky, is surrounded by green woods touched with brown and orange. Beyond, the woods are green before distant mauve mountains. A brown painted proscenium.

Oil on canvas. 22½ × 30¼ in. (57.1 × 76.8 cm.)
Signed and dated lower left: *T. Cole/ 1841.*
Collections: Jonathan Sturges, New York; Mrs. Andrew Chalmers Wilson (Mary Fuller), his granddaughter, New York.
Bequest of Mary Fuller Wilson. 63.271
Reference: H.T. Tuckerman, *Book of the Artists*, New York, 1870, p. 627.

245.

The Temple of Segesta with the Artist Sketching

Oil on canvas. 19½ × 30 in. (49.5 × 76.2 cm.)
Signed lower center on red and green portfolio: *T Cole.* Painted about 1842.
M. and M. Karolik Collection. 47.1198
Reference: *Karolik Catalogue*, 1949, no. 91 (repr.).

246.
fig. 230

River in the Catskills

Oil on canvas. 28¼ × 41¼ in. (71.1 × 104.7 cm.)
Signed and dated lower left: *T. Cole 1843.*
M. and M. Karolik Collection. 47.1201
Reference: *Karolik Catalogue*, 1949, no. 90 (repr.).

247.

View of the Thames

On the banks of the blue river, reflecting yellow touches in the blue sky, are green woods and fields and a brown towpath.

Oil on panel. 13¼ × 20¼ in. (33.6 × 51.4 cm.)
Painted on back center: *Painted by T. Cole/ from a sketch by/ C. Verbryck/ 1845.*
Collections: Jonathan Sturges, New York, 1845; Mrs. Andrew Chalmers Wilson (Mary Fuller), his granddaughter, New York.
Bequest of Mary Fuller Wilson. 63.270

Jonathan Sturges commissioned Cornelius Verbryck (1813–1844) to paint a landscape. The artist chose a composition from one of his English sketches but died before he could complete it. Cole, taking over the commission, painted the scene early in 1845.

References: L. Noble, *Cole*, New York, 1853, pp. 360, 363./ H.T. Tuckerman, *Book of the Artists*, New York, 1870, p. 627.

WILLIAM GROSVENOR CONGDON was born in Providence, R.I. in 1912 and studied with George Demetrios, Henry Hensch, and at the Pennsylvania Academy of the Fine Arts. He went to Italy after the Second World War, spent eight years working in Europe and the East, and in 1959 settled in Assisi, Italy, where he now lives.

248.
fig. 593

Naples Afternoon

Yellow houses shadowed in brown line a gray street which is filled with people and vehicles etched in yellow. The sky is pink.

Oil on masonite. 20¾ × 13¾ in. (52.7 × 34.9 cm.)
Painted in 1949.
Anonymous Fund. 50.2417

The date was given by the Betty Parsons Gallery, New York. "Looking down on the Via Santa Lucia . . . it is a painting of light, and only the light of Naples." (Letter from the artist, June 4, 1950.)

JOHN SINGLETON COPLEY (1738–1815), probably born in Boston, was virtually self-taught, but he was inspired by his leading contemporaries—his stepfather Peter Pelham, John Smibert, John Greenwood, Robert Feke, and Joseph Blackburn. He was also influenced by available European engravings. Active as a painter at the age of fifteen, by twenty he had become America's leading artist. His achievements in this country encouraged him to make the Grand Tour of study in Europe. His longest stay was in Italy in 1774–1775, and by the end of 1775 he had settled in London. He worked there, becoming a member of the Royal Academy in 1779, until his death. While active primarily as a portrait painter, his revolutionary historical paintings, which placed events of contemporary history in contemporary dress, were among his greatest achievements. His *Watson and the Shark* (Cat. no. 299) anticipates by forty years the discoveries of the nineteenth-century French Romantic painters.

249.
fig. 33

Mrs. Joseph Mann (Bethia Torrey)
Seated, three-quarter length, she faces front before brown rocks and a landscape of green and blue. With her left arm upon a brown pedestal, she wears a blue and white dress with a red stole and dangles a string of pearls.
Oil on canvas. 36×28¼ in. (91.4×71.7 cm.)
Signed and dated lower right: *J.S. Copley Pinx 1753.*
Collections: Susannah Torrey Metcalf, niece of the sitter; John George Metcalf, grandnephew of the sitter, Mendon, Mass., 1857; Frederick H. Metcalf, great-great-grandnephew, Melrose, Mass.
Gift of Frederick H. and Holbrook E. Metcalf. 43.1353
Bethia Torrey (1731–1798), daughter of William and Bethia Bass Torrey, married Joseph Mann (Cat. no. 250), a Boston baker, in 1748. She later lived in Wrentham. Copley used, as a prototype for the portrait, Isaac Beckett's mezzotint after the painting *Princess Anne* by Willem Wissing, dated 1683.
References: A.T. Perkins, *Copley*, Boston, 1873, p. 5 (supplement)./ F.W. Bayley, *Copley*, Boston, 1915, p. 170 (as *Mrs. Thomas Mann*)./ B.N. Parker and A.B. Wheeler, *Copley*, Boston, 1938, pp. 129–130 (pl. 3)./ A. Burroughs, "Young Copley," *Art in America*, 1943, XXXI, no. 4, p. 162 (fig. 2)./ B.N. Parker, "Documentary Portraits by Copley," *MFA Bulletin*, 1944, XLII, no. 248, pp. 33–34 (repr. p. 33)./ J.T. Flexner, *First Flowers of Our Wilderness*, Boston, 1947, p. 346 (repr. p. 202)./ —, *Copley*, Boston, 1948, pp. 24–25 (pl. 5)./ C.C. Sellers, "Mezzotint Prototypes of Colonial Portraiture," *Art Quarterly*, 1957, XX, no. 4, p. 431 (fig. 16A)./ J.D. Prown, *Copley*, Cambridge, Mass., 1966 (fig. 20).
Exhibitions: Colorado Springs Fine Arts Center, *Likeness of America, 1680–1820*, 1949, no. 11 (repr. no. 22); New–York Historical Society, *W.P. Belknap, Jr., Collection of Portraits and Silver*, 1955, p. 161 (pl. xv); Washington, D.C., National Gallery, New York, Metropolitan Museum, and Boston, MFA, *Copley*, 1965–1966, no. 4 (repr. p. 18).

250.
fig. 34

Joseph Mann
Three-quarter length, he stands facing front before brown rocks and a green landscape under blue sky. He wears a gray coat and long blue waistcoat, with one arm on a gray pedestal and the other holding a black tricorn hat.
Oil on canvas. 36×28¼ in. (91.4×71.7 cm.)
Signed and dated lower right: *I.S. Copley Pinx 1754.*
Collections: Same as Cat. no. 249.
Gift of Frederick H. and Holbrook E. Metcalf. 43.1352
Joseph Mann (1717–1807) was the son of Nathaniel and Elizabeth George Mann of Wrentham, Mass. The banns of his marriage to Bethia Torrey were published in Boston in 1748. He died childless in Wrentham. Pendant to the preceding.
References: A.T. Perkins, *Copley*, Boston, 1873, p. 5 (supplement)./ F.W. Bayley, *Copley*, Boston, 1915, p. 170 (as *Thomas Mann*)./ B.N. Parker and A.B. Wheeler, *Copley*, Boston, 1938, pp. 129–130 (pl. 3)./ J.H. Morgan, *Copley*, Windham, Conn., 1939, p. 11./ A.Burroughs, "Young Copley," *Art in America*, 1943, XXXI, no. 4, pp. 162–163 (fig. 3)./ B.N. Parker, "Documentary Portraits by Copley," *MFA Bulletin*, 1944, XLII, no. 248, pp. 33–34 (repr. p. 33)./ J.T. Flexner, *First Flowers of Our*

Wilderness, Boston, 1947, p. 346 (repr. p. 203)./ —, *Copley*, Boston, 1948, pp. 24–25./ J.D. Prown, *Copley*, Cambridge, Mass., 1966 (fig. 21).

Exhibition: Colorado Springs Fine Art Center, *Likeness of America, 1680–1820*, 1949, no. 12.

251.
fig. 32

Galatea

Galatea, robed in blue and white, rides upon a dolphin-drawn car attended by Neptune, sea nymphs, and sprites. The distant shore is green, the water is blue, and the sky is clouded.

Oil on canvas. 37 × 52 in. (94 × 132.1 cm.)
Painted about 1754.
Collections: Purchased at a sale (possibly *Thorndike*) by M.P. Sawyer, Boston, about 1840 to 1846; Mrs. C.B. Raymond, Newburyport, Mass., by 1873; Dr. Henry E. Spaulding, Boston, before 1899.
Picture Fund. 12.45

Traditionally entitled *Galatea*, the scene varies from the Sicilian legend of that sea nymph, who though pursued by the monster Polyphemus, loved Acis. Neptune, shown here, played no part. The subject may in fact be of Amphitrite, a nymph beloved by Neptune. Copley derived the subject, with only slight modifications, directly from an engraving called *Galatée Triomphe sur l'Onde* by Augustinus after a painting by Gregorio Lazzarini (1655–1735/40) (location unknown). Our picture was probably painted about 1754, judging by its close stylistic similarities to the signed and dated *Mars, Venus and Vulcan* (Mrs. James F. Chapman, Pueblo, Colo.). The Metropolitan Museum owns a third and similar early painting, *The Return of Neptune*, a pendant in composition to *Galatea*. A letter probably referring to the Boston painting is dated October 5th, 1774 and is from Charles Reak and Samuel Okey, printmakers of Newport, R.I., to Henry Pelham, Copley's half brother and agent (see below, *Copley-Pelham Letters*): "... you have a Fine Picture of a Lady in Car of a Sheperd or Nymph. it would make a Good Metzotint. at present wee cou'd not undertake it."

References: A.T. Perkins, *Copley*, Boston, 1873, p. 89./ Massachusetts Historical Society, *Copley-Pelham Letters*, Boston, 1914, p. 265./ F.W. Bayley, *Copley*, Boston, 1915, p. 110./ B.N. Parker and A.B. Wheeler, *Copley*, Boston, 1938, pp. 75–76 (pl. v)./ A. TenEyck Gardner, "A Copley Primitive," *Metropolitan Museum Bulletin*, New York, 1962, xx, no. 8, p. 257 (pl. 4)./ J.D. Prown, *Copley*, Cambridge, Mass., 1966 (fig. 7).

252.
fig. 36

Mother and Child

Full-length and turned three-quarters right sits a lady in a blue dress with white bows and lace; her child, in a pink dress with gray cuffs, leans on her knee holding flowers in one hand and points to a hummingbird perched on her mother's hand. Behind, a brown wall and column and a landscape of blue, gray, and green to the right.

Oil on canvas. 50¼ × 40 in. (127.6 × 101.6 cm.)
Painted about 1755–1756.
Collections: Martha Babcock Amory, the artist's granddaughter, Boston; Mrs. Susan Amory Dexter, her daughter, Boston; Gordon Dexter, her son, Boston; Mrs. Gordon Dexter; Herbert Lawton, Boston, 1942; Miss Frances J. Eggleston, Oswego, N.Y., about 1945; Miss Amelia Peabody, Boston, 1956.
Gift of Miss Amelia Peabody. 57.154

Comparison with early works by Copley, in particular *Ann Tyng (Mrs. Thomas Smelt)*, dated 1756 (Cat. no. 253), support the attribution and a date of about 1755–1756.
Reference: J.D. Prown, *Copley*, Cambridge, Mass., 1966 (fig. 43).

253.
fig. 37

Ann Tyng (Mrs. Thomas Smelt)

Three-quarter length, seated and turned three-quarters right, she is portrayed as a shepherdess and holds a crook in her right hand; her white satin dress is embellished with gray bows, lace, and a red shawl. Beyond the brown rock behind her is a green landscape under blue sky.

Oil on canvas. 50×40¼ in. (127×102.2 cm.)

Signed and dated center left: *J.S. Copley pinx. 1756.*

Collections: Mrs. William Tyng (*Elizabeth Ross*, Cat. no. 277), Gorham, Me.; Elizabeth Heddle Hilliard, her adopted daughter; William Tyng Hilliard, her son, by 1873; Mabel Harlow, his granddaughter, Boston; Hannah Marcy and Grace M. Edwards, Boston, about 1916.

Julia Cheney Edwards Collection, bequest of Grace M. Edwards in memory of her mother. 39.646

Ann Tyng (1733–1756) was born in Boston, the daughter of Edmund and Ann Waldo Tyng, and in 1756 married Thomas Smelt, an officer in the British Army. She died a month later, however, and was buried in King's Chapel, Boston. The concept of the lady as an elegant shepherdess was prompted by Blackburn's portrait of *Mary Sylvester* (Metropolitan Museum) painted two years before.

References: A.T. Perkins, *Copley*, Boston, 1873, p. 22./ F.W. Bayley, *Copley*, Boston, 1915, p. 228./ A. Burroughs, *Limners and Likenesses*, Cambridge, Mass., 1936, p. 66 (pl. 49)./ Metropolitan Museum, *Copley*, New York, 1936, p. 4./ B.N. Parker and A.B. Wheeler, *Copley*, Boston, 1938, pp. 89–90 (pl. 8)./ C.C. Cunningham, "From Gainsborough to Renoir," *Art News*, 1939, XXXVIII, no. 10, p. 8./ —, "Juliana Cheney Edwards Collection," *MFA Bulletin*, 1939, XXXVII, no. 224, p. 98, no. 3./ J.T. Flexner, *America's Old Masters*, New York, 1939 (repr. p. 116)./ J.H. Morgan, *Copley*, Windham, Conn., 1939, p. 11./ J.T. Flexner, *Copley*, Boston, 1948, p. 25 (pl. 3)./ E.P. Richardson, *Painting in America*, New York, 1956, p. 72./ J.D. Prown, *Copley*, Cambridge, Mass., 1966 (fig. 38).

Exhibitions: Boston, MFA, *Juliana Cheney Edwards Collection*, 1939–1940, no. 3./ Worcester, Mass., Art Museum, *New England Painting 1700–75*, 1943, no. 32./ Rhode Island School of Design Museum, *Old and New England*, 1945, no. 24 (repr. p. 23)./ Oberlin, O., Allen Memorial Art Museum, *Youthful Work by Great Artists*, 1963, no. 19 (repr. in the *Bulletin*, Spring 1963, XX, no. 3).

254.

fig. 38

Mary and Elizabeth Royall

Seated full-length upon a red and gold draped sofa, Mary, in blue, faces front and holds a hummingbird; Elizabeth, in beige, holds a black and white spaniel puppy. A deep red curtain is in the left background; the sky to the right is blue.

Oil on canvas. 57½×48 in. (146×121.9 cm.)

Painted about 1758.

Collections: The Royall family, Medford, Mass., until 1779; Gideon Snow, Boston; the Rev. Theodore W. Snow, Boston; H. Elizabeth Snow, Pomfret, Conn.

Julia Knight Fox Fund. 25.49

Mary MacIntosh and Elizabeth Royall were the daughters of Isaac Royall (Cat. no. 280) and Elizabeth MacIntosh Royall of Medford, Mass. Mary (1745–1786), the elder, married George Erving, a Tory merchant of Boston, in 1775 and fled to London with him via Halifax after the British evacuation of Boston the next year. She died there childless. Elizabeth (1747–1775) married William Pepperell Sparhawk, later (in 1774) to become Sir William Pepperell, Bart. Contrary to the traditional accounts that Lady Elizabeth Royall Pepperell died either in Halifax or at sea while fleeing to England, letters by her husband from Boston in November, 1775 and an obituary account in the *Boston News Letter* confirm her death there during the siege of the city by Washington's army (*see* M.A. Barclay, *below*). Painted about 1758, this portrait was acquired as a work by Joseph Blackburn, whose arrival in Boston in 1756 exerted a brief but strong influence over the young Copley's style. It was attributed to Copley by Mrs. Barbara N. Parker in 1934.

References: A.T. Perkins, *Copley*, Boston, 1873, p. 93./ Massachusetts Historical Society, *Copley-Pelham Letters*, Boston, 1914, p. 361./ L. Burroughs, "Copley," *Metro-*

politan Museum Bulletin, 1936, XXXI, no. 12, p. 253./ F.W. Coburn, "Blackburn," *Connoisseur*, 1937, XCIX, p. 75 (repr. p. 74)./ B.N. Parker and A.B. Wheeler, *Copley*, Boston, 1938, p. 72 (pl. 15)./ E.P. Richardson, *Painting in America*, New York, 1956, p. 72 (fig. 24)./ A.W. Rutledge, "American Loyalists," *Art Quarterly*, 1957, XX, no. 2, pp. 195–203 (fig. 5)./ M.A. Barclay, *Royall House Reporter*, 1966, VI, no. 1, pp. 1–6 (repr.)./ J.D. Prown, *Copley*, Cambridge, Mass., 1966 (fig. 83).

Exhibitions: Chicago Art Institute, *Century of Progress*, 1934, no. 367 (pl. LIV); New York, Metropolitan Museum, *Copley*, 1936–1937, no. 3 (repr.)./ —, *Life in America*, 1939, no. 13 (repr. p. 11)./ Toronto Art Gallery, *Great Paintings*, 1940, no. 53./ Medford, Mass., Royall House, *225th Anniversary of the Royall House*, 1957./ Boston, MFA and Wellesley College, Jewett Arts Center, *Four Boston Masters*, 1959, no. 1 (repr. p. 21)./ New York, Wildenstein and Co., *Masterpieces*, 1961, no. 25 (repr.)./ Raleigh, North Carolina Museum, *Carolina Charter: Tercentenary Exhibition*, 1963, no. 7 (repr.)./ Washington, D.C., National Gallery, New York Metropolitan Museum, and Boston, MFA, *Copley*, 1965–1966, no. 9 (repr. pl. 1).

255.

fig. 40

Mrs. Samuel Quincy (Hannah Hill)

Standing half-length, facing front before a brown background, she holds a sprig of larkspur in her folded hands. She wears a red satin dress trimmed in gold and green with white lace cuffs and an elaborate collar; white ostrich plumes adorn her black felt hat.

Oil on canvas. 35½ × 28¼ in. (90.2 × 71.7 cm.)

Painted about 1761.

Collections: Quincy Phillips, great-grandson of the sitter, Cambridge, Mass. by 1873; Emily Treadwell Phillips, his wife; Grace W. Treadwell, her niece, Kittery Point, Maine.

Lent by Miss Grace W. Treadwell. 2129.13

Hannah Hill was born in Boston in 1734, daughter of a wealthy distiller, Thomas Hill, and his wife Hannah. She married Samuel Quincy in 1761 and when he left for England in 1778 remained in Cambridge with her brother Henry. In 1782 she died without seeing her husband again. From its style, her portrait was probably painted before the pendant of her husband (Cat. no. 276), perhaps about the time of her marriage.

References: A.T. Perkins, *Copley*, Boston, 1873, p. 97./ F.W. Bayley, *Copley*, Boston, 1910, p. 82./ —, *Copley*, Boston, 1915, p. 204./ T. Bolton and H.L. Binsse, "Copley," *The Antiquarian*, 1930, XV, no. 6, p. 118./ B.N. Parker and A.B. Wheeler, *Copley*, Boston, 1938, p. 159 (pl. 27)./ J.H. Morgan, *Copley*, Windham, Conn., 1939, p. 14 (fig. 111)./ J.D. Prown, *Copley*, Cambridge, Mass., 1966 (fig. 97).

256.

fig. 39

Lady in a Blue Dress

Three-quarter length, turned three-quarters left, she is seated with her left arm resting on a cushioned table and holding a closed fan in her right hand. Pink ribbons decorate her lace cap and her blue dress with its white stomacher and lace. In the background is a red drapery before a green wall.

Oil on canvas. 50 × 40 in. (127 × 101.6 cm.)

Signed and dated on table's edge: *J.S. Copley pinx 1763*.

Collections: Martha Babcock Amory, granddaughter of the artist, Boston, before 1900; Mrs. F. Gordon Dexter, her daughter, Boston; Susan C. Amory, Boston; Martha Codman Karolik, Newport, R.I., 1938.

M. and M. Karolik Collection of Eighteenth Century American Arts. 39.249

The subject has been alternately identified as Mrs. Thomas Hutchinson, Sr. (Margaret Sanford) or her daughter-in-law Mrs. Thomas Hutchinson, Jr. (Sarah Oliver) (*see* Parker and Wheeler *below*).

References: F.W. Bayley, *Copley*, Boston, 1910, p. 56./ —, *Copley*, Boston, 1915, p. 154./ B.N. Parker and A.B. Wheeler, *Copley*, Boston, 1938, pp. 193–194 (pl. 29)./ E.J. Hipkiss, *M. and M. Karolik Collection of Eighteenth Century American Arts*, Boston, 1941, no. 8 (repr. p. 17)./ J.D. Prown, *Copley*, Cambridge, Mass., 1966 (fig. 118).

Exhibitions: Boston, MFA, *Copley*, 1938, no. 87./ Milwaukee Art Center, *Vignettes of the 18th Century in America*, 1960, p. 32 (repr. p. 18).

257.

John Spooner

Half-length, turned three-quarters right, shown through an oval aperture formed by brown spandrels, he wears an olive-gray suit laced with gold. The background is darker olive-brown.

Oil on canvas. 30 × 25¾ in. (76.2 × 65.4 cm.)

Signed and dated lower right: *J.S. Copley/ Pinx 1763.*

Collections: William Heath Spooner, great-grandson of the sitter; Lucy Reed Pettee, his daughter, by 1911; Mrs. Thayer; Philip L. Spalding, Milton, Mass., about 1914; Katherine A. Spalding, Philip Spalding, Oakes Ames Spalding, and Hobart Ames Spalding, her sons; Hobart Ames Spalding, 1964.

Lent by Hobart Ames Spalding. 1.50 (since withdrawn)

John Spooner (1728–1768), born in Boston, was the son of John and Elizabeth Wells Spooner. He was a merchant, and married first Hannah Jones in 1756, then in 1762 Margaret Oliver, daughter of Andrew Oliver. He died in London.

References: T. Bolton and H.L. Binsse, "Copley," *The Antiquarian*, 1930, xv, no. 6, p. 118./ B.N. Parker and A.B. Wheeler, *Copley*, Boston, 1938, pp. 187–188 (pl. 28)./ J.D. Prown, *Copley*, Cambridge, Mass., 1966 (fig. 113).

Exhibition: Boston, MFA, *One Hundred Colonial Portraits*, 1930, p. 85 (repr.).

258.

fig. 42

Mrs. John Amory (Katharine Greene)

Three-quarter length, she stands facing front, leaning on a brown carved pedestal and wearing a yellow-brown satin dress trimmed with mauve ribbons and white lace. Behind left, a green curtain and gray column; gray clouds in a blue sky.

Oil on canvas. 49½ × 40 in. (125.7 × 101.6 cm.)

Painted about 1763.

Collections: Arthur Amory Codman, great-grandson of the sitter; Misses Catherine E. and Maria P. Codman, his sisters, Bristol, R.I.; Martha Codman Karolik, their niece, Newport, R.I., about 1902.

M. and M. Karolik Collection of Eighteenth Century American Arts. 37.36

Katharine Greene (1731–1777) was born in Boston, daughter of Rufus and Katharine Stoubridge Greene. In 1757 she marred John Amory and in 1775 left five of their eight children in Boston to join her husband in England. She died in London. Copley used the 1746 mezzotint by John Faber, Jr., of Thomas Hudson's portrait of the *Rt. Hon. Mary, Viscountess Andover*, for three of his portraits: *Mrs. John Amory*, *Mrs. John Murray*, dated 1763 and owned by H. Daland Chandler, Boston, and *Mrs. Daniel Hubbard*, painted about 1764 and owned by the Chicago Art Institute. Similarities of style, pose, and costume indicate that they were painted at about the same time. The pendant portrait of her husband (Cat. no. 278) was painted in 1768.

References: A.T. Perkins, *Copley*, Boston, 1873, p. 30./ F.W. Bayley, *Copley*, Boston, 1910, p. 13./ —, *Copley*, Boston, 1915, p. 43./ M.C. Codman, *Journal of Mrs. John Amory*, Boston, 1923 (repr. opp. p. 3)./ T. Bolton and H.L. Binsse, "Copley," *The Antiquarian*, 1930, xv, no. 6, p. 116./ B.N. Parker and A.B. Wheeler, *Copley*, Boston, 1938, pp. 22–23 (pl. 41)./ E.J. Hipkiss, *M. and M. Karolik Collection of Eighteenth Century American Arts*, Boston, 1941, no. 5 (repr. p. 11)./ C.C. Cunningham, "The Karolik Collection—Some Notes on Copley," *Art in America*, 1942, xxx, no. 1, pp. 26–33 (fig. 1)./ J.T. Flexner, *First Flowers of Our Wilderness*, Boston, 1947, pp. 217, 220, 345 (repr. p. 215)./ —, *Copley*, Boston, 1948, p. 32./ F.A. Sweet, "Mezzotint Sources of American Colonial Portraits," *Art Quarterly*, 1951, XIV, no. 2, pp. 152–157 (fig. 4)./ J.D. Prown, *Copley*, Cambridge, Mass., 1966 (fig. 140).

Exhibitions: Washington, D.C., National Gallery, *Early American Paintings*, 1925–1926, no. 5./ Boston, MFA, *Copley*, 1938, no. 3./ — and Wellesley College, Jewett Arts Center, *Four Boston Masters*, 1959, no. 2./ Boston, MFA, *M. and M. Karolik Memorial Exhibition*, 1964.

259.

fig. 43

James Warren

Standing in three-quarter length and facing front, his right hand is in his pocket and

his left holds a walking stick; his gray coat is open to reveal a long black satin waist-coat. Beyond the red curtain and brown column is a green and blue landscape.
Oil on canvas. 51¼ × 41 in. (130.1 × 104.1 cm.)
Painted about 1763.
Collection: Winslow Warren, descendant of the sitter, Dedham, Mass.
Bequest of Winslow Warren. 31.211

James Warren (1726–1808), merchant, farmer, and patriot, was born in Plymouth, Mass. and married Mercy Otis (Cat. no. 260) in 1754. After the death of Joseph Warren (Cat. no. 292) at Bunker Hill, he became President of the Provincial Congress of Massachusetts. Because of his support of the lower classes and the enmity of John Hancock, he was relieved of his duties. In 1779–1780 he was a member of Congress, but lost the seat until 1787, when he was returned to the House of Representatives and elected Speaker. In 1788 he retired and pursued the study of scientific farming. Copley's portrait of his son Winslow (Cat. no. 300) is also in the MFA collection.

References: A.T. Perkins, *Copley*, Boston, 1873, p. 116./ F.W. Bayley, *Copley*, Boston, 1910, p. 130./ —, *Copley*, Boston, 1915, p. 250./ —, *Five Colonial Artists*, Boston, 1929 (repr. p. 277)./ T. Bolton and H.L. Binsse, "Copley," *The Antiquarian*, 1930, xv, no. 6, p. 118./ B.N. Parker and A.B. Wheeler, *Copley*, Boston, 1938, pp. 199–200 (pl. 42)./ J.D. Prown, *Copley*, Cambridge, Mass., 1966 (fig. 120).

Exhibition: Boston, MFA, *One Hundred Colonial Portraits*, 1930, no. 92 (repr.).

260.
fig. 44

Mrs. James Warren (Mercy Otis)

Three-quarter length, she stands in left profile, her head turned to the front, her fingers touching orange nasturtiums. Her blue dress, edged with gold, is embellished with lace, the material of her cap. To the right, beyond brown drapery, are green trees and blue sky.
Oil on canvas. 51¼ × 41 in. (130.1 × 104.1 cm.)
Painted about 1763.
Collection: Same as Cat. no. 259.
Bequest of Winslow Warren. 31.212

Mercy Otis (1728–1814), daughter of "Colonel" James Otis of Barnstable, Mass., married James Warren in 1754 and had five children by him. Politically knowledgeable, she wrote an entertaining three-volume history of the Revolution, as well as farces, satires, and poems. Pendant to the preceding.

References: A.T. Perkins, *Copley*, Boston, 1873, p. 116./ F.W. Bayley, *Copley*, Boston, 1910, p. 129./ —, *Copley*, Boston, 1915, p. 251./ —, *Five Colonial Artists*, Boston, 1929 (repr. p. 279)./ T. Bolton and H.L. Binsse, "Copley," *The Antiquarian*, 1930, xv, no. 6, p. 118./ B.N. Parker and A.B. Wheeler, *Copley*, Boston, 1938, pp. 200–201 (pl. 42)./ V. Barker, "Copley's American Portraits," *Magazine of Art*, 1950, XLIII, no. 3 (repr. p. 85)./ J.D. Prown, *Copley*, Cambridge, Mass., 1966 (fig. 121).

Exhibitions: Boston, MFA, *One Hundred Colonial Portraits*, 1930, no. 93 (repr.)./ — and Wellesley College, Jewett Arts Center, *Four Boston Masters*, 1959, no. 4 (repr. p. 17).

261.
fig. 41

Madam Cotton (Deborah Mason)

Seated in three-quarter length, turned three-quarters left, she rests her right arm on a table covered in red and with the other hand balances a closed fan on her lap. White lace adorns her blue satin dress, mauve ribbons her hair. The chair is red before a brown background.
Oil on canvas. 50¼ × 39½ in. (127.6 × 100.6 cm.)
Painted about 1763–1764.
Collections: Given by the sitter to the Rev. Abraham Williams, Sandwich, Mass.; Thomas Williams, his son, Sandwich, about 1784; Susanna Ann Williams Hayden, his daughter, Cambridge, Mass., about 1828; Horace John Hayden, her son, Boston, about 1871; Harold Buckminster Hayden, his son, Framingham, Mass., about 1900; Mrs. Harold B. Hayden, Platts-burgh, N.Y., 1928.
Lent by Mrs. Harold B. Hayden. 128.42

Born in Boston in 1730, Deborah Mason was married in 1760 to Roland

Cotton of Sandwich, Mass., an elderly gentleman at that time. He was a town Representative and Clerk of the House of Representatives. It is not known when Madam Cotton died. Dated according to her apparent age and stylistic similarities to the portrait of *Hannah Loring* (William Caleb Loring, Prides Crossing, Mass.) of 1763.

References: A.T. Perkins, *Copley*, Boston, 1873, p. 43 (as *Miss Catten*)./ F.W. Bayley, *Copley*, Boston, 1910, p. 26 (as *Miss Catten*)./ —, *Copley*, Boston, 1915, p. 75 (as *Miss Catten*)./ B.N. Parker and A.B. Wheeler, *Copley*, Boston, 1938, p. 63 (pl. 87)./ J.D. Prown, *Copley*, Cambridge, Mass., 1966 (fig. 123).

Exhibition: New York, Metropolitan Museum, *Colonial Portraits*, 1911, p. 38.

262.
fig. 45

Nathaniel Sparhawk

Standing full-length in a red velvet suit, he faces front and leans on the pedestal of a fluted column. In the background is extensive baroque architecture. A green landscape is visible through a portico, left; the sky is pink and blue.

Oil on canvas. 90 × 57½ in. (228.6 × 146 cm.)
Signed and dated on scroll in his hand: *John S. Copley/ pinx 1764.*
Collections: D.H. Sparhawk, great-nephew of the sitter, Boston, by 1873; Samuel B. Rindge, by 1880; Frederick H. Rindge, Los Angeles, Calif.; Mrs. Frederick H. Rindge.
Deposited by the Estate of Frederick H. Rindge. 536.80

Nathaniel Sparhawk (1715–1776), son of the Rev. John and Priscilla Hemans Sparhawk, was born in Bristol, Mass. After entering into business with Benjamin Coleman in Boston, he established a mercantile house in Kittery, Me. In 1742 he married Elizabeth Pepperell. He was Justice of the Peace in 1744, Justice in the Inferior Court of Common Pleas for York County from 1759 to 1772, and served on the Governor's Council from 1760 until his death.

References: A.T. Perkins, *Copley*, Boston, 1873, p. 107./ F.W. Bayley, *Copley*, Boston, 1910, p. 96./ —, *Copley*, Boston, 1915, p. 230./ —, *Five Colonial Artists*, Boston, 1929 (repr. p. 273)./ T. Bolton and H.L. Binsse, "Copley," *The Antiquarian*, 1930, xv, no. 6, p. 118./ B.N. Parker and A.B. Wheeler, *Copley*, 1938, p. 186 (pl. 44)./ J.H. Morgan, *Copley*, Windham, Conn., 1939, p. 12./ J.T. Flexner, *First Flowers of Our Wilderness*, Boston, 1947, pp. 220, 346 (repr. p. 221)./ L. Dresser, "Eighteenth Century Portraits," *Maine and Its Role in American Art*, New York, 1963, pp. 16, 20, 27 (repr. p. 20)./ J.D. Prown, *Copley*, Cambridge, Mass., 1966 (fig. 152).

Exhibition: Washington, D.C., National Gallery, New York, Metropolitan Museum, and Boston, MFA, *Copley*, 1965–1966, no. 22 (repr. p. 38).

263.
fig. 46

Mrs. Moses Gill (Sarah Prince)

Half-length and turned slightly right against a brown background, she wears a four-string pearl choker, a blue satin dress embellished with pearls, and a brown stole.

Pastel on paper. Sight size: 23¼ × 17¼ in. (59 × 43.8 cm.)
Drawn after 1764.
Collections: Estate of Louisa C.A. Nightingale, by 1903; Ward N. Boylston, Jr., Brattleboro, Vt.
Lent by the Estate of Ward N. Boylston, Jr. 302.25

Sarah Prince (1728–1771), the only daughter of the Rev. Thomas Prince of Boston, married Moses Gill, Lieutenant Governor of Massachusetts, in 1759. A replica by Copley after his full-length oil portrait painted about 1764 (Rhode Island School of Design Museum).

References: A.T. Perkins, *Copley*, Boston, 1873, p. 59./ F.W. Bayley, *Copley*, Boston, 1910, p. 41./ —, *Copley*, Boston, 1915, p. 119./ B.N. Parker and A.B. Wheeler, *Copley*, Boston, 1938, p. 220./ J.D. Prown, *Copley*, Cambridge, Mass., 1966 (fig. 130).

264.
fig. 48

John Hancock

Full-length, turned half right, he is seated at a table holding a quill pen and a large ledger inscribed at the top left corner, 1765. He wears a blue coat and waistcoat laced with gold, and black breeches. The curtain and tablecloth are pink.

Oil on canvas. 49½ × 40½ in. (125.7 × 102.8 cm.)
Signed and dated lower left: *J.S. Copley/ pinx 1765.*
Collections: John Hancock, the sitter's nephew, Boston; Charles Lowell Hancock and Washington Hancock, his sons, Boston, 1859; presented to the City of Boston, 1863.
Deposited by the City of Boston. 30.76d

John Hancock (1737–1793), son of the Rev. John and Mary Hawke Hancock, was born in Braintree, Mass. He was notorious among his peers for the crafty political maneuvers he used to gain his immense popularity with the people. As Treasurer of Harvard College from 1773 to 1777, he continually refused to render their accounts or securities. Yet, he was President of the Provincial Congress in 1774–1775, President of the Continental Congress from 1775 to 1777, and signer of the Declaration of Independence. He was elected first Governor of Massachusetts in 1780, and held that office, except between 1785 and 1787, until his death in Braintree. Independence Hall, Philadelphia, owns a copy of the head by S.F.B. Morse; Faneuil Hall, Boston, has a copy painted in 1876 by an unknown artist; a third copy by Edward Savage, dated 1785, owned in 1938 by John Hancock Tilton, was destroyed in 1942. Copley painted two half-length portraits as well (Henry L. Shattuck, Brookline, Mass. and James S. Copley, La Jolla, Calif.).

References: H.T. Tuckerman, *Book of the Artists*, New York, 1870, pp. 72, 75./ A.T. Perkins, *Copley*, Boston, 1873, p. 70./ W.H. Downes, "Boston Painters and Paintings," *Atlantic Monthly*, 1888, LXII, no. 369, p. 92./ S. Isham, *American Painting*, New York, 1905 (fig. 7)./ J.W. McSpadden, *Famous Painters of America*, New York, 1907 (repr. opp. p. 64)./ F.W. Bayley, *Copley*, Boston, 1910, p. 51./ —, *Copley*, Boston, 1915, p. 136./ —, *Five Colonial Artists*, Boston, 1929 (repr. p. 215)./ T. Bolton and H.L. Binsse, "Copley," *The Antiquarian*, 1930, XV, no. 6, p. 116./ B.N. Parker and A.B. Wheeler, *Copley*, Boston, 1938, pp. 96–97 (pl. 60)./ J.T. Flexner, *American Painting*, New York, 1950, pp. 10, 111 (repr. opp. p. 22)./ J.D. Prown, *Copley*, Cambridge, Mass., 1966 (fig. 153).

Exhibitions: Boston, MFA, *Contemporary Art*, 1879, no. 88./ —, *One Hundred Colonial Portraits*, 1930, p. 43 (repr.)./ Harvard University, *Tercentenary*, 1936, no. 18 (pl. 6)./ New York, Metropolitan Museum, *Copley*, 1936–1937, no. 14 (repr.)./ Washington, D.C., Corcoran Gallery, *Signers of the Declaration of Independence*, 1937–1938, p. 23, no. 15./ Williamsburg, Va., Colonial Williamsburg, *They Gave Us Freedom*, 1951, no. 22 (repr.)./ Washington, D.C., National Gallery, New York, Metropolitan Museum, and Boston, MFA, *Copley*, 1965–1966, no. 23 (repr. p. 39).

265.
fig. 47

Joseph Green
Bust-length and turned three-quarters right before a brown background, he wears a gray suit and a wig.
Pastel on paper mounted on linen. 22 × 17 in. (55.9 × 43.2 cm.)
Drawn about 1765.
Collections: Dr. Joshua Green, great-grandson of the sitter, Groton, Mass., by 1873; Dr. Samuel Abbott Green, Groton, by 1903.
Gift of Dr. Samuel Abbott Green. 10.34

Joseph Green (1703–1765), the son of the Rev. Joseph and Elizabeth Gerrish Green of Salem Village, Mass., became a successful Boston merchant and was commissioned a magistrate. Active in politics, he supported the Revolutionary side but died in Boston too soon to join the radical opposition to England.

References: *New England Historical and Genealogical Register*, 1861, XV, p. 108./ H.T. Tuckerman, *Book of the Artists*, New York, 1870, p. 72./ A.T. Perkins, *Copley*, Boston, 1873, p. 62./ F.W. Bayley, *Copley*, Boston, 1910, p. 49./ —, *Copley*, Boston, 1915, p. 124./ T. Bolton, *Early American Portrait Draughtsmen*, New York, 1923, p. 19, no. 20./ M. Vaughan, "Pastels in Colonial America," *International Studio*, 1928, LXXXIX, no. 370 (repr. p. 36)./ B.N. Parker and A.B. Wheeler, *Copley*, Boston, 1938, pp. 220–221 (pl. 126a)./ J.D. Prown, *Copley*, Cambridge, Mass., 1966 (fig. 151).

Exhibitions: Boston, MFA, *Copley*, 1938, no. 33./ — and Wellesley College, Jewett Arts Center, *Four Boston Masters*, 1959, no. 6.

266.

fig. 49

Mrs. Samuel Henley (Katharine Russell)

Half-length and facing slightly right, she wears a white dress embellished with lace, a lace choker, and has red and pink flowers in her hair. The background is gray.
Pastel on paper. 22¾ × 17¾ in. (57.8 × 45.1 cm.)
Drawn about 1765.
Gift of Rear Admiral T.O. Selfridge, 3rd, U.S.N. 24.266
Katharine Russell (1741–1812), probably the daughter of James and Katharine Graves Russell of Charlestown, Mass., became the second wife of Samuel Henley, a distiller and Treasurer of Charlestown, in 1762. There she bore him twenty children. Dated according to the style and the sitter's apparent age.
References: B.N. Parker and A.B. Wheeler, *Copley*, Boston, 1938, pp. 224–225./ J.D. Prown, *Copley*, Cambridge, Mass., 1966 (fig. 205).
Exhibition: Boston, MFA, *Copley*, 1938, no. 42.

267.

fig. 50

Mrs. Nathaniel Ellery (Ann Sargent)

Seated in three-quarter length, turned three-quarters right, in a mahogany sidechair with a black drapery over its back, she wears a brown satin dress with a broad white fichu and a white bonnet. She carries a sheer black shawl around her shoulders and a white rose is pinned at the base of her fichu. The background is dull green.
Oil on canvas. 51 × 40½ in. (129.5 × 102.8 cm.)
Painted about 1766.
Collections: Mrs. N. Martin Rogers, Cambridge, Mass., by 1873; Miss Fanny Rogers, Cambridge, Mass., 1915; Estate of Miss Fanny Rogers.
Lent by the Estate of Miss Fanny Rogers. 234.50
Ann Sargent (1692–1782) was the second daughter of William and Mary Duncan Sargent of Gloucester, Mass. In 1720 she married Nathaniel Ellery, a prosperous merchant of Gloucester, by whom she had six children. She died in Gloucester. Her pose, smoothly textured features, the emphasis of highlights on satin surfaces, and almost sisterly similarity to the portrait of *Mrs. Sylvanus Bourne* (Metropolitan Museum) dated 1766, indicate the date.
References: A.T. Perkins, *Copley*, Boston, 1873, p. 52./ *New England Historical and Genealogical Register*, Boston, XXVIII, 1874, p. 366./ F.W. Bayley, *Copley*, Boston, 1915, p. 99./ E.W. and C.S. Sargent, *Epes Sargent of Gloucester and His Descendants*, Gloucester, Mass., 1923, p. 5 (repr. opp. p. 2)./ T. Bolton and H.L. Binsse, "Copley," *The Antiquarian*, 1930, XV, no. 6, p. 116./ B.N. Parker and A.B. Wheeler, *Copley*, Boston, 1938, p. 265./ J.D. Prown, *Copley*, Cambridge, Mass., 1966 (fig. 180).

268.

fig. 55

Mrs. Timothy Rogers (Lucy Boylston)

Nearly full-length, turned three-quarters right, she is seated in an armchair upholstered in green and brown. She wears a gray satin dress with a pink stole; the background is dark brown.
Oil on canvas. 50 × 40 in. (127 × 101.6 cm.)
Painted about 1766–1767.
Collections: H.B. Rogers, Boston, by 1830; Mr. Boylston, Princeton, Mass., by 1873; Louisa C.A. Nightingale, Providence, R.I., by 1903; Mrs. Paul Webster Bean, Auburn, Me.
Lent by Mrs. Paul Webster Bean. 309.25
A daughter of Thomas and Sarah Morecock Boylston, Lucy Boylston was born in Boston in 1726. She married Captain Timothy Rogers, a shipowner and merchant, in 1745 and moved to Gloucester. She died there in 1759. Despite her death that year, the close stylistic similarity to the other portraits of the Boylston family, for example of her sister *Rebecca Boylston* (Cat. no. 270), all of 1766 and 1767, indicates that it was probably painted posthumously.
References: A.T. Perkins, *Copley*, Boston, 1873, p. 99./ F.W. Bayley, *Copley*, Boston,

1910, p. 84./ —, *Copley*, Boston, 1915, p. 210./ T. Bolton and H.L. Binsse, "Copley," *The Antiquarian*, 1930, xv, no. 6, p. 118./ B.N. Parker and A.B. Wheeler, *Copley*, Boston, 1938, pp. 164–165 (pl. 17)./ J.D. Prown, *Copley*, Cambridge, Mass., 1966 (fig. 187).

269.
fig. 54

Corkscrew Hanging on a Nail

Painted as a trompe l'oeil *on the frame of a paneled door: a dark gray steel cork-screw hangs from a hand-wrought nail set in the imitation mahogany-grained wood.*
Oil on panel. 3½ × 3¾ in. (8.9 × 9.5 cm., the painted area only).
Painted between 1766 and 1774.
Collections: Dr. Charles Russell, Lincoln, Mass.; Chambers Russell, his brother, 1780; Chambers Russell the younger, his son, 1784; the Hon. John Codman, son-in-law of Dr. Charles Russell, 1790; Charles Russell Codman, his son, 1803; house sold out of the family for many years; Ogden Codman, his son, until 1904; Dorothy Codman, his daughter.
Anonymous loan. 110.62

Family tradition relates that when Copley visited Dr. Charles Russell (1738–1780) in Lincoln, Mass., his host was embarrassed to find that he had mislaid his only corkscrew, and was thus unable to offer the artist refreshment. Copley immediately offered to provide him with a more permanent implement, and so painted this *trompe l'oeil* on the library door. A fragment of a portrait of *Dr. Charles Russell* (Massachusetts Historical Society) by Copley, showing the sitter at about thirty years of age, provides evidence for Copley's presence with brush and paint at the Russell house. Dr. Russell returned from London in 1766 and inherited the house from his uncle, Chambers Russell, that year. The corkscrew and the portrait were probably painted soon after, before Copley's departure for London in 1774.
Reference: P.T. Rathbone, "Rediscovery: Copley's Corkscrew," *Art in America*, 1965, no. 3, pp. 48–51 (repr.).

270.
fig. 53

Rebecca Boylston

Three-quarter length and facing front, she wears a white satin dress beneath a red lavender cloak with a blue shawl on her arm and holds a basket of red and white roses. She stands before an archway, left, and landscape in green and blue, right distance; her right arm leans against a brown griffin fountain.
Oil on canvas. 50 × 40 in. (127 × 101.6 cm.)
Signed and dated at base of fountain: *JSC 1767* (initials in monogram).
Collections: Mrs. Edwin J. Nightingale, great-grandniece of the sitter, by 1873; Mrs. Paul Webster Bean, Auburn, Me., about 1925.
Lent by Mrs. Paul Webster Bean. 308.25

Born in 1727, Rebecca Boylston was the daughter of Thomas and Sarah Morecock Boylston and the second wife of Moses Gill, whom she married in 1773. She lived in Boston and on the family estate in Princeton, Mass. A second portrait by Copley, painted about the time of her marriage, is in the Museum of the Rhode Island School of Design, Providence.
References: A.T. Perkins, *Copley*, Boston, 1873, p. 60./ F.W. Bayley, *Copley*, Boston, 1910, p. 42./ —, *Copley*, Boston, 1915, p. 117./ —, *Five Colonial Artists*, Boston, 1929 (repr. p. 207)./ B.N. Parker and A.B. Wheeler, *Copley*, Boston, 1938, p. 45 (pl. 81)./ J.D. Prown, *Copley*, Cambridge, Mass., 1966 (fig. 186).

271.
fig. 52

Joseph Green

Bust-length, he faces three-quarters left in a brown silk banyan and a beige turban. The background is gray.
Pastel on paper. 24 × 17 in. (61 × 43.2 cm.)
Signed and dated center right: *JSC 1767* (initials in monogram).
Collections: Gideon Snow, the sitter's nephew; the Rev. Theodore W. Snow, his son; H. Elizabeth Snow, his daughter, Pomfret, Conn.
Julia Knight Fox Fund. 25.50

Joseph Green (1706–1780), probably born in Boston, was graduated from

Harvard in 1726. He was a merchant by trade, but also a well-known wit and satirist. Although a ready parodist of the contemporary administration, he was a Loyalist at heart and in 1775 chose exile in London until his death. Pendant to the portrait of *Mrs. Joseph Green* (Cat. no. 272).

References: A.T. Perkins, *Copley*, Boston, 1873, p. 62./ J. Winsor, *Memorial History of Boston*, Boston, 1881, III, p. 132 (repr.)./ F.W. Bayley, *Copley*, Boston, 1910, pp. 48–49./ —, *Copley*, Boston, 1915, p. 125./ T. Bolton, *Early American Portrait Draughtsmen*, New York, 1923, p. 19, no. 21./ B.N. Parker and A.B. Wheeler, *Copley*, Boston, 1938, p. 221 (pl. 126b)./ J.D. Prown, *Copley*, Cambridge, Mass., 1966 (fig. 215).

Exhibitions: Boston, MFA, *One Hundred Colonial Portraits*, 1930, no. 40 (repr.)./ —, *Copley*, 1938, no. 34.

272.

fig. 51

Mrs. Joseph Green

Head and shoulders facing front, she wears a white scarf, fastened at the side with pearls over her dark hair. Her blue sacque edged with ermine is worn over a pink gown, the neck of which is trimmed with lace. A string of pearls is at her throat.

Pastel on paper, mounted on linen. 23¼ × 17¼ in. (59 × 43.8 cm.)

Drawn about 1767. Signed above left shoulder: *JSC* (in monogram).

Collections: Gideon Snow, the sitter's nephew; the Rev. Theodore W. Snow, his son; H. Elizabeth Snow, his daughter, Pomfret, Conn.

Julia Knight Fox Fund. 25.51

Little is known of Mrs. Green. She traveled to England with her husband in 1775 and is referred to as Elizabeth in his will. She lived in London until her death, which occurred between 1797, the date of her will, and 1800, the date of its registration. The pastel is probably of the same date as her husband's (Cat. no. 271).

References: A.T. Perkins, *Copley*, Boston, 1873, p. 63./ F.W. Bayley, *Copley*, Boston, 1910, p. 49./ —, *Copley*, Boston, 1915, p. 125./ M. Vaughan, "Pastels in Colonial America," *International Studio*, 1928, LXXXIX, no. 370 (repr. p. 36)./ B.N. Parker and A.B. Wheeler, *Copley*, Boston, 1938, pp. 221–222./ J.D. Prown, *Copley*, Cambridge, Mass., 1966 (fig. 216).

Exhibition: Boston, MFA, *Copley*, 1938, no. 35.

273.

fig. 56

Judge Martin Howard

He is seated, nearly full-length and turned three-quarters right, in a blue-green upholstered chair. His judge's robes are scarlet with brown cuffs. A brown leather book rests on the green covered table beside him; the curtain left is blue with a gold border.

Oil on canvas. 49½ × 39¾ in. (126 × 101 cm.)

Signed and dated center right: *JSC p. 1767* (initials in monogram).

Collections: Mrs. Martin Howard, wife of the sitter, Chelsea, Middlesex, England, 1781; Andrew Spooner, her grandson; Miss Anna Howard Spooner, his sister, Boston; Social Law Library, Boston, 1829.

Lent by the Proprietors of the Social Law Library. 18.37

The son of Martin and Ann Howard of Newport, R.I., the date and place of his birth are unknown. He studied law under James Honyman, Jr. and was admitted to the bar at Newport, R.I. An ardent Loyalist, his house was ransacked and destroyed in 1765; he sailed for England, but returned to become Chief Justice of the Superior Court of North Carolina. He married Abigail Greenleaf of Boston in 1767. In 1770 he was driven from his Court in North Carolina for favoritism to Tories but was allowed to remain in his home until 1777. In 1778 he settled in Chelsea, Middlesex, England, where he remained until his death in 1781.

References: A.T. Perkins, *Copley*, Boston, 1873, p. 126 (as *Judge Hayward*)./ H.H. Edes, "Martin Howard and His Portrait by Copley," *Colonial Society of Massachusetts Publications*, 1900, VI, p. 384 (repr.)./ F.W. Bayley. *Copley*, Boston, 1910, p. 56./ —, *Copley*, Boston, 1915, p. 149./ E.A. Jones, *Loyalists of Massachusetts*, London, 1930, p. 167 (repr. p. 176)./ B.N. Parker and A.B. Wheeler, *Copley*, Boston, 1938, pp. 114–115 (pl. 74)./ J.D. Prown, *Copley*, Cambridge, Mass., 1966 (fig. 192).

Exhibitions: New York, Metropolitan Museum, *Copley*, 1936–1937, no. 23 (repr.)./

274.
fig. 57

Daniel Rogers

Seated three-quarter length and facing front, he rests his right arm on a green covered table and the other on the back of the mahogany chair. He wears a red coat, black breeches, and a waistcoat elaborately edged with gold braid. A green curtain, left, is before a brown wall.

Oil on canvas. 50 × 40½ in. (127 × 102.8 cm.)
Signed and dated lower right: *JSC 1767* (initials in monogram).
Collection: Dr. Morrill Wyman, Cambridge, Mass., by 1873.
Bequest of Dr. Morrill Wyman. 17.1

Although bequeathed to the MFA as a portrait of *Mr. Rogers of Salem*, no such man is recorded. The subject is possibly Daniel Rogers (1734–1800), the son of the Rev. John and Susannah Whipple Rogers of Kittery, Me. In 1759 he married Elizabeth Gorham, whose portrait by Copley, signed and dated 1762, is owned by Mrs. Eugene Duffer, Arlington, Va. She died in 1767 and he married Rachel Ellery in 1770. The two women bore him twenty-one children. He died in Gloucester, Mass. Copley's portrait of *Joseph Hooper* (Mr. and Mrs. Jacob Blaustein, Baltimore) is virtually identical in pose, costume, and color.

References: A.T. Perkins, *Copley*, Boston, 1873, p. 99./ F.W. Bayley, *Copley*, Boston, 1910, p. 85./ Massachusetts Historical Society, *Copley-Pelham Letters*, Boston, 1914, pp. 66–73./ F.W. Bayley, *Copley*, 1915, pp. 208–209./ —, *Five Colonial Artists*, Boston, 1929 (repr. p. 261)./ T. Bolton and H.L. Binsse, "Copley," *The Antiquarian*, 1930, xv, no. 6, p. 118./ B.N. Parker and A.B. Wheeler, *Copley*, Boston, 1938, pp. 162–163 (pl. 76)./ J.D. Prown, *Copley*, Cambridge, Mass., 1966 (fig. 217).

Exhibitions: London, Society of Artists, 1768, no. 23./ Salem, Mass., Essex Institute, *Essex County—Its Patronage of Artists and Craftsmen*, 1955, no. 2.

275.
fig. 58

Nicholas Boylston

Three-quarter length and turned three-quarters right, he is seated at a table and rests his left arm on two large books. Dressed informally, his right hand holds back his brown silk banyan and reveals a purple waistcoat; he wears a red turban. A dark blue drapery is behind, and a green and brown seascape is to the right.

Oil on canvas. 50¼ × 40¼ in. (127.6 × 102.2 cm.)
Painted about 1767.
Collections: Moses Kimball, Boston, by 1873; David P. Kimball, Boston.
Bequest of David P. Kimball. 23.504

Nicholas Boylston (1716–1771), probably born in Boston, was the son of Thomas and Sarah Boylston. He was best known as a wealthy merchant and a benefactor of Harvard College. The College owns two versions of this portrait: one, signed and dated 1767, is probably the original from which our replica was done in the same year. The other is a full-length portrait by Copley copied from the original at the request of Harvard in 1773.

References: A.T. Perkins, *Copley*, Boston, 1873, p. 38./ W.H. Downes, "Boston Painters and Paintings," *Atlantic Monthly*, 1888, LXII, no. 369, pp. 92–93./ F.W. Bayley, Copley, Boston, 1910, p. 21./ —, *Copley*, Boston, 1915, p. 65./ T. Bolton and H.L. Binsse, "Copley," *The Antiquarian*, 1930, xv, no. 6, p. 116./ B.N. Parker and A.B. Wheeler, *Copley*, Boston, 1938, p. 44 (pl. 78)./ J.D. Prown, *Copley*, Cambridge, Mass., 1966 (fig. 184).

Exhibitions: New York, Metropolitan Museum, *Colonial Portraits*, 1911, no. 36./ Paris, Musée du Jeu de Paume, *Trois Siècles d'Art aux Etats-Unis*, 1938, no. 30 (pl. 2)./ London, Tate Gallery, *American Painting*, 1946, no. 45./ Boston, MFA and Wellesley College, Jewett Arts Center, *Four Boston Masters*, 1959, no. 10 (repr. p. 27).

276.
fig. 59

Samuel Quincy

Three-quarter length and facing front, he leans with his right arm on a green covered table and holds a white quill pen next to some papers. His barrister's robes are black with white cuffs and bands. A brown wall is half-hidden by a green curtain.

Oil on canvas. 35½ × 28¼ in. (90.2 × 71.7 cm.)

Painted about 1767.

Collections: Quincy Phillips, great-grandson of the sitter, Cambridge, Mass., by 1873; Emily Treadwell Phillips, his wife; Grace W. Treadwell, her niece, Kittery Point, Me.

Lent by Miss Grace W. Treadwell. 2128.13

Son of the merchant Josiah Quincy, Samuel Quincy (1735–1789) was born in Braintree, Mass. He graduated from Harvard in 1754 and was admitted to the bar in 1758. He left for England on business shortly after the battle at Lexington, but his Loyalist sympathies prevented his return and separated him permanently from his wife, Hannah Hill, who died in 1782. Despairing of his return to America, he accepted an appointment in 1779 as Comptroller of Customs in Antigua. He married Mrs. M.A. Chadwell and lived in Antigua until failing health forced his return to England. He died during the journey. Pendant to the portrait of *Mrs. Samuel Quincy* (Cat. no. 255) painted about 1761.

References: A.T. Perkins, *Copley*, Boston, 1873, p. 97./ F.W. Bayley, *Copley*, Boston, 1910, p. 82./ Massachusetts Historical Society, *Copley-Pelham Letters*, Boston, 1914, p. 135./ F.W. Bayley, *Copley*, Boston, 1915, p. 204./ —, *Five Colonial Artists*, Boston, 1929 (repr. p. 257)./ T. Bolton and H.L. Binsse, "Copley," *The Antiquarian*, 1930, xv, no. 6, p. 118./ E.A. Jones, *Loyalists of Massachusetts*, London, 1930, p. 241 (repr. p. 240)./ B.N. Parker and A.B. Wheeler, *Copley*, Boston, 1938, p. 158 (pl. 64)./ J.D. Prown, *Copley*, Cambridge, Mass., 1966 (fig. 197).

Exhibition: Boston, MFA, *One Hundred Colonial Portraits*, 1930, p. 73 (repr.).

277.
fig. 60

Elizabeth Ross

Three-quarter length, she stands turned three-quarters right in a pink coat trimmed with ermine over a white satin dress. She holds a white bird on a finger of her left hand. To one side is a brown rocky wall with dense green forest behind.

Oil on canvas. 50 × 40 in. (127 × 101.6 cm.)

Painted about 1767.

Collections: Mrs. Timothy Hilliard, the sitter's adopted daughter, Gorham, Me.; William Tyng Hilliard, her son, by 1873; Mrs. H.S. Harlow, his daughter; Miss Mabel Harlow, her daughter, Boston, before 1915; Herbert Lawton, Boston; *Lawton Sale*, American Art Association-Anderson Galleries, New York, April 3, 1937, no. 347 (repr. p. 125); Maxim Karolik, Newport, R.I., 1938.

M. and M. Karolik Collection of Eighteenth Century American Arts. 39.248

Elizabeth Ross (1751–1831), daughter of Alexander and Eliza Ross, was born in Portland, Me. and in 1769 married William Tyng, a Colonel in the British Army. In 1783 they were forced to flee to Canada but returned ten years later to live on her mother's estate in Gorham, Me., where she died. Dated according to family tradition and style. Copley based her pose and the bird device upon the engraving by Edward Fisher of 1762 after Reynolds' portrait of *The Ladies Amabel and Mary Jemima Yorke* (Cleveland Museum of Art).

References: T. Aldon, *Memoir of Edward and Wm. Tyng*, Boston, 1808./ A.T. Perkins, *Copley*, Boston, 1873, p. 23 (supplement)./ W. Gould, *Portland in the Past*, Portland, Me., 1886 (repr. p. 253)./ F.W. Bayley, *Copley*, Boston, 1915, p. 244./ T. Bolton and H.L. Binsse, "Copley," *The Antiquarian*, 1930, xv, no. 6, p. 118./ C.C. Cunningham, "Copley," *Art in America*, 1938, xxxvi, no. 20, p. 78./ B.N. Parker and A.B. Wheeler, *Copley*, Boston, 1938, pp. 165–166 (pl. 84)./ J.H. Morgan, *Copley*, Windham, Conn., 1939, p. 13./ E.J. Hipkiss, *M. and M. Karolik Collection of Eighteenth Century American Arts*, Boston, 1941, no. 7 (repr. p. 15)./ C.C. Cunningham, "Karolik Collection—Some Notes on Copley," *Art in America*, 1942, xxx, no. 1, p. 33 (repr.)./ J.T. Flexner, *Copley*, Boston, 1948, pp. 32–33 (pl. 3)./ L. Dresser, "Eighteenth Century Portraits," *Maine and Its Role in American Art*, New York, 1963, p. 27 (repr. p. 26)./ J.D. Prown, *Copley*, Cambridge, Mass., 1966 (fig. 175).

Exhibition: Boston, MFA, *Copley*, 1938, no. 67.

278.

fig. 62

John Amory

Three-quarter length, he stands turned three-quarters right, leaning on the back of a brown chair. Dressed in a green suit with gold buttons and lacings, he holds a letter addressed: For Mr. John Amory of . . ./ Boston. *Behind him is a red curtain and to the right a ship sails on green sea under a blue sky with gray clouds.*

Oil on canvas. 50 × 40 in. (127 × 101.6 cm.)
Painted in 1768.

Collections: Arthur Amory Codman, great-grandson of the sitter; Misses Catherine E. and Maria P. Codman, his sisters, Bristol, R.I.; Martha Codman Karolik, their niece, Newport, R.I., about 1902.

M. and M. Karolik Collection of Eighteenth Century American Arts. 37.37

John Amory (1728–1803), born in Boston the son of Thomas and Rebecca Holmes Amory, became extremely prosperous in a mercantile partnership with his brother Jonathan. He represented his firm in England during the Revolution but returned to Boston in 1784, where he lived until his death. The bill of payment for the portrait, in the Massachusetts Historical Society, reads: "Boston 1768/ Mr. Jno: Amory to Jno. S. Copley Dr./ To his own Portrait half length. £14–0–0/ Nov. 24, 1769. Paid as pr Receipt in Book." Copies of this portrait and its pendant (Cat. no. 258), done about 1860 by Bass Otis, belong to Mrs. Benjamin Schuyler Clark, Pound Ridge, N.Y. See also Cat. nos. 220, 916, and 917 for portraits of other members of the Amory family in the MFA collection.

References: A.T. Perkins, *Copley*, Boston, 1873, p. 30./ F.W. Bayley, *Copley*, Boston, 1910, p. 12./ —, *Copley*, Boston, 1915, p. 42./ M.C. Codman, *Journal of Mrs. John Amory*, Boston, 1923 (repr. opp. p. 14)./ T. Bolton and H.L. Binsse, "Copley," *The Antiquarian*, 1930, xv, no. 6, p. 116./ B.N. Parker and A.B. Wheeler, *Copley*, Boston, 1938, pp. 21–22 (pl. 89)./ E.J. Hipkiss, *M. and M. Karolik Collection of Eighteenth Century American Arts*, Boston, 1941, no. 4 (repr. p. 9)./ J.D. Prown, *Copley*, Cambridge, Mass., 1966 (fig. 220).

Exhibitions: Washington, D.C., National Gallery, *Early American Paintings*, 1925–1926, no. 6./ Boston, MFA, *Copley*, 1938, no. 2.

279.

fig. 61

Paul Revere

Half-length and facing front in a white shirt and blue waistcoat, he sits at a brown table, his right hand to his chin, the left holding a silver teapot which rests on a brown hammering pillow. Silversmith's needle and burins lie before him. The background is dark brown and blue.

Oil on canvas. 35 × 28½ in. (88.9 × 72.3 cm.)
Painted about 1768–1770.

Collections: John Revere, the sitter's grandson, Boston, by 1873; Mrs. John Revere, Canton, Mass., by 1915.

Gift of Joseph W., William B., and Edward H.R. Revere. 30.781

Paul Revere (1735–1818), son of Paul and Deborah Hitchbourn Revere of Boston, achieved his greatest fame for the legendary ride of the night of April 19, 1775. Although its military and historical significance have been exaggerated, he was an ardent patriot and frequently a courier. A man of immense versatility and charm, he was one of the finest silversmiths America has ever produced, and was also an engraver; he designed and printed paper currency, established a gunpowder plant, a foundry for church bells, a copper rolling mill, and even manufactured artificial teeth. He married Sarah Orne, daughter of John and Martha Lackey Orne of Boston in 1757, and in 1773 he married Rachel Walker. Portraits by Gilbert Stuart of Paul Revere and his second wife are in the MFA collection (Cat. nos. 929 and 930).

References: A.T. Perkins, *Copley*, Boston, 1873, p. 98./ F.W. Bayley, *Copley*, Boston, 1910, p. 80./ —, *Copley*, Boston, 1915, p. 206./ E.J. Hipkiss, "The Paul Revere Room," *MFA Bulletin*, 1931, xxix, no. 175, p. 84 (repr.)./ B.N. Parker and A.B. Wheeler, *Copley*, Boston, 1938, pp. 160–161 (pl. 63)./ E. Forbes, *Paul Revere and the*

World He Lived In, Cambridge, Mass., 1942, pp. 55, 112–114 (repr. frontispiece)./ J.T. Flexner, *First Flowers of Our Wilderness*, Boston, 1947, pp. 222–224, 346 (repr. p. 225)./ J.M. Phillips, *American Silver*, New York, 1949 (repr. frontispiece)./ V. Barker, "Copley's American Portraits," *Magazine of Art*, 1950, XLIII, no. 3, p. 87 (repr. p. 86)./ —, *American Painting*, New York, 1950, p. 143./ A. Eliot, *Three Hundred Years of American Painting*, New York, 1957, p. 14 (repr. p. 14)./ J.T. Flexner, "The Portrait in Health and Sickness," *Art in America*, 1958–1959, XLVI, no. 4 (repr. p. 18)./ J.D. Prown, *Copley*, Cambridge, Mass., 1966 (fig. 272).

Exhibitions: Boston, MFA, *Copley*, 1938, no. 64./ New York, Wildenstein and Co., *The American Vision*, 1957, no. 3 (repr.)./ Boston, MFA and Wellesley College, Jewett Arts Center, *Four Boston Masters*, 1959, no. 7./ Washington, D.C., National Gallery, New York, Metropolitan Museum, and Boston, MFA, *Copley*, 1965–1966, no. 45 (repr. p. 65).

280.

fig. 63

Isaac Royall

Seated three-quarter length in a dark red suit with large gilt buttons, he faces three-quarters right. His left arm rests over the back of the chair and indicates the papers on the table; his right holds another packet. The blue curtain, right, is against a brown background.

Oil on canvas. 50¼ × 40 in. (127.6 × 101.6 cm.)

Painted in 1769.

Collections: William Pepperell, grandson of the sitter; Lady Charles Palmer (Harriet Pepperell), his daughter, Wanlip Hall, Leicestershire, England; Sir Archdale Robert Palmer, 4th Bart., her son; Lady Augusta Amelia Shirley Palmer; Maxim Karolik, Newport, R.I., 1937.

M. and M. Karolik Collection of Eighteenth Century American Arts. 39.247

The Hon. Isaac Royall (1719–1781), born in St. John's Parish, Antigua, the son of Isaac and Elizabeth Brown Royall, moved to Medford, Mass. in 1737. A merchant and landowner of great wealth and lavish hospitality, he was active in political affairs. He was for twenty years in the Provincial House of Councillors and the first to become Brigadier General in America, in 1761. Considered a Loyalist due to family connections, he was in Halifax in 1775 and moved then to England, where he died of smallpox. Stylistically, the portrait relates to the *Isaac Smith* (Yale University) of 1769, although a bill for the pair of portraits of Mr. and Mrs. Royall (Public Records Office, London) bears the date June 8, 1774, but in another hand. Copley's portrait of his daughters, *Mary and Elizabeth Royall* (Cat. no. 254) is also in the MFA collection.

References: Massachusetts Historical Society, *Copley-Pelham Letters*, Boston, 1914, p. 284./ F.W. Bayley, *Copley*, Boston, 1915, p. 211./ B.N. Parker and A.B. Wheeler, *Copley*, Boston, 1938, pp. 166–167 (pl. 112)./ E.J. Hipkiss, *M. and M. Karolik Collection of Eighteenth Century American Arts*, Boston, 1941, no. 2 (repr. p. 5)./ J.D. Prown, *Copley*, Cambridge, Mass., 1966 (fig. 254).

Exhibitions: Boston, MFA, *Copley*, 1938, no. 68./ Medford, Mass., Royall House, *225th Anniversary of the Royall House*, 1957./ Boston, Vose Galleries, *Exhibition in Honor of Robert C. Vose*, 1961, no. 3.

281.

fig. 64

Mrs. James Smith (Elizabeth Murray)

Three-quarter length, she faces three-quarters right, her head turned forward, holding fruit in a fold of her gold dress and trailing a blue stole. A dark curtain is before a green landscape and pink and blue sky.

Oil on canvas. 49½ × 40 in. (125.7 × 101.6 cm.)

Painted in 1769.

Collections: Elizabeth Murray Robbins, niece of the sitter; James Murray Robbins, her son, Milton, Mass.; Mrs. Robert P. Rogers, his sister, Canton, Mass., by 1915; Joseph W.R. and Mary C. Rogers, her children.

Gift of Joseph W.R. and Mary C. Rogers. 42.463

Elizabeth Murray (1726–1785), daughter of John and Anne Bennet

Murray, left the place of her birth, Unthank, Roxburgshire, Scotland, to come to South Carolina by 1740 as housekeeper to her brother, James. An energetic and an excellent businesswoman, she had established a successful millinery and dry goods trade in Boston by 1749. She married three times: in 1755 to Thomas Campbell, a Scottish seacaptain; in 1760 to James Smith, a sugar baker; and in 1771 to Ralph Inman, a merchant. In a letter dated October 6 and 8, 1769, one Catherine Barnes told Dorothy Murray Forbes, the sitter's niece, that her aunt was sitting to Copley.

References: A.T. Perkins, *Copley*, Boston, 1873, p. 77./ N.M. Tiffany, *Letters of James Murray, Loyalist*, Boston, 1901 (repr. opp. p. 150 as *Mrs. Inman*)./ F.W. Bayley, *Copley*, Boston, 1915, p. 156./ B.N. Parker and A.B. Wheeler, *Copley*, Boston, 1938, pp. 185–186 (pl. 92)./ J.D. Prown, *Copley*, Cambridge, Mass., 1966 (fig. 259).

Exhibition: Boston, MFA, *Copley*, 1938, no. 73.

282.

fig. 65

Robert Hooper, Jr.

Standing in three-quarter length, facing front, he leans with his elbow on a dark brown rock; his left hand rests on the head of a cane. He wears a plum-colored suit with a black tie. Behind is a distant hilly landscape with a cloudy blue sky.

Oil on canvas. 49¾ × 40¼ in. (126.5 × 102 cm.)

Painted about 1769.

Collections: Greeley S. Curtis, Boston; General Robert H. Stevenson, his cousin, Boston, by 1873; Robert Hooper Stevenson, his son, Boston.

Future Donation

Robert Hooper (1747–about 1781) was the son of "King" Hooper of Marblehead, the prominent and powerful owner of a fleet of fishing schooners. His mother was Ruth Swett Hooper. In 1769, he married Anna Cowell of Marblehead, step-daughter of his father's third wife. This portrait was probably painted about the year of his marriage, a date which is stylistically consistent. A Copley portrait of his wife, listed by Perkins, has been unlocated since 1873.

References: A.T. Perkins, *Copley*, Boston, 1873, p. 74./ F.W. Bayley, *Copley*, Boston, 1915, p. 148./ T. Bolton and H.L. Binsse, "Copley," *The Antiquarian*, 1930, xv, no. 6, p. 118 (as Robert Chamblett Hooper)./ B.N. Parker and A.B. Wheeler, *Copley*, Boston, 1938, p. 113 (pl. 98)./ J.D. Prown, *Copley*, Cambridge, Mass., 1966 (fig. 281).

Exhibition: Boston, MFA, *One Hundred Colonial Portraits*, 1930, p. 49 (repr.).

283.

fig. 68

Mrs. Ebenezer Storer (Mary Edwards)

Bust-length, she faces three-quarters right, her head turned forward, and wears a brown dress, sheer black polkadot shawl, and black bonnet, trimmed and tied in white. The background is gray.

Pastel on paper mounted on linen. 23 × 17¼ in. (58.4 × 43.8 cm.)

Drawn about 1769.

Collections: William Storer Eaton, Boston; Miss G.G. Eaton, 1915; Mrs. Francis S. Eaton, Boston.

Gift of Mrs. Francis Storer Eaton. 55.505

Mary Edwards Storer (1700–1771) was the wife of a prosperous Boston merchant. A label, contemporary with the pastel, found on its back reads: *On the eighth of Dec 1771 died suddenly of a Lethargic/ disorder Mrs. Mary Storer aged 72, the virtuous relict/ of the late Ebenezer Storer Esq. . . . This portrait was taken by Copley a celebrated artist two years before her decease.* The Metropolitan Museum owns a pastel replica of this picture, with one of her husband, both of which it dates before 1761 on the basis of style and the death of Mr. Storer in 1761 (cf. H.W. Williams, Jr., "Two Early Pastels by Copley," *Metropolitan Museum Bulletin*, New York, 1941, xxxvi, no. 6, pp. 136–140); they assume nearly simultaneous origin. Both pastels of Mrs. Storer may date from the late sixties, however; both Mr. and Mrs. Storer face to the right and were not necessarily designed as complementary compositions.

Early copies of Mr. and Mrs. Storer also exist (Mrs. Francis S. Eaton).

References: A.T. Perkins, *Copley*, Boston, 1873, p. 110./ F.W. Bayley, *Copley*, Boston, 1910, p. 94./ —, *Copley*, Boston, 1915, p. 236./ T. Bolton, *Early American Portrait Draughtsmen*, New York, 1923, no. 49./ J.D. Prown, *Copley*, Cambridge, Mass., 1966 (fig. 235).

284.
fig. 67

Thomas Amory

Bust-length, facing front before a gray background, he wears a long wig and a blue robe with a white neckcloth.

Pastel on paper mounted on linen. 23 × 17¼ in. (58.4 × 43.8 cm.)
Drawn about 1770.

Collections: Jonathan Amory, the sitter's son, Boston, 1770; John Amory, Jr., his nephew, Boston; Misses Catherine E. and Maria P. Codman, his granddaughters, Bristol, R.I.; Martha Codman Karolik, their niece, Newport, R.I., about 1902.

M. and M. Karolik Collection of Eighteenth Century American Arts. 37.41

Thomas Amory (1683–1728) was born in Dublin, the son of Jonathan Amory, who in 1686 emigrated to Charleston, S.C. In 1706 Thomas established a flourishing transatlantic trade in the Azores. In 1721 he married Rebecca Holmes and settled in Boston. The pastel was commissioned by his sons Thomas and Jonathan, reputedly to be copied from an earlier English portrait destroyed in 1787. However, Anna Wells Rutledge and Mrs. Charles F. Middleton have suggested convincingly that the prototype was a now lost pastel by Henrietta Johnston, made in Charleston about 1721. A leaf from the account book of Jonathan and John Amory, owned by the MFA, reads: "Jon\(^a\): Amory Dr. to cash pd Jn\(^o\) S Copley in full for drawing/ his fathers Picture £9 - 16 -. August 16, 1770."

References: A.T. Perkins, *Copley*, Boston, 1873, p. 29./ F.W. Bayley, *Copley*, Boston, 1910, p. 12./ —, *Copley*, Boston, 1915, p. 445./ C.K. Bolton, *Founders*, Boston, 1919, II, p. 339 (repr. p. 34)./ T. Bolton, *Early American Portrait Draughtsmen*, New York, 1923, no. 1./ M.C. Codman, *Journal of Mrs. John Amory*, Boston, 1923 (repr. p. 46)./ B.N. Parker and A.B. Wheeler, *Copley*, Boston, 1938, p. 215./ E.J. Hipkiss, *M. and M. Karolik Collection of Eighteenth Century American Arts*, Boston, 1941, no. 3 (repr. p. 7)./ C.C. Cunningham, "The Karolik Collection—Some Notes on Copley," *Art in America*, 1942, XXX, no. 1, p. 33./ J.D. Prown, *Copley*, Cambridge, Mass., 1966 (fig. 240).

Exhibitions: Washington, D.C., National Gallery, *Early American Paintings*, 1925–1926, no. 4./ Boston, MFA, *Copley*, 1938, no. 4.

285.
fig. 66

Mrs. James Russell (Katherine Graves)

Three-quarter length and seated in a blue damask armchair, she is turned three-quarters right. She wears a brown satin dress, white lace cap, and lace-trimmed shawl, and holds a black and gold bound book in her lap. The background is brown.

Oil on canvas. 50¼ × 40¼ in. (127.6 × 102.2 cm.)
Painted about 1770–1771.

Collections: Mrs. John Lowell (Rebecca Graves), daughter of the sitter; Mrs. Warren Dutton (Elizabeth Lowell), her daughter; James Dutton Russell (formerly James Russell Dutton), her son; Mrs. Henry Rogers Dalton (Elizabeth Dutton Russell), his daughter; Henry Rogers Dalton, Jr., and Elizabeth Lowell Dalton, her children, Boston.

Gift of Elizabeth L. and Henry R. Dalton. 42.101

The daughter of the Hon. Thomas and Sibyll Avery Graves, Katherine Graves (1717–1778) married James Russell, a Representative, Councillor, and finally a Judge, in 1738. She bore him eleven children. Previously dated 1766 by Mrs. Parker (*see below*, Parker and Wheeler), Jules Prown has presented a convincing relationship with the polished style of about 1770–1771 as in *Mrs. Ezekiel Goldthwait* (Cat. no. 288).

References: A.T. Perkins, *Copley*, Boston, 1873, p. 100./ F.W. Bayley, *Copley*, Boston, 1910, p. 86./ —, *Copley*, Boston, 1915, p. 212./ B.N. Parker and A.B. Wheeler, *Copley*,

Boston, 1938, p. 170 (pl. 7)./J.D. Prown, *Copley*, Cambridge, Mass., 1966 (fig. 275).

Exhibitions: Dallas Museum of Fine Arts, *Famous American Paintings*, 1948, no. 2./ Saginaw Museum, *American Painting from Colonial Times until Today*, 1948, no. 10.

286.

fig. 69

Samuel Adams

Three-quarter length, he stands in a dark red-brown suit behind a blue covered table strewn with documents. His left hand points dramatically to one inscribed: Charter of William & Ma[ry] to Massachusetts; *his right grasps rolled papers inscribed:* Instructions of/ Town Boston. *The background is dark brown.*

Oil on canvas. 50 × 40¼ in. (127 × 102.2 cm.)

Painted about 1770–1772.

Collections: John Hancock, Boston, until 1793; heirs of John Hancock; City of Boston, 1836.

Deposited by the City of Boston. 30.76c

Samuel Adams (1722–1803), born in Boston and a graduate of Harvard, worked briefly as a lawyer, merchant, brewer, and assessor and collector for the city of Boston, before becoming a political organizer. As a member of the powerful Caucus Club, he was elected to the House of Representatives in 1765, and inaugurated the standing Committees of Correspondence. He was a delegate to the Continental Congress from 1774 to 1781, and a signer of the Declaration of Independence. He later was elected Lieutenant Governor of Massachusetts (1789–1794) and Governor from 1794 to 1797. Portrayed as confronting Governor Hutchinson on behalf of the citizens as he did the day after the Boston Massacre of March 5, 1770, the picture was painted probably for John Hancock, about 1770–1772. Copies are in Faneuil Hall, Boston; The Women's City Club, Boston; and Adams House, Harvard University. Engravings were made by Paul Revere (*Royal American Magazine*, April, 1774) and Samuel Okey (after J. Mitchell), Newport, 1775.

References: W.V. Wells, *Adams*, Boston, 1865, I, pp. 475–477./ A.T. Perkins, *Copley*, Boston, 1873, p. 27./ W.H. Downes, "Boston Painters and Paintings," *Atlantic Monthly*, 1888, LXII, no. 369, p. 92./ F.W. Bayley, *Copley*, Boston, 1910, p. 10./ —, *Copley*, Boston, 1915, pp. 39–40./ —, *Five Colonial Artists*, Boston, 1929 (repr. p. 153)./ T. Bolton and H.S. Binsse, "Copley," *The Antiquarian*, 1930, XV, no. 6, p. 116./ New York, Metropolitan Museum, *Catalogue of the Copley Exhibition*, 1936–1937, p. 5./ B.N. Parker and A.B. Wheeler, *Copley*, Boston, 1938, pp. 17–19 (pl. 114)./ J.T. Flexner, *First Flowers of Our Wilderness*, Boston, 1947, pp. 224–225 (repr. p. 223)./ J.D. Prown, *Copley*, Cambridge, Mass., 1966 (fig. 302).

Exhibitions: Boston, MFA, *Contemporary Art*, 1879, no. 89./ —, *One Hundred Colonial Portraits*, 1930, no. 2 (repr.)./ Harvard University, *Tercentenary*, 1936, no. 3 (pl. 1)./ Washington, D.C., Corcoran Gallery, *Signers of the Declaration of Independence*, 1937–1938, no. 22./ Williamsburg, Va., Colonial Williamsburg, *They Gave Us Freedom*, 1951, no. 10 (repr. p. 16)./ Toronto Art Gallery, *Comparisons*, 1957, no. 59./ Washington, D.C., National Gallery, New York, Metropolitan Museum, and Boston, MFA, *Copley*, 1965–1966, no. 48 (repr. p. 69).

287.

fig. 70

Ezekiel Goldthwait

Nearly full-length, he sits facing three-quarters left and looks front. He holds papers in his left hand, his arm resting against the chairback, and a quill in his right. He wears a full white wig, a dark red coat, and a waistcoat with black breeches. Behind is a green curtain before a dark brown wall.

Oil on canvas. 50 × 40 in. (127 × 101.6 cm.)

Signed lower right: *JSC* (in monogram). Painted in 1771.

Collections: Mrs. William Alline, great-granddaughter of the sitter, Boston, by 1873; Dr. John T. Bowen, great-great-great-grandson, Boston, about 1900.

Bequest of John T. Bowen in memory of Eliza M. Bowen. 41.85

Born in Boston, Ezekiel Goldthwait (1710–1782), the son of John and Jane Halsey Goldthwait, was Registrar of Deeds for the County of Suffolk from 1740 to 1776 and Town Clerk of Boston from 1741 to 1761. In 1760 he was one of the fifty-six Boston memorialists who arraigned themselves against the Crown officials, but in 1774 he was a Loyalist addressor of Hutchinson. Both successful and popular, his conservative Loyalist sympathies warranted exile only to Weston, Mass., from which he later returned. The receipt for this portrait (owned by the MFA) and its pendant (Cat. no. 288) is inscribed: *Boston July 1: 1771.*

References: A.T. Perkins, *Copley*, Boston, 1873, p. 57./ C. Goldthwait, *Descendants of Thomas Goldthwait*, Hartford, 1899, p. 86 (repr. p. 84)./ F.W. Bayley, *Copley*, Boston, 1910, p. 113./ —, *Copley*, Boston, 1915, p. 120./ T. Bolton and H.L. Binsse, "Copley," *The Antiquarian*, 1930, XV, no. 6, p. 116./ B.N. Parker and A.B. Wheeler, *Copley*, Boston, 1938, pp. 84–85 (pl. 106)./ B.N. Parker, "The Goldthwait Family," *MFA Bulletin*, 1941, XXXIX, no. 233, pp. 40–44 (repr. p. 42)./ E.P. Richardson, *Painting in America*, New York, 1956, p. 73 (fig. 25)./ J.D. Prown, *Copley*, Cambridge, Mass., 1966 (fig. 274).

Exhibitions: Boston, Copley Hall, *Portraits*, 1896, no. 67./ Boston, MFA, *One Hundred Colonial Portraits*, 1930, no. 37 (repr.).

288.
fig. 72

Mrs. Ezekiel Goldthwait (Elizabeth Lewis)

Three-quarter length, seated to the right with head toward the spectator, she wears a purple silk dress and a black lace fichu over her white lace collar. The chair back is blue damask. A plate of apples, peaches, and pears is placed on the mahogany table. The background is dark brown.

Oil on canvas. 50 × 40 in. (127 × 101.6 cm.)
Painted in 1771.
Collections: Same as Cat. no. 287.
Bequest of John T. Bowen in memory of Eliza M. Bowen. 41.84

Elizabeth Lewis (1713–1794) of Boston married Ezekiel Goldthwait (see pendant, Cat. no. 287) in 1732. Of her thirteen children, five daughters lived beyond childhood. She was an accomplished gardener.

References: A.T. Perkins, *Copley*, Boston, 1873, p. 57./ F.W. Bayley, *Copley*, Boston, 1910, p. 113./ —, *Copley*, Boston, 1915, p. 121./ T. Bolton and H.L. Binsse, "Copley," *The Antiquarian*, 1930, XV, no. 6, p. 116./ B.N. Parker and A.B. Wheeler, *Copley*, Boston, 1938, p. 85 (pl. 106)./ B.N. Parker, "The Goldthwait Family," *MFA Bulletin*, 1941, XXXIX, no. 233, pp. 40–44 (repr. pp. 43, 44)./ J.T. Flexner, *Copley*, Boston, 1948, p. 55 (pl. 18)./ V. Barker, *American Painting*, New York, 1950, p. 140./ —, "Copley's American Portraits," *Magazine of Art*, 1950, XLIII, no. 3, p. 86 (repr. p. 85)./ J.D. Prown, *Copley*, Cambridge, Mass., 1966 (fig. 273).

Exhibitions: Boston, MFA, *One Hundred Colonial Portraits*, 1930, no. 58 (repr.)./ Amsterdam, Municipal Museum, *American Paintings*, 1950, no. 3 (repr. p. 5)./ Berlin, Museum für Völkerkunde, Munich, Amerika Haus, and Vienna, Walsurni Gallery, *Amerikanische Malerei*, 1951, no. 2./ Vancouver Art Gallery, *Two Hundred Years of American Painting*, 1955, no. 5 (repr.)./ Washington, D.C., Corcoran Gallery, *The American Muse*, 1959, no. 1./ St. Louis City Art Museum, *200 Years of American Painting*, 1964, p. 2 (repr.)./ Washington, D.C., National Gallery, New York, Metropolitan Museum and Boston, MFA, *Copley*, 1965–1966, no. 43 (pl. VIII).

289.
fig. 75

Mrs. Joseph Barrell (Hannah Fitch)

Bust-length, facing front, she wears a blue dress with a pink rose and a sacque trimmed with ermine. The background is dark gray.

Pastel on paper mounted on linen. 23 × 17¼ in. (58.4 × 43.8 cm.)
Drawn about 1771.
Collections: Descended in the family of Mrs. Benjamin Joy, the sitter's daughter, to Mrs. Charles Joy, Boston; Mr. Benjamin Joy, Boston, 1939.
Gift of Benjamin Joy. 52.1472

Hannah Fitch (1753–1777), daughter of Timothy and Abigail Hall Fitch of Boston, became the second wife of Joseph Barrell of Charlestown, Mass. in 1771 and had five children by him. Judging from her age, the pastel was done at the time of her marriage.

References: A.T. Perkins, *Copley*, Boston, 1873, p. 33./ F.W. Bayley, *Copley*, Boston, 1910, p. 19./ —, *Copley*, Boston, 1915, p. 53./ T. Bolton, *Early American Portrait Draughtsmen*, New York, 1923, no. 7./ F.W. Bayley, *Five Colonial Artists*, Boston, 1929 (repr. p. 167)./ B.N. Parker and A.B. Wheeler, *Copley*, Boston, 1938, p. 218./ J.D. Prown, *Copley*, Cambridge, Mass., 1966 (fig. 233).

Exhibitions: Boston, MFA, *One Hundred Colonial Portraits*, 1930, no. 10 (repr.)./ Washington, D.C., National Gallery, New York, Metropolitan Museum, and Boston, MFA, *Copley*, 1965–1966, no. 33 (repr. p. 52).

290.

fig. 82

Mrs. Richard Skinner (Dorothy Wendell)

Three-quarter length, she sits on a blue chair turned three-quarters left, her arms resting on a mahogany table. She wears a white cap and dress printed with blue flowers similar to those she holds. The background is dark brown.

Oil on canvas. 39¾ × 30¾ in. (100.9 × 78.1 cm.)

Signed and dated center right: *John Singleton Copley pinx/1772/Boston.*

Collections: Lord Lyndhurst, the artist's son, London; *Lyndhurst Sale*, Christie's, London, 1864, no. 60 (as *Portrait of a Lady*); Mrs. Martin Brimmer, great-granddaughter of the artist, Boston.

Bequest of Mrs. Martin Brimmer. 06.2428

Dorothy Wendell Skinner (1733–1822), the daughter of John and Elizabeth Quincy Wendell, in 1756 married her stepbrother, Richard Skinner of Marblehead, and bore him four children. The sitter is identified by comparison with the portrait of *Dorothy Wendell* by Nathaniel Smibert dated 1755 (Mrs. Edward B. Alford, Brookline, Mass.); the Copley portrait of her first cousin *Dorothy Quincy* (Cat. no. 291) is nearly identical in pose and costume.

References: A.T. Perkins, *Copley*, Boston, 1873, p. 109 (as *Mrs. Spinner*)./ F.W. Bayley, *Copley*, Boston, 1910, p. 95./ —, *Copley*, Boston, 1915, pp. 34, 36, 226./ T. Bolton and H.L. Binsse, "Copley," *The Antiquarian*, 1930, xv, no. 6, p. 118./ B.N. Parker and A.B. Wheeler, *Copley*, Boston, 1938, pp. 182–183 (pl. 119)./ V. Barker, "Copley's American Portraits," *Magazine of Art*, 1950, XLIII, no. 3 (repr. p. 88)./ J.D. Prown, *Copley*, Cambridge, Mass., 1966 (fig. 315).

Exhibitions: Boston, MFA, *Copley*, 1938, no. 72./ Paris, Musée du Jeu de Paume, *Trois Siècles d'Art aux Etats-Unis*, 1938, no. 31./ New York, Metropolitan Museum, *Life in America*, 1939, no. 27 (repr. p. 19)./ Middletown, Conn., Wesleyan University, Davison Art Center, *Aspects of American Realism*, 1951, no. 2./ Baltimore Museum, *The Age of Elegance: Rococo and Its Effect*, 1959, no. 416./ Smith College Museum, *American Painting for a Professor of American Art*, 1964, no. 2 (repr.)./ Washington, D.C., National Gallery, New York, Metropolitan Museum, and Boston, MFA, *Copley*, 1965–1966, no. 50 (pl. IX).

291.

fig. 71

Dorothy Quincy (Mrs. John Hancock)

Three-quarter length, turned three-quarters left, she sits in a dark blue upholstered armchair; her right elbow rests on a mahogany table before her, the hand to her cheek. She wears a pink dress with white lace cuffs, apron, and a white lace cap. The background is dark brown.

Oil on canvas. 50 × 39 in. (127 × 99 cm.)

Painted about 1772.

Collections: Theodore Cushing, Little Harbor, N.H.; Mrs. George S. Rose, his great-granddaughter, Boston, by 1890.

Lent anonymously. 118.27

Dorothy Quincy (1747–1830), daughter of Edmund and Elizabeth Wendell Quincy, was born in Boston. Her marriage in 1775 to the wealthy John Hancock began a life of constant and extravagant entertaining. Hancock died in 1793, and she soon married Col. James Scott, to live with him in comparative quiet. After his death in 1809 she lived in Portsmouth, N.H., then returned to Boston, where she once more became known for her generous hospitality and brilliant conversation. She died in Boston. The close similarity in style, pose, and costume to the dated Copley portrait of her first cousin, *Mrs. Richard Skinner (Dorothy Wendell)* (Cat. no. 290), substantiates the date.

References: A.T. Perkins, *Copley*, Boston, 1873, p. 108 and supplement, p. 22./ F.W. Bayley, *Copley*, Boston, 1915, p. 220./ —, *Five Colonial Artists*, Boston, 1929 (repr. p. 219)./ T. Bolton and H.L. Binsse, "Copley," *The Antiquarian*, 1930, xv, no. 6, p. 116./ B.N. Parker and A.B. Wheeler, *Copley*, Boston, 1938, p. 156 (pl. 118)./ J.D. Prown, *Copley*, Cambridge, Mass., 1966 (fig. 316).

Exhibitions: Boston, Copley Hall, *Portraits of Women*, 1895, no. 90./ Boston, MFA, *One Hundred Colonial Portraits*, 1930, p. 44 (repr.).

292.

fig. 74

Joseph Warren

Nearly full-length, he sits facing front dressed in a black coat and breeches and white waistcoat. His left arm rests upon a table covered in red and obscure medical drawings of the human skull. The curtain is red and the wall is brown.

Oil on canvas. 50×40 in. (127×101.6 cm.)

Painted about 1772–1774.

Collections: Dr. John Warren, brother of the sitter, Boston; Rebecca Warren Brown, his daughter; Buckminster Brown, her son, 1886.

Gift of Buckminster Brown, M.D., through Warren Putnam Newcomb, Trustee. 95.1366

Joseph Warren (1741–1775), born in Roxbury, Mass. and educated at Harvard University, was a practicing physician in Boston. By 1767 he was active in politics, a member of the Committee of Correspondence in 1772, President of the Provincial Congress, Head of the Committee of Safety, and first Grand Master of the Masonic Lodge of Boston. He was commissioned a Major General of the Provincial Army in 1775 and shortly after was killed, as a volunteer, at the Battle of Bunker Hill. The apparent age of the sitter and the polished, mature style indicate a date of 1772–1774. A smaller half-length replica belongs to Dr. Richard Warren, Dedham, Mass. Perkins and Bayley record a full-length, nearly life size version by Copley, unlocated. Later copies also exist (*see* Prown). A portrait of Joseph Warren's niece, *Mrs. John Ball Brown (Rebecca Warren)*, by Chester Harding, is also in the MFA collection (Cat. no. 474).

References: A.T. Perkins, *Copley*, Boston, 1873, p. 115./ F.W. Bayley, *Copley*, Boston, 1910, p. 131./ —, *Copley*, Boston, 1915, p. 252./ T. Bolton and H.L. Binsse, "Copley," *The Antiquarian*, 1930, xv, no. 6, p. 118./ B.N. Parker and A.B. Wheeler, *Copley*, Boston, 1938, pp. 202–203 (pl. 122)./ J.D. Prown, *Copley*, Cambridge, Mass., 1966 (fig. 174).

Exhibitions: Boston, Copley Hall, *Portraits*, 1896, no. 60./ Harvard University, *Tercentenary*, 1936, no. 35./ Milwaukee Art Center, *Vignettes of the 18th Century in America*, 1960, p. 32 (repr. p. 16).

293.

fig. 76

Mrs. Joseph Warren (Elizabeth Hooton)

Three-quarter length, she sits turned three-quarters right and rests an elbow on the blue sofa. Her dress is deep red over a light blue skirt. A dark blue curtain is behind, and through a window, right, a classical urn is silhouetted against a blue sky.

Oil on canvas. 50×40 in. (127×101.6 cm.)

Painted about 1772–1774.

Collections: Same as Cat. no. 292.

Gift of Buckminster Brown, M.D., through Warren Putnam Newcomb, Trustee. 95.1367

Born in Boston, Elizabeth Hooton (1747–1773) was the only daughter of Richard Hooton, merchant, "... an accomplished young lady with a handsome fortune" (*Boston Gazette*, 1764). She married *Joseph Warren* (Cat. no. 292) in 1764 and had four children. Her portrait was probably painted about 1772–1774 and is a pendant to that of her husband. The rather romantic colors, the generalized handling of forms and her features, plus the presence of the urn, possibly a funerary symbol, suggest a posthumous portrait of 1773–1774, before Copley's departure for England. Jules Prown (*see below*) has proposed that the portrait is either a copy of an unlocated

Copley of Mrs. Warren, or a Copley painting finished probably by Henry Pelham. Of the two suggestions, the latter is the more plausible.

References: F.W. Bayley, *Copley*, Boston, 1910, p. 105./ —, *Copley*, Boston, 1915, p. 253./ B.N. Parker and A.B. Wheeler, *Copley*, Boston, 1938, p. 203 (pl. 121)./ J.D. Prown, *Copley*, Cambridge, Mass., 1966, 1, p. 243.

Exhibitions: Boston, Copley Hall, *Portraits of Women*, 1895, no. 98./ University of Minnesota Gallery, *Survey of Colonial and Provincial Painting*, 1939, no. 10. (pl. 10).

294.

fig. 78

Captain James Gambier

Three-quarter length, turned three-quarters left, he stands before brown columns, right, and a rural landscape under blue and pink sky. His blue uniform of a Captain in the Royal Navy, edged and buttoned with gold, is faced with buff, the color of his waistcoat and breeches. He leans on a brown cane and holds a black hat.

Oil on canvas. 50 × 40 in. (127 × 101.6 cm.)

Signed and dated lower right: *J.S. [obscure] Copley/1773 Boston.*

Collections: Lord Aberdare (d. 1895), husband of Constance Mary Hamilton, great-granddaughter of the artist, London; Miss Amelia Peabody, 1915.

Gift of Miss Amelia Peabody. 37.1208

James Gambier (1723–1789) led a successful career in the Royal Navy. A Lieutenant in 1743, he advanced to Commander-in-Chief on the North American Station from 1770 to 1773 as a Captain, and was later second in command under General Howe at New York. He was made Vice Admiral of the Blue in 1780 and Vice Admiral of the Red in 1787. He died in Bath, England.

References: J. Britton, "Copley and West in Boston," *Art News*, 1914, XII, no. 26, p. 3 (repr.)./ F.W. Bayley, *Copley*, Boston, 1915, p. 267./ T. Bolton and H.L. Binsse, "Copley," *The Antiquarian*, 1930, XV, no. 6, p. 116./ J.D. Prown, *Copley*, Cambridge, Mass., 1966 (fig. 325).

Exhibitions: Boston, Copley Society, *Retrospective Exhibition of the Decorative Arts*, 1911, no. 7./ Minneapolis Institute of Arts, *Early American Paintings*, 1915, no. 1./ New York, Duveen Galleries, *Soldiers and Sailors in American Wars*, 1945, no. 4 (repr. p. 14).

295.

fig. 79

The Rev. Thomas Cary of Newburyport

Three-quarter length, facing three-quarters left, he sits in an armchair resting his folded hands upon an open book; his banyan is blue with red lining, and his waistcoat is black. The bookcase and the wall behind are brown, the drapery right is red.

Oil on canvas. 50 × 40¼ in. (127 × 102.2 cm.)

Painted about 1773.

Collections: Thomas G. Cary, Cambridge, Mass., by 1873; Miss F.E. Cary, Cambridge, by 1915; Mr. and Mrs. Charles Pelham Curtis, Boston, 1922; Richard Cary Curtis, Brookline, Mass.

Gift of Mrs. Richard Cary Curtis. 57.67

Thomas Cary (1745–1808), born in Charlestown, Mass., was the son of Samuel and Margaret Graves Cary. Active as a preacher in the vicinity of Boston and on the North Shore in 1768, he was ordained Minister of the First Church, Newburyport, where he lived until his death. In 1775 he married Esther Carter of Newburyport. The date is derived from his apparent age and from a note in his almanac of dining with "Mr. Copely" [sic], early in 1773. A small nineteenth-century copy is owned by Miss Louisa H. Putnam of Boston.

References: A.T. Perkins, *Copley*, Boston, 1873, p. 42./ F.W. Bayley, *Copley*, Boston, 1910, p. 27./ —, *Copley*, Boston, 1915, p. 75./ —, *Five Colonial Artists*, Boston, 1929 (repr. p. 197)./ T. Bolton and H.L. Binsse, "Copley," *The Antiquarian*, 1930, XV, no. 6, pl. 116./ B.N. Parker and A.B. Wheeler, *Copley*, Boston, 1938, pp. 57–58 (pl. 113)./ J.D. Prown, *Copley*, Cambridge, Mass., 1966 (fig. 324).

Exhibitions: Boston, Copley Hall, *Portraits*, 1896, no. 47./ Boston, MFA, *Copley*, 1938, no. 16./ Washington, D.C., National Gallery, New York, Metropolitan Museum, and Boston, MFA, *Copley*, 1965–1966, no. 52 (repr. p. 73).

296.

fig. 80

Mr. and Mrs. Isaac Winslow (Jemima Debuke)

Three-quarter length, they sit together at a highly polished table, before a red curtain, left, and a brown wall. Holding a black hat and riding crop, he wears a dark blue coat and yellow breeches; his wife wears a changeable pink and green taffeta dress and a moonstone choker.

Oil on canvas. 40¼ × 48¾ in. (102.2 × 123.8 cm.)

Painted in 1774.

Collections: Dr. Walter Winslow, descendant of the sitters, London; Mrs. Walter Winslow, London; Maxim Karolik, Newport, R.I., 1939.

M. and M. Karolik Collection of Eighteenth Century American Arts. 39.250

Isaac Winslow (1709–1777), son of Col. Edward and Hannah Moody Winslow, joined his brother Joshua in a mercantile partnership in Boston. In 1747 he married Lucy, daughter of General Samuel Waldo, and in 1770 he married Jemima Debuke (1732–1790), represented here, the daughter of Thomas and Jemima Debuke of Boston. With the British evacuation of Boston in 1776, he fled to Halifax, Nova Scotia, where he died. Mrs. Winslow accompanied her husband to Halifax, reputedly next lived in New York until 1780, then in London, where she died. Copley's receipt for payment (with the MFA) is dated February 11, 1774. Portraits of Mr. Winslow by Robert Feke (Cat. no. 398) and Joseph Blackburn (Cat. no. 144) are also in the MFA.

References: T. Bolton and H.L. Binsse, "Copley," *The Antiquarian*, 1930, XV, no. 6, p. 118./ J.H. Morgan, "Some Notes on Copley," *Antiques*, 1937, XXXI, no. 3, p. 116 (repr.)./ C.C. Cunningham, "Copley," *Art in America*, 1938, XXXVI, no. 20, p. 78./ B.N. Parker and A.B. Wheeler, *Copley*, Boston, 1938, pp. 208–209 (pl. 116)./ J.H. Morgan, *Copley*, Windham, Conn., 1939, pp. 20–21 (fig. IV)./ A.M. Frankfurter, "Thirty-eight Candles for Royal Cortissoz," *Art News*, 1941, XL, no. 16, p. 24 (repr.)./ E.J. Hipkiss, *M. and M. Karolik Collection of Eighteenth Century American Arts*, Boston, 1941, no. 1 (repr. p. 3)./ J.T. Flexner, *First Flowers of Our Wilderness*, Boston, 1947, pp. 346–347 (repr. pp. 232–233)./ —, *Copley*, Boston, 1948, pp. 69–70./ L. Goodrich, "What Is American in American Art?" *Art in America*, 1958, XLVII, no. 3, p. 21 (repr. p. 20)./ J.D. Prown, *Copley*, Cambridge, Mass., 1966 (fig. 332).

Exhibitions: Boston, MFA, *Copley*, 1938, no. 85./ — and Wellesley College, Jewett Arts Center, *Four Boston Masters*, 1959, no. 14./ Museum of Fine Arts of Houston, *The Human Image*, 1958, no. 46 (fig. 46)./ Washington, D.C., National Gallery, New York, Metropolitan Museum, and Boston, MFA, *Copley*, 1965–1966, no. 56 (repr. p. 78).

297.

fig. 81

The Ascension

A hilly landscape with the eleven Apostles in robes of bright green, red, gold, and blue; they stand and kneel in the foreground, their arms outstretched to the white-robed Christ who rises above them into a clouded sky filled with golden light. Two angels in white stand at right.

Oil on canvas. 32 × 29 in. (81.2 × 73.6 cm.)

Painted in 1775.

Collections: Lord Lyndhurst, son of the artist, London; with M. Grist; Martha Babcock Amory, granddaughter of the artist; Susan Greene Dexter, her daughter, Boston.

Bequest of Susan Greene Dexter, in memory of Charles and Martha Babcock Amory. 25.95

Painted during Copley's first months in Rome, this painting is his first effort at a traditional "composition." The scene is from *Luke*, XXIV, 50–52. While in Rome, Copley, in a letter to Henry Pelham of March 14, 1775, gave a long account of his reasons for and method of completing the picture. There are three preparatory drawings for the painting (*see* Prown).

References: F.W. Bayley, *Copley*, Boston, 1910, p. 14./ Massachusetts Historical Society, *Copley-Pelham Letters*, Boston, 1914, pp. 294–300./ F.W. Bayley, *Copley*, Boston, 1915, pp. 46–47./ J.T. Flexner, *Copley*, Boston, 1948, pp. 75, 108 (pl. 21)./ V. Barker, *American Painting*, New York, 1950, p. 213./ J.D. Prown, *Copley*, Cambridge, Mass., 1966 (fig. 337).

Exhibitions: Boston, MFA, *Copley*, 1938, no. 6./ Washington, D.C., National Gallery, New York, Metropolitan Museum, and Boston, MFA, *Copley*, 1965–1966, no. 58 (repr. p. 84).

298.

fig. 77

Mr. and Mrs. Ralph Izard (Alice Delancey)

Three-quarter length, they are seated facing each other across a gilded table topped with red porphyry. He wears a gray suit and she a dress of blue and white with a white bonnet. The ornate gilded chair and sofa are upholstered in red. Behind them are a Greek vase by a column, a classical statue, and a red drapery. Beyond is the Colosseum under a blue and cloudy sky.

Oil on canvas. 69 × 88½ in. (175.3 × 224.7 cm.)

Painted in 1775.

Collections: Sold by Copley's widow to Dr. Gabriel Manigault, the sitters' grandson, 1825; Joseph Manigault, his son, Charleston, S.C., 1879; Estate of Dr. Gabriel Manigault, sold 1903.

Edward Ingersoll Browne Fund. 03.1033

Ralph Izard (1742–1804), of Charleston, S.C., was one of the richest men in the South. He moved to England in 1771 with his wife four years after their marriage. She was Alice Delancey (1745–1832), daughter of Peter Delancey of New York. She bore him thirteen children. Touring Italy in 1774, they met Copley in Florence; he painted their portrait early the next year in Rome. The Attic vase, a red-figured krater of 480–440 B.C., now lost, was probably by the Niobid painter. Mr. Izard holds a drawing for the sculpture group, a reduced version of the *Orestes and Electra* by Menelaos (Museo Nazionale, Rome), then in the Ludovisi Villa, Rome. Copley used the same table in his portrait of *Viscount Sidmouth*, 1795 (St. Louis City Art Museum).

References: H.T. Tuckerman, *Book of the Artists*, New York, 1870, p. 72./ A.T. Perkins, *Copley*, Boston, 1873, p. 78./ M.B. Amory, *Copley*, Cambridge, Mass., 1882, pp. 50–51, 445–449./ A.M. Earle, *Two Centuries of Costume*, New York, 1903, II, pp. 483–485 (repr. opp. p. 486)./ S. Isham, *American Painting*, New York, 1905, p. 37./ F.W. Bayley, *Copley*, Boston, 1910, p. 61./ Massachusetts Historical Society, *Copley-Pelham Letters*, Boston, 1914, pp. 295, 300./ F.W. Bayley, *Copley*, Boston, 1915, p. 156./ W. Dunlap, *History of the Arts of Design*, Boston, 1918, I, p. 124./ T. Bolton and H.L. Binsse, "Copley," *The Antiquarian*, 1930, XV, no. 6, p. 118./ A. Burroughs, *Limners and Likenesses*, Cambridge, Mass., 1936, p. 68 (repr. p. 54)./ J.T. Flexner, *America's Old Masters*, New York, 1939, pp. 146–147./ A. Greifenhagen, "Griechische Vasen auf Bildnissen der Zeit Winckelmanns und des Klassizismus," *Nachrichten Geschichtlichen Wissenschaften, Goettingen, Philologische-historische Klassizismus*, 1939, I, Altertumswissenschaft, N.F. III, No. 7./ J.H. Morgan, *Copley*, Windham, Conn./ 1939, pp. 20–22./ J.D. Beazley, *Attic Red-Figure Vase Painters*, Oxford, 1942, p. 424., J.T. Flexner, *Copley*, Boston, 1948, p. 74 (pl. 22)./ V. Barker, *American Painting*, New York, 1950, p. 213./ M.R. Scherer, *Marvels of Ancient Rome*, New York, 1955 p. 17, (pl. 27)./ E.P. Richardson, *Painting in America*, New York, 1956, p. 94./ Van Wyck Brooks, "Apollo and the Mohawk," *Art News*, 1958, LVII, no. 4, pp. 32–33 (repr. p. 33)./ J.D. Prown, *Copley*, Cambridge, Mass., 1966 (fig. 342).

Exhibitions: London, Royal Academy, 1776, no. 62 (as *Conversation*)./ Boston, MFA, *Copley*, 1938, no. 49./ Museum of the City of New York, *Four Centuries of Italian Influences in New York*, 1955–1956./ Rome, Palazzo delle Esposizioni, *Settecento a Roma*, 1959, no. 165 (pl. 64)./ University of Pennsylvania Museum and Detroit Institute of Arts, *Ruins of Rome*, 1960–1961, no. 30 (repr.)./ Washington, D.C., National Gallery, New York, Metropolitan Museum, and Boston, MFA, *Copley*, 1965–1966, no. 60 (pl. x).

299.

fig. 73

Watson and the Shark

In the foreground, a nude boy, floating helplessly in the green water, is attacked by a gray shark, right. Rescuers in a brown boat, clothed in gray, brown, or white, reach out for him. One is poised in the bow with a boat-hook; the Negro behind him holds a line. In the background, three-masted ships are anchored before the gray towers of Havana harbor. In the distance, right, Morro Castle is brown before a yellow horizon and the gray clouds in the blue sky.

Oil on canvas. 72 × 90¼ in. (182.9 × 229.2 cm.)

Signed and dated inside the stern of the boat: *J.S. Copley P.1778.*

Collections: Lord Lyndhurst, the artist's son, London; *Lyndhurst Sale*, Christie's, London, March 5, 1864, no. 61; Charles Hook Appleton, Boston, 1864; Mrs. George von Lengerke Meyer, his daughter, 1882.

Gift of Mrs. George von Lengerke Meyer. 89.481

Brook Watson (1735–1807), a prosperous merchant and Lord Mayor of London in 1796–1797, was fourteen in 1749 when he lost his leg to a shark in the waters of Havana harbor. Copley heard the story either from the victim himself, as they sailed for England in 1774 (Amory, *see below*), or more likely, from his brother-in-law Jonathan Clarke, who sailed to Canada with Watson in 1776 (letter from Richard Clarke to Isaac Winslow, May 4, 1776, Boston Public Library). Ours is a replica, also of 1778, after the original painting commissioned by Watson and bequeathed by him to Christ's Hospital, Horsham, Surrey, in 1807 (now National Gallery, Washington, D.C.). The picture is the earliest known example of the representation in painting on a grand scale of a specific incidental moment of contemporary history, a revolutionary concept later developed by the nineteenth-century French Romantics. Copley's painting antedates by forty years the celebrated *Raft of the Medusa* by Gericault (Louvre).

The Detroit Institute of Arts has a vertical version of the composition, a small study of the head of the Negro and four drawings for the original picture. Princeton University has a drawing, the MFA has another; all are listed by Prown (*see below*). A small oil version of the composition (Metropolitan Museum), long thought to be by Copley, has recently been considered possibly a contemporary study by Pelham (*see* Prown). Valentine Green engraved a mezzotint copy of the original painting in 1779. An oil copy of the subject, probably taken from the mezzotint, was owned by Lord Aberdare (sold Christie's, London, June 3, 1932, no. 81), and is on loan at the Worcester Art Museum. The Beaverbrook Art Gallery, Fredericton, N.B., has a copy in oil on copper. The MFA also has a small early copy by Henry Sargent (Cat. no. 847) after Green's engraving.

References: A. Pasquin, *Memoirs of the Royal Academicians*, London, 1796, pp. 136–137./ *Journals and Letters of Samuel Curwen*, New York, 1842, p. 296 (entry for Dec. 19, 1780)./ A.T. Perkins, *Copley*, Boston, 1873, pp. 118–119./ M.B. Amory, *Copley*, Boston, 1882, pp. 70–75./ F.W. Bayley, *Copley*, Boston, 1910, p. 128./ —, *Copley*, Boston, 1915, pp. 34, 36, 253–254./ W. Dunlap, *History of the Arts of Design*, Boston, 1918, I, pp. 133–134./ C.C. Cunningham, "Copley," *Art News*, 1938, XXXVI, no. 20, p. 9./ J.T. Flexner, *America's Old Masters*, New York, 1939, p. 106 (repr.)./ E.P. Richardson, "Watson and the Shark by Copley," *Art Quarterly*, 1947, X, no. 3, pp. 213, 218, note 2 (fig. 3)./ J.T. Flexner, *Copley*, Boston, 1948, pp. 6–7, 84–87, 109 (pl. 23)./ V. Barker, *American Painting*, New York, 1950, pp. 214, 217 (pl. 30)./ J.T. Flexner, *American Painting*, New York, 1950, pp. 15, 112 (pl. 8)./ —, *Light of Distant Skies*, New York, 1954, pp. 40–41, 139 (pl. 16)./ E.P. Richardson, *Painting in America*, New York, 1956, pp. 94, 316./ J.D. Prown, *Copley*, Cambridge, Mass., 1966 (fig. 372).

Exhibitions: Boston, MFA, *Copley*, 1938, no. 80./ Pittsburgh, Pa., Carnegie Institute, *Survey of American Painting*, 1940, no. 51./ New York, Museum of Modern Art, *Romantic Painting in America*, 1943, pp. 8–9, no. 57 (repr. p. 49)./ Boston, MFA and Wellesley College, Jewett Arts Center, *Four Boston Masters*, 1959, no. 16 (repr. p. 29)./ Washington, D.C., National Gallery, New York, Metropolitan Museum, and Boston, MFA, *Copley*, 1965–1966, no. 68b (repr. p. 94).

300.

fig. 84

Winslow Warren

Half-length and turned three-quarters right, he wears a gray-brown coat with dark brown velvet collar and a white stock. In the background are a green curtain and a brown column, with a distant blue and green landscape, right.

Oil on canvas. Painted oval. 30 × 25 in. (76.2 × 63.5 cm.)

Painted in 1785.

Collections: James and Mercy Otis Warren, Plymouth, Mass.; Henry Warren, the sitter's brother; Dr. Winslow Warren, Plymouth; Winslow Warren, Dedham, Mass., 1870; Winslow Warren, his grandson, Walpole, Mass., 1930.
Gift of Winslow Warren. 57.708

Born in Plymouth, Mass., the son of James (Cat. no. 259) and Mercy Otis (Cat. no. 260) Warren, Winslow Warren (1759–1791) sailed for London in 1780 and was twice arrested for political reasons during his year-and-a-half stay. He returned to America in 1783 but visited Europe again in 1785, just before being killed by the Indians in St. Clair's defeat at Miami, Ohio. Winslow Warren wrote of the portrait in a letter to his mother, dated March 7, 1785.

References: A.T. Perkins, *Copley*, Boston, 1873, p. 117./ F.W. Bayley, *Copley*, Boston, 1910, p. 129./ —, *Copley*, Boston, 1915, p. 253./ J.D. Prown, *Copley*, Cambridge, Mass., 1966 (fig. 473).

Exhibition: Boston, MFA, *Copley*, 1938, no. 78.

301.
fig. 85

Sir Henry Belasyse, Second Earl Fauconberg

Half-length and in right profile, his face turned front, he stands with his hands resting on a sword-hilt; he wears the red coat and gold epaulets of a British officer. To the left are a brown background and distant blue mountains and sky.

Oil on canvas. 31½ × 26½ in. (80 × 67.3 cm.)
Painted about 1785–1794.

Collections: Martha Babcock Amory, granddaughter of the artist; Susan Greene Dexter, her daughter, Boston.
Bequest of Susan Greene Dexter in memory of Charles and Martha Babcock Amory. 25.96

Henry Belasyse (1743–1802), son of Sir Thomas and Catherine Betham Belasyse, in 1774 succeeded his father as Second Earl Fauconberg of Newborough, York. He married twice: in 1776 Charlotte Lamb and later a Miss Chesshyre. The earldom became extinct at his death. He lived near the Copleys in George Street; in 1802, Mrs. Copley wrote her daughter, "We have lost our old neighbor, Lord Fauconberg. His death was awfully sudden: he went out to walk, and was brought back in a hearse" (*see* Amory, p. 224). His coat of arms, painted in the upper left corner, are those of Belasyse of Newborough and Belasyse of Scotland, quartered. The pose is like the three-quarter-length portrait by Copley of *General Thomas Gage* (Mrs. Harriet Moseley Bodley, Newburyport, Mass.) painted in Boston in 1768–1769. Engraved by A. Fogg in 1794, a replica is owned by Mrs. Robert Dickey, New York. The date is established by his apparent age and by the date of the engraving; stylistically, it is probably about 1790–1794.

References: A.T. Perkins, *Copley*, Boston, 1873, p. 53./ M.B. Amory, *Copley*, Boston, 1882, p. 470./ F.W. Bayley, *Copley*, Boston, 1910, p. 36./ —, *Copley*, Boston, 1915, p. 103./ J.D. Prown, *Copley*, Cambridge, Mass., 1966 (fig. 591).

302.
fig. 83

Thomas Lane and His Sister Harriot

A conversation piece; he lies full-length to the right on the grass and looks at his sister on his right; an open book is in his left hand. She is three-quarter length and in left profile, resting her hands on his left hand and shoulder. He wears black breeches and a blue coat over a yellow and mauve striped waistcoat; she wears a pink and white dress and a hat trimmed with white ribbon. Beyond, left, trees in the brown and green landscape are touched with yellow. The clouds in the blue sky are white.

Oil on canvas. 47 × 59 in. (119.4 × 149.8 cm.)
Painted about 1792.

Collections: Harriot Eleanor Lane, Camberwell, Surrey, by 1857; John Hawkins, her cousin, Camberwell, 1860; George Frederick Hawkins (1842–1922), his son, London; Mrs. Frances Alice Hawkins (1859–1951), his wife, Hartley Wintney, Hampshire, 1922; Estate of Mrs. Frances Alice Hawkins, 1951.

Emily L. Ainsley Fund. 54.573

Thomas (born 1768) and Harriot (1776–1860) were the children of John and Eleanor Everitt Lane of London, and grandchildren of Thomas Lane (d. 1784), who was head of Lane, Son & Fraser, an important London firm that supplied banking services and credit to the wealthy merchants of New England. A victim of tuberculosis, young Thomas, and his father, also of Lane, Son & Fraser, lived in Boston from 1786 to 1789. Thomas then went to Madeira for his health. After his return to England, he became business partner to a Mr. Taylor, and in 1792 left with him for Antigua. He later returned to Boston and in 1801 married Elizabeth Appleton (1768–1802), daughter of Nathaniel Appleton of Boston. She died childless the following year. Thomas was in London in 1818; in 1829, according to his father's will, he was a resident of Jamaica. It is not known when or where he died. Nothing is known of Harriot's later life except that, from her father's will, she was still a spinster in 1829. The last owner of the painting thought it to be by George Romney. The present attribution to Copley is based on the style and the knowledge that Copley did paint a portrait of John Lane (his will, Somerset House, London, bequeaths to his son, Thomas, ". . . my portrait painted by Copley . . ." Lane must have known Copley socially through the New England Club in London and, therefore, may well have also painted his children. From their apparent ages in the portrait, Thomas and Harriot were probably painted shortly before Thomas left for Antigua in 1792.

Reference: J.D. Prown, *Copley*. Cambridge, Mass., 1966 (fig. 484).

Exhibition: Montreal Museum of Fine Arts, circulated in Canada, and Toledo Museum, *British Painting in the 18th Century*, 1957–1958, no. 3 (repr. p. 137).

303. **John Quincy Adams**

fig. 86

Half-length and turned three-quarters right, he wears a black coat with a white stock. A red curtain is behind him, and in the right distance, a green landscape beneath a sunset sky.

Oil on canvas. Painted oval. 30 × 25 in. (76.2 × 63.5 cm.)

Painted in 1795.

Collections: Charles Francis Adams, the sitter's son, Boston, 1848; Charles Francis Adams, his son, Washington, D.C., 1886.

Gift of Mrs. Charles Francis Adams. 17.1077

John Quincy Adams (1767–1848) was the son of John Adams, President of the U.S., 1796–1800, and Abigail Smith Adams of Quincy, Mass. He was educated in Europe from 1777 to 1785, a graduate of Harvard in 1787, and a student of law before he began his brilliant career in politics. By 1794 he was Minister to The Hague; by 1803, U.S. Senator; in 1809, Minister to Russia; in 1817 Secretary of State; and in 1827 the sixth President of the U.S. After his failure at reelection, he represented Plymouth, Mass. in Congress until his death in Washington, D.C. The portrait was painted during his stay in London in 1795.

References: C. Bigot, *Life of G.P.A. Healy*, privately printed, n.d., pp. 52–53./ A.T. Perkins, *Copley*, Boston, 1873, p. 27./ M.B. Amory, *Copley*, Boston, 1882, p. 88./ F.W. Bayley, *Copley*, Boston, 1910, p. 10./ —, *Copley*, Boston, 1915, p. 39./ T. Bolton and H.L. Binsse, "Copley," *The Antiquarian*, 1930, xv, no. 6, p. 116./ J.T. Flexner, *Light of Distant Skies*, New York, 1954, p. 55./ J.D. Prown, *Copley*, Cambridge, Mass., 1966 (fig. 598).

Exhibitions: Harvard University, *Tercentenary*, 1936, no. 2./ Boston, MFA, *Copley*, 1938, no. 1./ Washington, D.C., National Gallery, New York, Metropolitan Museum, and Boston, MFA, *Copley*, 1965–1966, no. 92 (repr. p. 118).

304. **Saul Reproved by Samuel**

fig. 88

Saul, center, crowned and wearing a red cloak over his armor, grasps the mantle of the blue and gold tunic worn by Samuel, who turns to point accusingly at the King. David is behind Saul; to the right a soldier in blue armor controls a gray horse. The background is a burning city and a red and black sky.

Oil on canvas. 67 × 85½ in. (170 × 217 cm.)

Painted about 1798.

Collections: *Property of J. S. Copley*, Christie's, London, May 18, 1811, no. 41, bought in; Lord Lyndhurst, the artist's son, London; *Lyndhurst Sale*, Christie's, March 5, 1864, no. 84; Martha Babcock Amory, granddaughter of the artist; Susan Greene Dexter, her daughter, Boston.

Bequest of Susan Greene Dexter in memory of Charles and Martha Babcock Amory. 25.99

Saul, King of Israel, was commanded by the Lord, through Samuel, to destroy the entire civilization of Amalek. Saul, however, spared Agag, the King of the Amalekites, and the best of the animals in order to sacrifice them to the Lord. Samuel then reproved Saul, saying that to obey the Lord was better than to sacrifice to Him (*I Samuel*, xv, 27–28). Probably painted the year of its exhibition at the Royal Academy. Three studies for the painting, all drawings, two unlocated and one at the Addison Gallery, Andover, Mass., are listed by Prown (*see below*).

References: H.T. Tuckerman, *Book of the Artists*, New York, 1870, p. 79./ A.T. Perkins, *Copley*, Boston, 1873, pp. 127, 133./ M.B. Amory, *Copley*, Boston, 1882, pp. 172–173./ F.W. Bayley, *Copley*, Boston, 1915, pp. 32, 35./ W. Dunlap, *History of the Arts of Design*, Boston, 1918, I, p. 142./ C.C. Cunningham, "Copley," *Art News*, 1938, xxxvi, no. 20, p. 8./ J.T. Flexner, *America's Old Masters*, New York, 1939, p. 159./ —, *Copley*, Boston, 1948, p. 102./ J.D. Prown, *Copley*, Cambridge, Mass., 1966 (fig. 610).

Exhibitions: London, Royal Academy, 1798, no. 235./ Boston, MFA, *Copley*, 1938, no. 71 (repr. p. 13).

305.

fig. 87

John Codman

Three-quarter length, he sits turned three-quarters right, with one hand tucked into the coat of his brown suit. The chair, curtain, and sky beyond are blue.

Oil on canvas. 36¼ × 28 in. (92.1 × 71.1 cm.)

Painted about 1800.

Collections: Henry Codman, the sitter's grandson, Boston; John Amory Codman, his son, Boston, by 1873; Martha Codman Karolik, his daughter, Newport, R.I.

M. and M. Karolik Collection of Eighteenth Century American Arts. 37.38

John Codman (1720–1792) was the son of John and Parnell Foster Codman. A Boston merchant, he married Abigail Soley Asbury in 1754, and during the Revolution lived in Haverhill, Mass. He died in Boston. The present picture is Copley's copy after the lost original by Thomas Johnston. It was made in England after 1781 at the request of the Rev. John Codman, the sitter's son. Copley later portrayed Codman from life in Torquay, England.

References: A.T. Perkins, *Copley*, Boston, 1873, p. 45./ F.W. Bayley, *Copley*, Boston, 1910, p. 28./ —, *Copley*, Boston, 1915, pp. 33, 79–80./ E.J. Hipkiss, *M. and M. Karolik Collection of Eighteenth Century American Arts*, Boston, 1941, no. 6 (repr. p. 13)./ J.D. Prown, *Copley*, Cambridge, Mass., 1966 (fig. 658).

Exhibitions: Boston, Copley Hall, *Portraits*, 1896, no. 72./ Washington, D.C., National Gallery, *Early American Paintings*, 1925–1926, no. 7./ Boston, MFA, *Copley*, 1938, no. 18.

306.

fig. 89

Venus and Cupid

Surrounded by pink and yellow drapery, Venus and Cupid, both in half-length, clasp each other.

Oil on canvas. 24¾ × 20 in. (62.8 × 50.8 cm.)

Painted about 1800.

Collections: Lord Lyndhurst, son of the artist, London; *Lyndhurst Sale*, Christie's, London, March 5, 1864, no. 59; Martha Babcock Amory, granddaughter of the artist, Boston; Mrs. F. Gordon Dexter (Susan Greene Amory), her daughter, Boston.

Bequest of Susan Greene Dexter in memory of Charles and Martha Babcock Amory.
25.94

According to tradition, Mrs. Copley and her son John are said to have posed for this sketch, which would give it a date in the late 1770's. Stylistically, however, it is a much later work, perhaps of about 1800.

References: H.T. Tuckerman, *Book of the Artists*, New York, 1870, p. 79./ A.T. Perkins, *Copley*, Boston, 1873, p. 128./ F.W. Bayley, *Copley*, Boston, 1910, p. 30./ —, *Copley*, Boston, 1915, pp. 10, 34, 88./ J.D. Prown, *Copley*, Cambridge, Mass., 1966 (fig. 386).

307.
fig. 91

George IV When Prince of Wales

Mounted upon a black horse while reviewing his troops, the Prince wears a red dress uniform, black plumed hat, and boots. His officers behind him and the troops below wear red uniforms, the color of the horses' trappings. Cloudy blue sky above a green and brown landscape.

Oil on canvas. 146 × 124 in. (370.8 × 315 cm.)
Painted about 1804–1809.

Collections: Lord Lyndhurst, the artist's son, London; *Lyndhurst Sale*, Christie's, London, March 5, 1864, no. 88; to Cox; Martha Babcock Amory, granddaughter of the artist; Susan Greene Dexter, her daughter, Boston.

Bequest of Susan Greene Dexter in memory of Charles and Martha Babcock Amory.
25.98

The Prince is attended by Lieut. Gen. Francis Eliott, Second Lord Heathfield; Gen. Sir Tomkyns Turner, who brought the Rosetta Stone from Egypt to England; Col. Benjamin Bloomfield, chief equerry to the Prince, knighted in 1815; Baron Eben; and Col. George A. Quentin. The Prince wears the blue ribbon and star of the Order of the Garter; his saddlebag and cloth are decorated with the crossed batons of the Field Marshal. C. Turner made a mezzotint published by Copley and Colnaghi in 1813. Two drawings for the painting, *Head of the Prince Regent* and *Lord Heathfield* are in the M. and M. Karolik Collection of Eighteenth Century American Arts. Prown (*see below*) lists two others. An oil replica by Copley (39 × 33½ in.) is in the collection of her Majesty Queen Elizabeth II. Joseph Farington (*see below*) gives the date of 1809, but Graves, in the *Royal Academy Exhibitors*, 1905, lists the work only in the exhibition of 1810. F.W. Bayley, however, lists it in that of 1809.

References: H.T. Tuckerman, *Book of the Artists*, New York, 1870, p. 79./ F.W. Bayley, *Copley*, Boston, 1910, p. 43./ —, *Copley*, Boston, 1915, pp. 33, 35, 114./ J. Farington, *Farington Diary*, London, 1925, v, p. 135./ J.D. Prown, *Copley*, Cambridge, Mass., 1966 (fig. 661).

Exhibitions: London, Royal Academy, 1810, no. 58./ Washington, D.C., National Gallery, New York, Metropolitan Museum, and Boston, MFA, *Copley*, 1965–1966, no. 103 (pl. XVI).

308.
fig. 90

Battle of the Pyrenees

The Duke of Wellington, in a red and gold dress uniform on a gray charger center, gestures with a baton. The Prince of Orange and Lord March ride beside him. Below, red uniformed troops march. Green and brown mountains are partly obscured by gray and yellow smoke.

Oil on canvas. 78 × 85 in. (198.1 × 215.9 cm.)
Painted about 1813–1815.

Collections: Lord Lyndhurst, son of the artist, London; *Lyndhurst Sale*, Christie's, London, March 5, 1864, no. 87; with M. Grist; Martha Babcock Amory, granddaughter of the artist; Susan Greene Dexter, her daughter, Boston.

Bequest of Susan Greene Dexter in memory of Charles and Martha Babcock Amory.
25.97

An incident during the Peninsular War (1808–1814). The efforts of Maj.-Gen. Soult of the French Army to cross the Pyrenees into Spain were crushed by Wellington and the Allied troops in a series of skirmishes called the Battle of the Pyrenees, fought between July 25 and August 2, 1813. The painting remained unfinished in Copley's studio at his death.

References: F.W. Bayley, *Copley*, Boston, 1910, p. 24./ —, *Copley*, Boston, 1915, pp. 33, 57./ C.C. Cunningham, "Copley," *Art News*, 1938, XXXVI, no. 20, p. 8./ J.D. Prown, *Copley*, Cambridge, Mass., 1966 (fig. 673).

Exhibition: Boston, MFA, *Copley*, 1938, p. 14, no. 8.

309.

fig. 35

A Child of the Pierpont Family (attributed to Copley)

Full-length and dressed in blue and white, the child is seated on red drapery and holds a brown and white spaniel. The background is brown.

Oil on canvas. 34½ × 28 in. (87.7 × 71.1 cm.)

Painted about 1751–1753.

Collections: Ebenezer Pierpont III, Boston; Mrs. Moses Pierpont Davis, his daughter; Ellen A.W. Morrill, her great-great-granddaughter, Boston. *Bequest of Ellen A. Williams Morrill. 42.102*

Family tradition has identified the child, whose name is unknown, as one of the children of Ebenezer (born 1720) and Hannah Gridley Pierpont of Boston. The painting cannot be assigned to any known artist other than Copley who was working in Boston in the middle of the eighteenth century, but it bears a close connection to the Kneller tradition as manifested by John Smibert. The pose and *staffage* no doubt derived from a contemporary print; the stiff, undeveloped style but latent strength of brushwork indicates the strong possibility that the painting is one of the earliest efforts of Copley. Smibert and his colleague, Peter Pelham, Copley's stepfather, were the two earliest artistic influences on Copley before he rapidly developed his own technique during 1754, as seen in the portrait of *Joseph Mann* (Cat. no. 250) and *Galatea* (Cat. no. 251). The lack of any exactly comparable work in Copley's *oeuvre* prevents a positive attribution.

References: A.T. Perkins, *Copley*, Boston, 1873, pp. 95–96./ F.W. Bayley, *Copley*, Boston, 1910, p. 79./ —, *Copley*, Boston, 1915, p. 198./ B.N. Parker and A.B. Wheeler, *Copley*, Boston, 1938, p. 255./ B.N. Parker, "Problems of Attribution in Early Portraits by Copley," *MFA Bulletin*, 1942, XL, no. 239, pp. 54–57 (repr. pp. 54, 55)./ J.D. Prown, *Copley*, Cambridge, Mass., 1966 (rejects Copley attribution).

310.

John Tyng Tyler (attributed to Copley)

Half-length, the little boy stands three-quarters right before a hilly blue landscape. He wears a brown coat, yellow waistcoat, and black tie, and holds a black hat lined with blue and filled with cherries.

Pastel on paper mounted on linen. 23 × 18 in. (58.4 × 45.7 cm.)

Drawn about 1766.

Collections: Mrs. Samuel Tyler Whitwell, sister of the sitter, Newton, Mass., 1767; Samuel Whitwell, her son, Boston; Sophia Louisa, Henry, Samuel H., and Frederick A. Whitwell, his children; Frederick Silsbee Whitwell, Frederick A. Whitwell's son, Boston, 1876. *Helen and Alice Colburn Fund. 33.11*

John Tyng Tyler, the son of Joseph Tyler, who was one of the Sons of Liberty, and Frances Tyng Tyler of Boston, was born in 1761 and died at the age of six. The portrait was done in 1766, judging from the sitter's age, and is attributed to Copley by family tradition. Although unsigned, it resembles his pastel style closely enough to warrant strong consideration, and no alternate attribution can at present be made.

References: F.W. Bayley, *Copley*, Boston, 1915, p. 243./ T. Bolton, *Early American Portrait Draughtsmen*, New York, 1923, p. 21, no. 54./ B.N. Parker and A.B. Wheeler, *Copley*, Boston, 1938, p. 259.

311. **John Adams (after Copley)**

He stands full-length to the left, wearing a brown velvet suit and a sword. A scroll in his right hand, he gestures with his left to maps spread on a red Persian carpet laid over a large globe. Above left is a statue of Peace against a landscape background.

Oil on canvas. 20 × 13½ in. (50.8 × 34.3 cm.)

Painted after 1783.

Collection: Possibly Mrs. Newton Robinson, London.

Seth Kettell Sweetser Residuary Fund. 23.180

John Adams (1735–1826), son of John and Susannah Boylston Adams of Quincy, Mass., a lawyer, was appointed by Boston to oppose the Stamp Act. He was on the General Court of Massachusetts in 1770–1771, and at the Congress of Philadelphia in 1774, an influential leader among the radical nationalists. He was founder of the American Navy, with Jefferson formulated the Declaration of Independence, was first U.S. Minister to the Court of St. James, first American Vice-President, and second President. After retiring to his farm in Quincy, he wrote prodigiously. He is here represented as the harbinger of transatlantic peace. This replica of Copley's original life-size portrait of 1783 (Harvard University) was copied by an unknown hand in Copley's studio late in the eighteenth century.

Reference: V. Manners and G.C. Williamson, *Zoffany*, London, 1920 (repr. following p. 40), as *Admiral Lord George Auson* by Zoffany.

GARDNER COX, born in Holyoke, Mass. in 1906, attended the Art Students League in 1924, then studied painting at the Boston Museum School from 1928 to 1930 and architecture at Massachusetts Institute of Technology from 1929 to 1931. He was an architect until 1936, when he began to paint. From 1953 to 1957 he taught at the Boston Museum School and now lives in Cambridge, Mass.

312. **Basic No. 12**

An arrangement in gray, black, red, the pink-gray of a crab, and yellow sand. The sky above and the background pyramids are gray.

Oil on canvas. 22 × 31 in. (55.9 × 78.7 cm.)

Signed and dated lower left: *Gardner Cox 50.*

Abraham Shuman Fund. 51.697

"The objects depicted were chosen as symbols of timelessness in the sense of being primordial and at the same time presently familiar, i.e.—crab, rock egg, etc. In each case an attempt was made to express the character of the object painted through both texture and shape. The color was keyed rather somberly as it seemed fitting to the main theme. The newspaper was introduced as a foil to the 'timeless' objects—and as a necessary design element." (Letter from the artist, June 5, 1952.)

Exhibitions: University of Illinois, *Contemporary American Paintings*, 1951, no. 27 (pl. 93)./ Rockland, Me., William A. Farnsworth Art Museum, *Cox*, 1956, no. 22 (repr.)./ Lincoln, Mass., De Cordova Museum, *Margaret Brown Memorial Exhibition*, 1957, no. 6.

JAN COX was born in The Hague, Holland in 1919 and received his early education at the Barlaeus-Gymnasium in Amsterdam. When his family moved to Antwerp, he studied at the Institut National Supérieur d'Histoire de l'Art et d'Archéologie in Ghent and graduated in 1941. He then worked in Brussels in 1945 and joined there the "Jeune Peinture Belge" group. He joined the painting staff of the Boston Museum School in 1949 and is now its head.

313. **Second Loss of Eurydice**
fig. 608
Two symbolic flowerlike figures: Eurydice, on the right, is in red and white, surrounded by orange flame against a blue space; Orpheus is at the left, in black, red, green, and yellow, against a black background.

Oil on canvas. 60 × 60 in. (152.4 × 152.4 cm.)

Painted in 1959.
Sylvanus A. Denio Collection. 59.341

Cox has been fascinated by the Orpheus legend since 1953; this painting is one of a cycle of eight large panels on the myth. Represented by symbolic flower shapes and evocative colors is the moment of Eurydice's final return to the nether world and Orpheus' lament.

Exhibitions: Boston, MFA, *Myth of Orpheus*, 1959./ New York, Catherine Viviano Gallery, *Cox*, 1960, no. 7.

JASPER FRANCIS CROPSEY (1823–1900) was born in Rossville, N.Y. From 1836 to 1841 he worked as a draughtsman in the office of the architect Joseph Trench in New York, turning in 1841 to landscape painting to become one of the foremost artists of the Hudson River School. He traveled through Europe from 1847 to 1849 and on his return worked in New England and Pennsylvania. From 1856 to 1863 he lived in London. The following year he settled permanently in Hastings-on-Hudson, N.Y., and during the 1870's and 1880's drew numerous plans for residences. He died at Hastings-on-Hudson.

314.

Schatacook Mountain, Housatonic Valley, Connecticut
Oil on canvas. 30¾ × 46¼ in. (78.1 × 117.4 cm.)
Signed and dated lower right on rocks: *J.F. Cropsey 1845.* Inscribed on back: *the Valley of the Housatonic, Kent, Conn.*
M. and M. Karolik Collection. 47.1208
Reference: Karolik Catalogue, 1949, no. 92 (repr.).

315.

Study of a Clump of Trees
Oil on canvas. 15½ × 14 in. (39.4 × 35.5 cm.)
Signed and dated lower center: *J.F. Cropsey/ L Arrica/ Sept 1848.*
M. and M. Karolik Collection. 47.1246
Reference: Karolik Catalogue, 1949, no. 93 (repr.).

316.

Eagle Cliff, New Hampshire
Oil on canvas. 37 × 53 in. (94 × 134.6 cm.)
Signed and dated lower right: *J.F. Cropsey 1851.*
M. and M. Karolik Collection. 47.1190
Reference: Karolik Catalogue, 1949, no. 94 (repr.).

317.
fig. 311

Niagara Falls from the Foot of Goat Island
Oil on canvas. 15¼ × 24 in. (38.7 × 61 cm.)
Signed and dated lower right on rock: *J.F. Cropsey/ 1857.*
M. and M. Karolik Collection. 47.1238

Two drawings of similar composition are in the M. and M. Karolik Collection of Water Colors and Drawings: one, entitled *American Falls* (54.1647) is dated *Sept 4th 1855*; the other is entitled *Niagara Falls: the American Falls* (62.75).
Reference: Karolik Catalogue, 1949, no. 95 (repr.).

318.

Italian Landscape
Oil on canvas. 32¼ × 52¼ in. (81.9 × 132.7 cm.)
Signed and dated lower right: *J.F. Cropsey/ 1860.*
M. and M. Karolik Collection. 47.1204
Reference: Karolik Catalogue, 1949, no. 96 and 96A (repr.).

319.
fig. 312

Early Autumn on the Hudson
The woods surrounding the blue and gray water are in brown, green, yellow, and red. The sky is blue on the left, becoming yellow, pink, and gray.
Oil on canvas. 14 × 24 in. (35.5 × 61 cm.)
Signed and dated lower left: *J.F. Cropsey/ 1873.*
Bequest of Maxim Karolik. 64.444

JOHN STEUART CURRY (1897–1946), born in Dunavant, Kansas, was a student at the Art Institute of Chicago. From 1921 to 1926 he was a magazine and book illustrator, then went to Paris in 1926 to study at Schoukhaieff's Russian Academy and at the Louvre. He next taught at the Cooper Union, New York, and at the Art Students League from 1932 to 1936, when he became artist-in-residence at the Agricultural College of the University of Wisconsin. He died in Madison, Wis.

320.

fig. 573

Storm Over Lake Otsego

On a bright and dark green windswept hill above a blue lake, a man, in blue trousers and yellow shirt, controls two frightened horses. Beyond, the sky is dark gray over purple hills.

Oil on canvas. 40 × 50 in. (101.6 × 127 cm.)
Signed lower right: *John Steuart Curry.* Painted in 1929.
Collection: Mrs. Donald C. Starr, Boston, about 1943.
Gift of Mr. and Mrs. Donald C. Starr. 55.369

Painted in Westport, Conn., in 1929, from sketches made in upper New York State.

Reference: L. E. Schneikebier, *Curry's Pageant of America*, New York, 1943, p. 113 (repr. no. 60).

Exhibition: Chicago, Lakeside Press Galleries, *Curry*, 1939, no. 15.

HENRY F. DARBY (1829–1897) was born in North Adams, Mass. A self-taught portraitist, except for advice from itinerant limners, he was working in oils by 1842, and in 1847 went to teach at the South Carolina Female College, Barhamville. He soon returned to work in New York until about 1860; he was ordained an Episcopalian minister and then lived in Oxford, England, until 1865, when he returned to become rector of St. John's at Whitesboro, N.Y. He resigned in 1869 and lived in Fishkill, N.Y. until his death.

321.

fig. 256

The Rev. John Atwood and His Family

In their parlor, Mrs. and the Rev. Mr. Atwood, in black, sit on either side of a table covered with a green cloth. The children seated about them wear white, blue, and gray. A red-brown drape flutters left by the mahogany piano. The carpet is gray with painted figuration in green and brown. The wallpaper is brown with figures in gray and green. A colored mezzotint and a memorial painting hang on the back wall; a gold framed mirror sits next to a vase of flowers on the white mantle, right.

Oil on canvas. 72 × 96¼ in. (182.9 × 240.6 cm.)
Signed and dated lower right: *H.F. Darby, Painter/ 1845.*
Collections: The Rev. John Atwood, Concord and New Boston, N.H.; Solomon Dodge Atwood, his son, New Boston, 1873; Misses Florence and Annie Atwood, his daughters, New Boston, 1915.
M. and M. Karolik Collection. 62.269

John Atwood (1795–1873), born in Nottingham West, N.H., was ordained Pastor of the First Baptist Church of New Boston, N.H. in 1825 and in 1843 elected State Treasurer and Chaplain of the State Prison in Concord. Because of his antislavery attitude, he bolted his party and consequently failed in his run for the governorship in 1850. He retired to New Boston, where he lived until his death. In 1826 he married Lydia Dodge (1806–1886), daughter of Deacon Solomon Dodge of New Boston. The Atwood children from left to right are: Solomon Dodge, 1839–1915, a general store owner in New Boston; Mary Frances, 1837–1892, a teacher who died unmarried; Ann Judson, 1835–1874, who married the missionary Rev. J.L. Atwell Fish; Sarah Elisabeth, 1829–1916, married to John Blair of Alton, Ill.; Lydia Dodge, 1827–1909, unmarried; and Roger William, 1833–1917, a successful businessman of Alton, Ill. On the wall behind hangs a memorial dedicated to John. Two children who died in infancy were John Blodgett and John Henry. Beside it hangs a mezzotint (here colored) by the English engraver James S. Lucas, disciple of John Martin, of *Samson Carrying off the*

Gates of Gaza. In his Diary (*see* References) Darby remembered that at the age of sixteen he spent three months in "Concord, New Hampshire the capital to paint the Atwoods all on one canvas. The father was represented sitting in the midst of his admiring wife and children, expounding his Bible. . . ."

References: H.F. Darby, *Diary*, MS, 1894, p. 41./ I. Hacker, "Discovery of a Prodigy," and T.N. Maytham, "Two Faces of New England Portrait Painting," *MFA Bulletin*, 1963, LXI, no. 323, pp. 23 and 31 respectively.

Exhibition: Boston, MFA, *New Paintings in the M. and M. Karolik Collection*, 1962–1963.

ARTHUR BOWEN DAVIES (1862–1928) was born in Utica, N.Y. He studied at the Chicago Academy of Design until 1880 when he went to Mexico as a civil engineer. On his return in 1882 he attended the Art Institute school and in 1885 started work in New York with the Gotham Art Students, at the Art Students League, and as an illustrator. After the first visit to Europe in 1893, he returned every year but also worked in New York as painter, sculptor, and tapestry designer. President and leading organizer of the 1913 Armory Show and one of "The Eight," he died in Florence, Italy.

322.

Valley of the Jonathan

A landscape of varied greens and gray hills. The houses on the left and the sky are gray touched with brown.

Oil on canvas. 18 × 30 in. (45.7 × 76.2 cm.)

Signed and dated lower left: *A.B. Davies/ 09.*

Collections: Mrs. Cornelius J. Sullivan, New York; *C.J. Sullivan Sale*, Parke-Bernet, New York, Dec. 7, 1939, no. 39.

Charles Henry Hayden Fund. 39.797

Reference: R. Cortissoz, *Davies*, New York, 1931, p. 35.

Exhibitions: New York, Metropolitan Museum, *Davies Memorial*, 1930, no. 34./ Utica, N.Y., Munson-Williams-Proctor Institute and circulated in the U.S., *Davies Centennial*, 1962–1963, no. 33.

323.
fig. 568

Heliodora

In full length, a girl draped in white kneels before a brown and blue tree trunk. The red background is scattered with green leaves and yellow, blue, and pink flowers.

Oil on canvas. 24 × 18¼ in. (61 × 46.3 cm.)

Signed and dated lower left: *A.B. Davies/ 26.*

Collections: The artist, New York; Ferargil Galleries, New York, 1928.

Charles Henry Hayden Fund. 58.1198

The subject is reputedly a figure from Greek tragedy. The artist's daughter recalls that she had named her blonde-haired doll Heliodora from a story that her father had read. The doll was saved from a tragic studio fire in 1926 and apparently prompted the artist to do the painting. Davies had contemplated using the design for a tapestry; as far as is known, he never carried it out.

Exhibitions: New York, Museum of Modern Art and circulated in the U.S., *The Classical Motif*, 1953–1955 (lent by Ferargil Galleries)./ Utica, N.Y., Munson-Williams-Proctor Institute and circulated in the U.S., *Davies Centennial*, 1962–1963, no. 80 (repr.).

CHARLES HAROLD DAVIS (1856–1933) was born in Amesbury, Mass. He studied at the Boston Museum School for three years until in 1880 he went to Paris to study at the Académie Julian under Lefebvre and Boulanger. In France for ten years, he painted often at Barbizon and Fontainebleau. On his return he worked in Mystic, Conn. until his death.

324.

Forsaken Homestead

A brown, bleak landscape is touched with green. At sunset a ruined house is silhouetted against the pink and gray clouds in the blue sky.

Oil on canvas. 18 × 26 in. (45.7 × 66 cm.)
Signed lower left: *C.H. Davis.* Inscribed on back: *329.* Painted about 1891.
Collection: Charles T. Baker, Boston, 1891.
Bequest of Charles T. and Susan P. Baker. 21.1255
It was the artist's habit to number each painting on the back in chronological order; if he repainted, he would cross out the original number and apply a new one.
Exhibition: Boston, Doll and Richards, *Davis,* 1891, no. 18.

325.   **Morning Sunlight**
Gray farm buildings are surrounded by trees in fields of green and yellow, which in the foreground are touched with purple and brown. The sky is blue.
Oil on canvas. 20 × 30 in. (50.8 × 76.2 cm.)
Signed lower left: *C.H. Davis.* Inscribed on back: *397.* Painted about 1895.
Collection: George H. Champlin, Boston, 1895.
Gift of the Estate of Mrs. George Hebron Champlin. 11.1278
Exhibition: Boston, Doll and Richards, *Davis,* 1895, no. 6.

326.   **Summer Twilight**
The pink moon is reflected in pale blue water beyond gray rocks on the dark green shore. Distant land is gray and green under gray sky.
Oil on canvas. 20¼ × 27¼ in. (51.4 × 69.2 cm.)
Signed lower left: *C.H. Davis.* Inscribed on back: *45-C.* Painted about 1896.
Collections: Elizabeth Howard Bartol, Boston; Mary W. Bartol, John W. Bartol, and Abigail W. Clark, Boston.
Gift of Mary W. Bartol, John W. Bartol, and Abigail W. Clark. 27.98
Exhibition: Boston, Doll and Richards, *Davis,* 1896, no. 5.

327.   **The Clouds**
Above a hillside of various shades of green, the clouds are white in a blue sky.
Oil on canvas. 22 × 27 in. (55.9 × 68.6 cm.)
Signed lower left: *C.H. Davis.* Painted between 1900 and 1910.
Gift of the heirs of George Adams Kettell. 13.475

328.   **Gray Twilight**
A brown and purple landscape of brush and trees. The sky is gray with a faint touch of rose at the horizon.
Oil on canvas. 20¼ × 27¼ in. (51.4 × 69.2 cm.)
Signed lower left: *C.H. Davis.* Inscribed on back: *653.* Painted about 1904.
Collection: With T.C. Noe, New York, 1904.
Bequest of Ernest Wadsworth Longfellow. 23.501
Exhibition: Philadelphia, Pennsylvania Academy of the Fine Arts, *100th Anniversary Exhibition,* 1905, no. 547.

329.   **Midsummer**
A hillside and trees are bright green before gray and white clouds in a blue sky. Two figures in blue and orange cross a gray stone wall.
Oil on canvas. 25 × 30 in. (63.5 × 76.2 cm.)
Signed lower left: *C.H. Davis.* Inscribed on back: *725.* Painted about 1908.
Collections: Miss A.A. Davis (Mrs. H.H. Logan), Boston, 1908.
Gift of Mrs. Hiram Hyde Logan. 22.819

330.   **Autumn**
In the foreground is underbrush of brown, green, and yellow. The landscape beyond is purple with gray sky and water.
Oil on canvas. 25 × 30 in. (63.5 × 76.2 cm.)
Signed lower left: *C.H. Davis.* Inscribed on back: *820.* Painted about 1913.
Bequest of Dora N. Spaulding. 41.531

331.   **Summer Landscape**
A rocky green meadow has a gray stone wall. In the distance a red house with trees.

Beyond, blue water beneath yellow sky.
Oil on canvas. 20 × 30 in. (50.8 × 76.2 cm.)
Signed lower right: *C.H. Davis.* Painted by 1930.
Collection: Miss Nellie P. Carter, Boston, by 1930.
Gift of the Estate of Nellie P. Carter. 35.1687

STUART DAVIS (1894–1964), born in Philadelphia in 1910, left school to study with Robert Henri in New York and exhibited at the Armory Show of 1913 while working as a magazine illustrator. The year 1928–1929 he spent in Paris, and in 1931 he began teaching at the Art Students League, New York. From 1934 to 1939 he was editor of *Art Front* and was associated with the Artist's Congress. In 1940 he started to teach at the New School for Social Research, New York. He lived and worked in New York as painter, critic, and lecturer until his death. At first influenced by Van Gogh and Gauguin, his later exposure to Cubism developed a new direction of personal interpretations.

332. **Autumn Landscape**
fig. 551 *The foreground is pink with green bushes before a hill of black, ochre, and purple. In the background the foliage is brown and yellow. The sky is white.*
Oil on canvas. 23½ × 30 in. (59.7 × 76.2 cm.)
Signed on back, upper right: *Stuart Davis.* Painted in 1915–1916.
Collection: Private collection, Cape Cod, Mass., until 1959.
Abraham Shuman Fund. 59.523

333. **Hillside Near Gloucester**
A blue rock and two mauve trees on a green hillside. White houses and the trees stand before a purple-blue sky.
Oil on canvas. 22½ × 18¾ in. (57.1 × 47.6 cm.)
Painted in 1915–1916.
Collection: Same as Cat. no. 332.
Abraham Shuman Fund. 59.522

"I am sure they [*Hillside near Gloucester* and *Autumn Landscape,* Cat. no. 332] were done in Gloucester or environs, not Cape Cod. My guess is that the dates are 1915–16. They are examples of outdoor sketches from Nature . . . the method was product [sic] of direct and spontaneous reactions to certain landscapes. They should be regarded as exercises carried out in that spirit without other important consideration . . . I had a knowledge and enormous admiration for Van Gogh and Gauguin at that time, and still have." (Letters from the artist, Nov. 24 and Dec. 18, 1959.)

CHARLES DEAS (1818–1867)

334. **The Voyageurs**
fig. 282 Oil on canvas. 13 × 20½ in. (33 × 52 cm.)
Signed and dated on brown rock lower left: *C. Deas/ 1846.*
M. and M. Karolik Collection. 46.855
Reference: Karolik Catalogue, 1949, no. 97 (repr.).

JOSEPH RODEFER DE CAMP (1858–1923) was born in Cincinnati. A pupil of Thomas Noble at the School of Design in Cincinnati, he also worked with Frank Duveneck in Munich, Florence, and Venice from 1878 to 1880. Upon his return he settled in Boston to work. He died in Boca Grande, Fla.

335. **The Guitar Player**
fig. 490 *A woman, seated in three-quarter length on a green sofa, faces front playing a guitar. Her dress is lavender and white lace. The wall is gray.*
Oil on canvas. 50½ × 46½ in. (128.2 × 118.1 cm.)
Signed and dated lower right: *JOSEPH—DE—CAMP—1908.*
Charles Henry Hayden Fund. 08.204
References: W.H. Downes, "De Camp," *American Magazine of Art,* 1913, IV, no. 6,

pp. 920–922./ R.V.S. Berry, "De Camp," *American Magazine of Art*, 1923, XIV, no. 4, p. 184./ A. Burroughs, *Limners and Likenesses*, Cambridge, Mass., 1936, p. 178 (fig. 149).

Exhibitions: Cincinnati Art Museum, *15th Annual*, 1908, no. 14 (repr. opp. p. 7)./ Philadelphia, Pennsylvania Academy of the Fine Arts, *Ten American Painters*, 1908, no. 1 (repr.)./ Washington, D.C., Corcoran Gallery, *2nd Exhibition—Contemporary American Artists*, 1908–1909, no. 81./ Berlin, Königliche Akademie der Künste, *Ausstellung Amerikanischer Kunst*, 1910, p. 47 (repr.)./ Boston, St. Botolph Club, *De Camp Memorial*, 1924, no. 9.

336.

fig. 491

The Blue Cup

A young woman, in right profile and three-quarter length, stands holding a cup to the light. She wears white and brown. The china on the table beside her is white with red and blue decorations; the background is gray.

Oil on canvas. 50½ × 41½ in. (128.2 × 105.4 cm)

Signed and dated lower left: *JOSEPH—DE—CAMP—1909.*

Collection: Frank G. Webster, Boston, by 1924.

Gift of Edwin S. Webster, Laurence T. Webster, and Mary M. Sampson, in memory of their father, Frank G. Webster. 33.532

Reference: R.V.S. Berry, "De Camp," *American Magazine of Art*, 1923, XIV, no. 4, p. 186.

Exhibition: Boston, St. Botolph Club, *De Camp Memorial*, 1924, no. 13.

THOMAS WILMER DEWING (1851–1938) was born in Boston. A lithographer, he first studied at the Boston Art School. In Paris in 1876 he studied under Boulanger and Lefebvre, and upon his return in 1879–1880 he taught at the Art Students League in New York. He was a member of the "Ten American Painters" and was elected to the National Academy in 1888. He lived principally in New York, where he died.

337.

fig. 425

Autumn

Two women, dressed in yellow, are seated on a classical white marble bench. One plays the lyre; another reclines and plays a flute. Grass and flowers foreground with a white peacock. The sky is pale blue.

Oil on canvas. 16 × 40 in. (40.6 × 101.6 cm.)

Signed and dated lower left: *T.W. Dewing 1883.*

Collections: Thomas B. Clarke, New York, by 1891; George H. Webster, Boston.

Bequest of George H. Webster. 34.131

Reference: C. Cook, *Art and Artists of Our Time*, New York, 1888, p. 268 (repr. as *A Garden*).

Exhibitions: Philadelphia, Pennsylvania Academy of the Fine Arts, *The Clarke Collection*, 1891, no. 58 (as *A Garden*)./ New York, Durlacher Brothers, *Dewing*, 1963, no. 2.

PRESTON DICKINSON (1891–1930) was born in New York. He studied at the Art Students League but derived much of his training from painting in the Louvre when living in Paris from 1910 to 1915. Thereafter he worked in New York, making frequent trips to Europe and Canada. He died in Spain.

338.

The Factory

A complex of factory buildings, chimneys, and pipes in yellow, green, and gray, with blue shadows. Men work by piles of orange pipes.

Oil on cardboard. 14 × 20 in. (35.4 × 50.8 cm.)

Signed lower left: *P. Dickinson*. Painted about 1918.

Charles Henry Hayden Fund. 41.482

Baur (*see below*) gives *The Factory* an approximate date of 1918, in Dickinson's semiabstract period.

Reference: J.I.H. Baur, *Revolution and Tradition in Modern American Painting*, Cambridge, Mass., 1951, p. 59 (fig. 75).

339.

Port Jefferson, Long Island

A blue street between houses and a yellow, brown, and purple church leads to a brown wooded hill. Green trees and white sky, touched with blue and purple.

Pastel on paper. 22¾ × 17¼ in. (57.8 × 43.8 cm.) sight size.

Signed lower right: *Dickinson*. Drawn about 1920–1930.

Collection: John T. Spaulding, Boston.

Bequest of John T. Spaulding. 48.539

Exhibition: Boston, MFA, *The Spaulding Collections*, 1948, no. 23.

340.
fig. 564

Quebec

Viewed down a street from a hill. Soft blues in the foreground and on the roofs; white and buff buildings; blue-green and green foliage; blue-gray sky.

Oil on canvas. 14¼ × 24 in. (36.2 × 61 cm.)

Signed lower right: *Preston Dickinson*. Painted about 1920–1930.

Collection: John T. Spaulding, Boston.

Bequest of John T. Spaulding. 48.538

This work and *Port Jefferson, Long Island* (Cat. no. 339) were probably painted during the last decade of Dickinson's life.

Exhibition: Boston, MFA, *The Spaulding Collections*, 1948, no. 22.

DIETZ

341.

Milford, North Wales, Pennsylvania

Oil on canvas. 22 × 28½ in. (55.9 × 72.3 cm.)

On the back before relining, an old label inscribed: *House Jonathan Jones Wheeler was born in the family fleeing to it when the British occupied Philadelphia. North Wales, Montgomery Co. Gwined Township, Pennsylvania.* Painted about 1825–1833.

M. and M. Karolik Collection. 47.1209

Reference: *Karolik Catalogue*, 1949, no. 98 (repr.).

THOMAS DOUGHTY (1793–1856), born in Philadelphia, was a leather currier until 1820, when he abandoned his trade for a career as a landscape painter, the first American to specialize in that mode. He worked first in Philadelphia but traveled often to Baltimore, Washington, and Boston, where he moved in 1832. From 1837 to 1839 he worked in England, then returned to Newburgh-on-the-Hudson, New York and in 1841 settled in New York. He returned to Europe in 1845–1846 but worked thereafter in New York until his death.

342.
fig. 213

View of Baltimore from Beech Hill

Oil on canvas. 14¼ × 18¼ in. (36.3 × 46.3 cm.)

Signed and dated lower right: *Doughty 1822*.

M. and M. Karolik Collection. 47.1203

Reference: *Karolik Catalogue*, 1949, no. 99 (repr.).

343.

Landscape with Fishermen

Oil on canvas. 17 × 24½ in. (43.2 × 62.2 cm.)

Signed and dated lower left: *Doughty 1826*.

M. and M. Karolik Collection. 47.1244

Reference: *Karolik Catalogue*, 1949, no. 100 (repr.).

344.

The Naval Home, Gray's Ferry, Philadelphia

Oil on panel. 23½ × 36½ in. (59.7 × 92.7 cm.)

Signed and dated lower center: *Doughty 1828*.

M. and M. Karolik Collection. 47.1194

Reference: *Karolik Catalogue*, 1949, no. 101 (repr.).

345.

fig. 215

New Hampshire Lake

A thickly wooded hillside in the foreground is dark green touched with brown. Far distant hills are mauve beyond blue water; clouds are white in the pale blue sky.

Oil on canvas. 26 × 36 in. (66 × 91.4 cm.)

Signed lower left: *T. Doughty.* Painted about 1828–1830.

Collection: Maxim Karolik, Newport, R.I., by 1952.

Bequest of Maxim Karolik. 64.425

The clarity and detail of style suggest an early work before the more Romantic generalizations which arose in the early 1830's.

Reference: T.N. Maytham, "A Trove of Doughtys," *Antiques,* 1965, LXXXVIII, no. 5, p. 682 (repr. p. 681).

Exhibitions: Worcester, Mass., Art Museum, *The Private Collection of Maxim Karolik,* 1952, no. 14./ Washington, D.C., Smithsonian Institution, circulated in the U.S., *19th Century American Paintings,* 1954–1956, no. 17.

346.

View from Stacey Hill, Stoddard, New Hampshire

Oil on canvas. 22¼ × 30¼ in. (56.5 × 76.8 cm.)

Inscribed and dated on back: *T. Doughty 1830.*

M. and M. Karolik Collection. 47.1184

Reference: Karolik Catalogue, 1949, no. 102 (repr.).

347.

Winter Landscape

Oil on canvas. 13½ × 19½ in. (34.3 × 49.5 cm.)

Signed and dated lower right: *T. Doughty/ 1830.*

M. and M. Karolik Collection. 47.1180

Reference: Karolik Catalogue, 1949, no. 103 (repr.).

348.

fig. 216

Beach Scene with Rocks, I

Beyond brown rocks and beach the sea is green, white, and blue; the distant shore and buildings are all brown and gray. The blue sky is swept with white and gray clouds.

Oil on cardboard. 12¼ × 17½ in. (31.1 × 44.5 cm.)

Signed and dated lower left, on a rock: *T.D. 1834.*

Collections: Possibly Henry Codman, Boston, 1847; John Amory Codman, his son, Boston; Martha Codman (Mrs. Maxim Karolik), his daughter, Washington, D.C.; Maxim Karolik, Newport, R.I., 1948.

Bequest of Maxim Karolik. 64.599

Beach Scene with Rocks, II, 1835 (Cat. no. 353) is a version.

Reference: T.N. Maytham, "A Trove of Doughtys," *Antiques,* 1965, LXXXVIII, no. 5, p. 682 (repr. p. 683).

349.

Mountain and Lake

The green, brown, and yellow trees and distant pink mountains are reflected in the water. A fisherman's boat is gray under blue sky with pink and gray clouds.

Oil on panel. 15½ × 23 in. (39.4 × 58.4 cm.)

Signed and dated lower right, on lake shore: *T. Doughty 1834.*

Collection: Maxim Karolik, Newport, R.I., about 1937.

Bequest of Maxim Karolik. 64.408

Same size and type of panel as *Romantic Landscape with a Temple,* 1834 (Cat. no. 350).

Reference: T.N. Maytham, "A Trove of Doughtys," *Antiques,* 1965, LXXXVIII, no. 5, p. 682 (repr.).

350.

fig. 214

Romantic Landscape with a Temple

A pink and gray temple is in a landscape of green, brown, and pink. Gray water is in the foreground; the sky is blue with pink and gray clouds.

Oil on panel. 15½ × 23 in. (39.4 × 58.4 cm.)

Signed and dated lower center, on the bank: *T. Doughty 1834.*

Collections: Probably Henry Codman, Boston, 1847; John Amory Codman, his son, Boston; Martha Codman (Mrs. Maxim Karolik), his daughter, Washington, D.C.; Maxim Karolik, Newport, R.I., 1948.

Bequest of Maxim Karolik. 64.597

Reference: T.N. Maytham, "A Trove of Doughtys," *Antiques*, 1965, LXXXVIII, no. 5, p. 682 (repr.).

351.   **The Glades at Cohasset**

A windswept rocky coast of brown and pink. In the foreground a fisherman in gray walks above white foam from the green waves; the clouds in the blue sky are pink and gray.

Oil on panel. 11 × 14 in. (27.9 × 35.5 cm.)

Signed lower right: *T. Doughty/ 1834.*

Collection: Maxim Karolik, Newport, R.I., about 1943.

Bequest of Maxim Karolik. 64.414

The location is a rocky cove near North Scituate beach known as the Glades.

Reference: T.N. Maytham, "A Trove of Doughtys," *Antiques*, 1965, LXXXVIII, no. 5, p. 682 (repr. p. 683).

352.   **Lighthouse at Nantasket Beach**

The shoreline is brown and green before a gray and green sea; the lighthouse beyond is white beneath gray clouds.

Oil on cardboard. 9¼ × 12 in. (23.5 × 30.5 cm.)

Inscribed on back: *Lighthouse at Nantasket Beach/ by T. Doughty/ belonging to Eliz. A.E. Codman/ Boston.* Painted about 1834.

Collections: Miss Elizabeth A.E. Codman, Boston; Martha Codman (Mrs. Maxim Karolik), her great-niece, Washington, D.C.; Maxim Karolik, Newport, R.I., 1948.

Bequest of Maxim Karolik. 64.598

The style is the same clear, objective one as in *The Glades at Cohasset* (Cat. no. 351) and *Beach Scene with Rocks, I* (Cat. no. 348), both dated works of 1834.

Reference: T.N. Maytham, "A Trove of Doughtys," *Antiques*, 1965, LXXXVIII, no. 5, pp. 681–682 (repr.).

353.   **Beach Scene with Rocks, II**

Seen from a rocky brown beach across the green and white bay, buildings on the distant brown shore and sailboats are white. Gray and white clouds almost obscure the blue sky.

Oil on canvas. 18 × 24¼ in. (47.5 × 61.6 cm.)

Signed and dated lower left, on a rock: *T. Doughty/ 1835.*

Collection: Maxim Karolik, Newport, R.I., about 1948.

Bequest of Maxim Karolik. 64.426

A replica of *Beach Scene with Rocks, I*, 1834 (Cat. no. 348). Another version, called *Coming Squall*, is also probably 1835 (Mrs. Hugo Ambrosi, Tacoma Park, Maryland).

Reference: T.N. Maytham, "A Trove of Doughtys," *Antiques*, 1965, LXXXVIII, no. 5, p. 682 (repr. p. 683).

354.   **Cove of a Mountain Lake**

Gray water reflects the green, brown, and yellow of wooded banks. Mountains are brown and pink below the white and gray clouds in a blue sky.

Oil on canvas. 12 × 17 in. (30.5 × 43.2 cm.)

Signed and dated lower center, on the rocks: *T. Doughty/ 1835.*

Collections: Maxim and Martha Codman Karolik, Newport, R.I., in 1936; Maxim Karolik, Newport, 1948.

Bequest of Maxim Karolik. 64.601

Reference: T.N. Maytham, "A Trove of Doughtys," *Antiques*, 1965, LXXXVIII, no. 5, p. 682 (repr. p. 684).

355.   **View on New Hampshire Lake**

The green and brown of wooded mountains are reflected in the lake, on which are brown boats, one with a white sail. The hills in the distance are mauve; the sky is blue with white and gray clouds.

Oil on panel. 11¾ × 17 in. (29.7 × 43.2 cm.)
Signed lower left: *T. Doughty*. Painted about 1835.
Collections: William Doughty, the artist's brother; Margarett Doughty, his granddaughter; William Stewart Doughty, her brother, Englewood, N.J.; Elizabeth Noll Doughty, his daughter; Howard N. Doughty, Ipswich, Mass. by 1937; Maxim Karolik, Newport, R.I., by 1963.
Bequest of Maxim Karolik. 64.468

Similar to *Cove of a Mountain Lake* (Cat. no. 354), dated 1835.

Reference: T.N. Maytham, "A Trove of Doughtys," *Antiques*, 1965, LXXXVIII, no. 5, p. 682 (repr. p. 684).

356.   **Fishing by a Waterfall**
Oil on canvas. 17 × 14 in. (43.2 × 35.5 cm.)
Signed lower center: *T. Doughty*. Painted about 1835–1840.
M. and M. Karolik Collection. 47.1187

Reference: *Karolik Catalogue*, 1949, no. 104 (repr.).

357.   **A Lake in a Mountain Valley**
The pink and gray surrounding mountains are reflected in the lake; the sky is blue with pink and gray clouds.
Oil on canvas. 18 × 24 in. (45.7 × 61 cm.)
Signed and dated lower left: *T. Doughty/ 1836*.
Collections: Probably Henry Codman, Boston, 1847; John Amory Codman, his son, Boston; Martha Codman (Mrs. Maxim Karolik), his daughter, Newport, R.I.; Maxim Karolik, Newport, R.I., 1948.
Bequest of Maxim Karolik. 64.600

Reference: T.N. Maytham, "A Trove of Doughtys," *Antiques*, 1965, LXXXVIII, no. 5, pp. 681, 682 (repr. p. 685).

358.   **Two Men Fishing in a Mountain Lake**
A lake is surrounded by rocky pink and brown mountains under a cloudy gray sky. The men wear red, blue, and brown.
Oil on canvas. 14 × 16 in. (35.5 × 40.6 cm.)
Signed lower right: *T. Dought . . ./ 1837*.
Collections: Probably Henry Codman, Boston, 1847; John Amory Codman, his son, Boston; Martha Codman (Mrs. Maxim Karolik), his daughter, Newport, R.I.; Maxim Karolik, Newport, R.I., 1948.
Bequest of Maxim Karolik. 64.596

Reference: T.N. Maytham, "A Trove of Doughtys," *Antiques*, 1965, LXXXVIII, no. 5, pp. 681, 685 (repr.).

359.   **View in Paris**
fig. 212
A view from a balcony where two girls clean a table; nearby a red chair and red Persian carpets. The foreground houses are brown, the turreted building beyond green trees is red and white, all with gray roofs. The distant wooded landscape is green under a cloudy blue sky.
Oil on oval canvas. 19¼ × 17 in. (48.7 × 43.5 cm.)
Signed lower left: *T. Doughty*. Painted in 1847.
Collections: *Closure Sale*, American Art Union, New York, 1852, no. 176, bought S. Van Buren; Susan A.D. McKelvey, Boston, by 1905.
Bequest of Susan A.D. McKelvey. 64.1916

Probably painted when Doughty visited Paris in 1847.

Reference: T.N. Maytham, "A Trove of Doughtys," *Antiques*, 1965, LXXXVIII, no. 5, pp. 681, 685 (repr.).

ARTHUR GARFIELD DOVE (1880–1946) was born in Canandaigua, N.Y. He first worked as an illustrator in New York, then from 1907 to 1909 traveled and worked with Alfred Maurer and William Glackens in Europe, where he was influenced by the new Fauve and Cubist movements. He moved to Westport, Conn. in 1910, then for seven years during the 1920's lived aboard a yawl, working about Long Island. In 1938 he returned to his family home in Geneva, N.Y. for several years, then back to Long Island until his death in Centerport, N.Y.

360.
fig. 567

Long Island

A collage of twigs and leaves before a sandy dunelike hill; at the base a rank of mussel shells. A black car, cut from a magazine, drives down the crest of the hill. The background is blue.

Collage on painted panel. 15 × 20¾ in. (38.1 × 52.7 cm.)

Signed and dated on back, upper right: *Long Island/ 1925/ Dove.*

Collections: Estate of the artist; with the Downtown Gallery, New York, 1946.

Abraham Shuman Fund (Director's Discretionary Fund). 62.1128

Exhibitions: New York, Anderson Galleries, *Seven Americans*, 1925, no. 4./ New York, Downtown Gallery, *Collages Dove*, 1955, no. 6.

GUY PÈNE DU BOIS (1884–1958) was born in Brooklyn, N.Y. He attended the Chase School there from 1899 to 1905 and studied with Robert Henri and Frank Du-Mond. In Paris he painted under Steinlen in 1905–1906; he was again in France from 1924 to 1930. He worked primarily in New York, where he was art critic for many of the New York papers and editor of *Arts of Decoration*. He died in Boston.

361.
fig. 580

The Old Trouper

Half-length, nearly full front, her dress is black and pink feathers adorn her green-lined hat. The background is dark blue.

Oil on canvas. 30 × 25 in. (76.2 × 63.5 cm.)

Signed and dated lower right: *Guy Pène du Bois 42.*

Collection: Mrs. Booth Tarkington, Kennebunk, Me.

Emily L. Ainsley Fund. 46.1144

"... The model's name is [Pasquale] Devoe and she is literally an old trouper. She was about 74 in '42 and was then trying to get a job on the radio—her deafness was a drawback she was trying to overcome." (Letter from the artist, Nov. 23, 1946.)

Exhibitions: New York, National Academy of Design, *116th Annual*, 1942, no. 171./ London, Tate Gallery, *American Painting*, 1946, no. 25.

ASHER BROWN DURAND (1796–1886) was born in Jefferson Village (now Maplewood), N.J. He was apprenticed to the engraver Peter Maverick in 1812 and soon became one of the most prominent engravers of New York. In about 1836 he abandoned engraving for painting, especially of landscapes. The year 1840–1841 he spent studying in Europe, primarily in Rome, and returned to become a leader of the Hudson River School. President of the National Academy of Design from 1846 to 1861, he worked frequently in the mountainous districts of New York and New England until his death in Jefferson Village.

362.
fig. 304

View in the Catskills

Cattle graze beside a stream and under a tree that dominates an extensive green meadow. A blue sky with dark clouds is at the right.

Oil on canvas. 37¾ × 54 in. (95.8 × 137.2 cm.)

Signed and dated lower left: *A.B. Durand 1844.*

Collection: Charles D. White, New York, about 1915.

Gift of Charles D. White. 36.644

Reference: C.C. Cunningham, "American Landscapes," *MFA Bulletin*, 1938, XXXVI, no. 215, p. 39 (fig. 1; the date 1847 is an error).

Exhibitions: Pittsburgh, Pa., Carnegie Institute, *Century of American Landscape*, 1939, p. 31, no. 45./ Chicago Art Institute and New York, Whitney Museum, *Hudson River School*, 1945, no. 102 (repr. p. 44).

363.   **The Babbling Brook**
Oil on canvas. 32 × 43¼ in. (81.2 × 109.8 cm.)
Signed and dated lower right: *A B Durand/ 1851.*
M. and M. Karolik Collection. 47.1234
Reference: Karolik Catalogue, 1949, no. 105 (repr.).

364.   **Landscape with Birches**
fig. 307
Two birches on a hill overlook the green Catskill Mountains. The blue sky is cloudy.
Oil on canvas. 24 × 18 in. (61 × 45.7 cm.)
Painted about 1855.
Collections: Jonathan Sturges, New York about 1855; Mrs. Andrew Chalmers Wilson (Mary Fuller), his granddaughter, Newport, R.I.
Bequest of Mary Fuller Wilson. 63.268
Landscape with Birches and *Woodland Interior* (Cat. no. 365) were both painted for Jonathan Sturges, a collector and benefactor of Durand, probably from the series of woodland studies painted for Jonathan Sturges about 1855, of which *In the Woods* (Metropolitan Museum, repr. *Metropolitan Museum Bulletin,* New York, 1965, XXIII, no. 8, p. 270, fig. 10) is a characteristic example.

365.   **Woodland Interior**
On a steep forest mountainside, a path filled with gray and green rocks cuts through green woods. The sky is yellow.
Oil on canvas. 23¾ × 18 in. (60.3 × 45.7 cm.)
Signed lower right: *ABD.* Painted about 1855.
Collections: Same as Cat. no. 364.
Bequest of Mary Fuller Wilson. 63.269

366.   **Lake George, New York**
fig. 306
Oil on canvas. 16¾ × 23¾ in. (42.5 × 60.3 cm.)
Signed lower right: *A.B.D.*
M. and M. Karolik Collection. 47.1233
Reference: Karolik Catalogue, 1949, no. 106 (repr.).

GEORGE HENRY DURRIE (1820–1863) was born in New Haven, Conn. He began to paint portraits in 1839, and with his brother John he studied with the New Haven painter Nathaniel Jocelyn. From 1840 to 1842 he traveled through Connecticut and New Jersey as a portraitist, then settled in New Haven. By about 1850 he had begun to paint landscapes and after 1857 he concentrated on them. He died in New Haven.

367.   **David R. Van Derveer**
fig. 260
Half-length, seated and facing front, he wears a black coat and stock over a white shirt. The background is brown.
Oil on canvas. 30 × 25 in. (76.2 × 63.5 cm.)
Inscribed on back, lower center, on a palette: *Portrait of David R. Van Derveer/ Aged 50/ Painted by G. H. Durrie/ March 1842* (H and D in monogram).
Collections: Unknown family near Frenchtown, N.J.; Mr. and Mrs. Harry L. Tepper, South Orange, N.J.
Gift of Mr. and Mrs. Harry L. Tepper. 58.1365
David Van Derveer (1792–1869) was born in the family mansion on Prospect Hill, Marlboro, N.J. His profession is not known; in 1814 he married Eliza Ellis (pendant portrait, Cat. no. 368). According to Durrie's account book (*see below*), one of their two daughters, Martha Matilda, was portrayed by Durrie at the same time as the parents (location unknown).
Reference: G.H. Durrie, "Account Book," MS, Feb. 1942 (The Old Print Shop Inc., New York).

368.
fig. 259

Mrs. David R. Van Derveer (Eliza Holmes Ellis)

She is seated in half-length and faces front before a brown background. Her dress is black with a white lace collar; her cap is decorated with pink ribbon.

Oil on canvas. 30 × 25 in. (76.2 × 63.5 cm.)

Inscribed on back, lower center, on a palette: *Portrait of Mrs. David R. Vanderveer/ Aged 47/ Durrie Pinxt/ March 1842.*

Collections: Same as Cat. no. 367.

Gift of Mr. and Mrs. Harry L. Tepper. 58.1366

Eliza Holmes Ellis was born in 1795. She was described in her husband's obituary as "a lady possessed of all those beautiful and rare qualities which so well adorn the female character." She died, presumably in Marlboro, N.J. in 1858 and was buried in the Old Tennent Church. Pendant to the preceding.

Reference: G.H. Durrie, "Account Book," MS, Feb. 1842 (The Old Print Shop, Inc., New York).

369.
fig. 258

Winter Landscape: Gathering Wood

Oil on canvas. 28 × 34¼ in. (71.1 × 87 cm.)

Signed and dated lower left: *G H Durrie/ N.Haven/ 1859.*

M. and M. Karolik Collection. 46.853

Reference: *Karolik Catalogue*, 1949, no. 107 (repr.).

370.

Summer Landscape

Oil on canvas. 22 × 30 in. (55.9 × 76.2 cm.)

Signed and dated lower right: *G.H. Durrie/ 1862.*

M. and M. Karolik Collection. 47.1261

Reference: *Karolik Catalogue*, 1949, no. 108 (repr.).

FRANK DUVENECK (1848–1919) was born in Covington, Ky. of German parents, as Frank Decker, but took his stepfather's name. He left school as a youth to decorate church interiors, with early success. He studied at the Royal Academy, Munich under Wilhelm Dietz from 1870 to 1873, then returned to work in Chicago and Cincinnati again as a church decorator and as a portraitist. A Boston exhibition in 1875 was a major success, but he returned to Munich and Venice. He established his own successful school in Munich in 1878, then moved to Florence, an influential teacher. He began to etch in 1880 in Venice and was also a sculptor. In 1888 he returned to work and teach in Cincinnati until his death.

371.
fig. 412

Caucasian Soldier

Full-length, he is seated on the ground against a gray wall; cartridge pouches line his loose gray coat; his leggings are brown and he wears a black bearskin.

Oil on canvas. 50¼ × 41¼ in. (127.6 × 104.7 cm.)

Signed and dated upper left: *F. Duveneck/ Munich 1870.*

Collection: Miss Alice Hooper, Boston, 1875.

Gift of Miss Alice Hooper. 76.296

Reference: Cincinnati Art Museum, catalogue, *Exhibition of the Work of Frank Duveneck*, 1936, p. 53 (not exhibited; included in checklist).

Exhibition: probably Boston Art Club, *Duveneck*, 1875.

372.
fig. 411

The Old Professor

An elderly and spectacled man, bust-length and facing front, wears a brown coat and scarf. The background is black and brown.

Oil on canvas. 24 × 19¼ in. (61 × 48.9 cm.)

Signed and dated upper left: *FD Munich/ 1871* (initials in monogram).

Collection: Henry C. Angell, Boston, 1875.

Gift of Martha B. Angell. 19.96

The traditional title of *The Old Professor* is misleading, for the gentleman portrayed was a Munich pharmacist, Clemens von Sicherer, who also posed for Wilhelm Leibl, Philipp Helmer, and Wilhelm Trübner.

References: H.C. Angell, "Our Pictures and About Them," MS, 1909, p. 1 (owned by MFA)./ N. Heerman, *Duveneck*, Boston, 1918, p. 4 (repr. opp. p. 4 as *The Old Schoolmaster*)./ A. Burroughs, *Limners and Likenesses*, Cambridge, Mass., 1936, p. 186 (fig. 163)./ Cincinnati Art Museum, catalogue, *Exhibition of the Work of Frank Duveneck*, 1936, p. 71 (not exhibited; included in checklist)./ R.H.I. Gammell, *Twilight in Painting*, New York, 1946 (pl. 53).

Exhibitions: Boston, Massachusetts Charitable Mechanics Association, *13th Exhibition*, 1878, no. 36./ Boston, St. Botolph Club, *Duveneck, Meakin, Steele and Sharp*, 1903, no. 17.

373.

fig. 413

Girl Reading

Three-quarter length, seated and turned three-quarters left, wearing a dark brown bonnet, coat, and gloves with a red blouse, she reads a newspaper. The background is dark brown.

Oil on panel. 23¾ × 20 in. (60.3 × 50.8 cm.)
Signed and dated lower right: *F. Duveneck 1877.*
Charles Henry Hayden Fund. 23.119

Reference: Cincinnati Art Museum, catalogue, *Exhibition of the Work of Frank Duveneck*, 1936, p. 67 (not exhibited; included in checklist).

Exhibitions: Hartford, Conn., Wadsworth Atheneum, *American Painting and Sculpture of the 18th, 19th and 20th Centuries*, 1935, no. 19./ New York, Whitney Museum, *Duveneck*, 1938, no. 13.

374.

Head of a Young Girl

Bust-length, facing front, she has black hair and a black dress. The background is dark green.

Oil on canvas. 20½ × 17¼ in. (52 × 43.8 cm.)
Painted before 1880.
Collections: Joseph De Camp, Boston; Mrs. Joseph De Camp, Boston, by 1925.
Charles Henry Hayden Fund. 28.235

De Camp worked with Duveneck in Munich and Italy until his return to America in 1880.

Reference: Cincinnati Art Museum, catalogue, *Exhibition of the Work of Frank Duveneck*, 1936, p. 73 (not exhibited; included in checklist).

Exhibition: New York, Whitney Museum, *Duveneck*, 1938, no. 29 (as *Head of a Woman*).

375.

Head of a Child

Bust-length, facing front, the child wears a brown bonnet, edged in red, and a white dress. The brown background is unfinished.

Oil on canvas, mounted on board. 10½ × 10 in. (26.6 × 25.4 cm.)
Signed upper right: *FD* (in monogram).
Gift of Miss Marion C. Jackson. 29.895

Possibly a sketch of Amy Folsom, the donor's niece. The Jackson family were close friends of the Duvenecks.

Reference: Cincinnati Art Museum, catalogue, *Exhibition of the Work of Frank Duveneck*, 1936, p. 65 (not exhibited; included in checklist).

THOMAS EAKINS (1844–1916) was born in Philadelphia and began study at the Pennsylvania Academy of the Fine Arts about 1861, while taking anatomy courses at the Jefferson Medical College. In 1866 he studied in Paris with Gérôme at the École des Beaux Arts, then in 1868 and 1869 traveled in Italy and Germany, spending a winter in Spain. He settled permanently in Philadelphia in 1870, worked as a portrait and genre painter, and resumed his studies at Jefferson College. From 1876 to 1886 he taught the life class at the Academy and became its Director in 1882. When he resigned the position in 1886, he and his students formed the Philadelphia Art Students League. He died in Philadelphia. He was, with Winslow Homer, one of the leading American nineteenth-century Realist painters.

376.

fig. 441

Starting out after Rail

Two men sail a brown skiff with white sail across the blue and brown water. Beyond, other white sails and distant green trees under blue sky.

Oil on canvas. 24 × 20 in. (61 × 50.8 cm.)

Signed and dated on stern of boat: *Eakins 74.*, and lower left: *Eakins.*

Collection: Purchased from the artist by Miss Janet Wheeler, Philadelphia, 1915.

Charles Henry Hayden Fund. 35.1953

Eakins did an identical composition in watercolor, *Harry Young, of Moyamensing, and Sam Helhower, "The Pusher," going Rail Shooting* (Wichita Art Museum, Kansas) in 1874 and a horizontal version in oil called *Sailing* (Philadelphia Museum). Young and Helhower were friends of Eakins, and Moyamensing was the part of the Philadelphia marshlands on the Delaware River from which gunning parties started after birds.

References: A. Burroughs, "Catalogue of Eakins' Works," *Arts*, 1924, v, no. 6, p. 329./ L. Goodrich, *Eakins*, New York, 1933, p. 166, no. 78./ C.C. Cunningham, "A Sporting Picture by Eakins," *MFA Bulletin*, 1936, xxxiv, no. 201, pp. 11–12 (repr. p. 12)./ R. McKinney, *Eakins*, New York, 1942 (repr. p. 69).

Exhibitions: Paris, Goupil Gallery, about 1874./ Philadelphia, Pennsylvania Academy of the Fine Arts, *Eakins Memorial*, 1917–1918, no. 63./ New York, Museum of Modern Art, *Art in Our Time*, 1939, no. 30 (repr.)./ Washington, D.C., Phillips Memorial Gallery, *Emotional Design*, 1940, no. 25./ Utica, N.Y., Munson-Williams-Proctor Institute, *Homer-Eakins*, 1946–1947, no. 17./ Milwaukee Art Center, *Sports and Adventure in American Art*, 1947, no. 29./ Boston, MFA, *American Marine Paintings*, 1955, no. 20 (repr.)./ Philadelphia, Pennsylvania Academy of the Fine Arts, *150th Anniversary*, 1955, no. 97 (repr. p. 65).

377.

fig. 444

Walt Whitman

A sketch. The head of the elderly man faces front on a brown background.

Oil on panel. 5¼ × 5¼ in. (13.3 × 13.3 cm.)

Painted about 1887.

Collections: Mrs. Thomas Eakins, Philadelphia; Samuel Murray, Philadelphia.

Helen and Alice Colburn Fund. 30.122

Walt Whitman (1819–1892), American poet, was born in West Hills, N.Y. First a free-lance journalist, he published *Leaves of Grass*, one of the greatest contributions to American literature, in 1855. Further significant works were *Drum-Taps* (1865), a collection of war poems, and, in prose, *Specimen Days* (1882), again concerning the Civil War and his own reminiscences. This picture is the first study and color scheme for the large portrait, dated 1887, in the Pennsylvania Academy of the Fine Arts, Philadelphia.

Reference: L. Goodrich, *Eakins*, New York, 1933, p. 179, no. 221.

Exhibition: Philadelphia, Pennsylvania Academy of the Fine Arts, *Eakins Memorial*, 1917–1918, no. 2.

378.

fig. 442

The Dean's Roll-Call

The bearded figure stands full-length, turned slightly left, and holds an open brown folder; his black robes with green trim are those of a Doctor of Medicine. The background is a warm gray-brown.

Oil on canvas. 84 × 42 in. (213.4 × 106.7 cm.)

Signed and dated lower right: *Eakins/ 1899.*

Collections: Mrs. James W. Holland, wife of the sitter, Philadelphia; Rupert Sargent Holland, Lucy Sargent Holland Putnam, and Leicester Bodine Holland, children of the sitter, Philadelphia.

Abraham Shuman Fund. 43.211

Dr. James William Holland (1849–1922), born in Nashville, Tenn., was a noted urologist and Professor of Chemistry at Jefferson Medical College, Philadelphia, after 1855. He was also Dean of the College for thirty years and is portrayed reading the roll of candidates to receive their diplomas, a practice which he conducted religiously. The portrait was originally painted for the College but was not accepted, owing to the Dean's tense, almost haggard expression. Eakins, as a friendly gesture, gave the picture to the subject's wife. (Letter from Leicester Holland, Oct. 24, 1943.)

References: A. Burroughs, "Catalogue of Eakins' Works," *Arts*, 1924, v, no. 6, p. 330./ L. Goodrich, *Eakins*, New York, 1933, pp. 115, 190, no. 327 (pl. 52)./ B.N. Parker, "The Dean's Roll-call by Eakins," *MFA Bulletin*, 1943, XLI, no. 246, p. 60 (repr. cover)./ L.E. Scanlon, "Eakins as Functionalist," *College Art Journal*, 1960, XIX, no. 4, p. 325 (fig. 3).

Exhibitions: Philadelphia, Pennsylvania Academy of the Fine Arts, *69th Annual*, 1900, no. 310./ —, *Eakins Memorial*, 1917–1918, no. 132./ Washington, D.C., National Gallery, Chicago Art Institute, and Philadelphia Museum of Art, *Eakins*, 1961–1962, no. 76 (repr. p. 109).

379.   Mrs. Gilbert L. Parker
fig. 443

Half-length and turned slightly left, an elderly lady wears a high-collared brown dress with a yoke of white lace. The background is brown.
Oil on canvas. 24 × 20 in. (61 × 50.8 cm.)
Inscribed on back: *To his friend/ Mrs. Parker/ Thomas Eakins/ 1910.*
Collections: Gilbert S. Parker, the sitter's son, Philadelphia; Ernest L. Parker, his brother, Philadelphia.
Charles Henry Hayden Fund. Res. 32.28

Mrs. Gilbert Lafayette Parker was the wife of Dr. Gilbert L. Parker, an old friend of Eakins. Her sons, Gilbert and Ernest Parker, were successive Curators of Paintings at the Pennsylvania Academy of the Fine Arts. The companion portrait of her husband, formerly owned by Miss Katherine Parker, the sitter's granddaughter, is at present unlocated.

References: A. Burroughs, "Catalogue of Eakins' Works," *Arts*, 1924, v, no. 6, p. 333./ L. Goodrich, "Eakins-Realist," *Arts*, 1929, XVI, no. 1 (repr. p. 79)./ —, *Eakins*, New York, 1933, p. 205, no. 470./ R. McKinney, *Eakins*, New York, 1942 (repr. p. 94)./ W.S. Baldinger, "The Art of Eakins, Homer and Ryder: A Social Revaluation," *Art Quarterly*, 1946, IX, no. 3, pp. 227–228, 231 (fig. 3).

Exhibitions: Pittsburgh, Pa., Carnegie Institute, *16th Annual*, 1912, no. 95./ New York, Metropolitan Museum, *Eakins*, 1917, no. 54 (repr.)./ Philadelphia, Pennsylvania Academy of the Fine Arts, *Eakins*, 1917–1918, no. 45 (repr. p. 30)./ New York, Babcock Galleries, *Eakins*, 1929./ Washington, D.C., National Gallery, Chicago Art Institute, and Philadelphia Museum of Art, *Eakins*, 1961–1962, no. 96 (repr. p. 129).

RALPH EARL

(1751–1801), born in Worcester County, Mass., had a studio in New Haven, Conn. by 1775. A Loyalist, in 1778 he left for England, studied with Benjamin West in London, and worked there, in Norfolk, and in Windsor until his return to America in 1785. Then, as a portrait painter, he traveled and worked extensively from Vermont to New York, especially in Connecticut, until his death in Bolton, Conn.

380.   Ezra l'Hommedieu
fig. 101

Half-length and turned three-quarters right, he sits in a red upholstered armchair before a red drapery and shelves of brown leather-bound law books; he holds a sheet of white paper in his right hand. He wears a dark gray jacket and light gray waistcoat.
Oil on canvas. 33 × 27 in. (83.8 × 68.6 cm.)
Signed and dated lower left: *R. Earl Pinxt 1792.*
Collection: Descended through the sitter's family to Mrs. F. Carrington Weems, Manchester, Mass., 1949.
Lent by Mrs. F. Carrington Weems, 1949. 130.54

Ezra l'Hommedieu (1734–1811), lawyer, legislator, and agriculturist, was born at Southold, New York, the son of Benjamin and Martha Bourne l'Hommedieu. He graduated from Yale in 1754, was admitted to the bar, and was later a framer of the Constitution of 1777. He was a member of all the N.Y. Provincial Congresses, of the Assembly until 1783, and thereafter, at the state Senate. He was a delegate to the Continental Congress and in 1784 became Clerk of Suffolk County. In addition, he was the principal author of the University of the State of N.Y. as reconstituted in 1787. The New-York Historical Society owns a replica of the portrait by Earl, signed and dated 1792.

381. **Huldah Bradley**
fig. 102

Three-quarter length, seated and turned half right, the young girl wears a pink dress with a white sash and wide collar; she holds a green parasol in her lap. Behind, a green landscape slopes down to blue water under a blue sky with pink and black clouds.
Oil on canvas. 44 × 32 in. (111.7 × 81.2 cm.)
Signed and dated lower left: *R. Earl/Pinxt. 1794.*
Collections: William Bradley, the sitter's grandnephew, Greenfield Hill, Fairfield, Conn.; Mrs. E.B. Morehouse, his daughter, Greenfield Hill; Louis E. Morehouse, her son, Fairfield.
Ellen Kelleran Gardner Fund. 40.3

Huldah Bradley (1773–1842), daughter of Squire Samuel and Sarah Wakeman Bradley, was born in Greenfield Hill, Fairfield, Conn. She never married and lived in the family home until her death. When this painting hung with its pendant portrait of her sister *Lucy Bradley* (Detroit Institute of Arts), the two landscapes formed a continuation of each other as a view from Greenfield Hill toward Long Island Sound. Earl painted portraits of her parents, brother, and sister-in-law in 1788 (*see below*, Yale, *Earl*, nos. 1–4).
Reference: B.N. Parker, "Huldah Bradley," *MFA Bulletin*, 1940, XXXVIII, no. 228, pp. 54–55 (repr. p. 54).
Exhibitions: Yale University Art Gallery, *Earl*, 1935, p. 8, no. 5 (repr. p. 11)./ Rhode Island School of Design Museum, *Old and New England*, 1945, no. 27 (repr. p. 22)./ New York, Whitney Museum and Worcester, Mass., Art Museum, *Earl*, 1945–1946, no. 35.

SETH EASTMAN (1808–1875)

382. **Sioux Indians Breaking up Camp**
fig. 287

Oil on canvas. 25½ × 35 in. (64.8 × 88.9 cm.)
Old label on the original stretcher is inscribed: *Sioux Indians Breaking up Camp Am. Art Union, painted by Seth Eastman U S A Distributed December 22, 1848.* Painted before 1848.
M. and M. Karolik Collection. 46.850
Reference: *Karolik Catalogue*, 1949, no. 109 (repr.).

JOHN WHETTEN EHNINGER (1827–1889)

383. **Turkey Shoot**

Oil on canvas. 25 × 43½ in. (63.5 × 110.5 cm.)
Signed and dated lower right: *J.W. Ehninger N.A. 1879.*
M. and M. Karolik Collection. 46.854
Reference: *Karolik Catalogue*, 1949, no. 110 (repr.).

JACOB EICHHOLTZ (1776–1842)

384. **Man in a Yellow Waistcoat**

Oil on canvas. 30 × 25¼ in. (76.2 × 64.1 cm.)
Inscribed and dated on the back: *Eichholtz 1824.*
M. and M. Karolik Collection. 47.1136
Reference: *Karolik Catalogue*, 1949, no. 111 (repr.).

385. **An Incident of the Revolution**

Oil on canvas. 48½ × 66 in. (107.9 × 165.1 cm.)
Signed and dated lower right on step: *J. Eichholtz—1831.*

M. and M. Karolik Collection. 47.1149
Reference: Karolik Catalogue, 1949, no. 112 (repr.).

LOUIS MICHEL EILSHEMIUS (1864–1941) was born in Laurel Hill Manor, near Newark, N.J. of well-to-do parents. He studied in Dresden from 1875 to 1881, then attended Cornell University from 1882 to 1884. He studied at the Art Students League in New York from 1884 to 1886 and with Robert Minor, and in 1886–1887 was at the Académie Julian. He lived in New York except for frequent travels to Europe and to North Africa, Samoa, and the South Seas. In despair at his lack of recognition he gave up painting in 1921. In the 1920's and 1930's his work developed an active following which included both French and American painters such as Matisse, Duchamps, Stella, Lachaise, and Demuth. He died in New York.

386.
fig. 521

Fishing, Adirondacks

A man fishes from a boat in a blue pond set in a yellow-green landscape with brown buildings. Distant blue hills under a gray sky.
Oil on canvas. 20 × 30 in. (50.8 × 76.2 cm.)
Signed lower left: *Elshemus.* Painted about 1900.
Collection: Purchased from the artist by Valentine Dudensing, New York, about 1930.
Charles Henry Hayden Fund. 35.28

The soft delicate style is characteristic of his work about 1900. From 1890 to 1914 he simplified his signature to "Elshemus," thinking that the longer form encouraged criticism. A similar subject in watercolor is called *Arkville, Catskill, N.Y.* (Mr. and Mrs. Laurance Rockefeller, New York.)
Reference: W. Schack, *And He Sat Among the Ashes,* New York, 1939, p. 145 (repr. p. 139).

387.

The Startled Nymphs

Two women. One reclines on the brown shore, the other stands in the green water in a green and brown landscape touched with the white of moonlight. The distant mountain is blue and the clouded sky is brown.
Oil on cardboard. 18¼ × 28½ in. (46.3 × 72.3 cm.)
Signed and dated lower left: *Eilshemius 1914.* Inscribed on back: *The Startled Nymphs/ by Louis M. Eilshemius/ 118 E. 57th St./ N.Y. City.*
Collections: Bought from the artist by Julius Zirinsky, New York, 1937–1938; James N. Rosenberg, Scarsdale, New York, 1942.
Gift of Mr. and Mrs. James N. Rosenberg in memory of Joseph M. Herman. 46.560

CHARLES LORING ELLIOTT (1812–1868)

388.

Pieter van Buren (formerly Sanford Thayer)

Oil on canvas. 30¼ × 25½ in. (76.8 × 64.8 cm.)
Inscribed on back of original canvas before relining: *Painted by C.L. Elliott/ 1842/ And presented to S. Thayer/ by the Artist.*
M. and M. Karolik Collection. 47.1160

The earlier identification of the sitter as Sanford Thayer (1820–1880), painter and friend of Elliott, was assumed on the basis of the inscription. The latter part of the inscription, although later and in another hand, may well be true, but indicates only ownership. In 1842 Thayer was only twenty-two; this man is elderly. Identification as Pieter van Buren (1768–1860) of Kinderhook, then Cherry Valley, New York, shown at seventy-four, was made by Mrs. Nigel Cholmeley-Jones of Westport, Conn., great-great-granddaughter of van Buren, whose sister, Mrs. Sturgis Whitman, New York, has a nearly identical family portrait of Pieter van Buren. From photographs, the softer more generalized execution of the Whitman picture suggests that it is a copy, perhaps contemporary with the Boston portrait.
Reference: Karolik Catalogue, 1949, no. 113 (repr.).

JOHN JOSEPH ENNEKING (1841–1916), born in Minster, O., studied lithography in Boston after serving in the Civil War. From 1873 to 1876 he studied painting in Munich and Venice, then under Bonnat and Daubigny in Paris. Except for another year of work in Paris and Holland in 1878, he worked as a landscape painter in Boston until his death. Stylistically he was influenced by both the Barbizon and Impressionist painters.

389.   **Autumn Sunset**

Deep red and yellow sunset seen through trees, bare except for the oaks, which retain some dark red leaves.
Oil on chipboard. 12¼ × 18¼ in. (31.1 × 46.3 cm.)
Signed and dated indistinctly lower right: *Enneking 94*.
Gift of the Estate of Nellie P. Carter. 35.1685

390.   **Spring Hillside**
fig. 511

Pink and white apple trees blossom on a green wooded hillside above a blue stream.
Oil on canvas. 24½ × 34½ in. (62.2 × 87.7 cm.)
Signed and dated lower right: *Enneking* and *Enneking 99–2.*
Gift of the Heirs of George Adams Kettell. 13.474

Having signed and dated the painting, Enneking folded its right side back over the stretcher and signed it again without a date.

Exhibition: University of New Mexico Art Gallery and San Francisco, M.H. de Young Memorial Museum, *Impressionism in America*, 1965, no. 10 (repr. p. 27).

STEPHEN MORGAN ETNIER was born in York, Pa. in 1903 and studied painting at the Pennsylvania Academy of the Fine Arts from 1925 to 1929, then privately with Rockwell Kent and John Carroll. He has traveled in the Americas, Europe, and the West Indies, has worked in New York, and now lives in South Harpswell, Me.

391.   **Railroad Cut, Brunswick, Maine**

The cut and tracks beyond the gray signals are brown, as is the rest of the landscape. Gray clouds in a blue sky.
Oil on canvas. 34 × 30 in. (86.3 × 76.2 cm.)
Signed and dated lower right: *Stephen Etnier '41.*
Charles Henry Hayden Fund. 42.113

Exhibitions: Dayton Art Institute, *Railroad in Painting*, 1949, no. 21./ Rockland, Me., William A. Farnsworth Art Museum, *Etnier*, 1953 (repr.).

PHILIP EVERGOOD, born in New York in 1901, left Cambridge University in England in 1921 to study at the Slade School, London, with Henry Tonks and Howard Thomas. He studied at the Art Students League, New York, in 1923 with Von Schlegell and Luks, and in 1924 at the Académie Julian, Paris. He traveled in France, Italy, and Spain in 1924–1925 and 1930–1931, then returned to work and teach in New York and Michigan until 1952. Also a lecturer and writer, he has since lived in Southbury, Conn.

392.   **Fat of the Land**

A road lined with bare brown trees runs between pink and green fields, where dilapidated gray and red farm buildings stand. White and yellow clouds appear in a blue sky.
Oil on canvas. 28 × 46 in. (71.1 × 116.8 cm.)
Signed lower right: *Philip Evergood*. Painted in 1941.
Charles Henry Hayden Fund. 41.687

Painted in Michigan in the early summer of 1941. (Letter from the artist, Jan. 21, 1942.)

Exhibitions: Chicago Art Institute, *52nd Annual*, 1942, no. 67./ Toronto Art Gallery, *Museum's Choice*, 1945, no. 13./ New York, American Contemporary Art Gallery, *20 Years—Evergood*, 1946, p. 30 (repr. p. 53).

THOMAS CHARLES FARRER (1839–1891), born in London, was elder brother of the better known watercolorist Henry Farrer. Active in New York after 1861, he exhibited at the National Academy between 1867 and 1871, showing flower pieces and landscapes. He had returned to London by 1872. A frequent exhibitor at the Royal Academy, he was an active printmaker and water-colorist. Few works in oil are known. He died in London.

393. **Mount Hope Bay, Rhode Island**

fig. 291

The bright blue bay is surrounded by rich green meadows dotted with dark green trees; a few white clouds float in a blue sky.
Oil on canvas. 11¾ × 25 in. (29.8 × 64 cm.)
Signed and dated lower right: *TCF 63* (initials in monogram).
Collection: Maxim Karolik, Newport, R.I., 1955.
M. and M. Karolik Collection. 62.265

Although *Mt. Hope Bay, R.I.* is inscribed on the stretcher, there is no record that Farrer strayed from the New York-Hudson River area. The scene does bear similarities however with that area of Narragansett Bay formed by the north end of Aquidneck Island on which Newport is situated. The painting has long been anonymous, the monogram having been deciphered as "TC" or its reverse. The true identification was made by Miss Maria K. Naylor of New York on the basis of style and familiarity with the monogram.

LYONEL CHARLES FEININGER (1871–1956) was born in New York. In 1887 he studied music in Hamburg but abandoned that career for painting, which he pursued in Hamburg, in the Berlin Academy under Waldemar Friedrich until 1891, and under Colarossi in Paris in 1892–1893. Until 1907 he was a cartoonist and illustrator for German, French, and Chicago newspapers. After working in Berlin, he joined the Blaue Reiter group with Klee and Kandinsky in 1913, then taught painting and graphics at the Bauhaus, Weimar, from 1919 to 1932. He returned in 1937 to New York, where he worked until his death.

394. **Regler Church, Erfurt**

fig. 583

A composition of geometric planes, the two towers are yellow, brown, and blue. From the left streams yellow and pink light, making shadows of blue, gray, and green. Below is brown and yellow.
Oil on canvas. 50 × 40¼ in. (127 × 102.2 cm.)
Signed upper left: *Feininger*. Painted in 1930.
Collections: Magistrate of Dessau, Germany; Anhaltisches Landesmuseum, Dessau, until 1939; G. David Thompson, Pittsburgh, Pa., 1953.
Charles Henry Hayden Fund. 57.198

Mrs. Julia Feininger has given the date for the painting. The medieval church was so called after the Regler family of Erfurt but was dedicated to St. Augustine.

References: H. Devree, "New York Letter," *Magazine of Art*, 1941, XXXIV, no. 4, p. 219 (repr. p. 209 as *Village Church 1926*)./ J.W. Lane, "Feininger's Counterpoint in Paint," *Art News*, 1941, XL, no. 3, p. 51 (repr. p. 39 as *Village Church*)./ H. Hess, *Feininger*, New York, 1961, p. 146, no. 324.

Exhibitions: Detroit Institute of Arts, *Feininger*, 1941, no. 9 (repr. as *Village Church*)./ New York, Buchholz and Willard Galleries, *Feininger*, 1941, no. 9 (repr.)./ Hartford, Conn., Wadsworth Atheneum, *Fifty Painters of Architecture*, 1947, no. 18 (pl. 7 as *Cathedral*)./ Cleveland Museum, *Feininger*, 1951, no. 20./ Cleveland Museum and circulated in the U.S., *Feininger Memorial*, 1959–1961, no. 42.

395. **Sunset**

fig. 582

A composition in abstract angular planes of blue and yellow with orange and brown.
Oil on canvas. 19 × 30½ in. (48.2 × 77.5 cm.)
Signed and dated lower right: *Feininger/ '30*. Written on back: *Lyonel Feininger 1930 Sunset*.
Charles Henry Hayden Fund. 41.568

"The Sunset was painted in 1930, in Dessau [Germany], during my connection with the former Bauhaus. It represents, as to subject, the estuary of a small river [the Rega, on the Baltic Coast], with the sea in the back. During twelve successive years I spent several months on the Baltic Coast at Deep; the Sunset is one of a number of paintings and water colors made from experiences I had at the place." (Letter from the artist, July 7, 1941.)

Reference: H. Hess, *Feininger*, New York, 1961, no. 322.

Exhibitions: Berlin, Nationalgalerie, *Feininger*, 1931, no. 96./ Cleveland Museum, *Feininger*, 1951, no. 19 (pl. v)./ Deerfield, Mass., Deerfield Academy, Hilson Gallery, *Feininger*, 1955, no. 7./ Cambridge, Mass., Busch-Reisinger Museum, *Feininger*, 1958, p. 3./ Cleveland Museum and circulated in the U.S., *Feininger Memorial*, 1959–1961, no. 41./ England, York, City Art Gallery and London, Arts Council Gallery, *Feininger*, 1960, no. 21./ Dallas, Museum for Contemporary Arts, *Feininger*, 1963, no. 28.

ROBERT FEKE (active before 1741–after 1750) was probably born in Oyster Bay, N.Y. about 1705. Except for the influence of John Smibert, nothing is known of his training in portraiture. First recorded by a signed and dated work in Boston in 1741, he then lived primarily in Newport, R.I., although he was in Philadelphia in 1745 and 1750 and in Boston in 1748. He disappeared in 1750; tradition says he died in the West Indies, and his daughter's marriage certificate of 1767 describes him as deceased.

396.
fig. 21

John Channing

Three-quarter length, standing turned three-quarters right, he leans upon a stone parapet. His coat is green and his waistcoat black. A cloudy sky beyond the brown background.
Oil on canvas. 50 × 40½ in. (127 × 102.8 cm.)
Painted about 1747–1749.
Collections: William Ellery Channing, the sitter's grandson, Boston; Frederick Augustus Eustis, his son-in-law; William E.C. Eustis, his son, Milton, Mass.; Augustus Eustis, his son, Milton.
Gift of Augustus Eustis. 64.1008

John Channing was born in 1714, son of John and Mary Antram Channing of Newport, R.I. A merchant and importer of dry goods from England, he had considerable means, but was in reduced circumstances when he died in Newport in 1771. From its style, his portrait was probably painted either in 1747 or in 1749, before or after Feke's Boston visit of 1748.

References: E.T. Channing, *Notes Concerning the Channing Family*, Boston, 1895, p. 4./ H.W. Foote, *Feke*, Cambridge, Mass., 1930, pp. 85, 132, no. 1 (repr.)./ —, "Feke," *Art in America*, 1947, xxxv, no. 1, p. 65.

Exhibition: New York, Whitney Museum, Huntington, N.Y., Heckscher Art Museum, and Boston, MFA, *Feke*, 1946, no. 31.

397.
fig. 22

Mrs. John Channing (Mary Chaloner)

Seated in three-quarter length and turned three-quarters left, she holds red flowers. Her dress is green and white, the chair and curtain are red, the background is brown.
Oil on canvas. 50 × 40½ in. (127 × 102.6 cm.)
Painted about 1747–1749.
Collections: Same as Cat. no. 396.
Gift of Augustus Eustis. 64.1009

Mary Chaloner (1721–1790) was the daughter of Ninyon Chaloner of Newport. Her first husband, Dr. James Robinson, died in 1745, and in 1746 she married John Channing. Her portrait was doubtless painted with its pendant (Cat. no. 396), in 1747 or 1749. Another portrait of her, also by Feke, is owned by Henry M. Channing, Sherborn, Mass.

References: E.T. Channing, *Notes Concerning the Channing Family*, Boston, 1895, pp. 4–5./ H.W. Foote, *Feke*, Cambridge, Mass., 1930, pp. 85, 133, no. 1 (repr. opp. p. 86)./ —, "Feke," *Art in America*, 1947, xxxv, no. 1, p. 65.

Exhibition: New York, Whitney Museum, Huntington, N.Y., Heckscher Art Museum, and Boston, MFA, *Feke*, 1946, no. 32.

398. **Isaac Winslow**
fig. 23

Three-quarter length, turned three-quarters right, he stands outdoors, his right hand resting on a wall. With his left hand he gestures to the blue sea. His coat is brown over a long gold-embroidered white waistcoat. Behind, a tree and view of distant hills are under a blue and pink sky.

Oil on canvas. 50 × 40 in. (127 × 101.6 cm.)
Painted about 1748.

Collections: Elizabeth Winslow Pickering, great-niece of the sitter; Arthur Pickering, her son, Roxbury, Mass., in 1873; Susan Howard Pickering, his daughter, Boston; Russell Wiles, Chicago, 1936.

Gift in memory of the sitter's granddaughter (Mary Russell Winslow Bradford, 1793–1899), by her great-grandson, Russell Wiles. 42.424

The style and the subject's apparent age indicate that Isaac Winslow (1709–1777) was painted by Feke in 1748 or 1749, when Feke was in Boston and when Winslow was thirty-nine. In 1755 Joseph Blackburn painted a portrait of Winslow, his first wife, Lucy Waldo, and their two children (Cat. no. 144), and in 1774 John Singleton Copley portrayed him and his second wife, Jemima Debuke (Cat. no. 296). For details of Winslow's life, see the descriptions listed under these two catalogue numbers. Until the 1930's, the painting was thought to be by Copley.

References: A.T. Perkins, *Copley*, Boston, 1873, supplement, p. 24./ B.N. Parker and A.B. Wheeler, *Copley*, Boston, 1938, p. 257./ B.N. Parker, "Member of the Winslow Family in Boston," *MFA Bulletin*, 1942, XL, no. 241, p. 87 (repr.)./ J.T. Flexner, *First Flowers of Our Wilderness*, Boston, 1947, pp. 144–146, 308, 349 (repr. p. 145)./ —, "Feke," *Magazine of Art*, 1947, XL, no. 1, p. 7 (repr. p. 6)./ H.W. Foote, "Feke," *Art in America*, 1947, XXXV, no. 1, p. 68./ H. Comstock, "American Painting in the 18th Century," *Connoisseur*, 1955, CXXXIV, p. 296 (fig. 3)./ —, "Feke and the Nelsons of Virginia," *Antiques*, 1959, LXXV, no. 5, p. 458.

Exhibitions: New York, Whitney Museum, Huntington, N.Y., Heckscher Museum, and Boston, MFA, *Feke*, 1946, no. 30 (repr.)./ London, Tate Gallery, *American Painting*, 1946, no. 84./ Cincinnati Art Museum, *Rediscoveries in American Art*, 1955, no. 43.

ERASTUS SALISBURY FIELD (1805–1900) was born in Leverett, Mass. He was largely self-taught except for a few months in the New York studio of Samuel F.B. Morse in 1824–1825. Until after 1850 he worked as an itinerant portraitist in Massachusetts, the Connecticut Valley, and from 1841 to 1848 in New York City. After 1859 he abandoned portrait painting for religious, contemporary, or historical subjects. He lived in Sunderland, Mass. until his death.

399. **Joseph Moore and His Family**
fig. 249

Life size and full-length, the four children stand by the seated adults. They all wear black with white accessories, excepting the brown trousers of the youngest boys and the girl's white dress. The furniture is brown and the carpet is yellow, patterned in red and green; behind in the gray wall the shutters are green, the curtains red.

Oil on canvas. 82¾ × 93¼ in. (210.2 × 238.1 cm.)
Painted in 1839.

Collection: Helen E. Farrar, great-granddaughter of Joseph Moore, Sherborn, Mass.

M. and M. Karolik Collection. 58.25

Joseph Moore (1804–1855) was the son of George Francis and Ellen Louisa Moore of Windham, Vt. He grew up in Ware, Mass., where in 1828 he married Almira Gallond. He was a hatter, and in summer a traveling dentist. Almira Moore (1807–1892) was the daughter of Jeremiah and Dorcas Babbit Gallond of Petersham, Mass. They had three children, two of whom are portrayed: on the right Joseph Lauriston, born in 1829, grandfather of Helen Farrar, and George Francis, probably the boy behind his father, born in 1835 only to die in 1842. Their daughter, Ellen Louisa, was born in 1843. The boy and girl beside Mrs. Moore are thought to be Frederick Babbit Cook, born in 1835, and Louisa Ellen Cook, born in 1837, the children of Almira's younger sister, Louisa Ellen (Mrs. Nathaniel Cook), who died in 1838. The date of 1839 is derived from the style and from the ages of George Francis Moore and Louisa Ellen Cook.

Reference: T.N. Maytham, "Two Faces of New England Portrait Painting," *MFA Bulletin*, 1963, LXI, no. 323, pp. 31–38 (fig. 1).

Exhibitions: Brussels, World's Fair, *Universal and International Exhibition*, 1958, no. 81./ Boston, MFA, *New Paintings in the M. and M. Karolik Collection*, 1962–1963./ Williamsburg, Va., Abby Aldrich Rockefeller Folk Art Collection, *Field*, 1963, no. 76.

400.
fig. 250

The Garden of Eden
Oil on canvas. 34¾ × 46 in. (88.2 × 116.8 cm.)
Painted about 1860–1870.
M. and M. Karolik Collection. 48.1027
Reference: *Karolik Catalogue*, 1949, no. 114 (repr.).

401.
fig. 251

Miss Gilmore (attributed to Field)
Seated in a red chair full-length, facing front, the young girl wears a blue dress, trimmed in white, with red slippers, and several strands of pearls. In her hands she holds a patterned fan and a book. A gray cat rests at her feet on the carpet of green, red, and blue. Beside her is a table and book. The background is brown.
Oil on canvas. 54 × 34 in. (137.2 × 86.3 cm.)
Painted about 1845.
Collections: Mr. and Mrs. Hilliker, Shelton, Conn., until about 1949; Maxim Karolik, Newport, R.I., 1960.
Bequest of Maxim Karolik. 64.451

Possibly done by Field when he was in New York, as suggested by Mrs. Mary Black. A softness of style prevents a firm attribution to Field. Miss Gilmore's first name is traditionally given as Margaret.

Exhibition: Williamsburg, Va., Abby Aldrich Rockefeller Folk Art Collection, *Field*, 1963, no. 71.

ERNEST FIENE

was born in Elberfeld, Germany in 1894 and emigrated to the United States in 1912. In New York he studied at the National Academy of Design from 1914 to 1918, at the Beaux Arts Institute, and in 1923 at the Art Students League. In 1929 and 1932 respectively he worked at the Académie de la Grande Chaumière, Paris, and learned fresco painting in Florence. Since then he has worked and taught primarily in New York.

402.

Zinnias and Apples
A jug of yellow, red, and pink zinnias, a basket of apples, and a green bottle on a purple table with a colored cloth stand before a wall which is half-covered by drapery.
Oil on canvas. 25 × 30 in. (63.5 × 76.2 cm.)
Signed and dated lower right: *Ernest Fiene. 1921.*
Collection: Purchased from the artist by John T. Spaulding, Boston.
Bequest of John T. Spaulding. 48.541
Reference: W. Murrell, *Fiene*, Woodstock, N.Y., 1922 (pl. 6).
Exhibition: Boston, MFA, *The Spaulding Collections*, 1948, no. 25.

ALVAN FISHER

(1792–1863) was born in Needham, Mass. He studied painting in Boston with John Ritto Penniman, was painting portraits by 1814, and in 1815 established himself as a landscape and genre painter. He worked throughout New England; from 1822 to 1825 he lived in Hartford, Conn. and traveled in the southern states. In 1825 he visited Europe, studied briefly in Paris, then in 1826 returned to settle permanently in Dedham, near Boston, where he died.

403. **Lakes and Mountains**
Oil on canvas. 25 × 32¾ in. (63.5 × 83.2 cm.)
Painted in the 1820's or 1830's.
M. and M. Karolik Collection. 47.1147
Reference: Karolik Catalogue, 1949, no. 116 (repr.).

404. **Sugar Loaf Mountain**
Oil on canvas. 25½ × 33 in. (64.8 × 83.8 cm.)
Signed and dated lower right: *A. Fisher 1821.*
M. and M. Karolik Collection. 47.1154
Reference: Karolik Catalogue, 1949, no. 115 (repr.).

405. **Corn Husking Frolic**
fig. 227
A hay-filled barn in brown and yellow, and beyond, a moonlit farmyard. The interior, illuminated by a lantern, shows people dressed in red, white, and green.
Oil on panel. 27¾ × 24¼ in. (70.5 × 61.6 cm.)
Inscribed on back, center left: *A. Fisher/ To the care of H. Hovey & Co./ Boston.*
Painted in 1828–1829.
Collections: Josiah Putnam Bradlee, Boston, 1829; Maxim Karolik, Newport, R.I., 1957.
M. and M. Karolik Collection. 62.270

An old card, once attached to the back of the painting, read: "Husking Frolic. Fisher, July 3, 1828." In his "Catalogue of Paintings Executed After My Return From Europe in 1826," MS, under 1829, p. 3, Fisher wrote: "Husking Frolic sold J. P. Bradlee—$100 pd."

Exhibitions: Boston Athenaeum, *Exhibition,* 1829, no. 98./ Hartford, Conn., Wadsworth Atheneum, *Harvest of Plenty,* 1963, no. 14.

406. **Portrait of a Gentleman**
fig. 226
Half-length, turned three-quarters left, the elderly man is seated in a blue and yellow upholstered armchair; he wears a black suit and tie and holds an open letter in his left hand. The background is brown.
Oil on canvas. 34 × 27 in. (86.3 × 68.6 cm.)
Painted about 1835–1840.
Bequest of Maxim Karolik. 64.452

Painting style, costume, and furniture design indicate a date of about 1835–1840 for this portrait and its pendant (Cat. no. 407), after Fisher had finally settled in Boston. Portions of an inscription, "J.Br—," probably the sitter's name, remain on the letter.

407. **Portrait of a Lady**
Half-length, turned three-quarters right and seated in a brown and yellow upholstered armchair, she wears a black dress with a white lace bonnet and cuffs. The background is brown.
Oil on canvas. 34 × 27 in. (86.3 × 68.6 cm.)
Painted about 1835–1840.
Bequest of Maxim Karolik. 64.453
Pendant to the preceding (Cat. no. 406).

408. **Lake in the Mountains with Hunters**
fig. 225
In a landscape of blue mountains and nearby green hills, two hunters in dark clothes pose with their hounds; in the distance, right, a man rides a gray horse.
Oil on canvas. 14 × 17 in. (35.5 × 43.2 cm.)
Signed and dated lower right on rock: *AF 1857* (?) (initials in monogram).
Collections: Codman Family Collection, Boston; Martha Codman Karolik, Newport, R.I.; Maxim Karolik, Newport, 1948.
Bequest of Maxim Karolik. 64.602

JOHN F. FRANCIS (about 1810–1885)

409.   **Three Children**
Oil on canvas. 42 × 42 in. (106.7 × 106.7 cm.)
Signed and dated on back before relining: *Jno F. Francis pt 1840*.
M. and M. Karolik Collection. 47.1142

Reference: *Karolik Catalogue*, 1949, no. 117 (repr.).

410.   **Still-Life with Wine Bottles and Basket of Fruit**
Oil on canvas. 25 × 30 in. (63.5 × 76.2 cm.)
Signed and dated lower right: *J.F. Francis Pt 1857*.
M. and M. Karolik Collection. 47.1170

Reference: *Karolik Catalogue*, 1949, no. 118 (repr.).

411.   **Still-Life with Apples and Chestnuts**
fig. 292
Oil on canvas. 25 × 30 in. (63.5 × 76.2 cm.)
Signed and dated lower left: *J.F. Francis Pt 1859*.
M. and M. Karolik Collection. 47.1145

Reference: *Karolik Catalogue*, 1949, no. 119 (repr.).

THOMAS FRANSIOLI was born in Seattle, Wash. in 1906. He received an architectural degree at the University of Pennsylvania, then started to paint in 1947 at the Art Students League, New York. He has traveled extensively in Europe and now lives in Falls Village, Conn.

412.   **Beacon Hill**
fig. 581
A view of Boston from across the blue-gray river. The sky is gray with clouds, the buildings below are red and gray, and the trees on the green river bank in the foreground are brown.
Oil on canvas. 20 × 30 in. (50.8 × 76.2 cm.)
Signed and dated lower right: *T.F./ 1947*.
Abraham Shuman Fund. 48.284

Exhibitions: Rockland, Me., William A. Farnsworth Art Museum, *Paintings by Fransioli*, 1954, no. 4 (repr.)./ Lincoln, Mass., De Cordova Museum, *Margaret Brown Memorial Exhibition*, 1957, p. 2./ New York, Kennedy Galleries, Inc., *Fransioli*, 1958, no. 11./ Rockland, Me., William A. Farnsworth Art Museum, *10th Anniversary*, 1958, no. 23 (repr.).

FREDERICK CARL FRIESEKE (1874–1939) was born in Owosso, Mich. He studied at the Chicago Art Institute, the Art Students League, New York, and at the Académie Julian and the Whistler School, Paris. He then worked in New York until his death at Mesnil-sur-Blangy, France.

413.   **The Yellow Room**
fig. 508
A woman, in a yellow kimono patterned in red and blue, stands in a yellow interior. On the counter behind her stands a large blue and red china dish. A blue and green curtain is at the left, the rug on the dark gray floor is blue.
Oil on canvas. 32¼ × 32¼ in. (81.9 × 81.9 cm.)
Signed lower left: *F.C. Frieseke*. Painted in 1902 (?).
Collection: John T. Spaulding, Boston.
Bequest of John T. Spaulding. 48.543

A label on the back of the frame inscribed *1902* suggests a possible date for the painting.

Exhibitions: New York, Macbeth Galleries, *Frieseke*, 1912, no. 5./ Boston, MFA, *The Spaulding Collections*, 1948, no. 27.

JAMES FROTHINGHAM (1786–1864) was born in Charlestown, Mass. He first painted chaises built by his father, then was tempted to train himself to paint portraits. Although essentially self-taught, he received some instruction from a one-time student of Gilbert Stuart named Whiting, then frequently obtained criticism and encouragement from Stuart himself. He moved from Charlestown to Salem, then to Boston, and finally in 1826 to New York. A prolific and skilled artist, he was elected to the National Academy of Design in 1832. He lived in Brooklyn from 1844 until his death.

414.
fig. 201

Samuel Parker

Nearly half-length and turned three-quarters right, he wears a black coat with a white stock and waistcoat. To the right are pink clouds beyond an olive-brown wall.
Oil on panel. 27 × 21¾ in. (68.6 × 55.2 cm.)
Painted about 1812.
Collections: Rebecca Eaton Parker, daughter of the sitter, Boston; Mrs. Annie Kimball Brown, her niece, Boston.
Gift of the Estate of Mrs. Annie Kimball Brown. 22.849

Samuel Parker was born in Exeter, N.H. in 1773, fifth son of William Parker. He married Hannah Mather Crocker, widow of Joseph Crocker and a descendant of Cotton Mather, in 1802, and died in Cambridge, Mass. in 1862.

415.
fig. 199

Mrs. Peter Gilman Robbins (Polly Williams)

Turned three-quarters left, half-length, she wears a black dress with a white lace ruff and a red stole. Beyond a green wall, left, is a brown column before a blue sky.
Oil on panel. 26 × 21¼ in. (66 × 54 cm.)
Painted about 1818.
Collection: Mrs. George Hollingsworth, daughter of the sitter, Milton, Mass.
Bequest of Mrs. George Hollingsworth. 16.105

Daughter of John and Mary Sumner Williams, Polly Williams was born in Roxbury, Mass. in 1773. In 1809 she married Robert Hooper of Marblehead, grandson of "King Hooper"; after his death, she was remarried in 1818 to Dr. Peter Gilman Robbins. She then lived in the Bartlett Mansion, Roxbury, which Gilbert Stuart had occupied in 1812, and died there in 1864. The portrait was probably painted soon after the arrival of the artist in Salem, near Marblehead, in 1818.

416.

Edward Lander

Half-length, half-left, seated in a gilt armchair upholstered in light red matching the tablecloth, he is dressed in a black coat with white ruffled shirt and stock and writes with a white quill pen. The background is dark olive.
Oil on panel. 33½ × 25½ in. (85.1 × 64.8 cm.)
Painted about 1818–1825.
Collection: Mrs. Margaret Riker Haskell, Red Bank, N.J., about 1929.
Gift of Mrs. Jonathan Amory Haskell, in memory of her husband, Jonathan Amory Haskell. 39.737

Capt. Edward Lander (1787–1862), son of Peter Lander, was a ship owner of Salem, Mass. By his marriage in 1813 to Eliza West of Peabody, Mass., he had three children: Edward Lander (1816–1907), jurist; Frederick W. Lander (1822–1862), a general, explorer, and poet; and Louisa Lander (1826–1923), sculptress. Frothingham must have painted this portrait of Edward, and its pendant (Cat. no. 417), during his stay in Salem from 1818 to 1825. Frederick W. Lander led the western expedition which Bierstadt accompanied.

417.

Mrs. Edward Lander (Eliza West)

Half-length, three-quarters right, she is seated in an armchair upholstered in light red. Her dress is black, with white lace collar and cuffs; her wrap light red, edged with ermine. The background is light olive.
Oil on panel. 33½ × 25½ in. (85.1 × 64.8 cm.)
Painted about 1818–1825.
Collection: Same as Cat. no. 416.
Gift of Mrs. Jonathan Amory Haskell, in memory of her husband, Jonathan Amory Haskell. 39.738

Eliza West (1790–1849) was one of the three daughters of Capt. Nathaniel and Elizabeth Derby West of Peabody, Mass. Before her marriage in 1813, she lived in the distinguished country house "Oak Hill," designed by Samuel McIntire and built in 1800–1801 by her maternal grandfather, the famed Salem merchant, Elias Hasket Derby, as a gift for her mother. Three rooms from "Oak Hill" are now installed in the MFA. Pendant to the preceding.

418.

Isaac Wood

A young man, half-length and turned three-quarters left, wears a black coat with a white stock. The background is brown.
Oil on canvas. 29 × 24 in. (73.6 × 61 cm.)
Painted about 1820.
Collection: Henry Herbert Edes, great-nephew of the sitter, Boston.
Gift of Mr. and Mrs. Henry Herbert Edes. 36.65

Isaac Wood (1782–1805) was the unfortunate son of Col. David and Margaret Sprague Wood. He was expelled from Harvard College, where he was a member of the class of 1804, because he rode his horse through the hall of Wadsworth House, then the home of President Willard, while the President and his family were at dinner. As punishment, his father sent him to sea, where he was drowned. Frothingham was nineteen at the time of Isaac Wood's death; this is probably a posthumous portrait, painted in 1820 when his brother Timothy sat for his own portrait (Massachusetts Historical Society, Boston).

419.
fig. 200

Samuel Bayard

Half-length and turned slightly left, the elderly gentleman wears a black coat with a white neckcloth. The background is brown.
Oil on canvas. 27 × 22 in. (68.6 × 55.9 cm.)
Inscribed on a stretcher: *Samuel Bayard James Frothingham Pinx*. Painted about 1830–1835.
Collections: Albert Rosenthal, New Hope, Pa.; LeRoy Ireland, Philadelphia, 1939; Maxim Karolik, Newport, R.I., 1943.
Bequest of Maxim Karolik. 64.427

Samuel Bayard (1767–1840), born in Philadelphia, was a jurist and then Clerk, appointed by Washington, to the U.S. Supreme Court in 1791. Later he became Presiding Judge in Westchester County, N.Y. and a founder of the New-York Historical Society. He died in Princeton, N.J. The picture is dated from its style and from the apparent age of the sitter.

420.
fig. 202

William Cullen Bryant

Bust-length, turned three-quarters left, he wears a black coat and stock. The background is brown.
Oil on canvas. 21 × 17½ in. (53.3 × 44.5 cm.)
Inscribed on back: *William Cullen Bryant/ Painted by James Frothingham/ 1833.*
Collections: Mrs. E.P. Simpson, Philadelphia (?); Maxim Karolik, Newport, R.I., 1947.
M. and M. Karolik Collection. 62.271

William Cullen Bryant (1794–1878), son of the surgeon Peter Bryant and Sarah Snell Bryant, was born in Cummington, Mass. Extremely precocious, his education was derived from family tutoring rather than from formal sources. Although he was first a lawyer, he was acclaimed after his time as a great poet of nature and as an orator. A Unitarian and an ardent Democrat, as editor of the New York *Evening Post* from 1829 to 1878 he exerted a major influence on politics, as well as on the development of journalism in America. He died in New York.

Exhibitions: New York, National Academy of Design, 1834, no. 24./ Minneapolis Institute of Arts and circulated in the U.S., *19th Century American Paintings from the Collection of Maxim Karolik*, 1953–1954./ Washington, D.C., Smithsonian Institution, circulated in the U.S., *19th Century American Paintings*, 1954–1956, no. 24./ Boston, MFA, *New Paintings in the M. and M. Karolik Collection*, 1962–1963.

GEORGE FULLER (1822–1884), landscape, portrait, and figure painter, was born in Deerfield, Mass. He took up painting in 1841 after accompanying his deaf and dumb brother Augustus, a miniaturist, on a walking tour of western New York state. He studied first in Albany, N.Y. with the sculptor, Henry Brown, then in Boston with Thomas Ball until 1847, during which time he was influenced by the work of Allston. From 1847 to 1859 he studied in New York and then worked there, in Philadelphia, and in the South. In 1860 he visited Europe briefly and returned to the Deerfield home for fifteen years. From 1878 until his death he worked in Boston.

421.

Fifteen

A girl, half-length and turned three-quarters right, wears a black dress with a white collar and a gray bow in her hair. The background is brown.
Oil on canvas. 21 × 17¼ in. (53.3 × 43.8 cm.)
Signed and dated lower left: *G.F./ 1859.*
Collections: Henry Lee Higginson, Boston, by 1884; Ida Agassiz Higginson, his wife.
Bequest of Ida Agassiz Higginson. 35.1170
References: J.B. Millet, ed., *Fuller Memorial Volume*, Cambridge, Mass., 1886, p. 90./ W.I. Homer and D.M. Robb, Jr., "Paintings by Fuller," *Art Quarterly*, 1961, XXIV, no. 3, p. 289.
Exhibition: Boston, MFA, *Fuller*, 1884, no. 103.

422.

A Young Boy

Half-length and facing front, he wears a dark brown jacket with a white collar and red tie. The background is very dark brown.
Oil on canvas. 24 × 19 in. (61 × 48.2 cm.)
Painted in 1876.
Collection: Dr. Robert W. Hooper, Boston.
Gift of Edward William Hooper. 85.422
The *Fuller Memorial Volume* and the Boston exhibition catalogue of 1884 (*see below*) give the date.
References: J.B. Millet, ed., *Fuller Memorial Volume*, Cambridge, Mass., 1886, p. 90./ W.H. Downes, "Boston Painters and Paintings," *Atlantic Monthly*, 1888, LXII, no. 371, p. 394./ —, "Fuller," *International Studio*, 1922, LXXV, no. 302, p. 271./ W.I. Homer and D.M. Robb, Jr., "Paintings by Fuller," *Art Quarterly*, 1961, XXIV, no. 3. p. 289.
Exhibition: Boston, MFA, *Fuller*, 1884, no. 106 (as *Ideal Head*).

423.

fig. 337

The Dandelion Girl (Lydia Bigelow)

The child, dressed in brown and white, stands full-length, turned three-quarters right, in a green, wooded pasture and blows the seeds from a dandelion. A cow grazes nearby.
Oil on canvas. 50 × 40¼ in. (127 × 102.2 cm.)
Signed and dated lower left: *G. Fuller 1877.*
Gift of Dr. and Mrs. George Faulkner, through the Trustees of the Faulkner Hospital. 11.2808

A study (unlocated) for the painting was sold in 1884 by Williams and Everett of Boston to Miss A.P. Dixwell, Boston. The daughter of the artist has identified the model as Lydia Bigelow of Deerfield.
References: J.J. Enneking, "Fuller's Methods in Painting," in J.B. Millet, ed., *Fuller Memorial Volume*, Cambridge, Mass., 1886, pp. 72–73, 90./ W.H. Downes, "Fuller," *International Studio*, 1922, LXXV, no. 302, p. 271./ W.I. Homer and D.M. Robb, Jr., "Paintings by Fuller," *Art Quarterly*, 1961, XXIV, no. 3, p. 289.
Exhibitions: Boston, Massachusetts Charitable Mechanics Association, *13th Exhibition*, 1878, no. 250./ Boston, MFA, *Fuller*, 1884, no. 121 (as *By the Wayside*)./ New York, Metropolitan Museum, *Fuller Centennial*, 1923, no. 1 (pl. 1).

424.

fig. 334

Negro Funeral

A barren landscape of brown and green, with one green tree. On the left, figures in white and black stand against a gray and pink sky.

Oil on canvas. 17¾ × 30 in. (45.1 × 76.2 cm.)

Signed lower left: *G. Fuller.* Painted in 1881.

Collections: Estate of the artist; Miss A.P. Rogers, 1884.

Bequest of Anna Perkins Rogers. 21.2174

Date given by the *Fuller Memorial Volume* and the catalogue of the 1884 Boston exhibition. Fuller often painted from memory scenes inspired by his southern trip in the 1880's.

References: J.B. Millet, ed., *Fuller Memorial Volume*, Cambridge, Mass., 1886, p. 92./ W.I. Homer and D.M. Robb, Jr., "Paintings by Fuller," *Art Quarterly*, 1961, XXIV, no. 3, p. 289.

Exhibitions: Boston, MFA, *Fuller*, 1884, no. 2./ Bowdoin College Museum, *The Negro in American Painting*, 1964, no. 59 (repr.).

425.

Arethusa

The nude, brown-skinned girl lies by a brown stream. Behind, several figures are barely discernible among green and brown trees.

Oil on canvas. 50¼ × 40¼ in. (127.6 × 102.2 cm.)

Signed lower right: *G. Fuller.* Painted in 1883.

Collection: Estate of the artist.

Gift by contribution. 87.22

Arethusa, follower of the goddess Artemis, celebrated in Shelley's poem, was pursued by the god Alpheus. To escape him she was transformed into a fountain by Artemis and sent to the island of Ortygia, near Sicily, where the sacred well of Arethusa now springs. Said to be Fuller's last work, and his only nude. The date was given by the exhibition catalogue of 1884.

References: J.B. Millet, ed., *Fuller Memorial Volume*, Cambridge, Mass., 1886, pp. 60, 93./ W.H. Downes, "Boston Painters and Paintings," *Atlantic Monthly*, 1888, LXII, no. 371, p. 395./ —, "American Paintings in the Boston Art Museum," *Brush and Pencil*, 1900, VI, no. 5, p. 209./ —, "Fuller," *International Studio*, 1922, LXXV, no. 302, p. 271./ W.I. Homer and D.M. Robb, Jr., "Paintings by Fuller," *Art Quarterly*, 1961, XXIV, no. 3, p. 290.

Exhibitions: Boston, MFA, *Fuller*, 1884, no. 50./ Boston, St. Botolph Club, *Exhibition*, 1884, no. 60./ New York, Metropolitan Museum, *Fuller Centennial*, 1923, no. 31 (pl. 31)./ Brooklyn Museum, *Nude Painting from the 18th, 19th and 20th Centuries*, 1961, no. 17.

426.

fig. 336

Ethel Reynolds Clarke

Three-quarter length, the young girl stands turned nearly right profile; her dress is white with daisies tucked into her belt. Behind, green fields lie under a dull, yellow-gray sky.

Oil on canvas. 44 × 30¼ in. (111.7 × 76.8 cm.)

Signed lower right: *G. Fuller.* Painted in 1883.

Collections: Dr. Frederick E. Clarke, Lawrence, Mass.; Harriet A. Clarke, his wife.

Bequest of Harriet A. Clarke. 22.705

Ethel Reynolds Clarke (about 1868–1883) was the daughter of Dr. Frederick E. and Harriet A. Clarke of Lawrence, Mass. According to the catalogue of the 1884 Boston exhibition, she was painted in 1883.

References: J.B. Millet, ed., *Fuller Memorial Volume*, Cambridge, Mass., 1886, p. 93./ W.I. Homer and D.M. Robb, Jr., "Paintings by Fuller," *Art Quarterly*, 1961, XXIV, no. 3, p. 290.

Exhibition: Boston, MFA, *Fuller*, 1884, no. 163.

427.

Landscape with Figure

The figure is brown and indistinct in a predominately brown and green landscape. The sky is yellow and gray.

Oil on canvas. 14¼ × 20 in. (36.2 × 50.8 cm.)
Painted in 1883.
Collections: Estate of the artist; Dr. W.F. Wesselhoeft, Boston, 1884.
Gift of Dr. W.F. Wesselhoeft. Res. 12.1
The date is given by the catalogue of the 1884 Boston exhibition.
References: J.B. Millet, ed., *Fuller Memorial Volume*, Cambridge, Mass., 1886, p. 93./
W.I. Homer and D.M. Robb, Jr., "Paintings by Fuller," *Art Quarterly*, 1961, XXIV,
no. 3, p. 290.
Exhibition: Boston, MFA, *Fuller*, 1884, no. 21.

LEE GATCH was born near Baltimore, Md. in 1902. From 1920 to 1924 he studied at
the Maryland Institute of Fine Arts with Leon Kroll and John Sloan. In
1924 he began study at the American School in Fontainebleau, France,
and after travels in Italy and France he worked in Paris with André Lhote
and Moïse Kisling at the Académie Moderne. On his return in 1925 he
worked in New York, and in 1935 he moved to Lambertville, N.J., where
he now lives.

428. **My Three Aunts**
*Three geometrically abstracted heads in right profile, painted in muted olive, gray and
the lower in orange, are silhouetted against a soft blue sky. Below are other areas
and lines in dark brown, orange and muted blues.*
Oil on canvas, mounted on panel. 17 × 10½ in. (43.2 × 26.5 cm.)
Signed and dated lower right: *Gatch /30.*
Collections: The artist until 1960; Private Collection, New York, 1963;
Private Collection, Boston, 1967.
Anonymous Gift. 67.649

Exhibition: University of Illinois, Urbana, Krannert Art Museum and Cheekwood,
Nashville, Tenn., Tennessee Fine Arts Center, *A Selection from the Josephine and
Phillip A. Bruno Collection*, 1961–1962, no. 35.

429.
fig. 601 **Night Gothic**
*A black abstract figure dances on a gray tree shadow, underlined by orange and green;
black and patches of blue and gray planar shapes form gothic arches. Above, two gray
clouds emanate rays of green, orange, and blue.*
Oil on canvas. 42¼ × 46¼ in. (107.3 × 117.4 cm.)
Signed lower left: *L Gatch.* Painted in 1957.
Charles Henry Hayden Fund. 57.666
"While I have long been moved by that period of History intensely religious
and profoundly intellectual referred to by some authors as the Gothic
night, I would rather lay claim that my inspiration was more the result of
direct visual experience.... In my youth I was a hunter and the night
forest fascinated me, especially the great arches made by the trees against
the brilliant, November sky. This was the visual experience that was to
find spiritual discipline many years later." (Letter from the artist, Nov. 5,
1957.) The frame, an intaglio of gray, gray-green, and gray-pink canvas
patches, was made by the artist. A dancing figure, very similar to that in
Night Gothic, appears in *Winter*, 1955 (Mr. and Mrs. R.A. Bernstein) and
another, similar though reversed, is in *Leda*, 1959–1960 (Sampson R. Field,
Long Island City, N.Y.).
References: M. Sawin, "Gatch," *Arts*, 1958, XXXII, no. 8, p. 32 (repr. p. 33)./ B.
Guest, "Avery and Gatch," *Art News*, 1960, LIX, no. 1, pp. 42–45./ A.S. Weller,
Art USA Now, New York, 1963, I, no. 4 (repr. p. 112).
Exhibitions: Cleveland Museum, *Some Contemporary Works of Art*, 1958, no. 16
(repr.)./ New York, World House Galleries, *Gatch*, 1958, no. 24 (repr.)./ Chicago
Art Institute, *63rd American Exhibition*, 1959, no. 34./ American Federation of Arts
circulated in the U.S., *Gatch Retrospective*, 1960–1961, pp. 12, 19–20, no. 37 (repr.)./
Washington, D.C., White House, *Festival of the Arts*, 1965, no. 12.

IGNAZ MARCEL GAUGENGIGL (1855–1932) was born in Passau, Bavaria. He studied in Munich with Raab and Wilhelm Dietz; after travel in Italy and France, he came to Boston in 1880. A popular painter of portraits and genre, he worked here until his death.

430.
fig. 507

Self-Portrait

A studio interior beyond gray curtains; the artist, in gray, works in a room decorated with green, yellow, and brown objects. In the brown foreground are a suit of armor and a white fur rug.
Oil on canvas. 17¼ × 12¾ in. (43.8 × 32.3 cm.)
Signed upper right: *I.M. Gaugengigl.* Painted about 1880–1890.
Gift of Mrs. Henry S. Shaw. 25.520
Exhibition: Boston, Guild of Boston Artists, *Gaugengigl*, 1919, no. 18.

431.

Scherzando 1903

In an eighteenth-century Italian interior, a couple sit on a bench. Her dress is red and white, and he, playing a lute, is in yellow. White dogs, a tiger skin, and green potted plants lie about the floor. On the gray wall behind is a fresco after Tiepolo.
Oil on canvas. 10 × 14 in. (25.4 × 35.5 cm.)
Signed and dated lower left: *Scherzando: 1903: I.M. Gaugengigl.*
Gift of Robert Jordan from the collection of Eben D. Jordan. 24.219
Exhibitions: Pittsburgh, Pa., Carnegie Institute, *International Exhibition*, 1914, no. 339./ Boston, St. Botolph Club, *Gaugengigl*, 1929, no. 5.

432.

James Brown Case

Three-quarter length and turned three-quarters right, he stands in a white suit beside some red gladioli and a rubber tree. The background is brown.
Oil on canvas. 49 × 34 in. (124.5 × 86.3 cm.)
Signed lower left: *I.M. Gaugengigl.* Painted about 1904.
Collection: Louisa W. and Marian R. Case, daughters of the sitter, Boston, 1907.
Gift of the Misses Louisa W. and Marian R. Case. 20.1861

James Brown Case (1825–1907) was born in Cranston, R.I. He established the wool merchant partnership of Leland and Case of Boston and twice became President of the National Bank of Redemption. He lived in Weston, Mass. until his death in Boston. The date, given by the sitter's great-niece, agrees with his apparent age in the portrait.

433.
fig. 506

The Visitor

A lady, dressed in purple, sits reading in the brown interior of a studio. The oriental rug is red; the curtains above are green and yellow.
Oil on canvas. 30 × 25 in. (76.2 × 63.5 cm.)
Signed lower left: *I.M. Gaugengigl.* Painted about 1925.
Gift of Frederick L. Jack. 35.1223
The costume indicates the date.

JEFFERSON GAUNTT (1806–1864) exhibited at the Pennsylvania Academy of the Fine Arts from 1828 to 1832, but moved to Brooklyn, N.Y. in 1833. He exhibited at the American Academy in New York that year and at the National Academy in 1834, 1838, and 1843. He is believed to have been active until 1857, although no paintings executed after 1843 are known.

434.
fig. 248

Two Children (formerly attributed to J. Grant)

Oil on canvas. 50 × 40 in. (127 × 101.6 cm.)
Signed and dated on the back (a transcription on lining canvas of the original inscription): *Painted by J. Gaunt* [sic] *Brooklyn 1843.*
M. and M. Karolik Collection. 47.1161

The present attribution to Jefferson Gauntt was suggested by John J. Bowden, Huntington Station, N.Y. Two other portraits by Gauntt are extant: *The Spies Children* (Brooklyn Museum) and *Rebecca Garrison* (Dr.

and Mrs. Murray Hershberg, Whitestone, N.Y.). Both are signed and dated. A comparison of the styles and signatures of these two paintings and ours substantiates the attribution.

References: *Karolik Catalogue*, 1949, no. 122 (repr.)./ A. von Saldern, "Two Unpublished Family Portraits," *Brooklyn Museum Annual*, 1960–1962, II–III, p. 50 (fig. 2).

WALTER GAY (1856–1937), nephew of the painter Winckworth Allen Gay, was born in Hingham, Mass. In 1876 he studied with Bonnat in Paris. Despite extensive European travel, he settled permanently near Paris, but maintained a home in Boston. In his use of bright colors he was influenced by the Impressionists, and he specialized in genre subjects and interiors. He died at his home, the Château de Breau, near Barbizon.

435. **Monk Reading**

The Franciscan stands full-length reading. His habit and the background are brown.
Oil on panel. 13¼ × 9½ in. (33.6 × 24.1 cm.)
Signed and dated lower left: *Walter Gay 82.*
Gift of the artist. 36.563

436. **The Broken Thread**

A young peasant girl is seated at a loom weaving soft yellow cloth. She wears a white cap, gray kerchief, pink blouse, and blue apron.
Oil on panel. 16¼ × 11¾ in. (41.2 × 29.7 cm.)
Signed lower left: *Walter Gay.* Painted in 1886.
Bequest of Ernest Wadsworth Longfellow. 23.490

Similar in composition and subject to *The Weaver* (Cat. no. 437) dated 1886.

437. **The Weaver**

An old woman in black and brown peasant costume is seated weaving brown cloth. The interior is gray and brown; through the window, a green landscape.
Oil on canvas. 59¾ × 46¼ in. (151.8 × 117.4 cm.)
Signed and dated twice, lower right: *Walter Gay/ Allery 1886* and *Walter Gay/ Allery '86.*
Collection: Mrs. Walter Gay, Château de Breau, Barbizon, France.
Gift of Mrs. Walter Gay. 39.736
Reference: T.N. Maytham, "The Weaver," *MFA Bulletin*, 1961, LIX, no. 315, p. 8 (fig. 3).
Exhibition: Boston, St. Botolph Club, *Gay*, 1892, no. 9.

438. **Interior of Palazzo Barbaro, Venice**

fig. 493

A gray and gilded interior, with a brown floor and gilt furniture upholstered in green. The many paintings are red, brown, blue, and gray.
Oil on canvas. 35½ × 39½ in. (90.2 × 100.3 cm.)
Signed lower right: *Walter Gay/ Palazzo Barbaro.* Painted in 1902.
Collection: Purchased from the artist.
Charles Henry Hayden Fund. 11.1537

Represented is the ballroom of the Palazzo Barbaro. The two large paintings are, left, *The Rape of the Sabines* by Sebastiano Ricci, and right, *Jephthah's Oath* by Fontebasso. The full-length portrait between them is *Senator Grimani* by Bernardo Strozzi. The three ovals are early nineteenth century, and the ceiling was completed by Zanchi. Gay was a close friend of the son of Daniel Sargent Curtis, who had bought the palazzo in 1892, and which is now owned by his grandson, Ralph W. Curtis. In a letter of Sept. 5, 1936, Gay said that he had painted this picture in 1902.

Reference: A.E. Gallatin, *Gay*, New York, 1920 (repr. no. 15).

Exhibitions: New York, Gimpel and Wildenstein, *Gay*, 1920, no. 27./ New York, Metropolitan Museum, *Gay Memorial*, 1938, no. 20./ Yale University Art Gallery, *Portraits of Interiors*, 1955, no. 12.

439.
fig. 492

La Cheminée

The white mantlepiece is covered with photographs, various brown objects, and a pair of silver candlesticks.
Oil on upsom board. 21¾ × 18 in. (55.2 × 45.7 cm.)
Signed lower left: *Walter Gay.* Painted about 1909.
Collections: Louis Gillet, Château de Châalis, France, in 1921; the artist, Château de Breau, in 1923; Mrs. Walter Gay.
Gift of Mrs. Walter Gay. 39.735
Painted in Gay's apartment in Paris, no. 11, rue de l'Université.
Reference: L. Gillet, "Gay," *La Revue de l'Art*, 1921, XXXIX (repr. p. 44, as painted in 1909).
Exhibition: Yale University Art Gallery, *Portraits of Interiors*, 1955, no. 11.

440.

French Interior

The corner of a room, where the walls and furniture are gray and gilt. The flowers before the four green mirrors are white and the floor is brown.
Oil on canvas. 25¾ × 21½ in. (65.4 × 54.6 cm.)
Signed lower left: *Walter Gay.*
Collection: Mrs. John Gardner Coolidge, Boston.
Bequest of Helen S. Coolidge. 63.172
The Green Salon by Gay (Metropolitan Museum) represents a room in the Château de Breau; the strong architectural and decorative similarities to this indicate the *French Interior* may have been painted at that time.

SANFORD ROBINSON GIFFORD (1823–1880), born in Greenfield, N.Y., studied painting in New York with John Rubens Smith about 1845 and worked there until 1855, when he left for two years' study in Europe. He walked from England to Italy and spent a winter in Rome. He left New York again to make a walking tour of Europe and the Near East between 1859 and 1861. In America he spent summers in the Catskills and the Adirondacks, visited the Rockies and Alaska in 1870, and lived in New York until his death.

441.
fig. 290

Marina Grande near Sorrento

The bay and distant mountains, seen from a beach, are all painted in pink and gray. In the foreground fishermen in red, white, and brown work with the brown boats and orange, yellow, brown, and white sails.
Oil on canvas. 9 × 14 in. (22.9 × 35.5 cm.)
Signed and dated lower left: *Marina Grande June 20th 1857 SRG.*
Collections: Estate of the artist, New York, 1880, *Gifford Collection Sale*, Chickering Hall, New York, April 11–12, 28–29, 1881, no. 60; Sir Donald Alexander Smith, Baron Strathcona and Mount Royal, Montreal, Quebec; Quebec, Montreal Museum of Fine Arts; Maxim Karolik, Newport, R.I., 1954.
Bequest of Maxim Karolik. 64.428
Exhibitions: New York, Metropolitan Museum, *Gifford Memorial*, 1881, no. 113./ Washington, D.C., Smithsonian Institution, circulated in the U.S., *19th Century American Paintings*, 1954–1956, no. 25./ Ogunquit Museum, *8th Annual—Luminist and Trompe l'Oeil Painters*, 1960, no. 4.

FRANÇOIS RÉGIS GIGNOUX (1816–1882) was born in Lyons, France. He first studied historical painting at the École des Beaux Arts, Paris, and was a pupil of Vernet and Delaroche. He then took up landscape painting and in 1840 settled in Brooklyn, N.Y., where George Inness became his pupil. He worked in New York, New England, Canada, and the southern states before returning to France in 1870. He died in Freiburg, Germany.

442.
fig. 222

Sunset in a Swamp

The brown swamp and the brown and green trees reflect and are lighted by the red sunset. The sky changes from red, to yellow, and to blue.
Oil on canvas. 31¼ × 47 in. (79.4 × 119.4 cm.)

Signed lower left: *R. Gignoux*. Painted between 1840 and 1850.
Collections: N.W. Lincoln, Burlington, Vt.; Henry Herbert Edes, Boston,
by 1910.
Bequest of Henry Herbert Edes. 23.184

The painting was bequeathed to the MFA with the name *Sunset in the Dismal
Swamp*. In the exhibition record of the American Academy and Art Union,
1850, no. 230 is listed a "View, Dismal Swamp, N.C. 47 × 31. A sunset view
of water, beside which rise trees." This and *Sunset in a Swamp* are probably
one and the same.

Exhibitions: New York, American Academy and Art Union, 1850, no. 230./ Cambridge, Mass., Busch-Reisinger Museum, *Rivers and Seas—Changing Attitudes Toward
Landscape, 1700–1962*, 1962, no. 32.

443.   **Winter Scene in New Jersey**
Oil on canvas. Painted oval. 20 × 24 in. (50.8 × 61 cm.)
Signed and dated lower left center on rock: *Gignoux/ 1847*. Inscribed in the
artist's hand on the back of the canvas: *Vue prise dans le New Jersey/ par
Régis Gignoux/ 1847*.
M. and M. Karolik Collection. 48.424
Reference: Karolik Catalogue, 1949, no. 120 (repr.).

EDWARD GIOBBI was born in Waterbury, Conn. in 1926. He studied between 1946 and 1951
at the Whitney School of Art, New Haven, the Vesper George School of
Art, Boston, and with Zorach at the Art Students League, New York;
from 1951 to 1954 he was at the Academy of Fine Arts, Florence. He
traveled extensively in Spain, Holland, France, and Italy and now paints
in Katonah, N.Y.

444.   **For Brecht No. 2**
fig. 610
*Painted in a tondo, flanked by four unpainted spandrels, heads of various colors, lower
center, emerge from red and green areas before a black background. Horizontal bands
of blue, green, and yellow are seen above.*
Oil on canvas. 42 × 42 in. (106.6 × 106.6 cm.)
Signed and dated center right: *Giobbi 63*.
Ellen Kelleran Gardner Fund. 64.1945

". . . part of a series of paintings . . . inspired by Brecht plays. The painting is not specifically related to any of the writings of Brecht but rather
inspired by the general message of his works. Brecht to me, captured the
true expressionistic spirit of Germany in the thirties, and he seems to me,
to be a romantic as well. . . . The use of the tondo is related to a series of
paintings I started in Italy in 1959 when I became involved with [the]
combination of geometric forms with expressionism . . ." (Letter from the
artist, Oct. 21, 1964.)

C. GIROUX   Nothing is known of the artist.

445.   **Cotton Plantation**
Oil on canvas. 22 × 36 in. (55.9 × 91.4 cm.)
Painted between 1850 and 1865.
M. and M. Karolik Collection. 47.1144
Reference: Karolik Catalogue, 1949, no. 121 (repr.).

WILLIAM JAMES GLACKENS (1870–1938) was born in Philadelphia. He was an illustrator
for Philadelphia papers and studied at the Pennsylvania Academy of the
Fine Arts until 1896, when he went to Paris to work independently. There
he was strongly influenced by the Impressionist painters. On his return he
was an illustrator for New York papers and was commissioned by *McClure's*
to cover the Spanish-American War in Cuba. In 1908 he joined the social-
realist group, "The Eight" and in 1913 was chairman of the Armory Show

and first President of the Society of Independent Artists. From 1925 to 1932 he worked in France and New York, where he died.

446.
fig. 539

Flying Kites, Montmartre

Painted primarily in blue and gray, with touches of brown and green, a scene where boys fly their kites before some yellow houses on a hill overlooking Paris.

Oil on canvas. 26 × 34¼ in. (66 × 87 cm.)

Signed lower left: *W. Glackens.* Painted in 1906.

Collection: Purchased from the artist by Mrs. Richard E. Dwight, New York, about 1907.

Charles Henry Hayden Fund. 38.7

"It was painted in Paris in 1906." (Letter from the artist, March 25, 1938.)

References: C.C. Cunningham, *MFA Bulletin*, 1938, XXXVI, no. 215, pp. 39–41 (fig. 2)./ I. Glackens, *Glackens and the Ashcan Group*, New York, 1957, p. 71 (repr.).

Exhibitions: New York, Whitney Museum, *Glackens*, 1938–1939, no. 2./ Pittsburgh, Pa., Carnegie Institute, *Glackens Memorial*, 1939, no. 65./ Philadelphia Museum of Art, *Artists of the Philadelphia Press*, 1945, no. 5./ New York, Kraushaar Galleries, *Glackens*, 1949, no. 8./ Dartmouth College, Carpenter Art Galleries, *Glackens*, 1960, no. 6.

447.
fig. 538

Italo-American Celebration, Washington Square

A crowd, painted primarily in blue, stands in the square before the yellow arch and red buildings. Green trees are in the foreground; the ground is pink, green, and yellow under blue sky.

Oil on canvas. 26 × 32 in. (66 × 81.2 cm.)

Signed lower left: *W. Glackens.* Painted about 1912.

Collections: Ira Glackens, the artist's son, New York, 1938; Joseph Katz, Baltimore, 1957.

Emily L. Ainsley Fund. 59.658

A contemporary version of the same subject, *Parade, Washington Square*, dated 1912, is owned by the Whitney Museum, New York.

Exhibitions: New York, 10 West 9th St. (Glackens' studio), *Glackens Memorial*, 1944, no. 30./ New York, Kraushaar Galleries, *Glackens*, 1949, no. 13./ Saginaw Museum, *20th Century American Painting*, 1949./ University of Chicago, Renaissance Society, *American Pioneers of the 20th Century*, 1955, no. 8./ New York, Hirschl & Adler Galleries, *Exhibition of the Collection*, 1959, no. 6 (repr. as *Italian Parade*).

ARTHUR CLIFTON GOODWIN (1866–1929) was born in Portsmouth, N.H. Essentially self-taught, he began to paint in Boston in 1902, occasionally working in the studio of Louis Kronberg. From 1921 to 1928 he worked in Old Chatham, N.Y. and in New York City as a painter and illustrator. He returned to Boston just before his death with the intention of going to Europe. Prolific in both paint and pastel, he is best known for his views of the city and its everyday life.

448.

Public Garden, Boston

People in black stand under a green shelter by the blue Frog Pond. The large tree is brown in the green park; the buildings beyond are gray under pale green sky. Arlington Street and Commonwealth Avenue are in the distance.

Pastel on paper. 11¾ × 18 in. (29.7 × 45.7 cm.)

Signed lower left: *A.C. Goodwin.* Drawn about 1902.

Bequest of Grenville H. Norcross. 37.495

449.
fig. 525

Public Garden, Boston, Late Afternoon

People dressed in blue and black sit in the autumn foliage of the Garden. Behind them is the statue of Washington by Thomas Ball, the spire of Arlington Street Church, and gray buildings. The sky is blue.

Pastel on paper. 12 × 18½ in. (30.5 × 47 cm.)

Signed lower left: *A.C. Goodwin.* Drawn about 1905.

Collection: Grace M. Edwards, Boston, 1913.

Juliana Cheney Edwards Collection. Bequest of Grace M. Edwards in memory of her mother. 39.649

Exhibition: Boston, MFA, *Juliana Cheney Edwards Collection*, 1939–1940, no. 14. (Catalogue: MFA *Bulletin*, 1939, XXXVII, p. 100.)

450.
fig. 529

Copley Square, Boston

The red buildings and the streets are covered with snow and gray ice; blue and green haze in the distance.
Oil on canvas. 30 × 36 in. (76.2 × 91.4 cm.)
Signed lower right: *A.C. Goodwin*. Painted about 1908.
Bequest of John T. Spaulding. 48.550

A version, *Scene on Boylston Street* (oil on canvas, 25¼ × 30½ in., signed lower left) was in the *Goodwin* exhibition, Addison Gallery, Andover, Mass., 1946.

451.
fig. 528

Park Street, Boston

Looking down Tremont Street toward the Park Street Church; painted in green, gray, and gold.
Oil on canvas. 19 × 26 in. (48.2 × 66 cm.)
Signed lower right: *A C Goodwin*. Painted about 1908.
Bequest of John T. Spaulding. 48.551

A pastel (19¼ × 23 in.) and a large oil study (33¼ × 40¼ in.) were nos. 32 and 10 respectively in the *Goodwin* exhibition at the Addison Gallery, Andover, Mass. in 1946.
Exhibition: Boston, MFA, *The Spaulding Collections*, 1948, no. 35.

452.

Customs House Tower from the Public Garden, Boston

Seen from the Garden with its brown trees and wet pink-gray road, the buildings are gray under a blue-gray and yellow sky.
Pastel on paper. 16¼ × 20¼ in. (41.2 × 51.4 cm.)
Signed lower right: *A.C. Goodwin*. Drawn about 1914.
Bequest of John T. Spaulding. 48.556
Exhibition: Boston, Doll and Richards, *Goodwin*, 1915, no. 15.

453.
fig. 526

Mt. Vernon Street, Boston

Gray, blue-shadowed snow covers the street and orange houses looking over the Charles River. The trees are brown beneath blue and yellow sky.
Pastel on paper. 16¾ × 20½ in. (42.5 × 52 cm.)
Signed lower left: *A.C. Goodwin*. Drawn about 1914.
Bequest of John T. Spaulding. 48.557

454.
fig. 527

The Barnstormer, Old South Theatre, Boston

Yellow light plays on the actor and the conductor, both in black suits. The audience appears black in the foreground; a dull green stage is in the background.
Oil on cardboard. 12¾ × 15 in. (32.3 × 38.1 cm.)
Signed lower right: *ACG*. Inscribed with date on back: *AC Goodwin/ The Barnstormer/ Old South Theatre/ Boston/ 1918*.
Bequest of John T. Spaulding. 48.554

455.

Broadway Burlesque

Between an audience and stage of black, brown, and yellow, and before a chorus dressed in blue, a couple take their bow. He is in gray and she wears blue and red.
Pastel on paper. 17 × 21 in. (43.2 × 53.3 cm.)
Signed lower right: *A.C. Goodwin*. Drawn probably after 1918.
Bequest of John T. Spaulding. 48.552

The title, taken from a label on the back, suggests that the locale is New York City.
Exhibition: Boston, MFA, *The Spaulding Collections*, 1948, no. 36.

456. **The Spotlight**

The stage and the pink and blue scenery are seen over an audience in black and brown. The yellow light falls on a bowing couple, right, who wear black and pink.
Oil on canvas. 14 × 18 in. (35.5 × 45.7 cm.)
Signed and dated lower left: *To my friend J.T. Spaulding/ A.C. Goodwin, Apr.24/ 19.*
Bequest of John T. Spaulding. 48.553

Exhibitions: Boston, Guild of Boston Artists, *Goodwin*, 1919, no. 19./ Boston, MFA, *The Spaulding Collections*, 1948, no. 37.

457. **Strand Theatre, Boston**

Before the green and red scenery and the yellow boxes, a couple in black and white stand in the yellow floodlight. The audience in the foreground is black.
Oil on chipboard. 17½ × 21½ in. (44.5 × 54.6 cm.)
Signed on back: *Arthur C. Goodwin/ Strand Theatre.* Painted about 1919.
Bequest of John T. Spaulding. 48.555

In style and subject this painting is similar to *The Spotlight* (Cat. no. 456), which is dated 1919.

458. **Herald Square, New York**

The buildings are brown, pink, yellow, and green; the people and vehicles are in black. The brown wet streets reflect blue and gray from the sky, which is touched with pink and yellow.
Oil on canvas. 38 × 44 in. (96.5 × 111.7 cm.)
Signed lower right: *A C Goodwin.* Painted between 1921 and 1928.
Collections: Miss Goodyear, Newport, R.I.; Douglas Lorie, Newport; Maxim Karolik, Newport, 1946.
Bequest of Maxim Karolik. 64.409

Goodwin worked in New York City from about 1921 until late in 1928.

J. GRANT *See* Jefferson Gauntt.

ETHAN ALLEN GREENWOOD (1779–1856) was born in Hubbardston, Mass. He studied painting in New York with Edward Savage, who owned, in Boston, the New England Museum, a collection of curios and paintings. Greenwood acquired it and returned to Boston and Hubbardston to run it until about 1840. He continued to be active as a portrait painter in Boston and northern New England until his death.

459. **Horace Collamore**
fig. 157

Half-length and turned three-quarters left, he wears a black coat with a white stock, frilled shirt, and waistcoat. The background is dark green.
Oil on panel. 25¼ × 20½ in. (64.1 × 52 cm.)
Signed and dated lower left: *Greenwood/ Pinx/ –1813.*
Bequest of Lillie C. Smith in memory of her mother, Lydia Beal Collamore and her father, Morris T. Smith. 35.1978

Horace Collamore was married in 1814 and lived in Boston until 1821, when he bought a farm in North Pembroke, Mass. Greenwood's diary (American Antiquarian Society, Worcester, Mass.), lists a portrait of Horace Collamore for June 9, 1813.

Reference: C. Shipton, "List of Portraits Painted by E.A. Greenwood," American Antiquarian Society, *Proceedings*, Worcester, Mass., 1946, LVI, no. 1, p. 141.

460. **Judge Ellis**

Half-length, he faces three-quarters left and writes with a quill pen. His coat is black, his stock and frill shirt are white. The background is red.
Oil on panel. 26 × 20¾ in. (66 × 52.7 cm.)
Painted about 1815–1820.
Collections: Mrs. James Palmer Ellis, daughter-in-law of the sitter; Miss Ruth C. Presbrey, her granddaughter, Brookline, Mass.

Gift of Miss Ruth C. Presbrey in memory of her father, Edward A. Presbrey. 46.857

Close similarities of style, pose, and even size of panel to the portrait of Horace Collamore (Cat. no. 459) identify this portrait and its pendant (Cat. no. 461) as the work of Ethan Allen Greenwood, an attribution first proposed by Nina Fletcher Little.

461.   **Mrs. Ellis**

fig. 156

Bust-length, facing three-quarters right, she wears a gray empire dress with a white lace shawl, a bonnet, and neck ruffle. The background is brown.
Oil on panel. 26 × 20¾ in. (66 × 52.7 cm.)
Painted about 1815–1820.
Collections: Same as Cat. no. 460.
Gift of Miss Ruth C. Presbrey in memory of her father, Edward A. Presbrey. 46.858
Pendant to the preceding.

JOHN GREENWOOD (1727–1792), born in Boston, apprenticed himself in 1742 to the painter and engraver Thomas Johnston. He became a popular Boston portrait painter until his sudden departure in 1752 for Surinam (Dutch Guiana), where he continued to paint until 1758. He then studied mezzotint engraving with Michiel Elgersma in Amsterdam. In 1762 he settled in London, established a successful art dealing business, and continued to paint and engrave until his death in Margate, Kent.

462.   **The Greenwood-Lee Family**

fig. 20

Five ladies are arranged about a table covered with a green cloth on which is a basket of sewing and a piece of flame-stitching. From left to right, the ladies wear dresses of blue satin, gray (seated), pink, brown, and ivory. The man, behind right, wears a long blue coat, white shirt, and dark red turban. A green curtain is at the upper right.
Oil on canvas. 56 × 68 in. (142.2 × 172.7 cm.)
Painted about 1747.
Collections: Mrs. Benjamin Lee Waterhouse, Boston; Henry Lee; Henry Lee Shattuck, his grandson, Boston.
Future Donation.

Represented from left to right are Hannah Greenwood (born 1740), youngest sister of the artist; she stands beside her seated mother, Mary Charnock Greenwood (born 1709/10). Behind her is Mary or Elizabeth Greenwood (born 1731 and 1732 respectively); seated center, with her hand on a volume of *The Spectator*, Martha Lee (born 1728); and right, her sister Elizabeth Lee (1729/30–1808), first cousin and fiancée of the artist, Greenwood who appears behind. A nineteenth-century label on the back of the painting has identified the seated lady center as the artist's fiancée (the engagement was later broken off and Miss Lee married Andrew Newell in 1759). Elizabeth Charnock Lee, mother of the Lee girls, was sister of Mrs. Mary Greenwood. The composition was inspired by the Smibert of 1729, *Bishop Berkeley and His Entourage* (Yale University Art Gallery). The *Berkeley Group*, the *Isaac Royall Family* (Harvard Law School) of 1741 and the *Greenwood-Lee Family* are among the most ambitious and important paintings executed in America prior to the advent of Copley in the third quarter of the eighteenth century.

References: *New England Historical and Genealogical Register*, LXXVI, 1922, p. 204./ A. Burroughs, *Greenwood in America*, Andover, Mass., 1943, pp. 22, 23, 59, 66 (fig. 13)./ J.T. Flexner, *First Flowers of Our Wilderness*, Boston, 1947, pp. 201, 349 (repr. p. 200)./ S.P. Feld, "Loan Collection, 1965," *Metropolitan Museum Bulletin*, 1965, XXIII, no. 8, p. 278 (repr.).

Exhibition: New York, Metropolitan Museum, *Three Centuries of American Painting*, 1965, no catalogue (see *Bulletin*, above).

463.   **Mrs. Henry Bromfield (Margaret Fayerweather)**

fig. 18

Facing front, over half-length, she rests her left arm on a gray stone pedestal and holds

a rose in her right hand. Her dress is blue and white. A brown wall is left, and in the distance, right, is a green landscape with a blue pond below gray clouds.
Oil on canvas. 36 × 25½ in. (91.4 × 64.8 cm.)
Painted about 1749–1750.
Collections: Mrs. I.H.T. Blanchard, granddaughter of the sitter, Harvard, Mass., 1872; Miss Margaret Bromfield Slade, Boston; Mrs. Henry E. Warner, South Lincoln, Mass., 1943; Mrs. Jean-Frédéric Wagniere (Margaret Warner), 1955.
Emily L. Ainsley Fund. 62.173

Margaret Fayerweather (1732–1761), daughter of Thomas and Jerusha Fayerweather, was born in Boston. By her marriage to Henry Bromfield in 1749, she had five children. Her obituary said of her: "On the 3d inst. died at Brookfield (Mass.) of the Small Pox, Mrs. Margaret Bromfield of the Town. . . . The external Advantage of her Person was accompanied with a Sweetness of Temper, and an Assemblage of Virtues that form'd a distinguish'd and very amicable Character . . ." Long considered a work by Copley of about 1753, Alan Burroughs (*see below*) attributed the painting to Greenwood in 1943. It was probably painted about the time of her marriage, in 1749. Greenwood painted three other members of her family the following year.

References: D.D. Slade, *The Bromfields*, Boston, 1872, p. 11./ B.N. Parker and A.B. Wheeler, *Copley*, Boston, 1938, p. 48 (pl. 2)./ A. Burroughs, *Greenwood in America*, Andover, Mass., 1943, pp. 44–45, 63 (fig. 35)./ T.N. Maytham, "Some Recent Accessions," *MFA Bulletin*, 1962, LX, no. 322, pp. 140–141 (repr. p. 141).

464.
fig. 19

John Langdon

Seated in half-length, his right hand rests on a letter on the green covered table before him. He faces three-quarters right and wears a brown coat over a black waistcoat. A brown wall is left, and in the distance, right, a ship sails on a blue sea under gray clouds.
Oil on canvas. 36 × 28 in. (91.4 × 71.1 cm.)
Painted about 1750.
Collections: Langdon family to John Langdon Coffin; Mary Langdon Williams Pearse; Langdon Pearse, great-great-great-grandson of the sitter, Winnetka, Ill.
Gift of Langdon Pearse. 52.1732

John Langdon (1722–about 1783), son of Edward and Susanna Wadsworth Langdon, was a merchant of Boston. He married Mary Greenough in 1744 and had eight children by her. According to tradition, the portrait was painted when the sitter was twenty-nine.

References: M.C. Rogers, *Glimpses of an Old Social Capital*, Boston, 1923, p. 88 (repr. erroneously as John, son of Capt. Tobias and Mary Langdon of Portsmouth)./ A. Burroughs, *Greenwood in America*, Andover, Mass., 1943, p. 67.

ROBERT GWATHMEY was born in Richmond, Va. in 1903. He attended the Maryland Institute in 1925–1926, then the Pennsylvania Academy of the Fine Arts until 1930. He spent much time, especially summers, in the South, and lived in Paris in 1949–1950. He has taught at Cooper Union in New York since 1942.

465.
fig. 579

Sharecropper and Blackberry Pickers

A Negro in white shirt and bright blue trousers leans on his hoe and wipes his face with his arm. Behind, two women in yellow and pink pick from green bushes. The sky is gray above the brown ground.
Oil on canvas. 32 × 24 in. (81.2 × 61 cm.)
Signed lower right: *Gwathmey*. Painted in 1941.
Charles Henry Hayden Fund. 41.688

"The plight of the sharecropper, the evils of the usual one crop farming . . . and the worn earth have all too long been smothered by a traditional romanticism. . . . The canvas was finished in North Carolina during August of this year." (Letter from the artist, Oct. 6, 1941.) The Negro in this painting and *Hoeing* (Carnegie Institute, Pittsburgh; repr. p. 245 in *Carnegie Magazine*, 1944, XVII, no. 8), is derived from a "working drawing" which Gwathmey repeatedly used.

Exhibition: Toronto Art Gallery, *Museum's Choice*, 1945, no. 14.

GEORGE HENRY HALL (1825–1913), genre and still-life painter, was born in Manchester, N.H. He grew up in Boston and painted there from 1842 to 1849, then left to study in Düsseldorf and to live in Paris until 1852. He then settled in New York, where he died, having made frequent visits to Spain, Italy, and North Africa between 1860 and 1895.

466.
fig. 314

Roman Wine Cart
A peasant man and woman ride in a covered, brown two-wheeled cart. She wears a blue skirt and white blouse and holds a tambourine; he wears green knickerbockers, red vest, and blue coat. Behind, the Colosseum is brown under blue, cloudy sky.
Oil on canvas. 43 × 39½ in. (109.2 × 100.3 cm.)
Signed and dated lower left: *G.H. Hall/ Rome Dec/ 22d 1851*. Inscribed on back: *Roman Wine Cart/ Dec 22./ 1851*.
Collection: E.P. Winans, New York?, by 1853.
Gift of Miss Jennie Brownscombe. 16.44
Exhibition: New York, National Academy of Design, 1853, no. 394.

EDWARD WILBUR DEAN HAMILTON (1864–1943) was born in Sommerfield, Pa. Although he studied at the École des Beaux Arts in Paris, he was especially influenced by the Impressionists. He then worked in Boston as a portrait and landscape painter and became a member of the Boston Guild of Artists. He taught at the Massachusetts School of Art, Boston University, and at the Rhode Island School of Design. He died in Kingston, Mass.

467.

Canal, Venice
Touches of green, blue, and yellow appear on the stucco houses surrounding the canal; their blue shadows are reflected in the green water.
Oil on canvas. 10 × 14 in. (25.4 × 35.5 cm.)
Signed lower left: *E.W.D. Hamilton/ Venezia*. Painted about 1885–1890. No doubt painted in the late 1880's during or after the artist's period of study in Paris.
Gift of Mrs. Josiah Bradlee. 17.3143

468.
fig. 524

Summer at Campobello, New Brunswick
Several men and women in blue, white, brown, and gray stand or sit on a broad white and gray verandah. Bright red flowers and green foliage are to the right and center; the distant shore is pink and gray under a blue sky.
Oil on canvas. 28 × 28 in. (71.1 × 71.1 cm.)
Painted about 1890–1900.
Collections: Mrs. G.W. Stafford, the artist's niece, Madison, N.J., 1934; Maxim Karolik, Newport, R.I., 1961.
Bequest of Maxim Karolik. 64.463
The strongly Impressionist style and the costumes establish the date. Campobello Island was a popular summer resort in the late nineteenth and early twentieth centuries.
Exhibition: University of New Mexico Art Gallery and San Francisco, M.H. de Young Memorial Museum, *Impressionism in America*, 1965, no. 22 (repr.).

JOHN J. HAMMER (1842–1906)

469.

A Peaceful Day in the Mohawk Valley
Oil on canvas. 22 × 38 in. (55.9 × 96.5 cm.)
Signed lower right: *John J. Hammer*. Painted about 1860–1870.

M. and M. Karolik Collection. 47.1141
Reference: Karolik Catalogue, 1949, no. 123 (repr.).

470. **The Sculptor's Studio**
Oil on canvas. 17 × 14 in. (43.2 × 35.5 cm.)
Signed lower right: *John J. Hammer.* Painted about 1870–1873.
M. and M. Karolik Collection. 47.1148
Reference: Karolik Catalogue, 1949, no. 124 (repr.).

CHESTER HARDING (1792–1866) was born in Conway, N.H. In 1817 he was a sign painter
in Pittsburgh but soon began to paint portraits. He worked briefly in Paris,
Ky., in St. Louis until 1821, then in Washington, D.C. In 1822 he arrived
in Boston to see Gilbert Stuart, and prospered there. He spent the successful
years 1823 to 1826 in England, where he came under the influence of Sir
Thomas Lawrence and became a prolific portrait painter. On his return
he lived in Boston, then Springfield, Mass. with many trips to Washington,
Richmond, Baltimore, and other cities; he made another trip to England
in 1846. He also founded Harding's Gallery in Boston, the first association
of artists in America to promote group exhibitions of contemporary work.
He died in Boston.

471. **Ebenezer Bliss**
Bust-length, turned three-quarters left, he wears a black coat and white stock. The
background is brown.
Oil on panel. 30 × 23½ in. (76.2 × 59.7 cm.)
Painted about 1822.
Bequest of Maxim Karolik. 64.457
The sitter's name is traditional. He may have been Ebenezer Bliss (1779–
1827), son of Ebenezer and Abigail Parsons Bliss of Belchertown, Mass.,
who became a clothier in Ware, Mass. and who in 1803 married Betsy
Nevins. The costume and less accomplished technique suggest that the
portrait may have been done immediately after Harding's arrival in Boston.

472. **Eben Rollins**
fig. 205
Bust-length, turned three-quarters left, the young man wears a brown fur-collared
coat with a white stock. The background is brown.
Oil on panel. 28 × 23 in. (71.1 × 58.4 cm.)
Painted about 1822–1825.
Collection: John Torrey Morse, Jr., step-grandson of the sitter, and Miss
Charlotte G.S. Morse, Needham, Mass.
Gift of John Torrey Morse, Jr. and Miss Charlotte G.S. Morse. 59.959
Eben Rollins (1783–1832), son of Eliphalet and Patty Sargent Rollins, was
born in East Bradford (now Groveland), Mass. He became a prominent
Boston merchant and a director of a bank and an insurance company. His
wife was Frances Morse, widow of John T. Morse, daughter of Samuel and
Catherine Gore Torrey and niece of Governor Christopher Gore. In 1832
Rollins went to Havana, Cuba for reasons of health and died there. From
his youthful appearance, he was probably portrayed shortly after Harding's
arrival in Boston.

473. **Dr. John Ball Brown**
fig. 207
Half-length, turned three-quarters left, he wears a dark brown coat with a white stock.
Behind him is a red curtain before a blue sky.
Oil on canvas. 30 × 25 in. (76.2 × 63.5 cm.)
Painted about 1826.
Collection: Buckminster Brown, M.D., son of the sitter, Boston.
Bequest of Buckminster Brown, M.D. 14.424
John Ball Brown (1784–1862) was born in Wilmington, Mass. the son of
Dr. Jabez and Anna Brown. A prominent Boston doctor, he specialized in

orthopedics, having his own infirmary on Chambers Street, and was an associate and consulting surgeon of the Massachusetts General Hospital. He died in Boston. From his apparent age, about forty, his portrait was painted soon after Harding's return from London. It is pendant to Cat. no. 474.

474.

fig. 208

Mrs. John Ball Brown (Rebecca Warren)

Seated in half-length and turned three-quarters right, she is wearing a gray dress and gray ermine-trimmed cape. Her white lace bonnet has yellow ribbons. The background is gray.

Oil on canvas. 30 × 25 in. (76.2 × 63.5 cm.)

Painted about 1826.

Collection: Same as Cat. no. 473.

Bequest of Buckminster Brown, M.D. 14.425

Rebecca Warren (1789–1855) was the daughter of Dr. John and Abigail Warren and niece of Joseph Warren (Cat. no. 292), about whom she published the patriotic little book, *Stories about Gen. Warren in Relation to the 5th of March Massacre and the Battle of Bunker Hill* (1835). She married Dr. Brown in 1814. Her portrait was painted at the same time as the pendant of her husband (Cat. no. 473).

Exhibition: Springfield, Mass., Connecticut Valley Historical Museum, *Harding*, 1952.

475.

fig. 206

Mrs. Ward Nicholas Boylston (Alicia Darrow)

Half-length and facing front, she is seated before a brown wall and dark red curtain, left. She wears a black satin dress with shawl, a wide white lace collar, and white lace cap.

Oil on canvas. 36 × 28¾ in. (91.5 × 73 cm.)

Painted about 1826–1830.

Collections: Probably Ward Nicholas Boylston, M.D., her grandson, Princeton, Mass.; Mrs. Louisa C.A. Nightingale, his sister, Providence, R.I., 1887; Ward Nicholas Boylston, Jr., her nephew, Brattleboro, Vt., 1925; Mrs. Barbara Boylston Bean, his sister, Auburn, Me., 1963.

Lent by Mrs. Paul Webster Bean. 60.63

Alicia Darrow Boylston (1763–1843) of Yarmouth, England, was the second wife of Ward Nicholas Boylston (1749–1828), of whom the MFA owns two portraits by Gilbert Stuart (Cat. nos. 947, 948), a Boston merchant and benefactor of Harvard College. She lived with her husband, a Loyalist, in London from their marriage about 1785 until they returned to Boston in 1800. In 1819–1820 Mr. Boylston established an extensive country estate in Princeton, Mass., between Boston and Springfield. Harding returned to Boston from London in 1826 and moved to Springfield a few years later; the portrait, considering its costume and style, was probably painted soon after his return, and possibly at Princeton.

Exhibition: Pittsburgh, Pa., Carnegie Institute, *Survey of American Painting*, 1940, no. 52 (as *Portrait of a Lady*).

476.

Alderman Jabez Ellis

An elderly gentleman, bust-length and turned three-quarters right, wears a black suit and stock with a white shirt. The background is brown.

Oil on canvas. Painted oval. 30 × 25 in. (76.2 × 63.5 cm.)

Painted about 1832–1835.

Collections: Mrs. Charles B. Darling, daughter of the sitter, Boston; Miss Mary Elizabeth Ellis Darling, her daughter; the donors, her nephew and niece, New York.

Gift of Laurence Ballard Darling and Catherine Ellis Darling. 48.506

Jabez Ellis (1770–1855) was born in West Dedham, Mass. A successful Boston merchant, known for his integrity and righteousness, he was a member of the Boston Common Council in 1830 and 1831, a member of the

Massachusetts Legislature from 1830 to 1832, and an Alderman from 1832 to 1834. Tradition and the apparent ages of the sitters suggest the date for this portrait and its pendant (Cat. no. 477).

477.

Mrs. Jabez Ellis (Elizabeth Newell)
Half-length and turned three-quarters left, an elderly lady is seated before a brown background. Her dress is black with a white lace collar and cap.
Oil on canvas. Painted oval. 30 × 25¼ in. (76.2 × 64.1 cm.)
Painted about 1832–1835.
Collections: Same as Cat. no. 476.
Gift of Laurence Ballard Darling and Catherine Ellis Darling. 48.507
Elizabeth Newell, born in Needham, Mass. in 1770, married Mr. Ellis in 1797. They had five children and lived in a mansion on Harrison Avenue, Boston, where she died in 1863. Pendant to the preceding.

478.
fig. 210

Abbott Lawrence
Full-length, he stands by a green-draped table, resting his right hand on an upright book. He wears a black cape and suit with a white stock. Behind is green and gold drapery to the right of a gray column.
Oil on canvas. 28¾ × 18½ in. (73 × 47 cm.)
Painted about 1840–1845.
Collections: Mrs. Augustus Lowell, Boston; Abbott Lawrence Lowell, Boston; Mrs. Horatio A. Lamb, Milton, Mass.; the Misses Aimée and Rosamond Lamb, Boston.
Gift of the Misses Aimée and Rosamond Lamb. 61.239
Abbott Lawrence (1792–1855) was born in Groton, Mass. the son of Samuel and Susanna Parker Lawrence. Partner with his brother Amos (Cat. no. 482) in the A. & A. Lawrence Co., dry goods merchants, he was President of the Essex Company, a cotton and woolen mill they had founded in Lawrence, Mass., and of the Pacific Mills. Twice U.S. Representative and once Minister to England, he was a generous benefactor of Groton Academy and Harvard University, where he established the Lawrence Scientific School. He died in Boston. The portrait is dated from his apparent age. Although approximately of the same date, the portrait of Mrs. Abbott Lawrence (Cat. no. 479) is not a pendant.
Reference: M.E. White, ed., *A Sketch of Chester Harding, Artist*, Boston, 1890, p. 246 (possibly this portrait).

479.
fig. 211

Mrs. Abbott Lawrence (Katherine Bigelow)
Seated full-length in a Victorian Gothic chair and facing three-quarters right, she wears a long black dress with a white fichu and veil and knits a red scarf. Beside her are books and a vase of roses on a red and black covered table. Beyond are a green drapery and, right, a yellow-green landscape with pink clouded sky.
Oil on canvas. 27½ × 22¼ in. (69.2 × 56.5 cm.)
Painted about 1840–1850.
Collections: Same as Cat. no. 478.
Gift of the Misses Aimée and Rosamond Lamb. 61.240
Katherine Bigelow (1793–1860) was the daughter of Timothy and Lucy Prescott Bigelow of Medford, Mass. In 1819 she married Abbott Lawrence and had five children by him. She died in Boston. The portrait is dated according to her costume and the furnishings.

480.

Benjamin Pickman
Oil on canvas. 30 × 25 in. (76.2 × 63.5 cm.)
Painted in 1843.
M. and M. Karolik Collection. 48.425
Reference: *Karolik Catalogue*, 1949, no. 125 (repr.).

481.

Self-Portrait
Half-length, turned slightly right, he wears a black suit and stock with a white shirt.

The background is brown.
Oil on canvas. 30 × 25 in. (76.2 × 63.5 cm.)
Painted about 1843.
Collection: Russell Harding, the artist's grandson, Springfield, Mass.
Bequest of Isabel R. Harding (Mrs. Russell Harding). 30.108
Judging from the subject's age, the date of his painting is probably about 1843, the year in which he displayed a self-portrait in the Boston Artist's Association exhibition.
Reference: A. Burroughs, *Limners and Likenesses*, Cambridge, Mass., 1936, p. 126.
Exhibitions: Probably Boston, Harding's Gallery, *Boston Artist's Association*, 1843, no. 48 (lent by the artist)./ Springfield, Mass., Connecticut Valley Historical Museum, *Harding*, 1952.

482.
fig. 209

Amos Lawrence

Full-length, turned three-quarters left and seated in a green upholstered chair, he wears a red paisley dressing gown. His velvet cap, the tablecloth, and curtain are red; the column is gray, and the wall is brown.
Oil on canvas. 34¼ × 23½ in. (87 × 59.7 cm.)
Painted about 1844–1845.
Collections: Abbott Lawrence, the sitter's brother, Boston; Mrs. Benjamin S. Rotch, his daughter, Milton, Mass.; Mrs. Horatio A. Lamb, Milton; the Misses Aimée and Rosamond Lamb, Boston.
Gift of the Misses Aimée and Rosamond Lamb. 59.857
Amos Lawrence (1786–1852), son of Major Samuel and Susanna Parker Lawrence, was born in Groton, Mass. He and his brother Abbott (Cat. no. 478) formed the A. & A. Lawrence Co., one of the leading importers in New England of dry goods from England. After his retirement in 1831, Amos became known for his philanthropic gifts to many educational and civic institutions. He died in Boston. This is probably a study for the life-size portrait of Lawrence now in the National Gallery, Washington, D.C., painted about 1845. A replica of the latter is in the Williams College Art Museum, Williamstown, Mass. An engraving of the figure done probably after the National Gallery version was made by Joseph Andrews, 1845–1856 (published as the frontispiece to *Extracts from the Diary and Correspondence of the Late Amos Lawrence*, edited by his son, William R. Lawrence, Boston, 1856). The sitter's apparent age and the fact that the Williams replica was commissioned in 1845 suggest a date just prior to that.
Reference: M.E. White, ed., *Sketch of Chester Harding, Artist*, Boston, 1890, p. 246.
Exhibition: Springfield, Mass., Connecticut Valley Historical Museum, *Harding*, 1952.

483.

Henrietta Clark
Turned three-quarters left, half-length, she is seated in a red and gray brocade chair. Over her black dress and white bodice she wears a red-lined ermine stole. The background is brown.
Oil on canvas. 30 × 25 in. (76.2 × 63.5 cm.)
Painted about 1849.
Collection: Russell Harding, grandson of the sitter and of the artist.
Bequest of Isabel R. Harding (Mrs. Russell Harding). 30.109
Henrietta was the wife of J.P. Clark, merchant of Detroit; Chester Harding's son William married Mary, their daughter, in 1849. The painting was probably done at the time of this marriage.

484.

John Lemist (attributed to Harding)
Bust-length, turned three-quarters right, he wears a high-collared black coat and stock with a white waistcoat. The background is brown.
Oil on oval canvas. 24 × 20 in. (61 × 50.8 cm.)
Painted about 1823.
Gift of the Estates of Eunice McLellan Cruft and Frances Cordis Cruft. 42.387

A label on the back of the painting reads: *Portrait of| John Lemist| Born Aug. 25–1785| died Jan. 13–1840| Married Mary (Condis)| widow of Capt. Haswell| June 2–1816| Lost on Steamer Lexington| coming from New York to| Boston.* Stylistically, the portrait is quite similar to the work of Harding around 1840, as in the portraits of *Jabez Ellis* (Cat. no. 476), about 1835, and of *Benjamin Pickman* (Cat. no. 480) before 1843. However, the painting is either not by Harding or not of Lemist. Lemist would have been fifty-five in 1840, and the clothing style in this portrait was in use by the 1830's.

JEREMIAH PEARSON HARDY (1800–1887) was born in Pelham, N.H. and in 1811 moved with his family to Hampden, Me. Although self-taught, at an early age he became a competent book plate engraver, and about 1821 studied in Boston with David Brown at his Academy. He then reputedly worked with S.F.B. Morse in New York, but by 1827 he had returned to Hampden. In 1838 he settled permanently in Bangor, Me. and worked there, a popular portrait and genre painter, until his death.

485. **Mary Ann Hardy**
Oil on panel. 18 × 14½ in. (45.7 × 36.8 cm.)
Inscribed on back: *Mary A[n]n Hardy| Drawn, March 1821 in the| 12th year of her AE| J.P. Hardy del| 1.*
M. and M. Karolik Collection. 47.1135
Reference: Karolik Catalogue, 1949, no. 126 (repr.).

486. **The Reverend Cyrus Hamlin, D.D.**
A bust portrait, in left profile, his black coat has a brown fur collar, and the background is brown.
Oil on canvas. 27¼ × 22 in. (69.2 × 55.9 cm.)
Painted about 1839.
Collection: Miss Anna E. Hardy, the artist's daughter, Bangor, Me., 1887.
Gift of Miss Anna E. Hardy. 16.387

Cyrus Hamlin (1811–1900), missionary and educator, born near Waterford, Me., was a graduate of Bowdoin College and the Bangor Theological Seminary. He founded and managed a school in Bebek, Turkey from 1840 to 1860, was a founder and President of Robert College there from 1863 to 1877, and was President of Middlebury College in Vermont from 1881 until 1885. From his apparent age the portrait was probably done before he left for Turkey.
Exhibition: Boston, Massachusetts Charitable Mechanics Association, 1874, no. 172.

487. **Catharine Wheeler Hardy and Her Daughter**
Oil on canvas. 29¼ × 36 in. (74.3 × 91.4 cm.)
Painted about 1842.
M. and M. Karolik Collection. 47.1146
Reference: Karolik Catalogue, 1949, no. 127 (repr.).

A Pic Nick, Camden, Maine
See Jerome B. Thompson, Cat. no. 974.

WILLIAM MICHAEL HARNETT (1848–1892), born in Clonakilty, County Cork, Ireland, emigrated to Philadelphia; he studied engraving there until 1869 and attended night classes at the Pennsylvania Academy. He then became a silver engraver in New York and studied at the night schools of the Cooper Union and the National Academy; in 1874 he began to paint. He worked at the Pennsylvania Academy from 1876 to 1880, when he left to study in Frankfurt and Munich until 1884. Returning via Paris and London, he lived in New York from 1886 until his death.

488. **Old Models**
fig. 449
Against a green cupboard door with rusty hinges, a light blue music book hangs behind a brass horn. On the shelf below, a sheet of music and a blue-figured white jug stand

on books bound in brown and yellowed white. Beside them are a violin and bow.
Oil on canvas. 54 × 28 in. (137.2 × 71.1 cm.)
Signed and dated lower left: *WMHarnett/ 1892* (initials in monogram).
Collections: Estate of the artist, 1892; *Harnett Estate Sale*, Thomas Birch's Sons, Philadelphia, Feb. 23–24, 1893, no. 27 (repr. frontispiece); *A. Ludwig Collection Sale*, Fifth Avenue Art Galleries, New York, Feb. 1–2, 1898, no. 93; William J. Hughes, Washington, D.C.
Charles Henry Hayden Fund. 39.761

Said to have been the artist's last painting, and considered his masterpiece, *Old Models* was also known as *The Old Cupboard* and the *Old Cupboard Door*. The former title caused the confusion that existed between our painting and the one commissioned by William Bement of Philadelphia (completed 1889 and now owned by Graves Art Gallery, Sheffield, England).

References: "The Blemly Scrapbook," MS. owned by the Downtown Gallery, New York./ *The Collector*, 1893, IV, no. 19, p. 294./ B.N. Parker, "The Old Cupboard Door," *MFA Bulletin*, 1940, XXXVIII, no. 225, p. 17 (repr. p. 18)./ W. Born, *Still Life Painting in America*, New York, 1947, p. 33 (pl. 89)./ A. Frankenstein, *After the Hunt*, Berkeley, Calif., 1953, pp. 89 (note 57), 92, 95, 108, 174 (pl. 82)./ A. TenEyck Gardner, "Harnett," *Metropolitan Museum Bulletin*, 1964, XXII, no. 5, p. 164 (repr.).

Exhibitions: Philadelphia, Earle's Galleries, *Harnett*, 1892, no. 20./ New York, M. Knoedler and Co., *Harnett*, 1893./ *St. Louis Exposition*, 1896, no. 221./ London, Tate Gallery, *American Painting*, 1946, no. 97./ New York, Downtown Gallery, *Harnett Centennial*, 1948, no. 20 (repr. cover)./ San Francisco, California Palace of the Legion of Honor, *Illusionism and Trompe l'Oeil*, 1949 (repr. p. 33)./ Washington, D.C., Corcoran Gallery, *De Gustibus*, 1949, no. 32./ New York, American Federation of Arts, circulated in Germany and Italy, and Whitney Museum, *American Painting in the Nineteenth Century*, 1953–1954, no. 40./ Cincinnati Art Museum, *Rediscoveries in American Painting*, 1955, no. 46 (repr. frontispiece)./ Washington, D.C., St. Albans School, *50th Anniversary Celebration*, 1959, no. 20./ Toronto Art Gallery and circulated in Canada, and New York, Whitney Museum, *American Painting from 1865–1905*, 1961, no. 31 (pl. v).

PHILIP HARRY   (active 1843–1847)

489.   **Tremont Street, Boston**
fig. 278   Oil on panel. 13¾ × 16 in. (34.9 × 40.6 cm.)
Painted before 1843.
M. and M. Karolik Collection. 47.1150
Reference: Karolik Catalogue, 1949, no. 129 (repr.).

JAMES MACDOUGAL HART (1828–1901)

490.   **On the Lake Shore**
Oil on canvas. 13 × 23½ in. (33 × 59.7 cm.)
Signed and dated lower left: *James M. Hart Cay . . . July 1864.*
M. and M. Karolik Collection. 47.1140
Reference: Karolik Catalogue, 1949, no. 130 (repr.).

WILLIAM HART   (1823–1894), elder brother of James MacDougal Hart, was born in Paisley, Scotland. When he was eight, his family moved to Albany, N.Y., and at fifteen he was apprenticed to a coach-maker there. Illness forced abandonment of his trade and he turned to painting landscapes, portraits, and even window shade decorations. He studied in Scotland from 1849 to 1852 but settled in New York, then Brooklyn, then Mount Vernon, N.Y., where he died. In 1865 he became first President of the Brooklyn Academy of Design, and was President of the American Society of Water-Colorists.

491.   **River in Autumn**
fig. 369   *A gray river flows between wooded banks in autumn colors of brown, red, orange, and green. Beyond are brown hills under a blue sky.*
Oil on canvas. 18¼ × 32¼ in. (46.3 × 81.9 cm.)

Signed and dated lower left: *Wm. Hart 63.*
Collections: James Brown Case, Boston, by 1907; Louise W. Case and Marion
R. Case, his daughters, Boston.
Gift of Louise W. Case and Marian R. Case. 20.1871

492.   **After the Storm**
Oil on canvas. 14¼ × 24¼ in. (36.2 × 61.6 cm.)
Painted before the early 1870's.
M. and M. Karolik Collection. 47.1137
Reference: *Karolik Catalogue*, 1949, no. 131 (repr.).

493.   **Cows Drinking at a Pool**
*Several cows drink at a pool in the foreground that reflects the nearby green trees and
the distant cloudy blue sky.*
Oil on canvas. 10¼ × 8¼ in. (26 × 21 cm.)
Signed and dated lower right: *Wm. Hart/ 1886.*
Gift of Dr. Joseph P. Oliver, through Miss C.L.W. French. 06.2406

(EDMUND) MARSDEN HARTLEY (1877–1943) was born in Lewiston, Me., the youngest child
and only boy of nine children. The family moved to Cleveland, where he
studied in the School of Art. In New York in 1898 he entered the Chase
School, under F. Luis Mora, Frank du Mond, and William M. Chase, then
the National Academy. After 1900 he worked in Maine in the summers
and New York in the winters. His early work was Impressionist in manner
but he was soon aware of Cézanne and Picasso. He was in Paris and Berlin
in 1912 and 1913, when he came under the influence of Kandinsky and
the Blaue Reiter group, then in Berlin again in 1914–1915. Until his death
in Ellsworth, Me. he divided his time between America and Europe,
traveling extensively.

494.   **Black Duck**
fig. 578
The front of a black, white, and red-collared duck is depicted on a brown background.
Oil on masonite. 28 × 22 in. (71.1 × 55.9 cm.)
See also
cat. no 1048
Signed and dated lower right: *M.H./ 40–41.* Inscribed on back, upper right:
Black Duck/ no. 2.
Charles Henry Hayden Fund. 43.32

The bird depicted is actually the male Common Eider, which migrates to
New England during the winter from Labrador and the North. A similar
painting, entitled *Black Duck no. 1*, signed and dated M.H./ '41, is owned
by the Detroit Institute of Arts.

Exhibitions: New York, Museum of Modern Art, *Feininger and Hartley*, 1944, p. 93
(repr. p. 85)./ Chicago, Arts Club, *Hartley Memorial*, 1945, no. 52./ Toronto Art
Gallery, *Contemporary Art*, 1949, no. 87./ Boston, Shore Galleries, *Hartley*, 1962,
no. 37.

GEORGE HARVEY (about 1800–1878)

495.   **View on the Hudson**
fig. 217
Oil on panel. 12 × 19 in. (30.5 × 48.2 cm.)
Inscribed on back in pencil: *View on the Hudson/ by George Harvey/ April 1836.*
M. and M. Karolik Collection. 47.1134
Reference: *Karolik Catalogue*, 1949, no. 132 (repr.).

496.   **White Pelicans in Florida**
Oil on canvas. 14 × 24 in. (35.5 × 61 cm.)
Signed and dated lower left: *G.Harvey 1853* (unclear; possibly reads 1823).
M. and M. Karolik Collection. 47.1163
Reference: *Karolik Catalogue*, 1949, no. 133 (repr.).

FREDERICK CHILDE HASSAM (1859–1935) was born in Dorchester, Mass. At first employed as
an illustrator by a Boston wood engraver, he commenced to paint in the late

1870's under Gaugengigl. In 1883 he made a painting tour of Great Britain, the Lowlands, Spain, and Italy, and in 1886 moved to Paris. While at first in the conservative milieu of the Académie Julian, he soon embraced Impressionism. He experienced great success in Paris, and in New York after his return in 1889, and became with Twachtman one of the leading American Impressionist painters. He worked in New York in winter and visited his favorite New England haunts, Old Lyme and Cos Cob, Gloucester and the Isles of Shoals, during the summer. In 1897 he again visited Paris and Italy, and the following year founded with Twachtman, Weir, Theodore Robinson, and others the Impressionist-oriented group, the "Ten American Painters." There were later visits to western America and again to Europe, but after 1920 he worked regularly in New York and at his home in East Hampton, N.Y., where he died.

497.
fig. 519

Boston Common at Twilight
Figures, buildings, and vehicles are painted in muted browns with touches of orange; there is an orange-pink sunset in a pale blue sky.
Oil on canvas. 42 × 60 in. (106.7 × 152.4 cm.)
Signed and dated lower right: *Childe Hassam/ 1885–6.*
Collections: Mr. Appleton, Boston, by about 1895; Miss Maud E. Appleton, Boston, by 1927.
Gift of Miss Maud E. Appleton. 31.952
Reference: F.T. Robinson, "Hassam," *Living New England Artists*, Boston, 1888, p. 102.
Exhibitions: Probably exhibited Boston, Noyes, Cobb and Co., *Hassam*, 1889, no. 30./ Marquette University, Brooks Memorial Union Building, *American Painting of the Past Seventy-five Years*, 1956, no. 33./ New York, American Federation of Arts, circulated in the U.S., *A Hundred Years Ago*, 1958–1959./ Washington, D.C., Corcoran Gallery and circulated in the U.S., *Hassam*, 1965, no. 3 (repr. p. 10).

498.
fig. 518

Grand Prix Day
Gentlemen wearing brown and gray and ladies with pink parasols travel the ochre-pink street in carriages drawn by white and brown horses. A row of green trees before pink buildings and blue sky in the background. A corner of the Arc de Triomphe is at the left.
Oil on canvas. 24 × 34 in. (61 × 78.7 cm.)
Signed and dated lower left: *Childe Hassam Paris–1887.*
Collections: Celian M. Spitzer, Toledo, O., about 1900; Sidney Spitzer, 1919, a collateral descendant.
Ernest Wadsworth Longfellow Fund. 64.983
A busy thoroughfare in the vicinity of the Place de l'Étoile, Paris, with the Arc de Triomphe. Painted only a year after the somber realism of *Boston Common at Twilight* (Cat. no. 497), the painting displays the impact of French Impressionism on Hassam. A larger replica, probably also of about 1887, is at the New Britain Museum, New Britain, Conn. A pastel called *At the "Grand Prix de Paris"* (unlocated) was exhibited at Doll and Richards, Boston, 1891, no. 43.
Exhibitions: Possibly exhibited Boston, Noyes, Cobb & Co., 1889, no. 16./ Washington, D.C., Corcoran Gallery and circulated in the U.S., *Childe Hassam*, 1965, no. 5 (repr.).

499.

Chicken Yard Back of the Holly House
A fall landscape with distant red, yellow, and green trees and blue water. There are white chickens in the green yard foreground before white fences and houses with blue and brown roofs. The sky is vivid blue.
Pastel on cardboard. 10 × 11 in. (25.4 × 27.9 cm.)
Signed and dated lower left: *Childe Hassam/ 1902.*
Collection: Estate of the artist, New York.
Bequest of Kathleen Rothe. 65.1297
Exhibition: Boston, MFA, *Hassam*, 1965 (not in catalogue).

500. **Cos Cob**

A bridge and causeway over blue and brown falls and a stream leads to a yellow and brown house and trees in early fall colors of green with red and yellow. The moon in the pale blue sky is white.
Pastel on cardboard. 10 × 11 in. (25.4 × 27.9 cm.)
Signed and dated lower left: *Childe Hassam 1902.*
Collection: Estate of the artist, New York.
Bequest of Kathleen Rothe. 65.1298
Exhibition: Boston, MFA, *Hassam*, 1965 (not in catalogue).

501. **The Old Holly House**

fig. 517

A gray and white "salt box" house with two-story front porch stands behind a large tree. Fall leaves of yellow, orange, and brown are on the branches and on the ground near patches of green grass. The sky is blue-green.
Pastel on cardboard. 10 × 11 in. (25.4 × 27.9 cm.)
Signed and dated lower left: *Childe Hassam 1902.*
Collection: Estate of the artist, New York.
Bequest of Kathleen Rothe. 65.1299

The Old Holly House, or Bush Holly House, was built in the seventeenth century in the Cos Cob section of Greenwich, Conn. Early in this century it was known as the Holly Inn; Hassam and other artists stayed there.

Exhibition: Boston, MFA, *Hassam*, 1965 (not in catalogue).

502. **Bathing Pool, Appledore**

fig. 520

The gray and brown rocky coast, spotted with green grass, meets the bright blue and green sea. Figures wearing light-colored clothes, are in the foreground, and red and blue bathhouses are at the left; the blue sky is clouded.
Oil on canvas. 25 × 30 in. (63.5 × 76.2 cm.)
Signed and dated lower left: *Childe Hassam 1907.*
Collection: Robert Pollak, New York, 1948.
Ernest Wadsworth Longfellow Fund. 64.982

Appledore is one of the nine islands which form the Isles of Shoals off the Portsmouth, N.H. coast, where Hassam spent many summers painting. Numerous variations of the subject exist, spanning the years from about 1900 on.

503. **The Lady of the Gorge**

fig. 516

A nude figure sits on a rock and looks down into blue and brown water. The steep sides of the gorge are white, accented with green, yellow, brown, blue, and gray. The sky is blue.
Oil on canvas. 22¼ × 24 in. (56.5 × 61 cm.)
Signed and dated lower left: *Childe Hassam 1912.*
Collections: John P. Lyman, Boston; Miss Theodora Lyman, by 1915.
The John Pickering Lyman Collection. Gift of Miss Theodora Lyman. 19.1324
Exhibitions: Boston, Copley Gallery, *Hassam*, n.d., no. 18 (lent by Mr. Lyman)./ Buffalo, Albright Art Gallery, *Hassam*, 1929, no. 4 (erroneously listed as lent by the Brooklyn Museum).

CHARLES WEBSTER HAWTHORNE (1872–1930) was born in Lodi, Ill. In 1890 he studied in Frank du Mond's evening classes and at the Art Students League, New York, where he returned in 1894 as the student of George deF. Brush and Siddons Mowbray. He became William M. Chase's assistant in 1897, after a summer at his school. His interest in the sea took him to Holland in 1898. His fame as a teacher was made at the Art Students League and the National Academy in New York, the Chicago Art Institute, and at his own school, the Cape Cod School of Art, which he founded in 1899 in Provincetown, Mass. He died in Baltimore.

504.

fig. 531

The Bowl

A boy, wearing a white smock, stands behind a large green and white bowl on a gray table. In one hand he holds a fish. The background is purple.
Oil on canvas. 30 × 25 in. (76.2 × 63.5 cm.)
Signed upper left: *C.W. Hawthorne.*
Gift of Frederick L. Jack. 35.1222

505.

The Mother

A woman in green and yellow stands in three-quarter length holding her white-robed baby. Blue and white china is on a table covered with a white tablecloth. The chair is brown and the wall is green.
Oil on wallboard. 40 × 40 in. (101.6 × 101.6 cm.)
Signed upper left: *C.W. Hawthorne.* Painted about 1910.
Charles Henry Hayden Fund. 16.63

Exhibitions: Provincetown, Mass., Hawthorne Memorial Gallery, 1942./ Provincetown, Chrysler Art Museum, *Hawthorne Retrospective*, 1961, no. 95.

MARTIN JOHNSON HEADE (1819–1904), born in Lumberville, Pa., first studied there briefly with his friend Thomas Hicks. From about 1837 to 1840 he studied in Italy, France, and England, and on his return he lived periodically in New York, Trenton, N.J., and then Boston, St. Louis, and Chicago. He was a naturalist as well as a portrait and landscape painter. In 1863–1864 he worked in Brazil, in Nicaragua in 1866, and in Colombia, Puerto Rico, and Jamaica in 1870. He later lived in Washington, D.C. and New York. In 1885 he settled permanently in St. Augustine, Fla., where he died. (A more extensive biography is available in the MFA's *M. and M. Karolik Collection of American Water-colors and Drawings*, Boston, 1962, 1, p. 181.)

506.

fig. 326

Vase of Mixed Flowers

Oil on canvas. 17¼ × 13¾ in. (43.8 × 34.9 cm.)
Signed lower right: *M.J. Heade.* Painted in the 1850's.
M. and M. Karolik Collection. 48.427

Reference: Karolik Catalogue, 1949, no. 136 (repr.).

507.

Rocks in New England

Oil on canvas. 17 × 27¼ in. (43.2 × 69.2 cm.)
Signed and dated on a rock lower right: *M J Heade/ 1855.*
M. and M. Karolik Collection. 47.1171

Reference: Karolik Catalogue, 1949, no. 134 (repr.).

508.

Mary Rebecca Clark

Oil on canvas. 22 × 18 in. (55.9 × 45.7 cm.)
Signed and dated lower left: *M.J. Heade/ 1857.*
M. and M. Karolik Collection. 48.426

Reference: Karolik Catalogue, 1949, no. 135 (repr.).

509.

fig. 325

Rhode Island Landscape

Behind a fallen stone wall a young woman in a blue dress stands in a rocky green pasture beside a copse of trees, right, and surveys a gray inlet, a green point, and distant shoreline. Sheep graze next to a pair of stone walls. The sky is gray.
Oil on canvas. 12 × 20¼ in. (30.5 × 51.4 cm.)
Signed and dated lower right: *M. J. Heade/ 1858* (?).
Collections: Stephen C. Clark, 1944; Maxim Karolik, Newport, R.I., 1945.
Bequest of Maxim Karolik. 64.432

510.

Sunset, Black Rock, Connecticut

Oil on canvas. 13 × 26 in. (33 × 66 cm.)
Signed lower left: *M J Heade.* Painted in the early 1860's.
M. and M. Karolik Collection. 47.1174

Reference: Karolik Catalogue, 1949, no. 144 (repr.).

511.

fig. 329

Approaching Storm: Beach near Newport
Oil on canvas. 28 × 58¼ in. (71.1 × 147.9 cm.)
Painted in the 1860's.
M. and M. Karolik Collection. 45.889
Reference: *Karolik Catalogue*, 1949, no. 137 (repr.).

512.

Cloudy Day, Rhode Island
Oil on canvas. 11½ × 25¼ in. (29.1 × 64.1 cm.)
Signed and dated on fence rail lower center and again lower left: *M.J. Heade 1861.*
M. and M. Karolik Collection. 47.1158
Reference: *Karolik Catalogue*, 1949, no. 138 (repr.).

513.

Dawn
Oil on canvas. 12¼ × 24¼ in. (31.1 × 61.6 cm.)
Signed and dated lower right: *M.J. Heade –62.*
M. and M. Karolik Collection. 47.1143
Reference: *Karolik Catalogue*, 1949, no. 139 (repr.).

514.

fig. 327

Lake George
From the brown and green rocky shore a man pushes a boat into the green water. Gray distant mountains lie under a blue and pink sky.
Oil on canvas. 26 × 49¾ in. (66 × 126.3 cm.)
Signed and dated lower left: *MJ Heade/ 1862.*
Collections: S.M. Vose Galleries, the artist's agent, Providence, R.I.; Sumner Robinson, Boston; Maxim Karolik, Newport, R.I., 1948.
Bequest of Maxim Karolik. 64.430
Reference: J.I.H. Baur, *American Paintings in the Nineteenth Century*, New York, 1953 (repr. p. 14).
Exhibitions: Worcester, Mass., Art Museum, *The Private Collection of Maxim Karolik*, 1952, no. 18./ New York, American Federation of Arts, circulated in Germany and Italy, and Whitney Museum, *American Paintings in the Nineteenth Century*, 1953–1954, no. 22./ Washington, D.C., Smithsonian Institution, circulated in the U.S., *19th Century American Paintings*, 1954–1956, no. 27./ Boston, MFA, and circulated in the U.S., *American Paintings, 1815–1865*, 1957–1959, no. 157./ Ogunquit Museum, *8th Annual—Luminist and Trompe l'Oeil Painters*, 1960, no. 12.

515.

Hummingbirds with Nest
A green, red-breasted hummingbird perches with his brown, green, and gray mate beside their gray nest. Below them are green trees, above, gray sky.
Oil on canvas. 12 × 10½ in. (30.5 × 26.6 cm.)
Signed and dated lower right: *M.J. Heade/ 1863.*
Collection: Maxim Karolik, Newport, R.I., 1946.
Bequest of Maxim Karolik. 64.429
Painted on Heade's first South American expedition, to Brazil with the Rev. J.C. Fletcher, an amateur naturalist, with the intention of publishing an illustrated book on the hummingbirds of South America, never realized. For additional information on his bird pictures, see the *M. and M. Karolik Collection of American Water Colors and Drawings*, Boston, 1962, I, p. 183.
Exhibition: Southampton, N.Y., Parrish Museum, *American Paintings, 1815–1865*, 1961, no. 21 (repr. p. 30).

516.

Woodland Sketch
A brook runs through a wooded rocky glen dominated by a brown and green gnarled tree. Above, yellow clouds are in a blue sky.
Oil on canvas. 15 × 12 in. (38.1 × 30.5 cm.)
Signed and dated lower left: *M.J. Heade/–63–*
Collections: W.C. Thompson, North Attleboro, Mass.; Maxim Karolik, Newport, R.I., 1945.
Bequest of Maxim Karolik. 64.434

Despite the broad brushwork, its experimental nature and large-scale forms suggest a probable date in the 1850's.

517.   **Hunters Resting**
Oil on canvas. 12 × 24 in. (30.5 × 61 cm.)
Signed and dated lower left: *M J Heade—63.*
M. and M. Karolik Collection. 47.1139
Reference: *Karolik Catalogue*, 1949, no. 140 (repr.).

518.   **The Stranded Boat**
Oil on canvas. 22¾ × 36½ in. (57.8 × 92.7 cm.)
Signed and dated lower right: *M.J. Heade/ 1863.*
M. and M. Karolik Collection. 48.1026
Reference: *Karolik Catalogue*, 1949, no. 141 (repr.).

519.   **Salt Marshes, Newport, Rhode Island**
fig. 328
Oil on canvas. 15½ × 30¼ in. (39.4 × 76.8 cm.)
Signed lower left: *M.J. Heade.* Painted about 1863.
M. and M. Karolik Collection. 47.1152
Reference: *Karolik Catalogue*, 1949, no. 142 (repr.).

520.   **Sunset Over the Marshes**
Oil on canvas. 10¼ × 18¼ in. (26 × 46.3 cm.)
Signed lower left: *MJ Heade.* Painted about 1863.
M. and M. Karolik Collection. 47.1176
Reference: *Karolik Catalogue*, 1949, no. 143 (repr.).

521.   **Newburyport Marshes**
fig. 330
Two figures in the distance rake a broad green salt meadow beside a brown hay rick and red wagon. Trees, foliage, and gray hills are in the far distance. A gray pond is in the foreground, and gray, clouded sky is above.
Oil on canvas. 13 × 26 in. (33 × 66 cm.)
Signed lower left: *M.J. Heade.* Painted probably 1863–1865.
Collection: Maxim Karolik, Newport, R.I., by 1947.
Bequest of Maxim Karolik. 64.441
Similarity in subject and general style to *Salt Marshes, Newport, Rhode Island* (Cat. no. 519), probably of 1863, indicates that approximate date. However, *Newburyport Marshes*, although of nearly equal size, does not share the same clarity of definition and may be a later work.
Reference: H. Comstock, "Heade and Blythe," *Panorama*, 1947, II, no. 8 (repr. p. 86 as *Jersey Meadows*).
Exhibitions: Worcester, Mass., Art Museum, *19th Century American Painting*, 1952, no. 20./ Minneapolis Institute of Arts and circulated in the U.S., *19th Century American Paintings from the Collection of Maxim Karolik*, 1953–1954.

522.   **Orchids and Hummingbird**
Oil on canvas. 14½ × 22¼ in. (36.8 × 56.5 cm.)
Signed lower right: *M.J. Heade.* Painted about 1865.
M. and M. Karolik Collection. 47.1164
Reference: *Karolik Catalogue*, 1949, no. 146 (repr.).

523.   **Orchids and Spray Orchids with Hummingbirds**
Oil on canvas. 20 × 12 in. (50.8 × 30.5 cm.)
Signed lower left: *MJ Heade.* Painted about 1865.
M. and M. Karolik Collection. 47.1175
Reference: *Karolik Catalogue*, 1949, no. 147 (repr.).

524.   **Passion Flowers and Hummingbirds**
Oil on canvas. 15¼ × 21½ in. (39.4 × 54.6 cm.)
Signed lower left: *MJ Heade.* Painted about 1865.

M. and M. Karolik Collection. 47.1138

Reference: *Karolik Catalogue*, 1949, no. 145 (repr.).

525. **Rocky Shore**
Oil on canvas. 20 × 32 in. (50.8 × 81.2 cm.)
Signed and dated lower right: *M.J. Heade/ 1868.*
M. and M. Karolik Collection. 47.1172
Reference: *Karolik Catalogue*, 1949, no. 150 (repr.).

526. **South American River**
Oil on canvas. 26 × 22½ in. (66 × 57.1 cm.)
Signed and dated lower left: *M J Heade 68.*
M. and M. Karolik Collection. 47.1153
Reference: *Karolik Catalogue*, 1949, no. 149 (repr.).

527. **Spring Shower, Connecticut Valley**
fig. 331 Oil on canvas. 20 × 40 in. (50.8 × 101.6 cm.)
Signed and dated lower left: *M.J. Heade—68.*
M. and M. Karolik Collection. 47.1173
Reference: *Karolik Catalogue*, 1949, no. 151 (repr.).

528. **Off Shore: After the Storm**
Oil on canvas. 30 × 50 in. (76.2 × 127 cm.)
Signed lower left: *M J Heade.* Painted in the late 1860's.
M. and M. Karolik Collection. 47.1151
Reference: *Karolik Catalogue*, 1949, no. 148 (repr.).

529. **Sunset on Long Beach**
Oil on canvas. 10¼ × 22 in. (26 × 55.9 cm.)
Signed lower right: *MJ Heade.* Painted in the late 1870's or 1880's.
M. and M. Karolik Collection. 47.1159
Reference: *Karolik Catalogue*, 1949, no. 159 (repr.).

530. **The Bay of Panama**
Oil on canvas. 17 × 36¼ in. (43.2 × 92.1 cm.)
Signed on rock lower left: *M.J. Heade.* Painted about 1871.
M. and M. Karolik Collection. 47.1167
Reference: *Karolik Catalogue*, 1949, no. 152 (repr.).

531. **Sunset: Lake Champlain**
Oil on canvas. 25¼ × 50 in. (64.1 × 127 cm.)
Signed and dated lower left: *M.J. Heade/ 1874.*
M. and M. Karolik Collection. 47.1162
Reference: *Karolik Catalogue*, 1949, no. 153 (repr.).

532. **Magnolia Grandiflora**
Oil on canvas. 15 × 24 in. (38.1 × 61 cm.)
Signed lower left center: *M.J. Heade.* Painted in the 1880's.
M. and M. Karolik Collection. 47.1169
Reference: *Karolik Catalogue*, 1949, no. 157 (repr.).

533. **Magnolias**
Oil on canvas. 24 × 15 in. (61 × 38.1 cm.)
Signed lower right: *M.J. Heade.* Painted in the 1880's.
M. and M. Karolik Collection. 47.1157
Reference: *Karolik Catalogue*, 1949, no. 156 (repr.).

534. **Water Lily**
Oil on canvas. 10 × 18 in. (25.4 × 45.7 cm.)
Signed with initials lower right: *M J H.* Painted about 1884.
M. and M. Karolik Collection. 47.1165
Reference: *Karolik Catalogue*, 1949, no. 155 (repr.).

GEORGE PETER ALEXANDER HEALY (1813–1894), born in Boston, was precocious as an artist and with the encouragement of Thomas Sully opened a studio there in 1831. Patronage of Mrs. Harrison Gray Otis provided enough work to make possible a trip to Paris in 1834. He spent a year under Baron Gros and then met Couture. He worked in England, France, and America, painting portraits and some highly successful historical paintings. In 1855 he settled in Chicago, actively painting portraits. From 1867 to 1892 he lived primarily in Paris and Rome but returned to Chicago and died there two years later.

535. **Thomas Kemper Davis**

A young man, bust-length and wearing a black coat and cravat, is turned three-quarters right. The background is brown.
Oil on cardboard. 24 × 20 in. (61 × 50.8 cm.)
Painted about 1831–1834.
Collection: Charles G. Davis, Boston.
Gift of Mrs. Richard Hathaway Morgan and Miss Joanna W. Davis. 07.516
Thomas Kemper Davis (1808–1853) was the son of Isaac P. and Susan Jackson Davis of Boston. He received an M.A. degree at Harvard and, having studied law with Daniel Webster, was admitted to the bar in 1830. Promise of a brilliant career was cut short by a brain injury from which he never recovered. His portrait is dated from the style and from his apparent age.

536. **Father Taylor**
fig. 297

Half-length, facing front and seated in a red upholstered chair, he wears a black suit and tie. The background is brown.
Oil on canvas. 30 × 25 in. (76.2 × 63.5 cm.)
Inscribed on back: *Study of Father Taylor for W. Clapp*. Painted about 1845.
Collections: W. Clapp, probably Boston; Horatio G. Curtis, Boston.
Gift of Horatio Greenough Curtis. 16.335
Edward Thompson Taylor, born in Richmond, Va. in 1793, was trained as a sailor, but in 1819 was ordained into the Methodist-Episcopal Church and became a renowned preacher. He died in Boston in 1871. During his first sojourn in France, Healy frequently returned home; the portrait's style and the sitter's apparent age suggest its date. W. Clapp, for whom the portrait was painted, may have been William Warland Clapp, Sr., a nineteenth-century Boston journalist.
Reference: M. de Mare, *Healy*, New York, 1954, p. 22.

537. **President Franklin Pierce**
fig. 299

Oil on canvas. 30 × 25 in. (76.2 × 63.5 cm.)
Inscribed on the stretcher: *Portrait of Franklin Pierce by Healy/ Property of Francis Corse*. Painted about 1852–1856.
M. and M. Karolik Collection. 47.1156
Reference: *Karolik Catalogue*, 1949, no. 160 (repr.).

538. **Daniel Webster**
fig. 298

Turned three-quarters left, half-length, his coat is dark blue with a black collar, and his stock is white. The background is gray.
Oil on canvas. Painted oval. 30 × 25 in. (76.2 × 63.5 cm.)
Signed and dated center right: *G.P.A. Healy/ 1853*.
Gift of Miss Mary Haven and Mrs. Waldo O. Ross. 17.106
Daniel Webster (1782–1852), statesman, orator, and lawyer, was born in Franklin, N.H. and died in Marshfield, Mass. In his *Reminiscences*, 1894, p. 164, Healy wrote: "I painted Webster several times, the last being in 1848 . . ." This portrait is a version of that last one, which is now owned by the Virginia Museum, Richmond. A nearly identical version of the Boston

portrait, dated 1854, is with the New Hampshire Historical Society, Concord.

539.
fig. 300

Mrs. David E. Hughes (Anna Chadbourne Morey)

Seated at an easel full-length and turned three-quarters right, she wears a red velvet jacket over a yellow skirt and white blouse. The background is green.

Oil on canvas. 62¼ × 45 in. (158.1 × 114.3 cm.)

Painted in 1855.

Collection: Mrs. M.W. Mather, Robert L. Smith, and Charles P. Smith, Methuen, Mass., great-niece and great-nephews of the sitter.

Ellen Kelleran Gardner Fund. 21.2232

Anna Chadbourne was born in Concord, N.H. in 1826, daughter of Dr. Thomas Chadbourne. Her first husband, Charles Morey, inventor and partner with Charles Goodyear, was killed in Paris in 1856. The same year she married the rich scientist Prof. David Edward Hughes (1831–1900). She was a painter and friend of Healy. She died in Cambridge, Mass. in 1919. In her correspondence, she stated that her portrait was painted in Paris in 1855.

540.
fig. 301

Orestes A. Brownson

Nearly full-length, turned three-quarters left, a gray-bearded gentleman in a black suit is seated in a red upholstered carved armchair. The books beside him and the background are brown.

Oil on canvas. 55 × 43¼ in. (139.7 × 109.8 cm.)

Signed and dated center right: *G.P.A. Healy/ Chicago, 1863.*

Collection: Mrs. G.P.A. Healy, the artist's wife, Chicago, 1894.

Gift of Mrs. Louisa Healy. 95.1368

Orestes Augustus Brownson (1803–1876) was born in Stockbridge, Vt., son of Sylvester and Relief Metcalf Brownson. Minister, preacher, author and editor of his own journal, a socialist, he was successively a member of the Presbyterian, Universalist, Unitarian, and Roman Catholic churches; in 1836 he founded his own, the Society for Christian Union and Progress. He died in Detroit.

References: M. Bigot, *Healy*, Chicago, n.d., p. 50./ M. de Mare, *Healy*, New York, 1954, pp. 209–210./ L.E. Scanlon, "Eakins as Functionalist," *College Art Journal*, 1960, XIX, no. 4, p. 325 (fig. 2).

Exhibitions: New York, National Academy of Design, 1863, no. 181./ Chicago Art Institute, *Healy*, 1913, no. 13.

TIMOTHY HENNESSY was born in San Francisco in 1925 and grew up in Monterey, Calif., and St. Louis. He attended Harvard for two years until 1948 and then studied with André Lhote in Paris until 1950. He worked in Florence in 1950–1951, then Paris, Venice, and on the island of Hydra, Greece, spending each winter in America. He is a sculptor as well.

541.
fig. 604

Banner: Blue and Black with White

A black geometric pattern on three vertical bands, two of blue and one white, with a central circular emblem against blue.

Plastic paint and blue dye on unstretched cotton. 113 × 104 in. (287 × 264 cm.)

Signed and dated on back center: *Hennessy/ Venice/ August 4/ TH* (in monogram) *1960.*

Collection: Commissioned by Mrs. Peggy Guggenheim, Venice, 1960.

Gift of Mrs. Peggy Guggenheim. 61.1095

"I painted Mrs. Guggenheim's paintings [this *Banner* and its companion, Cat. no. 542] in Venice in 1960. They are part of a series of 10 paintings, the two largest. They were painted to be hung before her palace on days of fête . . . I am very interested to use painting in its architectural function, outside and in space. Though large they are very flexible and easy to move . . . the white and the vivid blue are the colors of the gondolieri of Mrs. Guggenheim, their arm bands being designed by Max Ernst." (Letter from the artist, Oct. 20, 1963.)

542.   **Banner: White and Black with Blue**

Three vertical bands, two white and one blue are backgrounds for a black geometric pattern. In the center is a white circular emblem.

Plastic paint and blue dye on unstretched cotton. 113 × 106 in. (287 × 269 cm.)

Signed and dated on back, in the center: *Hennessy/ August 4, 1960/ TH* (in monogram) *Venice.*

Collection: Same as Cat. no. 541.

Gift of Mrs. Peggy Guggenheim. 61.1096

ROBERT HENRI   (1865–1929) was born in Cincinnati, O. He studied first with Thomas Anshutz at the Pennsylvania Academy of the Fine Arts from 1886 to 1888, then in Paris in 1888–1889 at the Académie Julian, briefly at the École des Beaux Arts, and finally independently. He returned to Philadelphia in 1891 to teach, then returned to Paris in 1894–1895. He settled in New York in 1899. He was inspired by the realism of Courbet and the technique of Hals and Velasquez. By 1908 he formed the group called "The Eight," also dubbed "The Black Gang" or the "Ashcan School," a group oriented about social realism which included Luks, Sloan, Glackens, and Shinn. One of the most influential teachers of his time, he sought to revitalize the realist tradition, investigating a new realism of subject matter, daily city life. He returned frequently to Spain and Holland between 1906 and 1914, and spent many summers in Ireland; he also visited the American Southwest. He died in New York.

543.   **Café Bleu, St. Cloud**

A woman in a black coat and yellow and brown plumed hat and a man, to her right, wearing a gray suit and black derby, sit at a café table in the foreground. They are surrounded by green and yellow bushes and low trees touched with red.

Oil on panel. 3¼ × 6 in. (8.2 × 15.2 cm.)

Signed lower center, on table: *R. Henri.* Painted about 1895–1896.

Collections: Estate of the artist, 1929; Violet Organ, sister of the artist's wife, New York; John G. Pierce, Milton, Mass., 1955.

Anonymous gift in memory of John G. Pierce. 64.2007

Painted at the Café Bleu in St. Cloud, a Paris suburb, and dated according to a letter from the artist's sister-in-law in 1955.

544.   **Sidewalk Cafe**
fig. 541

Men and women seated at sidewalk tables wear brown or black and white. The street and buildings opposite are black and dark brown; the foliage above is dark green.

Oil on canvas. 32¼ × 26 in. (81.9 × 66 cm.)

Signed lower left: *Robert Henri.* Painted about 1899.

Collection: Estate of the artist, New York.

Emily L. Ainsley Fund. 59.657

No doubt the same subject as *Café Terrace* (also called *Café Lilas*) painted the same year (exhibited, New York, Metropolitan Museum, *Henri Memorial,* 1931, no. 4).

545.   **Gypsy Girl**

Half-length, turned three-quarters left, she wears a dark green dress touched with purple. The background is light green streaked with pink.

Oil on canvas. 24 × 20 in. (61 × 50.8 cm.)

Signed lower left: *Robert Henri.* Inscribed on back, upper center: *Robert Henri/ Gypsy Girl.* Painted about 1912.

Collections: Mrs. Marshall Field, Washington, D.C., by 1921; Mrs. Albert Beveridge, her niece, Beverly Farms, Mass.

Gift of Mrs. Albert J. Beveridge. 45.888

Henri painted in Spain in 1906, 1908, 1910, and 1912. The gypsy girl seems Spanish, and her picture is dated from its style.

References: W. Yarrow and L. Bouche, *Henri*, New York, 1921 (repr. no. 82)./N. Pousette-Dart, *Henri*, New York, 1922 (repr.).

546.
fig. 542

Irish Girl (Mary O'Donnel)

Half-length and turned three-quarters left, the young girl wears a blue jumper over a red sweater. The background is brown.
Oil on canvas. 24×20 in. (61×50.8 cm.)
Signed lower right: *Robert Henri*. Painted in 1913.
Collection: John T. Spaulding, Boston, about 1921.
Bequest of John T. Spaulding. 48.562

"The *Irish Girl* . . . was painted in 1913 in County Mayo, Ireland, on the Island of Achill . . . I hope you will always like the picture for Mary's sake and for my effort to find an order in it." (Letter from the artist to Mr. Spaulding, Nov. 28, 1921.)

Exhibitions: Boston, MFA, *The Spaulding Collections*, 1948, no. 42./ Philadelphia, Pennsylvania Academy of the Fine Arts, *150th Anniversary*, 1955, no. 103./ New York, American Academy of Arts and Letters, *Impressionist Mood in American Painting*, 1959, no. 46.

547.

Thammy

A young girl, half-length and facing front, who wears purple, blue, and red. The background is light green.
Oil on canvas. 24×20 in. (61×50.8 cm.)
Signed lower right: *Robert Henri*. Inscribed on back, upper center: *Robert Henri/ Thammy*. Painted about 1913.
Collections: Mrs. Marshall Field, Washington, D.C.; Mrs. Albert J. Beveridge, her niece, Beverly Farms, Mass.
Gift of Mrs. Albert J. Beveridge. 45.887

Probably painted on the first trip to Ireland, 1913; similar in style to *Gypsy Girl* (Cat. no. 545).

548.

Stephen Greene

A boy, half-length, is turned three-quarters left before a black and deep blue background. With a black jacket streaked with purple he wears a blue and green tie under a white collar.
Oil on canvas. 24×20 in. (61×50.8 cm.)
Signed and dated on back, upper center: *Robert Henri/ Portrait of Stephen Greene/ N.Y. City/ Dec. 31 1924*.
Collection: Mrs. Charlotte Nichols Greene, Boston.
Lent anonymously. 222.25

Stephen Greene, born in Boston in 1914, is the son of Edwin Farnham and Charlotte Nichols Greene. He graduated from Harvard in 1937, and in 1957 established The Stephen Greene Press in Brattleboro, Vt., where he now lives.

549.
fig. 543

The Pink Ribbon

A small girl, half-length and turned slightly left before a green background, wears a pink ribbon in her hair; her pinafore is white over a blue dress.
Oil on canvas. 24×20 in. (61×50.8 cm.)
Signed lower left: *Robert Henri*. Painted about 1927.
Collection: Estate of the artist, New York.
Charles Henry Hayden Fund. 32.421

Reference: MFA Bulletin, 1932, XXX, no. 182, pp. 80, 81 (repr. cover).

THOMAS HICKS (1823–1890), born in Newton, Pa., was a precocious painter. At thirteen he received instruction from his first cousin, Edward Hicks (1780–1849) and at fourteen in turn gave his first lessons to Martin J. Heade. He then studied at the Pennsylvania Academy and at the National Academy of Design. From 1845 to 1849 he continued his studies in London, Florence, and Rome, and in Paris with Thomas Couture. On his return, he settled in New York as a successful portrait, landscape, and genre painter. He died in Trenton Falls, N.Y.

550.
fig. 257

Calculating

A man sits with his brown dog in a brown and gray barn; he wears a gray coat and hat, green trousers, and a red waistcoat. Through the door is visible a green and brown landscape and a pale blue and pink sky.
Oil on canvas. 14 × 16¾ in. (35.5 × 42.5 cm.)
Inscribed on back of canvas before relining: *"Calculating"/ by T. Hicks/ 1844.*
Collection: Maxim Karolik, Newport, R.I., 1950.
M. and M. Karolik Collection. 62.273

Exhibitions: Worcester, Mass., Art Museum, *The Private Collection of Maxim Karolik,* 1952, no. 23./ Minneapolis Institute of Arts and circulated in the U.S., *19th Century American Paintings from the Collection of Maxim Karolik,* 1953–1954./ Washington, D.C., Smithsonian Institution, circulated in the U.S., *19th Century American Paintings,* 1954–1956, no. 31 (repr.).

JOSEPH H. HIDLEY (1830–1872) lived all his life in and about Poestenskill, N.Y., near Troy. Known for his views of the town and its environs, he was also a woodcarver, maker of shadow-box pictures, and a taxidermist.

551.

View of the Iron Works, Canton, Massachusetts

Black smoke from the red brick factory chimneys blows over the gray and white houses of Canton and the green landscape. A large rock in the foreground is gray under cloudy blue sky.
Oil on canvas. 27 × 34 in. (68.6 × 86.3 cm.)
Painted in 1850.
Collections: Lyman Kinsley, Canton, 1850; Frank F. Sylvia; Maxim Karolik, Newport, R.I., 1951.
M. and M. Karolik Collection. 62.274

One of a pair of paintings of the same title; the other is in the Shelburne, Museum, Shelburne, Vt. Both were supposedly painted for Lyman Kinsley in 1850, and the view here is of the Massapoag House from Lyman Kinsley's garden with the iron works on the right. The pendant shows the houses of Lyman Kinsley and a neighbor, Uriah Billings.

Exhibitions: Worcester, Mass., Art Museum, *The Private Collection of Maxim Karolik,* 1952, no. 25./ Minneapolis Institute of Arts and circulated in the U.S., *19th Century American Paintings from the Collection of Maxim Karolik,* 1953–1954./ Washington, D.C., Smithsonian Institution, circulated in the U.S., *19th Century American Paintings,* 1954–1956, no. 32.

FANNIE LOUISE HILLSMITH (Mrs. W.G. Welchman), born in Boston in 1911, studied at the Boston Museum School with Burns and Guthrie from 1930 to 1934. She then attended the Art Students League under Brook, Kuniyoshi, Zorach, and Sloan, and from 1946 to 1950 she studied with Stanley Hayter at Atelier 17. She has since lived in New York City, except for travels in Europe provided by a Museum School scholarship in 1959; in 1963 she was visiting critic at Cornell University, Ithaca, N.Y.

552.
fig. 584

Nocturne

Vertical angular planes of blues, grays, and purples, form a piano, right, a wall clock, chairs, a bed, and flowers.
Oil on canvas. 50½ × 56 in. (128.2 × 142.2 cm.)
Signed and dated lower right: *F. Hillsmith '54.*
Charles Henry Hayden Fund. 55.624

"*Nocturne* was painted . . . in Jaffrey, N.H. . . . an interior in the quietude of night complemented by objects of sound, a clock, a piano, making these shapes conform to a composition of vertical predominance to give a rhythmic feeling." (Letter from the artist, Dec. 3, 1955.)

Exhibitions: Washington, D.C., Corcoran Gallery, *24th Biennial*, 1955, no. 24./ Manchester, N.H., Currier Gallery, *New Hampshire Painters*, 1958, no. 2.

THOMAS HEWES HINCKLEY (1813–1896), born in Milton, Mass., was apprenticed to a Philadelphia merchant in 1829. While there he studied painting, probably with William Mason. In Milton in 1833 he was first a sign painter, then a portraitist and a painter of animals and landscapes. He visited Europe in 1851 and California in 1870. He lived in Milton from 1845 until his death.

553.   **Rotherham, Yorkshire, England**
Oil on canvas. 26 × 44 in. (66 × 111.7 cm.)
Signed and dated lower center: *T.H. Hinckley. 1852.*
M. and M. Karolik Collection. 47.1178
Reference: *Karolik Catalogue*, 1949, no. 161 (repr.).

554.   **Landscape with Dogs**
In a dark green wood, two English setters point a brace of woodcock. The sky is blue and cloudy.
Oil on canvas. 26 × 36¼ in. (66 × 92.1 cm.)
Signed and dated lower right: *T.H. Hinckley, 1868.*
Collection: James Brown Case, father of the donors, Boston, before 1907.
Gift of Louise W. and Marian R. Case. 20.1872

555.   **Wandering Boulder**
The gray boulder stands on a gray rocky ledge above green woods. Distant hills are mauve against a blue sky.
Oil on canvas. 12 × 16 in. (30.5 × 40.6 cm.)
Signed and dated lower right: *T.H. Hinckley/ 1875.*
Gift of Mary Hewes Hinckley, daughter of the artist, in memory of Thomas Hewes Hinckley. 27.221

The boulder still rests in Milton, Mass.

JOSEPH HIRSCH was born in 1910 in Philadelphia, where he studied at the Museum School of Industrial Art, then with George Luks and Henry Hensche at the Art Students League. In 1935–1936 he was in Paris. He was artist-correspondent for Abbott Laboratories in 1943, and later he toured the Pacific and Italy to find painting subjects in naval medicine. He was instructor at the Philadelphia Art Union and in 1959 at the University of Utah; he now lives in New York City, teaching at the Art Students League.

556.   **Portrait of an Old Man**
In three-quarter length, the tall figure of an elderly man wears a yellow-gray coat and a blue shirt, and holds a gray hat as he looks back over his shoulder. The background is russet.
Oil on canvas. 44 × 30 in. (111.7 × 76.2 cm.)
Signed and dated lower left: *J. Hirsch/ '39.*
Charles Henry Hayden Fund. 42.175

"The painting . . . is imaginary, that is, no model was used. I saw such a character on the street one day in 1938. . . . From memory I put it into sketch form and from the sketch, which I revised several times . . . I painted the canvas. I call it *Portrait of an Old Man* deliberately, because I feel that it is not so much a study of a beggar as a *portrait* of a man. . . . I was more concerned with getting that kingly bearing than with recording the picturesque shabbiness of his raiment. . . ." (Letter from the artist, April 7, 1942.)

Exhibitions: Pittsburgh, Pa., Carnegie Institute, *Directions in American Painting*, 1941, no. 41, pl. 79./ New York, Associated American Artists Galleries, *Hirsch*, 1942, no. 1./ New York, Museum of Modern Art, *Americans 1942,* 1942, no. 125./ Toronto Art Gallery, *Museum's Choice,* 1945, no. 15./ Philadelphia, Art Alliance, *Hirsch,* 1947, no. 11./ Berlin, Museum für Volkerkunde, Munich, Amerika Haus, and Vienna, Walsurni Gallery, *Amerikanische Malerei,* 1951, no. 34.

GEORGE HOLLINGSWORTH (1813–1882) was born in Milton, Mass. and studied painting in Boston and in Italy. While it is not known with whom he studied, his style shows an awareness of Chester Harding. He lived and worked in Milton, as a portrait and landscape painter, until his death. From 1851 to 1879 he was the first and chief instructor of drawing at the Lowell Institute, Boston.

557.
fig. 221

The Hollingsworth Family (formerly Anonymous: New England Family Group)
Oil on canvas. 42 × 72 in. (106.7 × 182.9 cm.)
Painted about 1840.
M. and M. Karolik Collection. 47.1227

The identification of this family group was provided by Mrs. Joseph R. Hodgson of Medford, Mass., a descendant of Maria Hollingsworth Cornell, the lady standing in the center. From left to right, the people are: Anderson Hollingsworth, seated; his brother George, the painter, standing behind their parents Mark and Waitstill Hollingsworth; Maria with Emmor Cornell, her husband; Cornelia Hollingsworth, at the piano; John Mark behind her; Lyman, seated on the right.

References: Karolik Catalogue, 1949, no. 12 (repr.)./ B.N. Parker, "George Hollingsworth and his Family," *MFA Bulletin,* 1952, L, no. 280, pp. 30–31 (repr. p. 30).

558.
fig. 220

Capt. Fisher of Milton
Half-length, he stands with folded arms, turned three-quarters left, in a gray coat and white neckcloth. The landscape beyond is green and blue below a gray and yellow sky.
Oil on canvas. 35½ × 29 in. (90.2 × 73.6 cm.)
Painted about 1840–1850.
Bequest of Polly Robbins Hollingsworth, wife of the artist. 16.109

A label on the back identifies Capt. Fisher as a blacksmith of Milton and "the village orator."

WINSLOW HOMER (1836–1910), born in Boston, was apprenticed there to the lithographer J.H. Bufford from 1854 to 1857. He worked in Boston and after 1859 in New York as a free-lance illustrator while studying at a Brooklyn drawing school; in 1861 he studied at the National Academy of Design and with Frederic Rondel. An "artist correspondent" with the Union Army during the Civil War, he spent 1866–1867 in Paris, then returned to settle in New York. In 1881–1882 he worked in Tynemouth, Northumberland, England. From 1883 until his death he lived in Prout's Neck, Me. but spent summers in the Adirondacks, Nassau, the Bahamas, Cuba, Florida, and Canada. His journalistic background contributed to an objective approach to painting. With Thomas Eakins he was one of the most important Realists of the late nineteenth century.

559.
fig. 434

Playing Old Soldier
Three Union soldiers, in blue uniforms, one of whom is seated and showing his tongue to the field doctor left. The wooden shelter is covered with green boughs; the sky is blue.
Oil on canvas. 16 × 12 in. (40.6 × 30.5 cm.)
Signed lower right: *Homer.* Painted in 1863.
Collections: Murray P. Ryder, Portland, Me., the 1860's; Murray Ryder, his son.
Ellen Kelleran Gardner Fund. 43.129

Mr. Ryder bought the painting at auction in New York. Sometimes called *The Malingerer,* the date of '63 was once barely discernible (letter from Lloyd Goodrich, Feb. 1, 1943), and is now illegible. It is one of Homer's first oil paintings.

Exhibitions: New York, American Artists' Fund Society, *4th Annual*, 1863, no. 108./ Philadelphia, Grand Central Fair in Logan Square, *For the Benefit of the U.S. Sanitary Commission*, 1864, no. 203./ Washington, D.C., National Gallery, *American Battle Painting*, 1944./ Washington, D.C., Corcoran Gallery, *American Processional*, 1950, no. 240 (repr. p. 187)./ San Diego, Fine Arts Gallery, *War, Peace and Union*, 1960, no. 16 (repr. p. 18)./ Washington, D.C., Corcoran Gallery and Boston, MFA, *The Civil War: The Artists' Record*, 1961–1962, no. 30 (repr.).

560.

fig. 436

Long Branch, New Jersey

Ladies, in white, gray, blue, and red, stand on the green and sandy brown bluff overlooking the blue-gray sea. The buildings are gray under a blue sky.

Oil on canvas. 16 × 21¾ in. (40.6 × 55.2 cm.)

Signed and dated lower right: *Winslow Homer/ 1869.*

Collections: Robert Vonnoh, Philadelphia, before 1906; Sherrill Babcock, New York.

Charles Henry Hayden Fund. 41.631

One of the best known of the early paintings by Homer, this painting is contemporaneous with the earliest work of the Impressionists, Boudin, and Manet. Despite his ignorance of their work, his own closely parallels it in spirit and technique. Similar subjects, also of Long Branch, appeared in at least three woodcuts (*Harper's Weekly*, Aug. 6, 1870 and Aug. 15, 1874 and *Appleton's Journal*, Oct. 21, 1869).

References: B.N. Parker, "An Early Painting by Homer," *MFA Bulletin*, 1942, XL, no. 237, pp. 9–10 (repr. p. 10)./ L. Goodrich, *Homer*, New York, 1944, pp. 41, 51 (repr. p. 9)./ —, "Young Homer," *Magazine of Art*, 1944, XXXVII, no. 2, p. 63 (repr.)./ —, "Realism and Romanticism," *Art Quarterly*, 1949, XII, no. 1, p. 17 (fig. 1)./ V. Barker, *American Painting*, New York, 1950, p. 643 (pl. 95)./ E.P. Richardson, *Painting in America*, New York, 1956, p. 315 (fig. 128)./ J. Walker, "Homer at the National Gallery," *Art in America*, 1958, XLVI, no. 3, p. 63 (repr. cover)./ L. Goodrich, *Homer*, New York, 1959 (pl. 24)./ A. TenEyck Gardener, *Homer*, New York, 1961 (repr. p. 37).

Exhibitions: Probably Brooklyn Art Association, 1869, no. 76./ Probably New York, National Academy of Design, *Third Winter Exhibition*, 1869–1870, no. 486./ Philadelphia, Pennsylvania Academy of the Fine Arts, *101st Annual*, 1906, no. 303./ Washington, D.C., Corcoran Gallery, *1st Annual Exhibition of Contemporary American Artists*, 1907, no. 42./ Worcester, Mass., Art Museum and New York, Whitney Museum, *Homer*, 1944, no. 5./ London, Tate Gallery, *American Painting*, 1946, no. 111./ New York, Wildenstein and Co., *Homer*, 1947, no. 11 (repr.)./ Smith College Museum and Williamstown, Mass., Lawrence Art Museum, *Homer*, 1951, no. 13./ Buffalo, Albright Art Gallery, *Painter's Painters*, 1954, no. 26./ Detroit Institute of Arts and San Francisco, M.H. de Young Memorial Museum, *Painting in America, the Story of 450 Years*, 1957, no. 132./ Washington, D.C., National Gallery and New York, Metropolitan Museum, *Homer*, 1958–1959, no. 15./ Boston, MFA, *Homer*, 1959, no. 14 (repr. frontispiece)./ Williamstown, Mass., Lawrence Art Museum, *A Symposium on American Art*, 1960, p. 9.

561.

fig. 433

Rocky Coast and Gulls

Four white gulls fly over the gray and brown sand. Behind gray rocks the sea is blue under pale green sky.

Oil on canvas. 16 × 28 in. (40.6 × 71.1 cm.)

Signed and dated lower right: *Winslow Homer/ 1869.*

Collections: Charles S. Homer, the artist's brother, New York; Mrs. Charles Homer; Mrs. Laura Norcross Marrs, the artist's cousin, about 1918; Grenville H. Norcross, Boston, 1926.

Bequest of Grenville H. Norcross. 37.486

Exhibition: Bowdoin College Museum and Colby College, Women's Union, *Homer*, 1954.

562.

fig. 437

Boys in a Pasture

Two boys sit in a green and brown field. One wears white and blue-gray with a gray hat, the other, gray and brown with a yellow hat. Beyond them are green trees against a blue sky.

Oil on canvas. 15¼ × 22½ in. (38.7 × 57.1 cm.)
Signed and dated lower right: *Winslow Homer N.A./ 1874.*
Collections: Purchased from the artist by a Mr. Tinker of Dublin, Ireland; Miss Tinker, his granddaughter; Patrick O'Connor, Dublin, 1953.
Charles Henry Hayden Fund. 53.2552
References: B.N. Parker, "Boys in a Pasture," *MFA Bulletin*, 1954, LII, no. 290, p. 89 (repr.). L. Goodrich, *Homer*, New York, 1959 (pl. 25)./ A. TenEyck Gardner, *Homer*, New York, 1961 (repr. p. 30).

Exhibition: Ontario, Art Gallery of Hamilton, *American Realists*, 1961, no. 28 (repr.)

563.
fig. 439

Twilight at Leeds, New York

A row of dark green trees cast shadows down a green hillside where cows graze. The sky is blue with gray clouds.

Oil on canvas mounted on masonite. 24 × 28 in. (61 × 71.1 cm.)
Signed and dated lower left: *Homer 1876.*
Collections: Charles S. Homer, the artist's brother, New York, 1910; Mrs. David P. Kimball, Boston, 1912.
Bequest of David P. Kimball, in memory of his wife, Clara Bertram Kimball. 23.521

The reproduction of *Twilight at Leeds*, in the catalogue of the 1877 exhibition at the National Academy of Design (*see Exhibitions*), is of a drawing made by Homer after the painting. The drawing (H.C. Bush Collection, Alexandria, Va.) shows more trees to the left than the painting, which apparently has been cut down. The measurements given in the 1877 catalogue are ten inches wider than the present measurements of the painting.

Reference: T. Bolton, "The Art of Homer," *Fine Arts*, 1932, XVIII, p. 53.

Exhibitions: New York, National Academy of Design, *52nd Annual*, 1877, no. 406 (repr. p. 41 as *Landscape*)./ Boston, Doll and Richards, *Homer*, 1912, no. 4 (as *Twilight at Leeds*)./ New York, Whitney Museum, *American Landscapes*, 1938, no. 49./ Stony Brook, N.Y., Suffolk Museum, *Homer*, 1950, no. 4./ Mountainville, N.Y., Storm King Art Center, *Homer in New York*, 1963, no. 4 (repr. p. 13).

564.
fig. 438

The Fog Warning

A fisherman on the Grand Banks, in dark brown oilskins, rows his halibut-laden brown dory across a rough gray-blue sea, under a gray and pink sky.
Oil on canvas. 30 × 48 in. (76.2 × 121.6 cm.)
Signed and dated lower left: *Winslow Homer 1885.*
Collections: With Doll and Richards, Boston, 1886; Miss Laura and Grenville H. Norcross, Boston, 1893–1894.
Otis Norcross Fund. 94.72

Painted at Prout's Neck, Me., the picture was first known as *Halibut Fishing*; however, by the Chicago exhibition of 1893 its title had been changed to the more dramatic *Fog Warning*.

References: W.H. Downes, "American Painting in the Boston Art Museum," *Brush and Pencil*, 1900, VI, no. 5, pp. 202–204./ F.W. Morton, "Homer," *Brush and Pencil*, 1902, X, no. 1, pp. 50, 54 (repr. p. 51)./ F.W. Coburn, "Homer's Fog Warning," *New England Magazine*, 1908, new series XXXVIII, pp. 616–617./ L. Mechlin, "Homer," *International Studio*, 1908, XXXIV, no. 136, p. CXXXV (repr. p. CXXX)./ C. Brinton, "Homer," *Scribner's Magazine*, Jan. 1911, p. 19 (repr. p. 20)./ W.H. Downes, *Homer*, Boston, 1911, pp. 137–140, 183 (repr. p. 130)./ K. Cox, *Homer*, New York, 1914, pp. 32, 36, 45./ L.M. Bryant, *American Pictures and Their Painters*, New York, 1917, p. 64 (fig. 32)./ N. Pousette-Dart, *Homer*, New York, 1923, p. ix (repr.)./ T. Bolton, "The Art of Homer," *Fine Arts*, 1932, XVIII, p. 54./ F. Watson, *Homer*, New York, 1942 (repr. p. 92)./ J.T. Soby and D. Miller, *Romantic Painting in America*, Museum of Modern Art, New York, 1943, p. 32./ L. Goodrich, *Homer*, New York, 1944, pp. 90–91, 100, 134, 180./ E.P. Richardson, *Painting in America*, 1956, p. 316./ L. Goodrich, *Homer*, New York, 1959 (pl. 47)./ A. TenEyck Gardner, *Homer*, New York, 1961, p. 214 (repr. p. 197).

Exhibitions: Boston, Doll and Richards, 1886./ Chicago, *World's Columbian Exposition*, 1893, no. 576./ Pittsburgh, Pa., Carnegie Institute, *12th Annual*, 1908, no. 156./ Boston, MFA, *Homer Memorial*, 1911./ Philadelphia Museum of Art, *Homer*, 1936, no. 15./ Pittsburgh, Pa., Carnegie Institute, *Survey of American Painting*, 1940, no. 172 (repr. frontispiece)./ Worcester, Mass., Art Museum and New York, Whitney Museum, *Homer*, 1944, no. 71./ Denver Art Museum, *American Heritage*, 1948, no. 44 (repr. p. 17)./ Washington, D.C., National Gallery and New York, Metropolitan Museum, *Homer*, 1958–1959, no. 51./ Boston, MFA, *Homer*, 1959, no. 47./ Dallas Museum of Fine Arts, *Directions in 20th Century American Painting*, 1961, no. 1 (repr.).

565.
fig. 435

Girl by the Seacoast

A young girl sits reading on a pinnacle of gray rocks, touched with green and brown, high above the green sea beyond. She wears a gray dress, striped in dark blue, and a yellow hat with a brown and blue ribbon. The blue sky is obscured by gray clouds.
Oil on canvas. 23 × 15 in. (58.4 × 38.1 cm.)
Signed and dated lower left: *Homer/ 1888.*
Gift of Walstein C. Findlay, Jr., in memory of William Wadsworth Findlay. 61.1294
Lloyd Goodrich has offered persuasive arguments that the painting is in fact an early work, of the 1870's, by J.G. Brown, and cites similarities of style, subject, and size to *The Old Stile* (Mrs. Pennell Phillips, Kennett Square, Pa. *See* Metropolitan Museum, *Life in America*, 1937, no. 226, repr.). and *Boy Robbing a Swallow Nest* (N.Y. art market). The painting style of our picture, however, seems more plastic, aggressive, and characteristic of the robust Homer of the 1880's than of the restrained genre of Brown a decade earlier. Brown's own debt to Homer in the seventies is apparent in the similarity of the *Swallow Nest* picture of 1877 to Homer's engraving of the same motif in 1874.

566.
fig. 440

The Lookout—"All's Well"

The head and shoulders of a seaman, clothed in oilskins, appears in front of the ship's bell, attached to the foremast and stanchion. All is dark brown, except for the deep gray-blue sky.
Oil on canvas. 40 × 30¼ in. (101.6 × 76.8 cm.)
Signed and dated lower right: *Homer/ 1896.*
Collections: With Doll and Richards, Boston, 1897; *Thomas B. Clarke Collection Sale*, American Art Association, New York, Feb. 14–17, 1899, no. 84.
William Wilkins Warren Fund. 99.23
Painted at Prout's Neck, Me. Several drawings, studies for the picture, are owned by the Cooper Union Museum, New York. Etched by W.H.W. Bicknell.

References: W.A. Coffin, "Two Paintings by Homer," *Century Magazine*, 1899, LVIII, no. 5, p. 653 (repr. p. 654)./ W.H. Downes, "American Paintings in the Boston Art Museum," *Brush and Pencil*, 1900, VI, no. 5, p. 202 (repr. p. 201)./ F.W. Morton, "Homer," *Brush and Pencil*, 1902, X, no. 1, pp. 49, 50 (repr. p. 54)./ L. Mechlin, "Homer," *International Studio*, 1908, XXXIV, no. 136, p. cxxxv./ C. Brinton, "Homer," *Scribner's Magazine*, Jan. 1911, p. 19 (repr.)./ W.H. Downes, *Homer*, Boston, 1911, pp. 181–185 (repr. p. 220)./ K. Cox, *Homer*, New York, 1914, pp. 33, 45, 51, 57 (repr. opp. p. 50)./ N. Pousette-Dart, *Homer*, New York, 1923, p. ix (repr.)./ T. Bolton, "The Art of Homer," *Fine Arts*, 1932, XVIII, p. 54./ H. Saint-Gaudens, "Homer," *Carnegie Magazine*, 1937, X, no. 9, p. 262 (repr.)./ F. Watson, *Homer*, New York, 1942 (repr. p. 76)./ J.T. Soby and D. Miller, *Romantic Painting in America*, Museum of Modern Art, New York, 1943, p. 32./ L. Goodrich, *Homer*, New York, 1944, pp. 141–145, 155, 156 (repr. p. 147)./ V. Barker, *American Painting*, New York, 1950, p. 647./ L. Goodrich, *Homer*, New York, 1959 (pl. 77)./ A. TenEyck Gardner, *Homer*, New York, 1961, p. 214 (repr. frontispiece).

Exhibitions: New York, Society of American Artists, 1897./ New York, Union League Club, 1898./ Paris, Exposition Universelle, *L'Exposition Décennale*, 1900, no. 154 and *Fine Arts Exhibition, U.S.A.*, no. 107./ New York, American Fine Arts Society, *Native and Foreign Art*, 1904, no. 35./ Indianapolis, Herron Museum of Art, *Inaugural Exhibition*, 1906, no. 97./ Pittsburgh, Pa., Carnegie Institute, *12th Annual*,

1908, no. 155./ Berlin, Königliche Akademie der Künste, *Ausstellung Amerikanischer Kunst*, 1910, p. 60 (repr.)./ Boston, MFA, *Homer Memorial*, 1911./ Chicago Art Institute, *Century of Progress*, 1933, no. 461./ New York, Whitney Museum, *Homer Centenary*, 1936, no. 29./ Philadelphia Museum of Art, *Homer*, 1936, no. 25 (repr. frontispiece)./ Pittsburgh, Pa., Carnegie Institute, *Homer Centenary*, 1937, no. 9 (repr. opp. p. 22)./ Hartford, Conn., Wadsworth Atheneum, *Night Scenes*, 1940, no. 54./ New York, Wildenstein and Co., *Homer*, 1947, no. 32 (repr.)./ Boston, MFA, *American Marine Paintings*, 1955, no. 19 (repr.)./ Washington, D.C., National Gallery and New York, Metropolitan Museum, *Homer*, 1958–1959, no. 68 (repr. p. 97)./ Boston, MFA, *Homer*, 1959, no. 62 (repr. p. 91).

JAMES HOPE (1818/19–1892) was born in Drygrange, Roxburghshire, Scotland. His father brought him to Canada as a child. Orphaned about 1834, he apprenticed himself to a wagon-maker in Fairhaven, Vt. and attended nearby Castleton Seminary for a year. In 1843 he established himself as a portrait painter in West Rutland, spent the next two years painting in Montreal, then returned to Castleton to teach painting at the Seminary, emphasizing landscapes in his own work. In the early 1850's he took a studio in New York and lived in Castleton summers. He saw action as a Captain in the Civil War and made numerous studies of the battles, later developed to greatly admired mural-size paintings. In 1872 he moved to Watkins Glen, N.Y., where he died.

567.
fig. 277

A Marble Quarry
Brown and gray buildings stand next to the gray and white quarry. The surrounding wooded hills are dark green under a cloudy blue sky.
Oil on canvas. 18 × 24 in. (45.7 × 61 cm.)
Signed and dated lower center: *J. Hope 1851/ Pinxt.*
Collections: Thelma Brady, Westbrook, Conn., by about 1905; William Oelschlager, Jackson Heights, N.Y., 1956; Maxim Karolik, Newport, R.I., 1957.
M. and M. Karolik Collection. 62.275

The block of stone being lifted from the pit, left, is inscribed *Washington Monument*. The picture's traditional title, *Granite Quarry*, presumably derives from the fact that the monument is largely of that stone. The actual material, however, was quarried on Vinal Haven, Me. (*Report on the Monument*, Thomas L. Casey, Engr., Dec. 6, 1883); Hope is not known to have visited Maine in 1851, the summer he built his house in Castleton, Vt., but marble quarries abound in the vicinity of Castleton. While documents indicate that most of the marble used to sheath the monument was obtained from Maryland and Massachusetts, some may have come from Vermont. A drawing by Seth Eastman of the monument under construction, also of 1851, is in the Karolik Collection of American Water Colors and Drawings (*Catalogue*, Boston, 1962, no. 271).

568.

Bird Mountain, Castleton, Vermont
Oil on canvas. 35 × 54¼ in. (88.9 × 137.8 cm.)
Signed and dated lower center: *J.Hope A. M./ Pinx. 1855*
M. and M. Karolik Collection. 48.429
Reference: *Karolik Catalogue*, 1949, no. 163 (repr.).

569.

Winter Scene: The Red Fox
Oil on canvas. 15¼ × 22¼ in. (38.7 × 56.5 cm.)
Signed and dated lower right: *J. Hope 1855.*
M. and M. Karolik Collection. 48.428
The painting has been discovered to be a reduced copy after a *Winter Landscape* (John A. Bingle, Los Angeles) signed by Prof. Georg E.O. Saal (German, 1818–1870) and dated 1845. Hope probably made his copy while the Saal was in the possession of Alexander Turney Stewart (1803–1876), an extremely wealthy textile merchant of New York who had an extensive

business chain throughout Europe and who was given to entertaining artists at his home. Hope maintained a New York studio winters from the early 1850's. A small simplified version of the composition, which substitutes a squirrel for the fox, was painted, and signed, by Cornelius Krieghoff (National Museum of Canada, Ottawa); it was probably also based on the Saal original.

Reference: *Karolik Catalogue*, 1949, no. 162 (repr.).

570. **The Army of the Potomac**
Oil on canvas. 17¾ × 41¾ in. (45.1 × 106 cm.)
Signed and dated lower right: *J. Hope/ 1865 Capt. U.S.V.* Inscribed on the back before relining: *The Army of the Potomac, at Cumberland Landing,/ On the Pamunky, Va. May 12th 1862/ Painted by James Hope, Capt. U.S.V. April 1865/ From a sketch taken by him on the spot.*
M. and M. Karolik Collection. *45.890*
Reference: *Karolik Catalogue*, 1949, no. 164 (repr.).

571. **Frowning Cliff, Watkins Glen, New York**
Oil on canvas. 24 × 20 in. (61 × 50.8 cm.)
Signed and dated lower right: *J. Hope 1872.* Inscribed on back: *"Frowning Cliff"/ Watkins Glen./ J. Hope/ 1872./ No. 644./ Copyright Reserved.*
M. and M. Karolik Collection. *48.430*
Reference: *Karolik Catalogue*, 1949, no. 165 (repr.).

EDWARD HOPPER (1882–1967) born in Nyack, N.Y. and studied first at a commercial art school in New York City in 1899–1900. From 1900 to 1906 he studied at the New York School of Art under Robert Henri and Kenneth Hayes Miller, just prior to Henri's formation of the realist group, "The Eight." In 1906, 1909, and 1910 he worked in Europe, especially in Paris, painting city scenes. His painting consistently pursued objective realism, often of city life. About 1919 he took up etching and in 1923 found quick success with watercolors. He worked in New York from 1908, spending summers on the New England coast.

572. **Drug Store**
fig. 557
A corner drug store at night; the lighted window displays blue boxes, blue and red streamer decorations, and hanging glass globes, one green, one red. Above are a blue and white sign and red canopy. The gray street has blue and black shadows.
Oil on canvas. 29 × 40 in. (73.6 × 101.6 cm.)
Signed lower right: *Edward Hopper.* Painted in 1927.
Collection: John T. Spaulding, Boston, before 1933.
Bequest of John T. Spaulding. 48.564

The date is according to the Museum of Modern Art's catalogue of 1933. The artist altered the legend on the drug store sign after the picture had been exhibited and photographed, thus giving rise to the idea that there were two versions of this subject.

Exhibitions: New York, Museum of Modern Art, *Hopper*, 1933, no. 3 (repr.)./ Arts Club of Chicago, *Hopper*, 1934, no. 20./ Boston, MFA, *The Spaulding Collections*, 1948, no. 44 (pl. VII)./ New York, Whitney Museum, Boston, MFA, and Detroit Institute of Arts, *Hopper*, 1950, no. 23./ Santa Barbara Museum, Pasadena Art Museum, Museum of Fine Arts of Houston, and Dallas, Southern Methodist University Art Center, *Illusion and Reality*, 1956, no. 30./ Ontario, Art Gallery of Hamilton, *American Realists*, 1961, no. 29 (repr.)./ Columbus, Ga., Museum of Arts and Crafts, *American Traditionalists of the 20th Century*, 1963, no. 153./ New York, Whitney Museum, Chicago Art Institute, Detroit Institute of Arts, and St. Louis City Art Museum, *Edward Hopper*, 1964–1965, no. 12.

573. **Room in Brooklyn**
fig. 558
In the corner of a brown and light blue interior a woman in a blue dress sits in a yellow-brown rocker before windows with a view of red brick houses and blue sky.

Beside her are tables draped in red and blue and a green carpet.
Oil on canvas. 29 × 34 in. (73.6 × 86.3 cm.)
Signed lower right: *Edward Hopper*. Painted in 1932.
Collection: With Frank K.M. Rehn, Inc., New York.
Charles Henry Hayden Fund. 35.66

Exhibitions: Pittsburgh, Pa., Carnegie Institute, *Modern Americans*, 1932./ New York, Museum of Modern Art, *Hopper*, 1933, no. 24 (repr.)./ Arts Club of Chicago, *Hopper*, 1934, no. 17./ Cincinnati Art Museum, *41st American Annual*, 1934, no. 59./ Toledo Museum, *Twenty-First Annual*, 1934, no. 30./ Pittsburgh, Pa., Carnegie Institute, *Hopper*, 1937, no. 18./ Chicago Art Institute, *54th American Annual*, 1943, no. 18./ New York, Whitney Museum, Boston, MFA, and Detroit Institute of Arts, *Hopper*, 1950, no. 41 (pl. 12)./ Venice, *Biennale di Venezia*, XXVI, 1952, no. 21./ Dallas Museum of Fine Arts, *The World of Realism*, 1958 (repr.)./ Clinton, N.Y., Hamilton College, Edward W. Root Art Center, *Hopper*, 1964, no. 4 (repr.)./ New York, Whitney Museum, Chicago Art Institute, Detroit Institute of Arts, and St. Louis City Art Museum, *Edward Hopper*, 1964–1965, no. 28 (repr.).

574. **Ryder's House**
fig. 556

A white house with green shutters and a dark gray roof, red chimneys and red foundation stands alone on one of many green and yellow hills. The sky is blue, with gray clouds.
Oil on canvas. 36 × 50 in. (91.4 × 127 cm.)
Signed lower right: *Edward Hopper*. Painted about 1933.
Gift of the National Academy of Design from the Henry W. Ranger Fund. 54.859

The painting was done directly from nature in the early thirties (letter from the artist, Dec. 23, 1956). The house, now changed in appearance, stands in South Truro, Mass. When Hopper painted the picture, it belonged to Albert Ryder's niece, who sold it about 1936.

Exhibitions: New York, Museum of Modern Art, *Hopper*, 1933, no. 25 (repr.)./ Arts Club of Chicago, *Hopper*, 1934, no. 7./ New York, National Academy of Design and Washington, D.C., Smithsonian Institution, *Henry Ward Ranger Centennial Exhibition*, 1958, no. 61.

JOHN BRADLEY HUDSON, JR. (1832–1903)

575. **Haying at Lapham's Farm, Auburn, Maine**
(formerly View in Maine)
Oil on canvas. 22 × 30 in. (55.9 × 76.2 cm.)
Before relining, inscribed on back in large scroll handwriting in pencil: *Painted by J.B. Hudson Jr./ Portland, Me . . . 1859.*
M. and M. Karolik Collection. 48.431

A sketch of the same view, without the man in the foreground or the distant haymakers, is in the "Journal of John Hudson, Jr.," MS. (Boston, MFA, Dept. of Prints and Drawings), 1855 to 1881, opp. p. 34. It is there entitled *The Lapham Farm*, and on page 35 of the text, Hudson noted that Mr. Lapham lived "about three miles from Auburn." The journal indicates Hudson's first visit as September 7, 1858. The painting was done in Portland, during the winter of 1858–1859.

Reference: *Karolik Catalogue*, 1949, no. 166 (repr.).

WILLIAM MORRIS HUNT (1824–1879), born in Brattleboro, Vt. left Harvard before graduating and was taken to Europe for his health. Having attempted sculpture in Rome and Paris, he enrolled in a class at Düsseldorf, but soon dropped out to work under Pradier in Paris. He returned briefly to America in 1846 but when again in Paris studied painting under Thomas Couture. Through the Boston painter William P. Babcock, Hunt met Millet and joined him in Barbizon. In 1855 Hunt married Louisa Perkins, a lady of Boston, but worked until 1862 in Brattleboro and Newport, R.I. before returning to Boston. Her social position and his enthusiasm for the Barbizon School resulted in the formation of numerous excellent private collections of Barbizon art, and many of these paintings form the greater portion of the collection of the MFA. For example the Allston Club, under his leadership, acquired *The Quarry* by Gustave Courbet (MFA) in 1866, the first important work by Courbet in an American collection. He visited the Azores in 1857–1858, Europe in 1866, and Mexico in 1875. He drowned at the Isles of Shoals, N.H.

576.
fig. 349

Self-Portrait

Bust-length, the portrait is of a man facing three-quarters right in a black "chapeau montagnard." His suit is black, the background dark brown. The spandrels are dark brown.
Oil on canvas. Painted oval. 11 × 8¾ in. (27.9 × 22.2 cm.)
Written on the stretcher: *Portrait de Wm. M. Hunt (peintre) de Boston U.S.A./ peint par lui-même Paris/ 1849.*
Gift of William P. Babcock. 92.2742

"It was painted in 1848, just after the revolution, when the 'chapeau montagnard' was in fashion with the Republicans . . . It is quite likely to be the first portrait Hunt painted of himself." (Letter from William P. Babcock, Dec. 6, 1892.) Painted shortly after he entered Couture's studio.
Exhibition: New York, American Academy of Arts and Letters, *The Great Decade in American Writing, 1850–1860*, 1954, no. 141.

577.

Head of a Girl

The half-length figure of a young nude girl is in left profile, her head turned forward. The background is dull green behind black spandrels.
Oil on canvas. Painted oval. 22 × 18 in. (55.9 × 45.7 cm.)
Painted about 1849.
Collections: William P. Babcock, Boston; Mr. Bradlee, Boston; Miss Sarah C. Bradlee, Boston; The Copley Society, Boston.
Gift of The Copley Society. 17.1686

A study, strongly influenced by Couture, probably executed about 1849 while in his studio. It was given by Hunt to his friend William Babcock.

578.

Boy and Dog

In a yellow landscape with his brown and white dog, a boy in a blue smock reaches for a branch of the brown tree.
Oil on canvas. 21½ × 16 in. (54.6 × 40.6 cm.)
Painted before 1850.
Collections: Gift of the artist to William P. Babcock, Boston; Mr. Bradlee, Boston; Miss Sarah C. Bradlee, Boston; The Copley Society, Boston.
Gift of The Copley Society. 17.1685

The date has been established by the character and quality of the painting.

579.

Along the River

Beyond the green river and trees are white cottages, roofed in brown, and a gray cathedral. The sky is gray and golden.
Oil on cardboard. 19½ × 13½ in. (49.5 × 34.3 cm.)
Signed lower right: *W. Hunt.* Painted about 1850–1855.
Bequest of Mrs. Edward Wheelwright. 13.457

This painting and the three following ones were probably painted before 1855, while Hunt was in France, judging by their characteristic dull coloration and the subject.
Exhibition: Boston, MFA, *Hunt Memorial*, 1924, no. 94.

580.

By the River

Before green trees and white and brown cottages, and under a gray and yellow sky, peasant women in dark skirts and white blouses wash white linen in a quiet green river.
Oil on panel. 10¾ × 17¼ in. (27.3 × 43.8 cm.)
Painted about 1850–1855.
Gift of Mrs. Edwin C. Cushman. 15.1143

A charcoal replica (location unknown) is reproduced in H. Knowlton's *Hunt*, Boston, 1899, opposite page 106. Both were probably done in France before 1855.

581.

French Peasant Woman with Pig

Beneath a blue sky, a woman wearing a black dress, white cap, and red kerchief walks her pig down a wood path.
Oil on panel. 17¼ × 11 in. (43.8 × 27.9 cm.)
Signed lower left: *WMH* (in monogram). Painted about 1850–1855.
Collection: Isaac Fenno, Boston, by 1879.
Gift from the Isaac Fenno Collection. 18.394
Probably done while with Millet at Barbizon.
Exhibitions: Boston, MFA, *Hunt*, 1879–1880, no. 26./ —, *Hunt Memorial*, 1924, no. 57.

582.

fig. 341

The Hurdy-Gurdy Boy

A boy, three-quarter length and facing front, stands in a red coat and dark blue trousers before a white stucco wall. He plays the brown hurdy-gurdy hung from a strap about his neck.
Oil on canvas. 42½ × 32¾ in. (107.9 × 83.2 cm.)
Signed and dated lower left: *Hunt 1851.*
Collection: Edmund Dwight, Boston, 1852–1853.
Bequest of Edmund Dwight. 00.503

The painting, done in Paris, was the first sold in America. Hunt made a lithograph from it in 1856. A companion painting, *Girl with Cat* (Cat. no. 592) is also in the MFA collection.
References: H.M. Knowlton, *Hunt*, Boston, 1899, p.26; M.A.S. Shannon, *Boston Days of Hunt*, Boston, 1923, p. 41./ V. Barker, *American Painting*, New York, 1950, p. 617.
Exhibitions: Boston Athenaeum, *Exhibitions*, 1858, no. 225; 1859, no. 300./ Boston, MFA, *Hunt*, 1879–1880, no. 130./ Boston, St. Botolph Club, *Hunt*, 1894, no. 32./ Boston, MFA, *Hunt Memorial*, 1924, no. 14./ Buffalo, Albright Art Gallery, *Hunt Centennial*, 1924, no. 3.

583.

Study for "The Fortune Teller"

A mother, child, and crone are clothed in black, green and white. The background is green and gray.
Oil on cardboard. 9 × 12 in. (22.9 × 30.5 cm.)
Painted about 1852.
Bequest of Maxim Karolik. 64.609
The Fortune Teller (Cat. no. 584) is signed and dated 1852.

584.

fig. 343

The Fortune Teller

A mother in a red dress and brown shawl holds her child, who is dressed in white; an old crone, right, wearing a brown mantle, reaches out. Behind is a gray and deep blue sky.
Oil on canvas. 54¾ × 51 in. (139 × 129.5 cm.)
Signed and dated lower left: *W.M. Hunt/ 1852.*
Collections: Frank B. Brooks, by 1853; James R. Gregerson, Boston; Miss Elizabeth Howes.
Bequest of Elizabeth Howes. 07.136

In 1944 a study for the head of the mother belonged to Mrs. Horatio N. Slater, daughter of the artist. A study for the composition (Cat. no. 583) is in the MFA's collection.
References: H.M. Knowlton, *Hunt*, Boston, 1899, p. 27./ J.W. Addison, *The Boston Museum*, Boston, 1910, p. 33 (repr. opp. p. 32)./ M.A.S. Shannon, *Boston Days of Hunt*, Boston, 1923, pp. 41, 158.
Exhibitions: Boston Athenaeum, *Exhibitions*, 1853, no. 134; 1855, no. 90; 1857, no. 120./ Boston, MFA, *Hunt Memorial*, 1924, no. 96.

585.

fig. 342

Sheep Shearing at Barbizon

In a dimly lit brown interior three men in gray, blue, and white shear brown sheep. Gray sky and a brown landscape are seen through the door.
Oil on panel. 10 × 15½ in. (25.4 × 39.4 cm.)
Painted about 1852.
Collection: Edward Wheelwright, by 1879.
Bequest of Mrs. Edward Wheelwright. 13.455

A copy of the original by J.F. Millet, which was owned by Mrs. Enid Hunt Slater, daughter of the artist. Hunt visited Millet in 1852.

Exhibitions: Boston, MFA, *Hunt*, 1879–1880, no. 10./ Buffalo, Albright Art Gallery, *Hunt Centennial*, 1924, no. 7.

586.

Girl Reading

Three-quarter view of a girl in a blue and white blouse, gray skirt, and orange scarf, who is reading a book in her lap.
Oil on canvas. 21½ × 16 in. (54.6 × 40.6 cm.)
Signed and dated lower right: *W.M. Hunt '53.*
Collection: Charles W. Dabney, Boston, by 1869.
Gift of Mrs. Charles W. Dabney. 93.1455

References: W.H. Downes, "Boston Painters and Paintings," *Atlantic Monthly*, 1888, LXII, no. 371, p. 389./ H.M. Knowlton, *Hunt*, Boston, 1899, p. 28./ W.H. Downes, "American Paintings in the Boston Art Museum," *Brush and Pencil*, 1900, VI, no. 5, p. 208./ *Masters in Art*, Boston, 1908, IX, no. 104, p. 42 (pl. x)./ J.W. Addison, *The Boston Museum*, Boston, 1910, p. 33./ M.A.S. Shannon, *Boston Days of Hunt*, Boston, 1923, p. 161 (repr. opp. p. 152).

Exhibitions: Boston Athenaeum, *Exhibition*, 1869, no. 303./ Boston, MFA, *Hunt*, 1879–1880, no. 2./ Indianapolis, Herron Museum of Art, *Inaugural Exhibition*, 1906, no. 99./ Boston, MFA, *Hunt Memorial*, 1924, no. 73./ Buffalo, Albright Art Gallery, *Hunt Centennial*, 1924, no. 1.

587.

fig. 344

La Marguerite

Three-quarter length, a young woman in a gray skirt and white blouse holding a white marguerite stands in a golden field of grain. The sky is gray and clouded.
Oil on canvas. 46 × 35½ in. (116.8 × 90.2 cm.)
Signed and dated lower left: *WMH/ 1853* (initials in monogram).
Collection: Martin Brimmer, Boston, 1854.
Bequest of Mrs. Martin Brimmer. 06.2429

The first version of *La Marguerite*, painted for the Salon of 1852 and one of ten chosen by Louis Napoleon for purchase, had already been spoken for and went to America (present location unknown). Martin Brimmer bought this second version, of 1853. D.C. Fabronius made a lithograph of the painting in Boston in 1863 (Peters, *see below*). Nearly the same pose in reverse can be seen in another version of the *Marguerite* theme owned by the MFA (Cat. no. 613).

References: A.T. Tuckerman, *Book of the Artists*, New York, 1870, p. 449./ W.H. Downes, "Boston Painters and Paintings," *Atlantic Monthly*, 1888, LXII, no. 373, p. 785./ H.M. Knowlton, *Hunt*, Boston, 1899, pp. 27–28./ M.A.S. Shannon, *Boston Days of Hunt*, Boston, 1923, pp. 41, 158 (repr. opp. p. 144)./ H.T. Peters, *America on Stone*, New York, 1931, pp. 183, 227 (pl. 52).

Exhibitions: Boston Athenaeum, *Exhibition*, 1854, no. 117./ Boston, MFA, *Hunt*, 1879–1880, no. 128./ —, *Hunt Memorial*, 1924, no. 4./ Buffalo, Albright Art Gallery, *Hunt Centennial*, 1924, no. 5.

588.

On the Edge of the Forest

A peasant woman in a red cap, white blouse, and blue dress pastures her black cow in brown woods. The foliage is green.
Oil on panel. 7½ × 11 in. (19 × 27.9 cm.)
Signed lower right: *W.M. Hunt*. Painted about 1853.
Collection: Edward Wheelwright, Boston, by 1879.
Bequest of Mrs. Edward Wheelwright. 13.466

Exhibition: Boston, MFA, *Hunt*, 1879–1880, no. 80.

589.

Sheep

Brown sheep and white lambs stand or lie on yellow straw on the floor of a brown barn.
Oil on canvas. 8¾ × 15¼ in. (22.2 × 38.7 cm.)
Signed lower right: *W. M. Hunt.* Painted about 1853.
Bequest of Mrs. Edward Wheelwright. 13.461

590.

Girl with Cap

In profile to the right, a young girl, half-length, wears a gray dress, red scarf, and white cap. The background is brown.
Oil on canvas. 22 × 18 in. (55.9 × 45.7 cm.)
Painted about 1855.
Collections: Mrs. W.M. Hunt, Boston, 1879; Warren Chambers Hunt, *W.C. Hunt Sale*, Boston, 1898, no. 5; Mrs. H.N. Slater, Readville, Mass., 1910.
Gift of H. Nelson Slater, Mrs. Esther Slater Kerrigan, and Mrs. Ray Slater Murphy, in memory of their mother, Mabel Hunt Slater. 44.46
The title of this picture in the exhibition of 1879, *Head—Daughter of Concierge*, indicates a date prior to his departure from France in 1855.
References: *Masters in Art*, Boston, 1908, IV, p. 313./ M.A.S. Shannon, *Boston Days of Hunt*, Boston, 1923, p. 44.
Exhibitions: Boston, MFA, *Hunt*, 1879–1880, no. 35 (as *Head—Daughter of Concierge*)./ Milton, Mass., Education Society, Town Hall, *Hunt*, 1905, no. 37 (repr. opp. p. 26)./ Berlin, Königliche Akademie der Künste, *Ausstellung Amerikanische Kunst*, 1910, p. 61./ Boston, MFA, *Hunt Memorial*, 1924, no. 95./ Buffalo, Albright Art Gallery, *Hunt Centennial*, 1924, no. 35.

591.

Twin Lambs

Two white lambs lie in a green field before gray rocks and clouded blue sky.
Oil on canvas. 38½ × 32 in. (97.8 × 81.2 cm.)
Painted about 1855–1862.
Collection: Mrs. G.W. Long.
Gift by subscription. 05.8
The date is according to the 1879 exhibition catalogue. Hunt was in Newport during this time.
Exhibitions: Boston, MFA, *Hunt*, 1879–1880, no. 78./ —, *Hunt Memorial*, 1924, no. 3.

592.

Girl with Cat

The girl, in three-quarter length and turned three-quarters left, is dressed in pink over white, and stands holding a gray cat. The background is brown.
Oil on canvas. 42 × 33½ in. (106.7 × 85.1 cm.)
Signed and dated lower right: *Wm. M. Hunt 1856.*
Collections: Commissioned by Edmund Dwight, Boston, 1856.
Bequest of Edmund Dwight. 00.504
Painted as a companion to *The Hurdy-Gurdy Boy* (Cat. no. 582) at the request of Edmund Dwight. In 1944 a small sketch was in the estate of Mrs. Horatio N. Slater of N.Y., daughter of the sitter.
Reference: M.A.S. Shannon, *Boston Days of Hunt*, Boston, 1923, p. 161.
Exhibitions: Boston, MFA, *Hunt*, 1879–1880, no. 99./ Boston, St. Botolph Club, *Hunt*, 1894, no. 33./ Boston, MFA, *Hunt Memorial*, 1924, no. 8./ Buffalo, Albright Art Gallery, *Hunt Centennial*, 1924, no. 4.

593.

fig. 345

The Belated Kid

A child in gray carries a kid as the white mother goat walks beside them on a brown field; behind is a golden sunset sky.
Oil on canvas. 54 × 38½ in. (137.2 × 97.8 cm.)
Painted in 1857.
Bequest of Elizabeth Howes. 07.135
The painting was begun in Europe and finished in Newport, R.I. in 1857.

Bradford Junior College owns a replica of the painting, dated 1857 (formerly Mrs. R.M. Saltonstall, Brookline, Mass.).

References: H.M. Knowlton, *Hunt*, Boston, 1899, p. 26./ M.A.S. Shannon, *Boston Days of Hunt*, 1923 (repr. p. 32)./ A. Burroughs, *Limners and Likenesses*, 1936, p. 172.

Exhibitions: Boston, MFA, *Hunt*, 1879–1880, no. 33./ —, *Hunt Memorial*, 1924, no. 40./ Buffalo, Albright Art Gallery, *Hunt Centennial*, 1924, no. 6.

594. **Morris Hunt**
Bust-length before a black background, the child faces front in a white dress trimmed with red bows.
Oil on canvas. 14¾ × 13 in. (37.5 × 33 cm.)
Painted in 1857.
Collections: Mrs. William Morris Hunt, Boston, 1879; Estate of Mrs. W.M. Hunt (Mrs. Enid Hunt Slater, Executrix), 1913.
Lent by Mrs. Enid Hunt Slater. 72.14

The artist's son and first child, Morris, was born on July 24, 1856 and died on September 11, 1857.

595. **The Snow Storm**
Beside bare gray tree trunks, a mother dressed in gray lies on the snow-covered ground, holding her child, who is wrapped in a purple shawl.
Oil on chipboard. 18½ × 12¼ in. (47 × 31.1 cm.)
Signed and dated lower left: *WM Hunt/ 1859* (initials in monogram).
Collections: W. Woolsey Borland, by 1860; James R. Gregerson, Boston, by 1894; Miss Elizabeth S. Gregerson, by 1914.
Bequest of Elizabeth S. Gregerson. 19.10

The scene was inspired by a quotation, found pasted on the back of the painting, taken, with emendations, from the poem *The Snow Storm* or *The Mother's Sacrifice* by Seba Smith. Mr. Smith (1792–1868), who wrote under the name of Major Jack Downing, was a New England journalist and satirist. The quotation reads:

"*The cold winds swept the mountain's height*
And pathless was the dreary wild,
When 'mid the cheerless hours of night
A mother wandered with her child . . .
Oh God, she cried, in accents wild,
If I must perish, save my child . . .
She tore the mantle from her breast
And bared her bosom to the storm,
Around the child she wrapped the vest
And smiled to think the babe was warm . . .
At morn a traveller passed by —
The babe looked up and sweetly smiled."
(Wm. Cullen Bryant, Ed., *Library of Poetry and Song*, New York, 1925, p. 86.)

Exhibitions: Boston Athenaeum, *Exhibition*, 1860, no. 225./ Boston, MFA, *Hunt*, 1879–1880, no. 25./ Boston, St. Botolph Club, *Hunt*, 1894, no. 51./ Boston, MFA, *Hunt Memorial*, 1924, no. 5./ Los Angeles, Municipal Gallery, *Old Favorites Revisited*, 1959, no. 25.

596. **Landscape at Newport**
Cows graze in a green pasture as a woman feeds several swans swimming in a gray pond.
Oil on panel. 9½ × 12½ in. (24.1 × 31.7 cm.)
Signed and dated lower right: *WMH 1860/ Newport* (initials in monogram).
Collections: Richard M. Hunt, New York; Mrs. H.N. Slater, the artist's daughter, New York, 1910.
Gift of H. Nelson Slater, Mrs. Esther Slater Kerrigan, and Mrs. Ray Slater Murphy, in memory of their mother, Mabel Hunt Slater. 44.45

Reference: G. Danes, "Hunt and his Newport Circle," *American Magazine of Art*, 1950, XLIII, no. 4, p. 150 (repr. p. 149).
Exhibition: Boston, MFA, *Hunt*, 1879–1880, no. 7.

597.   **Mrs. Robert C. Winthrop (Frances Pickering Adams)**
fig. 346

Three-quarter length, she stands turned half right in a purple dress embellished with black ribbon and white lace. The books on the table are red, the chair is green, and the background is brown.
Oil on canvas. 47 × 36¼ in. (119.4 × 92.1 cm.)
Signed and dated lower right: *WM Hunt/1861* (initials in monogram).
Gift through Miss Clara Bowdoin Winthrop. 24.339
Frances Adams, daughter of Benjamin Adams of Boston, was the first wife of Robert Winthrop. They married in 1857. Her portrait was painted a year after her death.
Reference: H.M. Knowlton, *Hunt*, Boston, 1899, p. 48.

598.   **The Drummer Boy**
fig. 347

A lad, wearing a white shirt and blue pants, stands, full-length center, on a slab of gray marble as he beats upon a red and gold drum. A gray clouded sky is the background.
Oil on canvas. 36 × 26 in. (91.4 × 66 cm.)
Signed lower right: *WM Hunt* (initials in monogram). Inscribed on marble slab: *1861. U.S. Volunteers! 1862*. Painted about 1862.
Collections: J.H. Wolcott, Boston, after 1862; Samuel H. Wolcott, his grandson, Boston, 1891; Mrs. Samuel H. Wolcott, 1935.
Lent by Mrs. Samuel H. Wolcott. 368.35
References: H.T. Tuckerman, *Book of the Artists*, New York, 1870, p. 450./ F.P. Vinton, "Hunt," *American Art Review*, 1880, I, no. 1, p. 98./ H.M. Knowlton, *Hunt*, Boston, 1899, p. 49./ M.A.S. Shannon, *The Boston Days of Hunt*, Boston, 1923, p. 59.
Exhibitions: Boston, MFA, *Hunt*, 1879–1880, no. 108./ Boston, St. Botolph Club, *Hunt*, 1894, no. 35./ Boston, MFA, *Hunt Memorial*, 1924, no. 65./ Washington, D.C., Corcoran Gallery and Boston, MFA, *The Civil War: The Artists' Record*, 1961, no. 11 (repr. opp. p. 35.).

599.   **The Wounded Drummer Boy**

The boy, in a blue and white uniform, lies beside his drum in a brown landscape. The sky is gray.
Oil on canvas. 14 × 19½ in. (35.5 × 48.9 cm.)
Signed lower right: *WMH* (in monogram). Painted about 1862–1865.
Gift from the Isaac Fenno Collection. 18.393
The subject was inspired by an incident in the Civil War.
Exhibitions: Boston, MFA, *Hunt*, 1879–1880, no. 49./ Boston, St. Botolph Club, *Hunt*, 1894, no. 69.

600.   **Hamlet**
fig. 351

He stands full-length, facing three-quarters right, in a black costume against a background of gray medieval architecture. The sky is gray and cloudy.
Oil on canvas. 93¾ × 57½ in. (240.6 × 146 cm.)
Painted about 1864.
Collections: Mrs. William Morris Hunt, Boston, 1879; Estate of Mrs. W.M. Hunt, 1913.
Lent by the Estate of Louisa D. Hunt. 2116.13 (c)
Painted about 1864, according to Knowlton (*see below*).
References: F.P. Vinton, "Hunt," *American Art Review*, 1880, I, no. 1, p. 52./ H.M. Knowlton, *Hunt*, Boston, 1899, pp. 36–37, 57./ *Masters in Art*, Boston, 1908, IX, no. 104, p. 27.
Exhibitions: Boston, MFA, *Hunt*, 1879, no. 160./ Boston, *Hunt Estate Exhibition and Sale*, 1880, no. 55 (repr. as *Large Hamlet*).

601.

Felix Regamy

Wearing a black medieval costume with brown and yellow sleeves, he stands full-length, his face turned left. The background is brown.
Oil on canvas. 85¼ × 41¼ in. (216.5 × 104.7 cm.)
Painted about 1864.
Collections: Mrs. William Morris Hunt, Boston, 1879; Estate of Mrs. W.M. Hunt (Mrs. Enid Hunt Slater, Executrix), 1913.
Lent by Mrs. Enid Hunt Slater. 2116.13 (b)
Reference: H.M. Knowlton, *Hunt*, Boston, 1899, p. 47.
Exhibition: Boston, MFA, *Hunt*, 1879, no. 15.

602.

fig. 350

The Gleaner

A girl, bust-length and facing three-quarters right, carries a sheaf of golden wheat on her head. She wears a white blouse. The background is blue.
Oil on canvas. 21¼ × 15¼ in. (54 × 38.7 cm.)
Signed and dated lower left: *WM Hunt/ 1865* (initials in monogram).
Gift of George R. White. 15.1

603.

fig. 353

Abraham Lincoln

Full-length, wearing a black suit, he stands against gray-brown panelling before a dark table draped with a gray cloth.
Oil on panel. 9 × 5 in. (22.9 × 12.7 cm.)
Painted in 1865.
Collections: James R. Gregerson, Boston, by 1894; Miss Elizabeth S. Gregerson, by 1914.
Bequest of Elizabeth S. Gregerson. 19.9
This study for a large portrait, destroyed in the Boston fire of 1872, was painted in May, 1865 after the death of the President. Mrs. Lincoln reputedly sent Mr. Pendell, the White House doorman, who was Lincoln's size, to pose for the portrait. One of Hunt's finest studies.
Reference: H.M. Knowlton, *Hunt*, Boston, 1899, p. 41.
Exhibitions: Boston, St. Botolph Club, *Hunt*, 1894, no. 55./ Boston, Copley Hall, *Loan Collection of Portraits*, 1896, no. 137.

604.

Man in Wheatfield

Under a cloudy blue sky a farmer, clothed in blue trousers and a white shirt, is reaping wheat in a brown and gold field.
Oil on millboard. 6 × 8¼ in. (15.2 × 21 cm.)
Signed and dated lower right: *WMH 65* (initials in monogram).
Collections: James R. Gregerson, Boston, by 1894; Miss Elizabeth S. Gregerson, by 1914.
Bequest of Elizabeth S. Gregerson. 19.8
Exhibition: Boston, St. Botolph Club, *Hunt*, 1894, no. 56.

605.

fig. 359

Mother and Child

Nearly full-length, with her back almost turned toward the viewer, she wears a lavender dress with black details and holds her small child. The background is green.
Oil on canvas. 56 × 36 in. (142.2 × 91.4 cm.)
Painted about 1865–1866.
Collections: Mrs. William Morris Hunt, Boston, 1879; Estate of Mrs. W.M. Hunt, 1913.
Lent by the Estate of Louisa D. Hunt. 2116.13 (d)
The subjects are the wife and child of the artist's brother, Richard H. Hunt of New York City. The apparent age of the child indicates the date.
References: F.P. Vinton, "Hunt," *American Art Review*, 1880, 1, no. 1, p. 52./ H.M. Knowlton, *Hunt*, Boston, 1899, p. 47.
Exhibitions: Boston, *Hunt Estate Exhibition and Sale*, 1880, no. 9./ Boston, MFA, *Hunt*, 1879–1880, no. 52./ —, *Hunt Memorial*, 1924, no. 142./ Buffalo, Albright Art Gallery, *Hunt Centennial*, 1924, no. 22 (repr. p. 8).

606.

fig. 348

Gainsborough Hat

Bust-length, the woman is dressed in brown with a gold buckle on her hat. The background is yellow.

Oil on canvas. 22 × 18¼ in. (55.9 × 46.3 cm.)

Signed lower right: *WMH* (in monogram). Painted about 1865–1870.

Gift of the Estate of Mrs. James T. Fields. 35.1979

Exhibitions: Boston, MFA, *Hunt*, 1879–1880, no. 69./ Dallas Museum of Fine Arts, *6 Centuries of Headdress*, 1955, no. 41.

607.

Enid

Bust-length, in right profile, she has chestnut hair and wears a yellow dress. The background is dark brown.

Oil on panel. 11¾ × 9¾ in. (29.7 × 24.7 cm.)

Signed and dated lower right: *WMH/ 1866* (initials in monogram).

Collections: James R. Gregerson, Boston, by 1894; Miss Elizabeth S. Gregerson, by 1914.

Bequest of Elizabeth S. Gregerson. 19.11

Exhibitions: Boston, St. Botolph Club, *Hunt*, 1894, no. 52./ Boston, Copley Hall, *Loan Collection of Portraits*, 1896, no. 136.

608.

fig. 352

Italian Peasant Boy

Three-quarter length, he stands with arms folded, turned three-quarters right, wearing a gray jacket and red waistcoat, brown trousers, and a gray flowered hat. The wall is pale yellow.

Oil on canvas. 38½ × 25 in. (97.8 × 63.5 cm.)

Signed and dated lower left: *WM Hunt/ 1866* (initials in monogram).

Collections: Francis Skinner, Boston, by 1873; George Peabody Gardner, Boston, by 1924.

Gift of George Peabody Gardner. 29.1117

This and a smaller but full-length, nearly identical version (Cat. no. 609) were painted on the European trip of 1866. A charcoal and white chalk drawing of another version of the composition is in the M. & M. Karolik Collection of American Water Colors and Drawings, Boston Museum (*Catalogue*, 1962, I, no. 393).

Reference: H.M. Knowlton, *Hunt*, Boston, 1899, p. 28.

Exhibitions: Boston Athenaeum, *Exhibition*, 1873, no. 153./ Boston, MFA, *Hunt*, 1879–1880, no. 219./ Boston, St. Botolph Club, *Hunt*, 1894, no. 19./ Boston, MFA, *Hunt Memorial*, 1924, no. 41./ Buffalo, Albright Art Gallery, *Hunt Centennial*, 1924, no. 33.

609.

Italian Peasant Boy II

Full-length and facing front, he wears a black jacket and hat, light gray trousers, and a red waistcoat; he leans against a gray wall.

Oil on canvas. 24 × 14 in. (61 × 35.5 cm.)

Signed lower right: *WMH* (in monogram). Painted about 1866.

Gift of Mrs. Ellerton James. 27.52

A version of Cat. no. 608.

610.

fig. 355

Self-Portrait

He stands half-length, turned three-quarters right with crossed arms, wearing a black suit. The background is pale yellow.

Oil on canvas. 30 × 25 in. (76.2 × 63.5 cm.)

Signed and dated center right: *WMH/ 1866* (initials in monogram).

Collection: Mrs. Eleanor Hunt Diederich.

William Wilkins Warren Fund. 97.63

References: J. deW. Addison, *The Boston Museum*, Boston, 1910, p. 32./ M.A.S. Shannon, *Boston Days of Hunt*, Boston, 1923 (repr. frontispiece)./ A. Burroughs, *Limners and Likenesses*, Cambridge, Mass., 1936, p. 172.

Exhibitions: Boston, MFA, *Hunt Memorial*, 1924, no. 17./ Buffalo, Albright Art

Gallery, *Hunt Centennial*, 1924, no. 2 (repr. p. 2)./ Williamstown, Mass., Lawrence Art Museum, *American Art*, 1960, p. 3 (checklist).

611. **Italian Girl**

Half-length, in profile to the left, she wears a white blouse and scarf, red bodice, and yellow kerchief. The background is black.

Oil on panel. 22 × 18½ in. (55.9 × 47 cm.)
Signed and dated lower right: *WM Hunt/ 67* (initials in monogram).
Collections: Mrs. A.T. Fenno, by 1879; Charles P. Curtis, Boston.
Gift of Charles P. Curtis. 24.409

Exhibitions: Boston, MFA, *Hunt*, 1879–1880, no. 142./ Boston, St. Botolph Club, *Hunt*, 1894, no. 70./ Boston, MFA, *Hunt Memorial*, 1924, no. 36.

612. **Lt. Huntington Frothingham Wolcott**

fig. 354

Nearly full-length, the young man stands full-front with arms folded in a dark blue officer's uniform of the northern army. He wears gold bars on his shoulders and a sword hangs from his left side. The indistinct landscape background is yellow-brown under a blue-gray sky.

Oil on canvas. 60 × 30 in. (152.4 × 76.2 cm.)
Signed and dated lower left: *WM Hunt 1867* (W and M in monogram).
Collections: Joshua Huntington Wolcott, father of the sitter, Milton, Mass., 1867; Governor Roger Wolcott, Milton, Mass.; Roger Wolcott, Jr., Milton, Mass.; Samuel Wolcott, Jr., Milton, Mass., 1966.
Gift of Samuel Wolcott, Jr. 67.76

Lt. Huntington Frothingham Wolcott (1846–1865), the eldest son of the Boston merchant, Joshua Huntington Wolcott and Cornelia Frothingham Wolcott, and brother of Roger Wolcott, Governor of Massachusetts (1898–1900), was commissioned a Second Lieutenant during the Civil War while serving under General Sheridan. In the spring of 1865 he contracted camp-fever and died shortly afterwards at his family's home in Milton, Mass. Hunt painted the portrait posthumously in Paris.

Reference: Possibly recorded in H.M. Knowlton, *Hunt*, Boston, 1899, p. 49 as H. Wolcott, Jr.

613. **Marguerite**

fig. 356

Three-quarter length, in profile to the left, a young girl, in a white dress with a broad red sash and holding a straw bonnet, stands before a green landscape. The sky is blue.

Oil on canvas. 50 × 38 in. (127 × 96.5 cm.)
Signed lower left: *WMH* (in monogram). Painted in 1870.
Collections: Richard M. Hunt, New York, 1878–1879; Francis L. Higginson, Boston.
Abraham Shuman Fund. 26.63

The portrait is said to be of Miss Williams of Roxbury. Another version of the same theme is Cat. no. 587.

Reference: H.M. Knowlton, *Hunt*, 1899, pp. 50–51 (repr. opp. p. 50).

Exhibitions: Boston, Massachusetts Charitable Mechanics Association, *13th Exhibition*, 1878, no. 248./ Boston, MFA, *Hunt*, 1879–1880, no. 87./ —, *Hunt Memorial*, 1924, no. 30./ San Francisco, M.H. de Young Memorial Museum and California Palace of the Legion of Honor, *American Painting*, 1935, no. 133 (repr.).

614. **Mrs. Ellerton James (Olivia Buckminster Tappan)**

fig. 357

Full-length, she stands in left profile, her face turned forward, and holds a closed fan; her brown satin dress is trimmed with gold lace. The background is dark green.

Oil on canvas. 61 × 33 in. (154.9 × 83.8 cm.)
Painted about 1870.
Gift of Mrs. Ellerton James. 27.457

615. **Portrait of a Lady**

Three-quarter length, she stands facing three-quarters right, wearing a black dress and cape. The background is green and orange.

Oil on canvas. 56¼ × 38¼ in. (142.8 × 97.1 cm.)
Painted about 1870.
Collections: Mrs. William Morris Hunt, Boston, 1879; Estate of Mrs. W.M. Hunt (Mrs. Enid Hunt Slater, Executrix), 1913.
Lent by Mrs. Enid Hunt Slater. 68.14

616.

fig. 366

Senator Charles Sumner

Against a black and green background he sits, three-quarter length and facing three-quarters left, dressed in a black suit and white shirt, with black tie.
Oil on canvas. 36 × 29¼ in. (91.4 × 74.9 cm.)
Painted about 1870.
Collections: Mrs. William Morris Hunt, Boston, 1879; Estate of Mrs. W.M. Hunt (Mrs. Enid Hunt Slater, Executrix), 1913.
Lent by Mrs. Enid Hunt Slater. 69.14

Charles Sumner (1811–1874), the son of Charles Pinckney and Relief Jacob Sumner, was born in Boston. When fifteen years old, he entered Harvard, graduating from the Law School in 1833. He was elected to the U.S. Senate from Massachusetts in 1851. A famed orator, he helped to organize the Republican party against the Whigs; politically extremely influential and active, he was a vehement proponent of emancipation. Also an art collector, his bequest was the first substantial donation of paintings to the newly formed MFA. Hunt painted an earlier profile portrait of Senator Sumner (Metropolitan Museum).

Exhibitions: Milton, Mass., Town Hall, Education Society, *Hunt*, 1905, no. 50./ Buffalo, Albright Art Gallery, *Hunt Centennial*, 1924, no. 43.

617.

Charles J. Morrill

Three-quarter length, he sits facing three-quarters left in a black suit. The background is green and brown.
Oil on canvas. 42 × 34 in. (106.7 × 86.3 cm.)
Signed lower right: *WMH* (in monogram). Painted about 1870–1875.
Collections: Charles J. Morrill, Boston; Miss A.W. Morrill, by 1905; Dr. John Dane, Boston.
Gift of Dr. John Dane. 23.219

Charles J. Morrill was born in 1820 and died in 1895.

Reference: H.M. Knowlton, *Hunt*, Boston, 1899, p. 49.

Exhibitions: Boston, MFA, *Hunt*, 1879–1880, no. 36./ —, *Hunt Memorial*, 1924, no. 49./ Buffalo, Albright Art Gallery, *Hunt Centennial*, 1924, no. 7a.

618.

Study for Anahita

The composition is done predominantly in gray, with touches of brown and black.
Oil on panel. 9 × 14½ in. (22.9 × 36.8 cm.)
Painted before 1872.
Collections: Miss Jane Hunt, the artist's sister, Newport, R.I.
Gift of Miss Jane Hunt. 97.203

In 1846 Hunt's brother sent him a translation of the Persian poem *Anahita*; the romantic concept possessed his imagination throughout his life and provided the inspiration for innumerable studies, and for his masterwork, the mural in the State Capitol, Albany (Cat. nos. 630, 631, 634, 635). The study, done on a Japanese tea tray during a visit with his sister in Newport, was one of the few not destroyed by the Boston fire of 1872.

References: H.M. Knowlton, *Hunt*, Boston, 1899, p. 81./ J. deW. Addison, *The Boston Museum*, Boston, 1910, p. 33.

619.

Isaac Fenno

Bust-length, the bearded gentleman in a black suit turns three-quarters left. The background is dark green.
Oil on canvas. 24¼ × 20¼ in. (61.6 × 51.4 cm.)
Signed lower left: *WMH* (in monogram). Painted in 1872.

Gift from the Isaac Fenno Collection. 18.392

Isaac Fenno (1823–1897), a prominent wool manufacturer and clothing merchant of Boston, maintained a grand home in Roxbury which he filled with an extensive collection of contemporary painting and sculpture.

Reference: H.M. Knowlton, *Hunt*, Boston, 1899, p. 49.

Exhibitions: Boston, MFA, *Hunt*, 1879–1880, no. 11./ —, *Hunt Memorial*, 1924, no. 85.

620.   **Meadows in Summer**

A cloudy blue sky is above a green meadow cut by a gray stone wall.
Oil on canvas. 30 × 20 in. (76.2 × 50.8 cm.)
Painted about 1872–1879.
Gift of Miss Mary C. Wheelwright. 31.206

621.   **Reflections in the Water**

The blue sky is seen through the green foliage of the white birches, which are reflected in the gray pool.
Oil on canvas. 24½ × 14¼ in. (62.2 × 36.2 cm.)
Signed lower left: *WMH* (in monogram). Painted about 1872–1879.
Collections: Mrs. A.C. Wheelwright, by 1917; Miss Mary C. Wheelwright.
Gift of Mary C. Wheelwright. 19.1443
Exhibition: Boston, MFA, *Hunt Memorial*, 1924, no. 78.

622.   **Portrait of a Lady with a White Collar**

Bust-length, she faces three-quarters left in a black dress with a broad white collar. The background is dark green.
Oil on canvas. 21 × 17½ in. (53.3 × 44.5 cm.)
Signed and dated center right: *WMH/ 73* (initials in monogram).
Collection: Charles P. Curtis, Boston, by 1894.
Gift of Charles P. Curtis. 24.410
Exhibitions: Boston, St. Botolph Club, *Hunt*, 1894, no. 49./ Boston, MFA, *Hunt Memorial*, 1924, no. 89.

623.   **Barthold Schlesinger**

Half-length, he faces three-quarters left, wearing a brown suit and tie and white shirt. The background is brown.
Oil on canvas. 30¼ × 25¼ in. (76.8 × 64.1 cm.)
Painted in 1873.
Lent by the Executors of the Estate of Mary Schlesinger. 83.25

The date of the painting is given in the St. Botolph Club catalogue.

Barthold Schlesinger (1828–1900) was a prominent Boston businessman who contributed much to the growth of the Back Bay in Brookline. He was co-owner, with Sebastian Schlesinger and George P. King, of the iron and steel concern, Naylor & Co., Boston and was associated with Albert Geiger in a substantial and highly successful real estate business. He was a generous patron of art and music in the Boston area.

Exhibitions: Boston, MFA, *Hunt*, 1879–1880, no. 63./ Boston, St. Botolph Club, *Hunt*, 1894, no. 37.

624.   **Beach Scene with Two-Horse Cart**
fig. 362

On the brown sand stand two figures beside a gray cart with a black horse and a gray horse. Behind them the sea is blue, and the sky pink with yellow clouds.
Oil on canvas. 15 × 24 in. (38.1 × 61 cm.)
Signed lower left: *WMH* (in monogram). Painted in 1874.
Collections: Henry C. Angell, Boston, 1875; Adelaide E. Wadsworth, Boston, 1915; Miss Mary Frothingham Hooper, Boston.
Bequest of Miss Mary Frothingham Hooper. 62.179

Recorded in Angell's catalogue (*see below*): "Beach Cart and Horses. [bought] 1875. $300. The horse doubtless painted by Tom Robinson." This statement is supported by the stylistic evidence in the picture itself.

Thomas Robinson (1834–1888) was a landscape, genre, and animal painter whom Hunt befriended when he first came to Boston in 1865. The date for the painting is given by the 1879 exhibition catalogue.

Reference: H.C. Angell, "Our Pictures and About Them," MS 1909 (owned by MFA), p. 8.

Exhibitions: Boston, MFA, *Hunt*, 1879–1880, no. 176./ Boston, St. Botolph Club, *Hunt*, 1894, no. 11.

625.　　**Mary B. Claflin**

Bust-length in nearly left profile, a young girl wears a gray dress with a white kerchief. The background is dark gray.

Oil on canvas. 20¾ × 16 in. (52.7 × 40.6 cm.)

Painted in 1875.

Collections: William Claflin, 1875; David P. Kimball, Boston.

Bequest of David P. Kimball, in memory of his wife, Clara Bertram Kimball. 23.536

A first posthumous portrait by Hunt was destroyed by the Boston fire of 1872. This painting was done from a charcoal study (unlocated) for the first.

References: H.M. Knowlton, *Hunt*, Boston, 1899, pp. 49, 77, 78./ M.A.S. Shannon, *Boston Days of Hunt*, Boston, 1923, p. 160 (repr. opp. p. 160)./ A. Burroughs, *Limners and Likenesses*, Cambridge, Mass., 1936, p. 172 (fig. 139).

Exhibition: Boston, MFA, *Hunt*, 1879–1880, no. 202.

626.　　**Study of Rocks, North Easton**

Yellow and gray rocks are strewn upon the green and brown ground before a gray stone wall and a grove of trees.

Oil on canvas. 16 × 20 in. (40.6 × 50.8 cm.)

Signed lower left: *WMH* (in monogram). Painted in 1876.

Collections: Estate of the artist, *Hunt Estate Sale*, Boston, Feb. 23, 1880, no. 16; Clement S. Houghton, Boston, by 1914.

Gift of Clement S. Houghton. 37.1302

During the summer of 1876 Hunt painted in North Easton.

Exhibition: Boston, MFA, *Hunt Memorial*, 1924, no. 141.

627.　　**Study of Miss S.**

The woman, half-length and turned half right, wears a bright yellow coat over a black dress. The background is black.

Oil on canvas. 24½ × 21 in. (62.2 × 53.3 cm.)

Signed center left: *WMH* (in monogram). Painted about 1876–1877.

Bequest of Miss Lucy Ellis. 99.306

The 1879 exhibition catalogue gives the date.

Reference: J. deW. Addison, *The Boston Museum*, Boston, 1910, p. 32.

Exhibitions: Boston, MFA, *Hunt*, 1879–1880, no. 84./ Boston, St. Botolph Club, *Hunt*, 1894, no. 57./ Boston, MFA, *Hunt Memorial*, 1924, no. 63.

628.　　**Gloucester Harbor**

fig. 361

The foreground boat and dock are dark gray on white water, touched with blue. The objects on the horizon are brown against the blue sky.

Oil on canvas. 21 × 31¼ in. (53.3 × 79.4 cm.)

Painted in 1877.

Collections: Estate of the artist, *Hunt Estate Sale*, Feb. 23, 1880, no. 65; John L. Gardner, Boston, 1880; Mrs. John L. Gardner, by 1894; Mrs. H.N. Slater, the artist's daughter, Readville, Mass., by 1914.

Gift of H. Nelson Slater, Mrs. Esther Slater Kerrigan, and Mrs. Ray Slater Murphy, in memory of their mother, Mabel Hunt Slater. 44.47

Knowlton states that Hunt painted this picture in one afternoon in the summer of 1877. Mrs. Jack Gardner presented the picture to Mrs. Slater for the Hunt Room at the time of its opening at the MFA in 1924.

References: H.M. Knowlton, *Hunt*, Boston, 1899, pp. 119, 131./ M.A.S. Shannon, *Boston Days of Hunt*, Boston, 1923, pp. 131–133 (repr. opp. p. 124)./ A. Burroughs,

Limners and Likenesses, Cambridge, Mass., 1936, p. 173./ V. Barker, *American Painting*, New York, 1950, p. 618.

Exhibitions: Boston, St. Botolph Club, *Hunt*, 1894, no. 85./ Boston, MFA, *Hunt Memorial*, 1924, no. 81./ Buffalo, Albright Art Gallery, *Hunt Centennial*, 1924, no. 41./ Brooklyn Museum, *The Coast and The Sea*, 1948–1949, no. 65./ New York, American Academy of Arts and Letters, *The Great Decade in American Writing, 1850–1860*, 1954, no. 103./ Williamstown, Mass., Lawrence Art Museum, *American Art*, 1960, p. 5 (checklist).

629.
fig. 358

Pine Woods, Magnolia
Among the brown trunks of pine trees, a man stands with a white horse; a bay is tethered nearby. The ground is carpeted with brown pine needles. The sky is blue.
Oil on canvas. 34 × 44 in. (86.3 × 111.7 cm.)
Painted in 1877.
Collections: Estate of the artist; *Hunt Estate Sale*, Boston, Feb. 23, 1880, no. 24 (as *Horses in "Pine Wood," Milton*).
Gift of the Pupils and Friends of Mr. Hunt. 10.231
Hunt summered at Magnolia in 1877.
Exhibition: Boston, MFA, *Hunt Memorial*, 1924, no. 97.

630.

Anahita
Anahita, partially draped in gray-brown, sits amid clouds of red, blue, yellow, and brown.
Oil on canvas. 25 × 21½ in. (63.5 × 54.6 cm.)
Painted in 1878.
Collection: Anna Perkins Rogers, Boston, by 1894.
Bequest of Anna Perkins Rogers. 21.2173
A study for the central figure of his mural in the Capitol, Albany, N.Y. Hunt was fascinated by the story of Anahita, the Persian nature goddess of night who rode her car of light, the moon, through the heavens. He painted the subject many times during the 1870's; a large canvas on the theme painted as early as 1872 was lost in the Great Boston Fire of that year. For other versions and studies, see Cat. nos. 618, 631, 634, and 635. In June, 1878, Hunt received a commission to paint two murals for the Assembly Chamber in the new Capitol Building at Albany. This picture and those noted above are some of the numerous studies made at his Boston studio in preparation for the murals. The Pennsylvania Academy of the Fine Arts at Philadelphia has a large finished cartoon.
Reference: M.A.S. Shannon, *Boston Days of Hunt*, Boston, 1923, pp. 147–148 (repr. opp. p. 128).
Exhibition: Boston, St. Botolph Club, *Hunt*, 1894, no. 63.

631.
fig. 364

Anahita. The Flight of Night
Anahita, draped in gray, rides across the blue sky on orange, red, and gray clouds driving three horses, brown, black, and white.
Oil on canvas. 62 × 99 in. (157.5 × 251.4 cm.)
Painted in 1878.
Collections: Mrs. H.N. Slater, the artist's daughter, Readville, Mass., by 1915.
Gift of H. Nelson Slater, Mrs. Esther Slater Kerrigan, and Mrs. Ray Slater Murphy, in memory of their mother, Mabel Hunt Slater. 44.48
References: H.M. Knowlton, *Hunt*, 1899, pp. 78–81 (repr. opp. p. 94)./ M.A.S. Shannon, *Boston Days of Hunt*, 1923, p. 158./ L. Goodrich, "Hunt," *Arts*, 1924, v, no. 5, p. 282 (repr. p. 279).

632.
fig. 363

Miss Ida Mason
Three-quarter length, seated and turned three-quarters left, her hands are folded in her lap. Her suit is maroon trimmed with gray fur. The background is gray.
Oil on canvas. 42 × 30¼ in. (106.7 × 76.8 cm.)

Signed and dated lower left: *WMH/ 1878* (initials in monogram).
Charles Henry Hayden Fund. 32.127

Reference: M.A.S. Shannon, *Hunt*, Boston, 1923 (repr. opp. p. 100).

Exhibitions: Boston, MFA, *Hunt Memorial*, 1924, no. 45./ Buffalo, Albright Art Gallery, *Hunt Centennial*, 1924, no. 19./ Paris, Musée du Jeu de Paume, *Trois Siècles d'Art aux États-Unis*, 1938, no. 98./ New York, American Federation of Arts, circulated in Germany and Italy, and Whitney Museum, *American Painting in the Nineteenth Century*, 1953–1954, no. 42./ Toronto Art Gallery and circulated in Canada, and New York, Whitney Museum, *American Painting from 1865–1905*, 1961, no. 40 (pl. III).

633.
fig. 360

Niagara
The falls are green and gray touched with pink and mauve before a distant brown shoreline and gray sky.
Oil on canvas. 62½ × 100 in. (158.1 × 254 cm.)
Painted in 1878.
Collections: Mrs. William Morris Hunt, Boston, 1879; Estate of Mrs. W.M. Hunt (Mrs. Enid Hunt Slater, Executrix), 1913.
Lent by the Estate of Mrs. Enid Hunt Slater. 67.14

In 1878 Hunt painted a series of pictures in oil and pastel of Niagara Falls and the river.

Reference: H.M. Knowlton, *Hunt*, Boston, 1899, p. 204.

Exhibition: Boston, MFA, *Hunt*, 1879, no. 74.

634.
fig. 365

Sketch for the State Capitol at Albany (The Discoverer)
A scalloped lunette. A man in a brown cloak stands in a brown boat before pink and gray clouds. A half-nude winged female figure behind him carries a flame and supports a sail; other figures float in the green water.
Oil on panel. 16 × 36¾ in. (40.6 × 93.3 cm.)
Painted in 1878.
Collections: Mrs. William Morris Hunt, Boston, 1879; Estate of Mrs. W.M. Hunt (Mrs. Enid Hunt Slater, Executrix), 1913.
Lent by Mrs. Enid Hunt Slater. 105.14

A sketch for the mural of *The Discoverer* in the Capitol building, Albany. Columbus is represented crossing the dark ocean attended by figures representing Faith, Hope, and like spirits.

635.

Sketch for the State Capitol at Albany (The Flight of Night)
A scalloped lunette. On brown and white clouds before blue sky and pink mist, Anahita, draped in brown, drives three brown, black, and white horses.
Oil on panel. 16 × 36¾ in. (40.6 × 93.3 cm.)
Painted in 1878.
Collections: Mrs. William Morris Hunt, Boston, 1879; Estate of Mrs. W.M. Hunt (Mrs. Enid Hunt Slater, Executrix), 1913.
Lent by Mrs. Enid Hunt Slater. 104.14

636.
fig. 367

Self-Portrait
Bust-length, the elderly white-bearded man faces three-quarters right in a brown coat edged in green. The background is brown.
Oil on canvas. 20 × 17¼ in. (50.8 × 43.8 cm.)
Signed and dated lower right: *WMH/ '79* (initials in monogram).
Collection: Peter Chardon Brooks, Jr., Boston, 1879.
Gift of Mrs. Richard M. Saltonstall. 20.595

Hunt's last work, it was painted in March, 1879.

Reference: H.M. Knowlton, *Hunt*, Boston, 1899, p. 165.

Exhibitions: Boston, MFA, *Hunt*, 1879–1880, no. 64./ —, *Hunt Memorial*, 1924, no 6.

637.

Girl at Piano
Three-quarter length, dressed in black, she sits at the brown upright piano before a gray wall.
Oil on canvas. 10¼ × 6¼ in. (26 × 15.9 cm.)

Signed lower left: *WMH* (in monogram).
Gift of the Estate of Mrs. James H. Beal. 20.437

638. **Head of a Child**

The bust of a child, wearing a black dress with white ruffles, is turned three-quarters right on a black background.
Oil on canvas. 18 × 14 in. (45.6 × 35.5 cm.)
Gift of Mary W. Bartol, John W. Bartol, and Abigail W. Clark. Res. 27.102

An identical version (19 × 15 in.), inscribed on the reverse, *W.M.H. May 8, 1854 (?) to F.H.*, is owned by the Santa Barbara Museum of Art.

639. **Portrait of a Lady**

A study. Bust-length, turned slightly left, the elderly lady wears a dark brown dress with white lace mantilla and collar. The background is black.
Oil on canvas. 21 × 17 in. (53.3 × 43.2 cm.)
Collections: Mrs. William Morris Hunt, Boston, 1879; Estate of Mrs. W.M. Hunt (Mrs. Enid Hunt Slater, Executrix), 1913.
Lent by Mrs. Enid Hunt Slater. 71.14

A study for the following picture.

640. **Portrait of a Lady**

Facing three-quarters left, bust-length, she wears a black dress trimmed with white lace and a white lace cap. The background is brown.
Oil on canvas. 24 × 20 in. (61 × 50.8 cm.)
Collections: Mrs. William Morris Hunt, Boston, 1879; Estate of Mrs. W.M. Hunt (Mrs. Enid Hunt Slater, Executrix), 1913.
Lent by Mrs. Enid Hunt Slater. 70.14

641. **Priscilla**

Bust-length, turned three-quarters left, her head in profile, she wears an olive-green and black dress with a white fichu and a white cap. The background is dark olive green.
Oil on canvas. 24 × 15¼ in. (61 × 38.5 cm.)
Signed center left: *WMH* (in monogram).
Collections: Mrs. W. Scott Fitz, Boston, by 1924; Edward Jackson Holmes; Mrs. Edward Jackson Holmes.
Bequest of Mrs. Edward Jackson Holmes. 65.432
Exhibition: Boston, MFA, *Hunt Memorial*, 1924, no. 83.

DANIEL HUNTINGTON (1816–1906)

see John F. Kensett, and Daniel Huntington, Cat. no. 682.

HENRY INMAN (1801–1846), born in Utica, N.Y., studied drawing in New York City. From 1814 to 1821 he was apprenticed to the portrait painter John Wesley Jarvis. By 1823 he was an established artist in New York, and in 1827 he was elected first Vice-President of the National Academy of Design. He worked in Philadelphia from 1831 to 1834, becoming Director of the Pennsylvania Academy of the Fine Arts. He then worked in New York until his death, except for a visit to England in 1844 to paint commissioned portraits of Wordsworth and Macaulay. He was completing a series of historical paintings, commissioned by the U.S. Congress for the Capitol in Washington, D.C., at the time of his death.

642. **John Inman**
fig. 233

Turned three-quarters left, half-length before a brown background, he wears a blue coat, yellow waistcoat, and black stock under a fur-collared brown coat lined in red.
Oil on canvas. 30 × 25 in. (76.2 × 63.5 cm.)
Painted about 1828.
Collection: Frank Inman, son of the sitter, Philadelphia.
William Wilkins Warren Fund. 03.1156

John Inman (1805–1850), the artist's brother, was a journalist and editor. He served on the editorial staffs of the *New York Mirror*, the *Commercial Ad-*

vertiser, and the *Columbian Lady's and Gentleman's Magazine*. The catalogue of the Art Union exhibition (*see below*) says that this was Henry Inman's first portrait in oils; the apparent age of the sitter suggests a slightly later date. A replica of the portrait was owned by Mrs. George H. Babbitt of Boston.

Reference: T. Bolton, "Inman," *Art Quarterly*, 1940, III, no. 4, p. 361, and supplement, "Catalogue of Paintings by Inman," no. 68.

Exhibition: New York, Art Union, *Inman Memorial*, 1846, no. 113.

643.

fig. 232

Georgianna Buckham and Her Mother

Seated in three-quarter length, Mrs. Buckham, in black with a blue and white bonnet, turns three-quarters right; at her knee stands young Georgianna, wearing red and green plaid. The chair is red, and the landscape to the right of a brown wall is green.

Oil on canvas. 34¼ × 27¼ in. (87 × 69.2 cm.)
Painted in 1839.

Collections: George Buckham, New York; Georgianna Buckham Wright, the sitter.

Bequest of Georgianna Buckham Wright. 19.1370

Georgianna Buckham (about 1833/35–about 1919) was the daughter of George and Anna Traphagen Buckham of New York City. Her first marriage was to George Wellman Wright and her second to William James Wright of Boston. The date was given by the Art Union exhibition catalogue.

References: A. Burroughs, *Limners and Likenesses*, Cambridge, Mass., 1936, p. 132 (fig. 107)./ T. Bolton, "Catalogue of Paintings by Inman," no. 167, and "Inman, an Account of his Life and Work," *Art Quarterly*, 1940, III, no. 4 (fig. 11)./ E.P. Richardson, *American Romantic Painting*, New York, 1945, no. 91 (repr.)./ —, *Painting in America*, New York, 1956, p. 203.

Exhibitions: New York, Art Union, *Inman Memorial*, 1846, no. 13./ San Francisco, M.H. de Young Memorial Museum and California Palace of the Legion of Honor, *American Painting*, 1935, no. 135 (repr.)./ New York, M. Knoedler and Co., *American Portraits by American Painters*, 1944, no. 16 (repr.)./ Cambridge, Mass., Fogg Art Museum, *American Spirit in Portraiture*, 1951, no. 23.

644.

Lord Cottenham

Bust-length, facing three-quarters right, he is dressed as Lord Chancellor in a long white wig and black robes trimmed with gold. The chair is upholstered in light red.

Oil on canvas. 30 × 24¾ in. (76.2 × 62.8 cm.)
Painted in 1844.

Bequest of Georgianna Buckham Wright. 19.1338

Sir Charles Christopher Pepys (1781–1851) was the second son of Sir William Weller Pepys and Elizabeth Dowdeswell. An eminent lawyer, he was responsible for the 1838 Judgement Act for the relief of insolvent debtors, and was twice Lord High Chancellor, from 1836 to 1841 and from 1846 to 1850. On his retirement in 1850 he was created Viscount Crowhurst and First Earl of Cottenham. Inman painted another portrait, entitled *Lord Cottenham*, of a young man standing in three-quarter length (catalogue of the *National Academy of Design Centennial Exhibition*, 1925–1926, repr. p. 6). Since Inman visited England only once, in 1844, this is possibly our Lord Cottenham's son, Charles Edward, Second Earl of Cottenham.

References: T. Bolton, "Catalogue of Paintings by Inman," *Art Quarterly*, 1940, III, no. 4, and supplement, no. 25.

Exhibition: New York, Art Union, *Inman Memorial*, 1846, no. 22.

645.

fig. 234

Dismissal of School on an October Afternoon

Oil on canvas. 26 × 36 in. (66 × 91.4 cm.)
Signed and dated lower left on rock: *Inman/ 1845.*
M. and M. Karolik Collection. 48.432

Reference: *Karolik Catalogue*, 1949, no. 167 (repr.).

GEORGE INNESS (1825–1894), born near Newburgh, N.Y., was self-taught except for a brief apprenticeship to a map engraving firm in New York and a period of study under Régis François Gignoux. By 1845 he had a studio in New York and had come under the influence of the Hudson River School. He studied in Rome in 1847, and in 1850–1851 he was in Florence. In 1854–1855 he worked in Paris, where the Barbizon painters strongly influenced him. From 1859 to 1864 he lived in Medfield, Mass., then in Eagleswood, N.J. and Brooykln; the years 1870 to 1874 were spent in France and Italy. After 1878 he lived in Montclair, N.J. until his death at Bridge of Allen, Scotland.

646.

Woodland Vista

Oil on canvas. 19¾ × 14¾ in. (50.1 × 37.5 cm.)
Signed and dated lower right: *G.I.*/ *1846*.
M. and M. Karolik Collection. 48.433
Reference: Karolik Catalogue, 1949, no. 168 (repr.).

647.
fig. 374

View near Florence

A gray and brown towered villa is surrounded by umbrella pines and green and brown cypresses. The sky is blue and cloudy.
Oil on canvas. 4½ × 7 in. (11.4 × 17.8 cm.)
Painted about 1850–1851.
Collections: Given by the artist to Mrs. Daniel Rogers, Medfield, Mass.; Mary B. Fowle, her daughter, Medfield; Harriet Adams Fowle, Medfield; Lodge of St. Andrew, Medfield.
Gift of the Lodge of St. Andrew. 21.99
Both Harriet Adams Fowle and a label on the back of the painting state that Inness painted this sketch on his trip to Italy before he settled in Medfield. Inness used this composition as the central element in the *Italian Landscape* (Ireland, no. 130, repr.) of 1857 and his *Souvenir of Italy* of 1872–1874 (Ireland, no. 598, repr. Collection Dr. T. E. Hanley).
Reference: L. Ireland, *Inness*, Austin, Tex., 1965, no. 76 (repr.).
Exhibitions: Detroit Institute of Arts and Toledo Museum, *Travelers in Arcadia*, 1951, no. 69./ Washington, D.C., Corcoran Gallery, *The American Muse*, 1959, no. 50./ New York, Grolier Club, *The Italian Influence on American Literature*, 1961, no. 270 (repr.).

648.
fig. 376

Summer at Medfield

A green summer landscape; a pond, meadow, and hills are in the distance. A white house, right, half hidden by trees, is under a cloudy, blue sky.
Oil on canvas. 16 × 24 in. (40.6 × 61 cm.)
Signed lower right: *G. Inness.* Painted about 1859–1864.
Collections: R.W. Johnson, Boston; Hiram Hyde Logan, Boston, 1911.
Gift of Mrs. Hiram Hyde Logan. 22.815
The house is said to have been Inness' home in Medfield from 1859 to 1864. The clarity of style agrees with an origin in the early 1860's. This work served as a study, with some changes, for *The Old Homestead* (36 × 54 in.) painted about 1876 (Pioneer Museum and Haggin Art Galleries, Stockton, Calif., Ireland, no. 821).
Reference: L. Ireland, *Inness*, Austin, Tex., 1965, no. 820 (repr.).
Exhibition: Boston, Vose Galleries, *Exhibition in Honor of Robert C. Vose*, 1961, no. 19.

649.
fig. 375

The Road to the Farm

A shepherd in blue drives his flock down the gray and brown path, bordered by green and brown trees. Gray clouds are in the blue sky.
Oil on canvas. 27 × 37 in. (68.6 × 94 cm.)
Signed and dated lower right: *Geo. Inness 1862.*
Gift of Robert Jordan from the collection of Eben D. Jordan. 24.221
The influence of Emile Jacque and Rousseau is apparent.
Reference: L. Ireland, *Inness*, Austin, Tex., 1965, no. 238 (repr.).

650.

Sunset

The dark landscape is green and brown; in the center black trees stand against the red, green, and yellow sky.

Oil on canvas. 18 × 26 in. (45.7 × 66 cm.)
Signed and dated lower right: *Geo. Inness 1864.*
Collections: Henry P. Kidder, Boston; Nathaniel T. Kidder, his son, Boston, about 1893.
Bequest of Nathaniel T. Kidder. 38.1418

An inscription, *Geo. Inness 1844*, scratched on the stretcher, is by a later hand.

Reference: L. Ireland, *Inness*, Austin, Tex., 1965, no. 285 (repr.).

Exhibition: Boston Athenaeum, *Exhibition*, 1864, no. 309 (perhaps this picture).

651.

Fishing

A lake is surrounded by brown and green fields and wooded hills in autumn foliage under gray and yellow clouds.
Oil on chipboard. 11¾ × 17¾ in. (29.7 × 45.1 cm.)
Signed and dated lower left: *G. Inness 1867* (last figure indistinct).
Gift of John R. Hall. 17.1620

Reference: L. Ireland, *Inness*, Austin, Tex., 1965, no. 404 (repr.).

652.
fig. 380

Elms in Summer

The green landscape is of meadows, stone walls, and tall elms which stand before a red and white house and distant gray hills under a cloudy blue sky.
Oil on canvas. 16 × 24 in. (40.6 × 61 cm.)
Signed and dated lower right: *G. Inness 1868.*
Collections: Thomas Wigglesworth, Boston; Mrs. W. Scott Fitz, his niece, Boston; Edward J. Holmes, her son, Boston.
Gift of Edward Jackson Holmes. 41.119

Reference: L. Ireland, *Inness*, Austin, Tex., 1965, no. 237 (repr.).

653.
fig. 372

Italian Landscape

The meadows are green and yellow, with a grove of trees in full foliage; the villa, on a green hillside, is white. The sea is blue on the distant horizon, under a pale blue sky.
Oil on canvas. 26½ × 42¾ in. (67.3 × 108.6 cm.)
Signed and dated lower right: *G. Inness 1872* (last figure indistinct).
Collections: Henry P. Kidder, Boston; Nathaniel T. Kidder, his son, Boston, about 1893.
Bequest of Nathaniel T. Kidder. 38.1417

A signed oil study (14¾ × 21¼ in.) for the painting is in the Philadelphia Museum of Art.

Reference: L. Ireland, *Inness*, Austin, Tex., 1965, no. 559 (repr.).

654.
fig. 381

Lake Nemi

In the foreground a priest walks near a white wall on the green hillside, far above a blue lake. A yellow haze covers the distant blue and green landscape beneath a blue sky.
Oil on canvas. 30 × 45 in. (76.2 × 114.3 cm.)
Signed and dated lower right: *Inness Nemi 1872.*
Collections: Commissioned by Mr. and Mrs. A.D. Williams, Roxbury, Mass., 1872; Miss Ada Hersey, Roxbury, 1905.
Gift of the Misses Hersey. 49.412

"I trust you will find the picture of Lake Nemi one of my very best, as I intended it should be, and I am happy to say it was so looked upon by all who saw it at my studio." (Letter from Inness to Mr. Williams, Aug. 13, 1872, written from Albano.) The building high upon the distant hill is the Villa Sforza-Cesarini above the town of Gensano. Inness spent the summer of 1872 in Albano.

Reference: L. Ireland, *Inness*, Austin, Tex., 1965, no. 560 (repr.).

655.
fig. 378

Lake Nemi

The blue lake is half hidden by wooded hills of green, brown, and gray. Distant hills

are mauve under blue sky.
Oil on canvas. 12¼ × 18¼ in. (31.1 × 46.3 cm.)
Signed lower right: *G. Inness*. Painted in 1872.
Charles Henry Hayden Fund. 21.290

Reference: L. Ireland, *Inness*, Austin, Tex., 1965, no. 572 (repr.).

Exhibitions: New York School of Applied Design for Women, *Inness*, 1912, no. 18./
New York, George H. Ainslee Galleries, *Inness*, 1917, no. 12.

656.
fig. 377

The Church Spire
The top of a distant spire appears in a green wooded landscape. The hills are gray and blue under a pale blue sky with gray and pink clouds.
Oil on canvas. 20 × 30 in. (50.8 × 76.2 cm.)
Signed and dated lower right: *G. Inness 1875.*
Collections: James Brown Case, Boston, before 1907; Mrs. James G. Freeman and the Misses Case, by 1919.
Gift of Louise W. and Marian R. Case. 20.1863
Reference: L. Ireland, *Inness*, Austin, Tex., 1965, no. 710 (repr.).

657.
fig. 373

Kearsarge Village
A green knoll with trees appears before a sunlit mountain meadow. Dark gray clouds obscure the mountain behind.
Oil on canvas. 16 × 24 in. (40.6 × 61 cm.)
Signed and dated lower right: *G. Inness 1875.*
Gift of Miss Mary Thacher in memory of Mr. and Mrs. Henry C. Thacher and Miss Martha Thacher. 30.102

Inness, in Boston in 1875, made a painting trip to the White Mountains of New Hampshire with his friend John Monks. A more broadly handled replica called *November in the Adirondacks* (Ireland, no. 1158, repr.), given a date of about 1885 by Ireland, is with the Auslew Gallery, Norfolk, Va.
Reference: L. Ireland, *Inness*, Austin, Tex., 1965, no. 751 (repr.).

658.
fig. 383

Rainbow over Perugia
Three peasant women in costumes of blue, red, and white, wash clothes at a fountain. The sun breaks through the clouds and shines on a white building at the top of the hill behind them; a rainbow arches in the sky at left.
Oil on canvas. 38½ × 63½ in. (97.8 × 161.3 cm.)
Signed and dated lower right: *G. Inness 1875.*
Collections: James Brown Case, Boston, before 1907; the Misses Louise W. and Marian R. Case, his daughters.
Gift of Louise W. and Marian R. Case. 20.169
Inness, in Boston in 1875, probably painted this from a sketch made at Perugia. Such a sketch, 10½ × 16 in., is in the John Bannon collection, New York (Ireland, no. 682). The buildings at the top of the hill may be the church of San Constanzo, seen from the northeast side.

References: W.H. Downes and F.T. Robinson, "Inness," *The Art Interchange*, 1894, XXXIII, no. 4, p. 102./ L. Ireland, *Inness*, Austin, Tex., 1965, no. 704 (repr.).

Exhibitions: Boston, Doll & Richards, *3rd Special Sale of Inness Paintings*, 1876, no. 14 (as *Scene in Perugia*)./ Boston, Copley Hall, *Modern Paintings*, 1898, no. 48./ San Francisco, M.H. de Young Memorial Museum and California Palace of the Legion of Honor, *American Painting*, 1935, no. 142 (repr.)./ Springfield, Mass., G.W.V. Smith Art Museum, N.Y., Brooklyn Museum, and Montclair Art Museum, *Inness*, 1946, p. 33, no. 24 (repr.)./ New York, Macbeth Gallery, *Italian Landscapes by Inness*, 1952, no. 11.

659.
fig. 379

The Rising Storm
A white horse pulls a cart in the foreground of a dark green and brown landscape. The clouds are gray at the horizon, becoming yellow and brown.
Oil on canvas. 30 × 45 in. (76.2 × 114.3 cm.)
Signed lower right: *G. Inness*. Painted about 1879.
Gift of George Higginson. 82.113

The title *A Hazy Morning* is handwritten on an old label on the stretcher. The picture is probably the one exhibited at the National Academy in 1879.

References: W.H. Downes, "American Paintings in the Boston Art Museum," *Brush and Pencil*, 1900, VI, no. 5, p. 210 (repr. p. 207)./ L. Ireland, *Inness*, Austin, Tex., 1965, no. 907 (repr.).

Exhibitions: New York, National Academy of Design, *54th Annual*, 1879, no. 384 (as *Hazy Morning*)./ Buffalo, Albright Art Gallery, *Inness Centennial*, 1925, p. 12, no. 40 (repr.).

660.
fig. 382

Georgia Pines—Afternoon

A clump of pines in a flat green landscape are silhouetted against gray clouds.
Oil on canvas. 24 × 36 in. (61 × 91.4 cm.)
Signed lower right: *G. Inness*. Painted in 1886.
Collections: Mrs. George Inness, Montclair, N.J.; William T. Evans, sold American Art Association, New York, Jan. 31, Feb. 1–2, 1900, no. 177 (repr.); Robert D. Evans, 1900.
Robert Dawson Evans Collection. Bequest of Mrs. Robert D. Evans. 17.3236
Inness worked in the South in 1886.

References: S. Hartmann, *American Painting*, Boston, 1901, I (repr. p. 87)./ "Inness," *Masters in Art*, 1908, IX, part 102, p. 40 (pl. IX)./ G. Inness, Jr., *Inness*, New York, 1917 (repr. p. 171)./ L. Ireland, *Inness*, Austin, Tex., 1965, no. 1886 (repr.).

GENICHIRO INOKUMA was born in Takamatsu, Japan in 1902. He learned calligraphy from his father, then received academic Western training at the Tokyo Academy of Art from 1922 to 1926. He worked in Tokyo until 1938, when he traveled for two years in Europe, where he developed a great admiration for the work of Matisse. From 1941 to 1945 he was an art reporter in the Orient; he then taught independently until 1955, when he came to the United States. His work in America has become increasingly abstract.

661.
fig. 598

Accumulate

A pattern of gray and black rectangles, some accented with white and blue, is on a light gray background.
Oil on canvas. 57 × 50 in. (144.7 × 127 cm.)
Signed top center: *guèn*. Painted in 1956–1957.
Collection: Institute of Contemporary Art, Boston, Provisional Collection, 1958.
Arthur Gordon Tompkins Residuary Fund. 61.199

Exhibitions: Columbus, O., Columbus Gallery and Boston, Institute of Contemporary Art, *Contemporary Painters of Japanese Origin in America*, 1958, no. 9 (repr.)./ Boston, Institute of Contemporary Art, *Provisional Collection*, 1961, no. 18.

ALEXANDER JAMES (1890–1946) was born in Cambridge, Mass. He studied at the Boston Museum School under Frank Benson and later with Abbott Thayer in Dublin, N.H. In 1918–1919 he was in California; until 1921 he taught the life class at the Corcoran School, Washington, D.C. From 1929 to 1930 he worked in Paris. He then lived in Richmond and Dublin, N.H. until his death.

662.

Portrait of a Professor (Philip Cabot)

Bust-length and turned three-quarters left, he wears a blue coat with a green scarf. The background is brown and green.
Oil on panel. 17¾ × 13 in. (45.1 × 33 cm.)
Signed upper left: *Alexander James*. Painted in 1934.
Gift of Mrs. Charles Gaston Smith's Group and by purchase. 34.1439
Philip Cabot (1872–1941), born in Beverly Farms, Mass., was the son of James and Elizabeth Dwight Cabot. He was a lecturer at the Harvard Business School from 1925 until his death in Boston. His portrait was painted in Dublin, N.H. in 1934, "after many studies in pencil . . . approximately 35 sittings . . . during the time I kept two portraits going, each

based on the same pencil drawing but painted independently of each other. One of these is owned by Mr. Cabot.'' (Letter from the artist, Jan. 12, 1935).

Exhibitions: New York, Walker Galleries, *James*, 1937, no. 4./ Manchester, N.H., Currier Gallery, Boston, MFA, and Washington, D.C., Corcoran Gallery, *James Memorial*, 1947, no. 15./ Fitchburg, Mass., Art Museum and Springfield, Mass., Museum of Fine Arts, *James*, 1950, no. 10.

663.   **The Embattled Farmer**

The farmer, in his white undershirt, sits half-length at a table, typing. The background is brown.

Oil on panel. 19¾ × 24 in. (50.1 × 61 cm.)
Signed lower left: *Alexander James*. Painted in 1939.
Collection: Mrs. Alexander James, Dublin, N.H., 1946.
Charles Henry Hayden Fund. 47.1465

Painted in Richmond, N.H. in 1939. ''Stepping into the Richmond house you might find the 'Embattled Farmer,' who was a Selectman of Richmond, stripped to his long winter underwear, doing the town accounts in the warm kitchen.'' (From the Memorial Exhibition catalogue.) Mrs. Alexander James owns a pastel study for the painting.

Exhibitions: New York, Maynard Walker, *New Paintings by James*, 1940, no. 1./ Manchester, N.H., Currier Gallery, Boston, MFA, and Washington, D.C., Corcoran Gallery, *James Memorial*, 1947, no. 47 (repr.)./ Fitchburg, Mass., Art Museum and Springfield, Mass., Museum of Fine Arts, *James*, 1950, no. 26 (repr.).

664.   **Siberian Cossack**

Half-length in a red shirt, he leans with folded arms over a brown object. The background is brown, yellow, and mauve.

Oil on panel. 24 × 20 in. (61 × 50.8 cm.)
Signed lower right: *Alexander James*. Painted in 1937.
Collection: Mrs. Alexander James, Dublin, N.H., 1946.
Charles Henry Hayden Fund. 47.1546

Gouri Ivanov-Rinov, son of P.P. Ivanov-Rinov, was a member of the Siberian Cossacks and an artist. He was painted in Dublin, N.H. in 1937.

Exhibitions: New York, Maynard Walker, *New Paintings by James*, 1940, no. 13./ Manchester, N.H., Currier Gallery, Boston, MFA, and Washington, D.C., Corcoran Gallery, *James Memorial*, 1947, no. 32./ Fitchburg, Mass., Art Museum and Springfield, Mass., Museum of Fine Arts, *James*, 1950, no. 19.

WILLIAM JAMES (1882–1961) was born in Cambridge, Mass. He first trained in medicine but then studied painting at the Boston Museum School and the Académie Julian in Paris. A portrait and landscape painter, he taught at the Museum School from 1913 to 1924 and was the MFA's Acting Director from 1936 to 1938. He died in Chocorua, N.H.

665.   **The Artist's Mother**

An elderly lady, bust-length in left profile, wears a black dress and hairband. The unfinished background is black and gray.

Oil on canvas. 27 × 22½ in. (68.6 × 57.1 cm.)
Signed lower right: *William James*. Painted in 1921.
Abraham Shuman Fund. 51.243

''It was painted in my studio . . . I think in 1921—in one sitting.'' (Letter from the artist, Jan. 20, 1951.)

JOHN WESLEY JARVIS (1781–1840)

666.   **De Witt Clinton**

Oil on canvas. 30 × 25 in. (76.2 × 63.5 cm.)
Painted about 1810.
M. and M. Karolik Collection. 45.895
Reference: Karolik Catalogue, 1949, no. 169 (repr.).

WILLIAM JEWETT (1789/90–1874)

See Samuel L. Waldo and William Jewett (Cat. no. 1009). *See also* p. 279 (Samuel Lovett Waldo).

DAVID JOHNSON (1827–1908), born in New York, studied under Jasper Francis Cropsey, but was largely a self-taught painter. He lived and worked principally in New York City, making numerous sketching trips throughout New England and upstate New York. Elected to the National Academy in 1861, he died in Walden, N.Y.

667.
fig. 279

North Conway, New Hampshire

The gray houses of the village stand in a brown and green landscape before the distant gray and white mass of Mt. Washington. The sky is pale gray.
Oil on canvas. 16×23 in. (40.6×58.4 cm.)
Signed and dated lower right: *D. Johnson 1852.* Inscribed on back, lower right: *White Mountains—from N. Conway, N.H.| D. Johnson—1852.*
Collection: Maxim Karolik, Newport, R.I., 1954.
M. and M. Karolik Collection. 62.276

Exhibitions: New York, National Academy of Design, 1852, no. 59./ Washington, D.C., Smithsonian Institution, circulated in the U.S., *19th Century American Paintings*, 1954–1956, no. 34 (repr.)./ Boston, MFA and circulated in the U.S., *The M. and M. Karolik Collection*, 1957–1959, no. 157./ North Conway, N.H., Library Association, *A Century of Art in the White Mountains*, 1965, p. 25 (repr. p. 2).

JONATHAN EASTMAN JOHNSON (1824–1906), born in Lovell, Me., in 1840 worked for about a year at Bufford's Lithography Shop, Boston. He then took up portraiture in crayons and from 1841 to 1849 worked in Augusta, Me., Boston, Newport, R.I., and Washington, D.C. In 1849 he left to study at the Royal Academy, Düsseldorf with Emmanuel Leutze, then from 1851 to 1855 studied in The Hague. On his return to America, he worked in Wisconsin in 1856–1857, in Cincinnati and Washington, D.C. in 1858, and in 1859 settled permanently in New York. He first visited Nantucket in the early 1870's and there painted many of the genre scenes for which he is best known. He died in New York.

668.

Measurement and Contemplation
Oil on chipboard. 20×24 in. (50.8×61 cm.)
Signed lower right: *E.J.* Painted in the early 1860's.
M. and M. Karolik Collection. 48.435
Reference: *Karolik Catalogue,* 1949, no. 171 (repr.).

669.
fig. 320

Writing to Father

The small blond boy, dressed in a gray Civil War uniform, sits on a brown chair, hunched over a green table, upon which he writes a letter. His gray cap lies on another yellow chair, left, above a red hassock on the floor of the brown interior. Red draperies hang from the open window, upper left, and in the background, right.
Oil on canvas. 12×9½ in. (30.5×23.5 cm.)
Signed and dated lower right: *E. Johnson.|—63.*
Collections: Mrs. Edward W. McMahon, about 1940; Maxim Karolik, Newport, R.I.
Bequest of Maxim Karolik. 64.435

Reference: J.I.H. Baur, *Eastman Johnson*, Brooklyn Museum, New York, 1940, p. 66, no. 149.

Exhibitions: Washington, D.C., Smithsonian Institution, circulated in the U.S., *19th Century American Paintings*, 1954–1956, no. 35 (repr. p. 22)./ Ogunquit Museum, *8th Annual—Luminist and Trompe l'Oeil Painters*, 1960, no. 16./ Washington, D.C., Corcoran Gallery and Boston, MFA, *The Civil War: The Artists' Record*, 1961–1962, p. 18, no. 209.

670.

The Letter Home
Oil on chipboard. 23 × 27½ in. (58.4 × 69.8 cm.)
Signed and dated lower left: *E. Johnson 1867.*
M. and M. Karolik Collection. 48.434
Reference: Karolik Catalogue, 1949, no. 170 (repr.).

671.
fig. 322

Winnowing Grain
Oil on chipboard. 15½ × 13 in. (39.4 × 33 cm.)
Signed lower right: *E.J.* Inscribed on back: *E.J.* Painted between 1873 and 1879.
M. and M. Karolik Collection. 48.436
Reference: Karolik Catalogue, 1949, no. 172 (repr.).

672.
fig. 321

The Little Convalescent
A woman in black, her back turned, sits by a boy propped up in bed reading. A white blanket screens a cupboard by the brown wall, on which stand white and brown bottles.
Oil on academy board. 12¾ × 11 in. (32.3 × 27.9 cm.)
Signed lower left: *E. J—.* Painted about 1873–1879.
Collections: Eastman Johnson Sale, American Art Association, New York, Feb. 26, 1907, no. 12; W.B. Cogswell, Syracuse, N.Y, 1907; the Misses F. Pearl and Elizabeth Browning, his granddaughters, Syracuse, by 1920.
Frederick Brown Fund. 40.90

The painting was probably done during the summers Johnson spent at his sister's farm in Kennebunkport, Me., from 1873 to 1879.

Exhibitions: Brooklyn Museum, *Johnson,* 1940, p. 46, no. 118 (pl. xxi)./ Philadelphia Art Alliance, *Johnson,* 1944, no. 25.

673.
fig. 323

Self Portrait
Bust length, turned three-quarters left, he wears a black jacket and tie with a white shirt. A black eyeshade casts a dark shadow across his eyes; his face is ruddy and his moustache, goatee, and hair are gray. The background is very dark brown.
Oil on canvas. 24 × 20 in. (60.9 × 50.8 cm.)
Signed lower left: *E.J.* Painted about 1885.
Collections: Mrs. Eastman Johnson; Lotos Club, New York, by 1906; M. Knoedler & Company, New York, 1962; Mr. and Mrs. Daniel Fraad, New York, 1962.
Emily L. Ainsley Fund. 67.604

A nearly identical version, but without the eyeshade and with a looser arrangement of the hair, is at the Brooklyn Museum of Art (J.I.H. Baur, *Eastman Johnson,* Brooklyn Museum, New York, 1940, check list no. 206).

Exhibitions: Douthitt Gallery, N.Y., *Eastman Johnson, "The Keystone Artist,"* 1940, no. 26./ M. Knoedler & Company, New York, *Paintings and Drawings by Eastman Johnson,* 1946, no. 4./ The Brooklyn Museum of Art and Andover, Mass., Addison Gallery, *Selections from the Collection of Daniel and Rita Fraad,* New York, 1964, no. 4 (repr.).

JOHN JOHNSTON (1753–1818), born in Boston, was trained by his father, Thomas Johnston (1708–1767), and perhaps by the house and sign painter John Gore. A Captain, he was severely wounded in the Revolutionary War and was discharged in 1777. He then established, with Daniel Rea, Jr., his brother-in-law, a house and sign painting business which he supplemented by painting portraits in oil and pastel. He died in Boston.

674.
fig. 95

A Man in a Gray Coat
Half-length, turned three-quarters right, his neckcloth is white under the gray coat. Gray and pink clouds are in a blue sky, right, beyond a brown background. The spandrels are gray.
Oil on canvas. Painted oval. 30 × 24¾ in. (76.2 × 62.8 cm.)
Painted about 1788.
Gift of William Brewster. 29.893

A handwritten label on the back of the canvas reads: *This portrait was painted by J. Johnson, Boston, 1788, and restored by J. Howith, Boston, April 1844.* The costume supports this date.

WILLIAM KEITH (1839–1911) was born in Old Meldrum, Aberdeenshire, Scotland. He came to New York about 1851 and learned wood engraving there. Until 1859 he worked as an illustrator for *Harper's*, then lived in California. Except for an influential visit with George Inness, he taught himself to paint. Then, in 1869, he studied in Düsseldorf, and on his return lived in California, with frequent visits to Europe, until his death in Berkeley.

675.

California Landscape
A small green valley where cows drink from a pool. Beyond, a blue mountain is against a pale blue sky.
Oil on canvas. 25 × 30 in. (63.5 × 76.2 cm.)
Signed lower right: *W. Keith/ SF* (San Francisco).
Gift of Mrs. I. Tucker Burr. 27.219

JOHN FREDERICK KENSETT (1816–1872) was born in Cheshire, Conn. He studied engraving with his father Thomas and his uncle, Alfred Daggett, until 1835, when he started work in Albany and New York City as a professional engraver. In 1840 he went abroad with Asher B. Durand, T.P. Rossiter and John W. Casilear; he worked as a landscape painter in France, England, Germany, Switzerland, and Italy, remaining in Europe until 1847. He settled in New York in 1848, became associated with the Hudson River group, and made frequent summer trips in New York State, New England, Mississippi, Colorado, and Canada. He died in New York.

676.

Niagara Falls and the Rapids
Oil on canvas. 16 × 24 in. (40.6 × 61 cm.)
Painted about 1851–1852.
M. and M. Karolik Collection. 48.439
Reference: Karolik Catalogue, 1949, no. 175 (repr.).

677.
fig. 308

Whirlpool, Niagara
Swirling green and white water flows between the brown and green wooded cliffs; the sky is blue with gray clouds.
Oil on canvas. 13½ × 22 in. (34.3 × 55.9 cm.)
Inscribed on back, left center: *J.F. Kensett*. Painted about 1851–1852.
Collections: J.R. Kellogg, the artist's great-nephew, New York; Maxim Karolik, Newport, R.I., 1945.
Bequest of Maxim Karolik. 64.436
Kensett visited Niagara only twice: in 1851 and 1852.
References: M. Breuning, *Art Digest*, 1945, xix, no. 9, p. 10./ "Kensett," *Old Print Shop Portfolio*, 1945, iv, no. 6 (repr. p. 125).

678.

Bash-Bish Falls, South Egremont, Massachusetts
Oil on canvas. 29½ × 24 in. (74.9 × 61 cm.)
Signed and dated lower right: *J.F.K. 1855* (initials in monogram).
M. and M. Karolik Collection. 48.437
Reference: Karolik Catalogue, 1949, no. 173 (repr.).

679.
fig. 309

Cliffs at Newport, R.I., Low Tide
Brown cliffs with green and yellow shrubs rise from the blue water. Boat sails are white under blue sky.
Oil on canvas. 22¼ × 36¼ in. (56.5 × 92.1 cm.)
Signed and dated lower right: *JFK '67* (J and F in monogram).
Collections: Maxim Karolik, Newport, R.I., 1950.
M. and M. Karolik Collection. 62.277
The New York Public Library owns a photograph of John F. Kensett in his studio which shows the painting on an easel before him.

References: E.H. Johnson, "Kensett Revisited," *Art Quarterly*, 1957, xx, no. 1, p. 83 (fig. 1)./ T.N. Maytham, "Some Recent Accessions," *MFA Bulletin*, 1962, LX, no. 322, p. 143 (repr.).

Exhibitions: Worcester, Mass., Art Museum, *The Private Collection of Maxim Karolik*, 1952, no. 28./ Minneapolis Institute of Arts and circulated in the U.S., *19th Century American Paintings from the Collection of Maxim Karolik*, 1953–1954./ Washington, D.C., Smithsonian Institution, circulated in the U.S., *19th Century American Paintings*, 1954–1956, no. 37./ Boston, MFA, *New Paintings in the M. and M. Karolik Collection*, 1962–1963.

680. **Cliffs at Newport, Rhode Island**
Oil on canvas. 12 × 20 in. (30.5 × 50.8 cm.)
Inscribed on back of stretcher: *Burton Av. Newport, R.I.*
M. and M. Karolik Collection. 48.440
Reference: *Karolik Catalogue*, 1949, no. 176 (repr.).

681. **Trenton Falls, New York**
Oil on canvas. 18¾ × 24 in. (47.6 × 61 cm.)
Inscribed in pencil on back of stretcher: *Suydam Falls, Trenton Falls, N.Y.*
M. and M. Karolik Collection. 48.438
Reference: *Karolik Catalogue*, 1949, no. 174 (repr.).

JOHN F. KENSETT and DANIEL HUNTINGTON (1816–1906)

682. **Seascape, Newport**
Oil on canvas. 36 × 60 in. (76.2 × 152.4 cm.)
Signed lower left: *J.F. Kensett & D. Huntington.* Painted between 1848 and 1851, or 1858 and 1872.
M. and M. Karolik Collection. 48.441
Reference: *Karolik Catalogue*, 1949, no. 177 (repr.).

ROCKWELL KENT born in Tarrytown Heights, N.Y. in 1882, studied in New York City with William M. Chase, Robert Henri, Kenneth Hayes Miller, and Abbott Thayer. He is a painter, illustrator, author, and lecturer and has worked in Alaska in 1919, Ireland in 1926, Greenland in 1931–1932, and in Monhegan, Me. He now lives in Ausable Forks, N.Y.

683. **Maine Coast, Winter**
fig. 550
The fir trees in the foreground are covered with blue-shadowed snow; those behind are dark green against a white hill. The sea is blue under gray sky.
Oil on canvas. 38 × 44½ in. (96.5 × 113 cm.)
Signed and dated lower left: *Rockwell Kent 1909.*
Bequest of John T. Spaulding. 48.567
Exhibition: Boston, MFA, *The Spaulding Collections*, 1948, p. 3, no. 47.

GYORGY KEPES was born in Selyp, Hungary in 1906 and studied from 1924 to 1928 at the Royal Academy of Fine Arts in Budapest. Until 1930 he was one of the Hungarian avant garde group, Munka, when he left to work in London and Berlin in film, stage, and exhibition design. In 1937 he went to Chicago as head of the Light and Color Department of the Institute of Design. Since 1946 he has been Professor of Visual Design at the Massachusetts Institute of Technology, Cambridge and is author of three books: *Language of Vision*, 1944, *The New Landscape in Art and Science*, 1956, and *Visual Arts Today*, 1960.

684. **Silver Dew**
fig. 606
Broad planes of orange, red, green, and purple are on a background of brown and gray. Below, a brown streak of sand separates them from the brown and blue-gray foreground.
Oil and sand on canvas. 60 × 60 in. (152.4 × 152.4 cm.)
Signed and dated on back, left center: *Gyorgy Kepes/ Silver Dew/ 1962/ GK.*
Gift of Mr. and Mrs. W. Ray Kitchel. 63.1051
Exhibition: Boston, Institute of Contemporary Art, *Contributions*, 1963.

WILLIAM AUSTIN KIENBUSCH was born in New York in 1914. On graduation from Princeton in 1936 he studied a year at the Art Students League in New York and one summer at the Colorado Springs Fine Arts Center. In 1937 he went to Paris to work under Abraham Rattner. On his return, in 1938, he worked for two years with Anton Refregier and one year with Stuart Davis at the New School for Social Research, New York. Since 1948 he has taught at the Brooklyn Museum School of Art and now spends his summers in Maine.

685. **Orange Trees I**

fig. 590

Broad strokes of bright orange with blue, green, and purple over a white background. Casein on paper, mounted on upsom board. 32 × 45 in. (81.2 × 114.3 cm.) Signed and dated lower left: *Kienbusch 61.*
Gift of the Ford Foundation. 62.205

"All three of the Orange Trees pictures were done at Trevett, Me., my summer home, last summer and yours is no. I. The picture relates to orange trees seen in Greece and Crete last Feb. & March." (Letter from the artist, March 14, 1962.)

CHARLES BIRD KING (1785–1862), born in Newport, R.I., studied there with the portrait painter Samuel King and from 1800 to 1805 with Edward Savage in New York City. Until 1812 he worked with Benjamin West in London and on his return lived in Philadelphia and Baltimore. From 1816 until his death he worked, primarily painting portraits, in Washington, D.C.

686. **Rip Van Winkle Returning from a Morning Lounge**

fig. 219

The brown interior has brown furniture and domestic objects of blue, yellow, gray, and white. At the door on the left stands Rip, in gray, brown, and blue; his wife, by the fireside, and his children wear red, green, and gray.
Oil on canvas. 44 × 56¼ in. (111.7 × 142.8 cm.)
Collection: Maxim Karolik, Newport, R.I., 1952.
Bequest of Maxim Karolik. 64.442

On the stretcher is inscribed: *Rip Van Winkle Returning from a Morning Lounge/ Original by C.B. King.* The story of Rip Van Winkle was written in 1819–1820 by Washington Irving and first published in the *Sketch Book.*
Reference: "The Editor's Attic," *Antiques,* 1932, XXI, no. 2, p. 67 (repr. cover).
Exhibition: Washington, D.C., Smithsonian Institution, circulated in the U.S., *19th Century American Paintings,* 1954–1956, no. 38.

FRANZ JOSEPH KLINE (1910–1962), born in Wilkes-Barre, Pa., studied at Girard College, Philadelphia, at Boston University from 1931–35 and at Heatherly's Art School, London in 1937 and 1938. He returned to New York in that year where he met Willem de Kooning who had a pronounced influence on his work. He taught at Black Mountain College, North Carolina, at the Pratt Institute, the Philadelphia Museum School and at Cooper Union in New York. His formidable, gestural paintings, confined largely to black and white, spring from the late 1940's, and he soon became a leading influential figure in the Abstract Expressionist movement. He continued to live in New York until his death.

687. **Probst I**

fig. 594

Broad angular black and dark brown bands are violently applied on a near white background streaked with areas of peach-pink and yellow. Strong yellow strokes appear in the opening near the top center.
Oil on canvas. 108 × 79⅝ in. (274.3 × 202.3 cm.)
Signed and dated on back center: *FRANZ KLINE –60.*
Collections: With Sidney Janis Gallery, New York, 1961; Susan Morse Hilles (Mrs. Frederick H.), New Haven, Conn., 1962.
Lent by Susan Morse Hilles. 597.66
Exhibitions: Sarasota, Florida, John and Mable Ringling Museum of Art, *The Sidney Janis Painters,* 1961, no. 14 (repr.)./ New York City, Whitney Museum of American

Art, *Annual Exhibition 1961, Contemporary American Painting*, no. 67 (repr.)./ Hartford, Conn., Wadsworth Atheneum, *Continuity and Change—45 American Abstract Painters and Sculptors*, 1962, no. 62 (repr. cover); New Haven, Conn., Yale University Art Gallery, *Two Modern Collectors: Susan Morse Hilles and Richard Brown Baker*, 1963, no. 20 (repr.)./ Washington, D.C., Gallery of Modern Art and Hartford, Conn., Wadsworth Atheneum, *20th Century Painting and Sculpture from Connecticut Collections*, 1965, nos. 33 and 35 in respective catalogues./ Boston, MFA, *Sculpture and Painting Today—Selections from the Collection of Susan Morse Hilles*, 1966, no. 49 (repr.).

KARL KNATHS was born in Eau Clair, Wisc. in 1891. His study at the Art Institute of Chicago was interrupted by the First World War; he is largely self-taught. In 1919 he went first to New York, then to Provincetown, Mass. where he now lives. During the winters from 1938 to 1950 he taught at the Phillips Memorial Gallery in Washington, D.C., and he has taught at Bennington College, Vt. The work of Picasso and the German Expressionists Klee and Kandinsky especially has influenced him.

688.
fig. 587

Day of Atonement
The scenes of heaven and hell are of many colors. Above, gray, white, yellow, and purple predominate in the figures; brown, white, green, and purple in the background. Below, the background is mainly purple, and the flames are red; the wolf and the figures are gray and green.
Oil on masonite, two panels joined horizontally. 96 × 96 in. (243.8 × 243.8 cm.)
Signed center right: *K Knaths*. Painted about 1939–1940.
Collections: Raymond L. Myrer, Boston, 1942.
Gift of Mr. and Mrs. Raymond L. Myrer. 60.796

"The painting, I believe, was painted around 1939. . . . So I took the heaven and hell idea on the story side so that the mood of the subject would transform itself into a mode for the structure of the painting. I think it was influenced by Picasso's *Guernica*—as far as I was able to comprehend it at that time." (Letter from the artist, June 19, 1960.) A study for the painting (crayon, pencil, and india ink, 15¾ × 15¾ in.) is in the Department of Prints and Drawings of the MFA.
Exhibitions: New York, Buchholz Gallery, *Knaths*, 1942, no. 18./ Washington, D.C., Phillips Memorial Gallery, *American Painting and Water Colors*, 1942./ Boston, Boris Mirski Gallery, *Knaths*, 1949./ Lincoln, Mass., De Cordova Museum, *Knaths*, 1953./ Boston University Gallery, *Works from Private Collections*, 1960, no. 41.

689.

Pine Bough
A green and pink pine bough, a red, purple, and white clock, a jug, and bread are composed on a table. Purple predominates, with touches of pink, gray, yellow, white, and green.
Oil on canvas. 36 × 42 in. (91.4 × 106.7 cm.)
Signed lower right: *Karl Knaths*. Painted in 1952.
Charles Henry Hayden Fund. 57.181

"The particular style of painting I believe grows out of the influence of Cézanne as modified by the fauves and cubists. Or rather what I could comprehend from these mainly and would serve for my painting methods." (Letter from the artist, March 24, 1957.) The date was given by the artist.
Exhibitions: Washington, D.C., Corcoran Gallery, *23rd Biennial*, 1953, no. 104./ New York, Paul Rosenberg and Co., *Knaths*, 1963, no. 16.

690.
fig. 586

Lilacs
A composition of abstracted angular planes of lavender with blue, white, and green against a background of pink, white, green, and purple.
Oil on canvas. 40¼ × 30 in. (102.2 × 76.2 cm.)
Signed lower left: *Karl Knaths*. Painted in 1955.
Ellen Kelleran Gardner Fund. 60.1159
Exhibition: New York, Paul Rosenberg & Co., *Knaths*, 1955, no. 14.

691.

Vermont Barns

Across a gray river with green banks are white and gray barns before a village of white, yellow, and gray buildings. Gray and yellow clouds in a blue sky.

Oil on chipboard. 15¾ × 12 in. (40 × 30.5 cm.)

Signed lower left: *Koch.* Painted in 1941.

Charles Henry Hayden Fund. 41.800

LEON KROLL

born in New York in 1884, studied from about 1900 to 1902 at the Art Students League with Twachtman and at the National Academy. In Paris he was a pupil at the Académie Julian and of Laurens. He then lived in New York, with summers in Gloucester, Mass. From 1911 to 1918 he taught at the National Academy, was President of the U.S. Committee of the International Association of Plastic Arts, and is a Director of the American Academy of Arts and Letters. He now lives in Gloucester.

692.

Nancy Wynne Parker

The head of a girl, facing front. Her dress is blue, with touches of red and green, and the background is yellow and mauve.

Oil on canvas. 18 × 15 in. (45.7 × 38.1 cm.)

Signed lower right: *Leon Kroll.* Painted in 1930.

Collection: John T. Spaulding, Boston, 1931.

Bequest of John T. Spaulding. 48.568

"The head of Nancy Wynne Parker was painted in 1930 at Folly Cove, Gloucester, Mass." (Letter from the artist, May 24, 1951.)

Reference: N. Wynne, "In the Studio of Leon Kroll," *Studio,* April, 1938, xv, pp. 202–205.

Exhibitions: Boston, MFA, *The Spaulding Collections,* 1948, no. 48./ New York, American Academy of Arts and Letters, *Kroll,* 1949.

JOHN LA FARGE

(1835–1910) was born in New York and studied law before he left in 1856 for Paris, where he worked briefly with Couture, then traveled throughout Europe. He returned in 1858, worked with W.M. Hunt in Newport in 1859 and worked as a still-life and landscape painter until 1876, when he turned to mural painting (as in Trinity Church, Boston) and stained-glass design, at which he became preeminent in this country. In 1886 he visited Japan, and in 1890–1891, the South Seas, Java, and Ceylon. In addition he was a writer, illustrator, lecturer, and critic. He died in Providence, R.I. A portrait of La Farge by Wilton Robert Lockwood (Cat. no. 728) is also in the MFA collection.

693.

Path Between Trees

The path, edged by green grass and bordered with trees, runs beside a white house toward a gray shed. Beyond are a green hillside and green-blue sky.

Oil on panel. 15¾ × 11 in. (40 × 27.9 cm.)

Painted in 1859.

Collection: Henry Lee Higginson, Sr., Boston, by 1910.

Bequest of Mrs. Henry Lee Higginson, Sr. 35.1168

The picture was probably painted in 1859, when La Farge was in Newport.

Reference: G. Danes, "Hunt and His Newport Circle," *American Magazine of Art,* 1950, XLIII, no. 4 (repr. p. 147).

Exhibition: Boston, MFA, *Contemporary Art,* 1879.

694.

Hillside, Long Island

A bare hillside of brown and green grass. Over its crest a brown tree and a house rise against blue sky.

Oil on panel. 11¾ × 9¼ in. (29.7 × 23.5 cm.)

Painted about 1860–1865.

Collection: Henry Lee Higginson, Sr., Boston.

Bequest of Mrs. Henry Lee Higginson, Sr. 35.1166

Exhibition: Boston, MFA, *La Farge,* 1911.

695.

In the Forest

Deep woods of dark green and brown, broken by blue sky and touches of red, gray, and white foliage.

Oil on panel. 9¾ × 12 in. (24.7 × 30.5 cm.)

Painted about 1860–1865.

Gift of the Estate of Arthur T. Cabot. 14.2

The early experimental style suggests its date.

Reference: R.B. Katz, "La Farge as Painter and Critic," PhD thesis, Radcliffe 1951, pp. 48, 58 (footnote 21) (fig. 10).

Exhibition: Boston, MFA, *La Farge*, 1911.

696.

Water Lily

A water lily floats on shadowy gray water, with its petals dimly reflected. The background is olive-gray.

Oil on panel. 7¾ × 5½ in. (19.7 × 14 cm.)

Signed upper left: *JLF*. Painted about 1860–1865.

Collection: Elizabeth H. Bartol, Boston, by 1881.

Bequest of Elizabeth Howard Bartol. Res. 27.93

"Some few were paintings of the water lily, which has . . . always appealed to the sense of something of a meaning—a mysterious appeal such as comes to us from certain arrangements of notes of music" . . . (From the artist; *see* R. Cortissoz, *La Farge*, Boston, 1911, pp. 135–136.) Most of his flower paintings of this type were done during the 1860's; this is probably an early example.

Exhibitions: New York, Macbeth Gallery, *La Farge*, 1948, no. 3./ Worcester, Mass., Assumption College, Galerie de la Maison Française, *La Farge*, 1956–1957, no. 2.

697.

Head of St. John

A young man with reddish hair and beard, in nearly left profile, wears a red robe. The background is gray.

Oil on canvas. 10¼ × 7½ in. (26 × 19 cm.)

Painted about 1862.

Collection: Elizabeth H. Bartol, Boston, by 1881.

Bequest of Elizabeth Howard Bartol. Res. 27.92

A study for the full-length figure of St. John (Whitney Museum of American Art, New York), painted in 1862–1863 as part of the unfinished triptych commissioned but rejected by a Roman Catholic church in New York.

References: C. Waern, *La Farge*, London, 1896, p. 31./ R.B. Katz, "La Farge as Painter and Critic," PhD thesis, Radcliffe, 1951, pp. 90–100 (fig. 38).

Exhibitions: Boston, MFA, *La Farge*, 1911./ New York, Macbeth Gallery, *La Farge*, 1948, no. 2./ Worcester, Mass., Assumption College, Galerie de la Maison Française, *La Farge*, 1956–1957, no. 3.

698.
fig. 407

Vase of Flowers

Red, yellow, and white flowers with green leaves are in a brown and black patterned vase. The table is brown before a gold background.

Oil on panel. 18½ × 14 in. (47 × 35.5 cm.)

Signed and dated lower right: *J. La Farge/ 1864.*

Collections: James Brown Case, Boston, before 1907; the Misses Case, his daughters.

Gift of Louise W. and Marian R. Case. 20.1873

References: W. Born, *Still Life Painting in America*, New York, 1947, p. 41 (pl. 109)./ R.B. Katz, "La Farge as Painter and Critic," PhD thesis, Radcliffe, 1951, p. 68 (fig. 17).

Exhibition: Worcester, Mass., Assumption College, Galerie de la Maison Française, *La Farge*, 1956–1957, no. 1.

699.
fig. 408

Hollyhocks and Corn

Two stalks of red and white flowers stand against a gold and brown background.

Below, the green ears of corn are torn open to show the yellow kernels.
Oil on panel. 23½ × 16½ in. (59.7 × 41.9 cm.)
Signed and dated center right: *J. La Farge* MCXXXLXV.
Gift of Dr. William Sturgis Bigelow. 21.1442

References: W. Born, *Still Life Painting in America*, New York, 1947, p. 41 (pl. 108)./ R.B. Katz, "La Farge as Painter and Critic," PhD thesis, Radcliffe, 1951, pp. 69–70 (fig. 18).

700.   **A Gray Day, Newport**

Two bare trees grow between gray boulders. The grass in the foreground is green; the distant misty landscape is gray under gray and yellow sky.
Oil on panel. 12½ × 9½ in. (31.7 × 24.1 cm.)
Signed and dated lower left: *La Farge 1867.*
Collection: Henry Lee Higginson, Sr., Boston, by 1910.
Bequest of Mrs. Henry Lee Higginson, Sr. 35.1167

Exhibitions: Boston, MFA, *Contemporary Art*, 1879, no. 311./ Worcester, Mass., Assumption College, Galerie de la Maison Française, *La Farge*, 1956–1957, no. 4.

701.   **Hilltop**
fig. 406

A brown hill is crowned by two brown and green pine trees. Beneath them are two women; one in blue is standing, the other in black is seated. The sky is blue and white.
Oil on canvas. 24 × 13 in. (61 × 33 cm.)
Painted about 1868.
Collection: Dr. William Sturgis Bigelow, Boston, by 1910.
Bequest of Dr. William Sturgis Bigelow. 26.771

Reference: R.B. Katz, "La Farge as Painter and Critic," PhD thesis, Radcliffe, 1951, p. 39 (fig. 6).

Exhibitions: San Francisco, M.H. de Young Memorial Museum and California Palace of the Legion of Honor, *American Painting*, 1935, no. 160 (repr.)./ New York, Metropolitan Museum, *La Farge*, 1936, no. 22 (repr.)./ Baltimore Museum, *200 Years of American Painting*, 1938, no. 21.

702.   **Halt of the Wise Men**
fig. 405

Of the three wise men robed in red and white, one is mounted and two walk; their horses are black, gray, and bay. The bleak landscape is brown, gray, and deep blue, and from the left a white light brightens the blue sky.
Oil on canvas. 32¾ × 42 in. (83.2 × 106.7 cm.)
Painted after 1868.
Gift of Edward W. Hooper. 90.151

A similar composition by La Farge, *The Wise Men Out of the East*, was used as a full-page illustration in *The Riverside Magazine for Young Children*, 1868, II, p. 529. The MFA's version was probably painted soon after. A watercolor version (7 × 9 in.) was owned by Frank Jewett Mather, Jr. of Princeton, N.J. in 1941.

References: W.H. Downes, "American Paintings in the Boston Art Museum," *Brush and Pencil*, 1900, VI, no. 5, p. 210 (repr. p. 205)./ R. Cortissoz, *La Farge*, Boston, 1911 (repr. opp. p. 74 as *The Three Kings*)./ L.M. Bryant, *American Pictures and Their Painters*, New York, 1917, pp. 84–85 (fig. 46)./ J.C. Van Dyke, *American Painting*, New York, 1919 (repr. opp. p. 138)./ R.B. Katz, "La Farge as Painter and Critic," PhD thesis, Radcliffe, 1951, p. 105 (fig. 47).

Exhibitions: New York, Wildenstein and Co., *La Farge and His Descendants*, 1931, no. 4./ New York, Metropolitan Museum, *La Farge*, 1936, no. 21 (repr.)./ Cleveland Museum, *American Painting*, 1937, no. 116./ Columbus, O., Columbus Gallery, *Romantic America*, 1948, no. 30./ New York, Macbeth Gallery, *La Farge*, 1948, no. 1./ Los Angeles, Municipal Art Gallery, *Old Favorites Revisited*, 1959, no. 29 (repr.)./ Toronto Art Gallery and circulated in Canada, and New York, Whitney Museum, *American Painting from 1865–1905*, 1961, no. 46 (pl. XXIII).

703.   **Nude (Ceres)**

A woman, with brown-toned skin, stands surrounded by green leaves.

Oil on canvas. 21½ × 11 in. (54.6 × 27.9 cm.)
Painted about 1881.
Collection: William Sturgis Bigelow, Boston, by 1910.
Bequest of Dr. William Sturgis Bigelow. 26.769
A preliminary sketch for one of the decorative panels in the dining room of the Vanderbilt mansion in New York City. Saint-Gaudens modeled the four panels, which represented Ceres, Pomona, Bacchus, and Vertumnus, after sketches by La Farge, who started the work in 1881. The subject here is probably Ceres.
Reference: R.B. Katz, "La Farge as Painter and Critic," PhD thesis, Radcliffe, 1951, p. 129 (fig. 58).
Exhibition: Boston, MFA, *La Farge*, 1911.

GEORGE COCHRAN LAMBDIN (1830–1896), born in Pittsburgh, Pa., moved to Philadelphia with his family in 1838. He studied painting with his father, the portrait painter James Reid Lambdin, but is best known for his flower pieces and sentimental genre subjects. Except for trips to Europe in 1855 and 1870, and two years in New York between 1868 and 1870, he worked primarily in Philadelphia, where he died.

704. **The Pruner**
Oil on canvas. 24 × 20 in. (61 × 50.8 cm.)
Signed and dated lower right: *Geo. C. Lambdin. 1868.*
M. and M. Karolik Collection. 48.442
Reference: *Karolik Catalogue*, 1949, no. 178 (repr.).

705. **Vase of Flowers**
Yellow, white, and red flowers in a clear glass vase stand beside grapes on a red and green tablecloth, with a green curtain behind.
Oil on canvas. 16 × 12 in. (40.6 × 30.5 cm.)
Signed and dated lower right: *Geo. C. Lambdin/ 1873.*
Collections: Private collection, N.J.; Maxim Karolik, Newport, R.I., 1961.
Bequest of Maxim Karolik. 64.458

FITZ HUGH LANE (1804–1865), christened Nathaniel Rogers Lane, was born in Gloucester, Mass. Although crippled by infantile paralysis, he worked in Pendleton's Lithography Shop in Boston from 1832 to 1837; from then until 1845 he was employed by the publishers Keith and Moore. In that same year he and J.W.A. Scott (1815–1907) set up a lithography business in Boston, but in 1848 Lane settled permanently in Gloucester. He visited Maine during the summers of 1850, 1852, 1855, and 1863, New York and Baltimore during the 1850's, and Puerto Rico. He died in Gloucester.

706. **A Maine Inlet**
Oil on canvas. 16½ × 25 in. (41.9 × 63.5 cm.)
Painted in the 1830's.
M. and M. Karolik Collection. 48.443
Reference: *Karolik Catalogue*, 1949, no. 179 (repr.).

707. **Fresh Water Cove from Dolliver's Neck, Gloucester**
fig. 262
Oil on canvas. 24 × 36 in. (61 × 91.4 cm.)
Painted in the late 1840's.
M. and M. Karolik Collection. 48.445
Reference: *Karolik Catalogue*, 1949, nos. 181 and 181A (repr.).

708. **Gloucester from Brookbank**
Oil on canvas. 20 × 30 in. (50.8 × 76.2 cm.)
Painted in the late 1840's.
M. and M. Karolik Collection. 48.444
Reference: *Karolik Catalogue*, 1949, no. 180 (repr.).

709.

Ships in Ice off Ten Pound Island, Gloucester
Oil on canvas. 12 × 19¾ in. (30.5 × 50.1 cm.)
Painted in the 1850's.
M. and M. Karolik Collection. 48.447
Reference: Karolik Catalogue, 1949, no. 183 (repr.).

710.
fig. 261

Castine, Maine
In the foreground are green meadows, separated by yellow fences, in which people stand or make hay. Beyond the gray and white buildings of the village is a gray harbor and distant blue-gray hills.
Oil on canvas. 21 × 33½ in. (53.3 × 82.5 cm.)
Signed and dated lower right: *F.H. Lane/ 1850.*
Collections: Probably Jonathan Lane, father of the artist, Gloucester, Mass.; Mrs. Leary Swan, West Roxbury, Mass., by 1938; Maxim Karolik, Newport, R.I.
Bequest of Maxim Karolik. 64.437

A detailed preliminary drawing without figures, inscribed *Castine from Port George/ Aug, 1850* is in the Samuel Mansfield Collection of the Cape Ann Scientific, Literary and Historical Association, Gloucester. Also on the drawing is the inscription, "A painting was made from this sketch and presented to my father." The MFA also has a panoramic view of Castine from another position, in watercolor and pencil, painted in 1851.
References: J.T. Flexner, "Painting and Sculpture, 1820–1865," *Maine and Its Role in American Art,* New York, 1963 (repr. pp. 66–67)./ J. Wilmerding, *Lane,* Salem, Mass., 1964, no. 42.
Exhibitions: Worcester, Mass., Art Museum, *The Private Collection of Maxim Karolik,* 1952, no. 29./ New York, M. Knoedler and Co., *Heade and Lane,* 1954, no. 5./ Washington, D.C., Smithsonian Institution, circulated in the U.S., *19th Century American Paintings,* 1954–1956, no. 39./ Boston, MFA and circulated in the U.S., *The M. and M. Karolik Collection,* 1957–1959, no. 160./ Waterville, Me., Colby College and circulated in the U.S., *Maine and Its Artists,* 1963–1964, no. 82.

711.
fig. 264

New York Harbor
Oil on canvas. 36 × 60 in. (91.4 × 152.4 cm.)
Signed and dated lower right: *Fitz H. Lane 1850.*
M. and M. Karolik Collection. 48.446
Reference: Karolik Catalogue, 1949, no. 182 (repr.).

712.
fig. 263

Boston Harbor
Two large gray three-masted ships and numerous other sailing craft, mostly with sails up, are nearly becalmed in gray-brown water. In the distance, under a yellow, pink and lavender sunset in a blue sky appears the Boston skyline.
Oil on canvas. 26¼ × 32 in. (66.8 × 106.7 cm.)
Painted about 1850–1855.
Collections: Probably Mrs. Charles M. Peirce (about 1840–1922), New Bedford, Mass.; Mrs. Willis E. Lougee, her daughter, New Bedford; Mrs. Grace H. Sargeant, her daughter, New Bedford; Mrs. Thomas W. Fransworth, Jr., her daughter, New Bedford, about 1960.
M. and M. Karolik Collection, by exchange. 66.339

The painting is one of several versions of the subject. One example is in a Massachusetts private collection (*see* J. Wilmerding, *Fitz Hugh Lane,* Salem, Mass., 1964, no. 20), another is the property of Bronson Trevor, New York (Wilmerding, no. 21).

713.
fig. 266

At the Fishing Grounds
Gray gaff-rigged schooners with white sails crowd the green water under cloudy blue sky. The fishermen wear red, green, brown, and black.
Oil on canvas. 17¼ × 26¼ in. (43.8 × 66.7 cm.)
Signed and dated lower right: *F.H. Lane/ 1851.*
Gift of Caroline W. Trask. 35.1981

Lane's painting style at this relatively early date was strongly influenced by the work of Robert Salmon.

Reference: J. Wilmerding, *Fitz Hugh Lane*, Salem, Mass., 1964, no. 54.

714.
fig. 265

Salem Harbor

Several three-masted vessels sail on calm green water. In the center of the fleet of black and brown boats with their white sails, a man in a brown row boat tows a broken spar. The blue sky is clouded.

Oil on canvas. 26 × 42 in. (66 × 106.7 cm.)

Signed and dated on sail of center boat: *FHL/ 1853.*

Collections: The Silsbee Family, Salem, Mass.; Maxim Karolik, Newport, R.I.

Bequest of Maxim Karolik. 64.465

A label on the back reads: *Belonged to my great-grandparents/ Nathaniel Silsbee Jr./ Dec. 18,—1804—July 9—1881/ and/ Marianne C.D. Silsbee/ Feb. 6,—1812—Aug. 4,—1889/ ——/ Marianne M. Beach/ sa—.* Possibly a painting of one of the Silsbee family's many ships.

Reference: J. Wilmerding, *Fitz Hugh Lane*, Salem, Mass., 1964, no. 78.

715.
fig. 267

Ipswich Bay

Beyond white breakers and brown rocks in the foreground the water is blue against the distant shore. The clouds in the blue and pink sky are pink and lavender.

Oil on canvas. 20 × 33 in. (50.8 × 83.8 cm.)

Inscribed on back, at the center: *View of Coffin's beach, from the rocks/ at the Loaf, after a sketch taken, August, 1862./ By Fitz H. Lane./ Presented to Dr. H.E. Davidson and Lady/ by the Artist.*

Collections: Dr. and Mrs. Herman Davidson, about 1862; Mrs. Barclay Tilton, their daughter, South Hamilton, Mass.

Gift of Mrs. Barclay Tilton in memory of Dr. Herman E. Davidson. 53.383

Reference: J. Wilmerding, *Fitz Hugh Lane*, Salem, Mass., 1964, no. 107.

716.

Owl's Head, Penobscot Bay, Maine

Oil on canvas. 16 × 26 in. (40.6 × 66 cm.)

Signed and dated on back of canvas: *Owl's Head—Penobscot Bay, by F.H. Lane, 1862.*

M. and M. Karolik Collection. 48.448

Reference: *Karolik Catalogue*, 1949, no. 184 (repr.).

717.

Brace's Rock, Eastern Point, Gloucester

Oil on canvas. 10 × 15 in. (25.4 × 38.1 cm.)

Painted in 1863.

Collections: MFA, Boston, M. and M. Karolik Collection; Private Collection, N.H.

Future Donation.

Reference: *Karolik Catalogue*, 1949, no. 186 (repr.).

718.

Brig "Antelope" in Boston Harbor

Oil on canvas. 21¼ × 36 in. (54 × 91.4 cm.)

Signed and dated on back of canvas: *F.H. Lane July 1863.*

M. and M. Karolik Collection. 48.449

Reference: *Karolik Catalogue*, 1949, no. 185 (repr.).

A. A. LAWRENCE

Nothing is known of the artist.

719.

Boat Race, Boston Harbor

Oil on canvas. 22 × 30 in. (55.9 × 76.2 cm.)

Signed and dated lower left: *A.A. Lawrence/ 1852.*

M. and M. Karolik Collection. 48.451

Reference: *Karolik Catalogue*, 1949, no. 187 (repr.).

ERNEST LAWSON (1873–1939) was born in San Francisco. In 1890 he began to study at the Art Students League, New York, and worked in Cos Cob, Conn. with John Twachtman and J. Alden Weir. In Paris he studied with Laurens and Constant at the Académie Julian. He then lived in New York City, and in 1908 joined "The Eight." Although a member of this Realist group, his stylistic origins and outlook were essentially Impressionist. He traveled extensively in America and France until his death in Miami, Fla.

720.   **Westchester Hills**

fig. 549   *The foreground meadows are bright green and dark blue before yellow-green meadows and gray-green woods on the distant hills. The clouds in the blue sky are white.*
Oil on canvas, mounted on plywood. 25 × 30 in. (63.5 × 76.2 cm.)
Signed and dated lower center: *E. Lawson/ 1917.*
Collection: John T. Spaulding, Boston, 1921.
Bequest of John T. Spaulding. 48.571
Exhibition: Boston, MFA, *The Spaulding Collections*, 1948, no. 50.

FREDERICO LEBRUN (1900–1964), born in Naples, Italy, attended night classes there at the Academy of Arts, and in 1922 became a designer for a stained glass factory. In 1924 he formed a branch of the firm in Springfield, Ill., then from 1925 to 1930 worked in New York as a commercial artist. From 1930 to 1936 he visited Europe, studying especially in Orvieto. He then taught at the Art Students League, New York, Yale University, at the Chouinard Art Institute, Los Angeles, and at the American Academy in Rome. He lived in Los Angeles, except for 1952 to 1954, spent in Mexico, and the year in Rome, 1959–1960, until his death. He has become best known for his intensely Expressionist studies, of a cadaverous nature, on tragic religious and secular themes.

721.   **The Slaughter House**

fig. 576   *In a pink, brown, and gray building, men in blue, white, and yellow handle brown carcasses. The sky is gray-blue.*
Oil on canvas. 20 × 34 in. (50.8 × 86.3 cm.)
Signed lower right: *Rico Lebrun.* Painted in 1940.
Charles Henry Hayden Fund. 42.176

"Painted in the winter of 1940 . . . During the years of 1939 and 1940 I was following an intensive program of study of the structure of animals in motion, this led me quite frequently to a nearby slaughter house . . . the painting in your collection was the result of a wish on my part to record the place as I had seen it." (Letter from the artist, April 15, 1942.)
Exhibition: New York, Museum of Modern Art, *Americans 1942*, 1942, no. 126.

JACK LEVINE was born in Boston in 1915. From 1929 to 1931 he studied with Denman Ross at the Fogg Art Museum in Cambridge, Mass. He worked for the Works Progress Administration, served in World War II, and since 1946 has lived in New York City. In 1947 and from 1950 to 1951 he traveled in Europe. He is one of America's most important social protest artists.

722.   **Street Scene No. I**

fig. 575   *Three men, with orange-red faces and hands, wear black vests over white shirts. The street around them is brown, touched with red, gold, and gray, and the sky is blue.*
Tempera, india ink, oil, and gold leaf on canvas. 30 × 40 in. (76.2 × 101.6 cm.)
Signed lower left: *J. Levine.* Painted in 1938.
Gift of the National Council of Jewish Women, Boston Section. 46.48

"*Street Scene* was a study for a much larger picture (owned by the Works Progress Administration). My objective was to express the almost mediaeval emblazonry which I find characteristic in many of Boston's streets. . . . It seemed reasonable and unanachronistic to make use of gold leaf to represent

signs and brass fittings although I don't think it had been done before.''
(Letter from the artist, Jan. 30, 1946.)

Exhibitions: New York, Downtown Gallery, *Levine*, 1939, no. 2./ Richmond, Virginia Museum of Fine Arts, *4th Biennial*, 1944, no. 88./ Washington, D.C., Corcoran Gallery, *19th Biennial*, 1945, no. 148./ Boston, Boris Mirski Gallery, *Levine*, 1950, no. 29./ Boston, Institute of Contemporary Art, *Levine*, 1952./ Boston, Young Men's Hebrew Association, *17 Jewish Artists*, 1955, no. 10 (repr.).

723.   **Man and Dog**

An elderly man with pink hands and face wears black trousers and vest with a white shirt. His dog beside him is white, touched with blue and green; the background is brown, blue, and green.
Oil on canvas. 19 × 12 in. (48.2 × 30.5 cm.)
Painted in 1939.
Gift of the Massachusetts Works Progress Administration. 61.1113
Man and Dog is a study for the picture *The Neighborhood Physician*, painted in 1939 (Walker Art Center, Minneapolis).

JONAS LIE   (1880–1940) was born in Norway and came to New York about 1893. He studied painting at the National Academy and the Art Students League, then in 1906 painted in Paris. He returned to work in New York and Plainfield, N.J., returning frequently to Paris and Norway until his death in New York.

724.   **The Fisherman's Return**

Fishermen, wearing blue and green, stand on the brown dock by a gray boat. Beyond are white sails between the green sea and gray sky.
Oil on canvas. 25 × 30 in. (63.5 × 76.2 cm.)
Signed and dated lower right: *Jonas Lie 191*? (last number illegible).
The John Pickering Lyman Collection. Gift of Miss Theodora Lyman. 19.1327

725.   **Vesper**

The blue water of the inlet reflects the red-brown and green of the cliffs. Gray boats have white sails, and the clouds are pink in a blue sky.
Oil on canvas. 20 × 30 in. (50.8 × 76.2 cm.)
Signed and dated lower right: *Jonas Lie '20.*
Gift of Miss Mary C. Wheelwright. 36.79

726.   **When the Boats Come In**

Fishermen clothed in yellow, red, and blue stand watching the dark blue and gray boats in the harbor. There is a yellow light on the water under the gray and blue sky.
Oil on canvas. 30 × 40 in. (76.2 × 101.6 cm.)
Signed lower left: *Jonas Lie.*
Collection: John T. Spaulding, Boston, 1922.
Bequest of John T. Spaulding. 48.572
Exhibition: Boston, MFA, *The Spaulding Collections*, 1948, no. 51.

BARNARD LINTOTT (1875–1951), born in London, studied at the Académie Julian with Laurens and Constant, and at the École des Beaux Arts, Paris. Author of *The Art of Water Colour Painting*, 1925, and art advisor to the London *Times*, he worked in London until 1931, when he settled in New York City. He worked there and in Peru, Vermont, and New Jersey until his death in Lynbrook, N.Y.

727.   **Cineraria and "New York Times"**

Purple and white flowers with green leaves stand in a red pot on the gray-shadowed paper beside a glass. The tabletop is brown, the wall behind, light green.
Oil on canvas. 25 × 30 in. (63.5 × 76.2 cm.)
Signed lower left: *Lintott.* Painted in 1935.
Gift of Marie Sterner Lintott, the artist's wife. 35.747

Exhibitions: Boston, Doll and Richards, *Lintott*, 1935 (not in catalogue)./ New York, French and Co., *Lintott*, 1946, no. 47.

WILTON ROBERT LOCKWOOD (1861–1914), born in Wilton, Conn., was a pupil of John La Farge and studied at the Art Students League, New York. For ten years he lived in Europe, studying at the Académie Julian, Paris, and in Munich. On his return he worked in New York and Boston until his death in Brookline, Mass.

728.
fig. 415

John La Farge

Seated in three-quarter length, he faces front and smokes a cigar. His suit is black and the background is brown.
Oil on canvas. 38 × 30 in. (96.5 × 76.2 cm.)
Signed and dated lower left: *Wilton Lockwood 1891.*
Charles Henry Hayden Fund. 09.208
Purchased from the artist John La Farge (1835–1910); for biography see p. 181.
Reference: R. Cortissoz, *La Farge*, Boston, 1911 (repr. opp. p. 206, incorrectly dated 1902).
Exhibitions: Boston, St. Botolph Club, *Lockwood*, 1906, no. 12./ —, *Lockwood Memorial*, 1915, no. 13.

729.

Peonies

White and pink peonies with green leaves are in a green vase; the background is gray and brown.
Oil on canvas. 30¼ × 30¼ in. (76.8 × 76.8 cm.)
Signed lower left: *Wilton Lockwood.* Painted about 1910.
Charles Henry Hayden Fund. 10.558
This picture was possibly painted about the time of its first exhibition and purchase.
Exhibitions: Washington, D.C., Corcoran Gallery, *3rd Annual*, 1910, no. 63./ Boston, St. Botolph Club, *Lockwood Memorial*, 1915, no. 15.

MORRIS LOUIS (1912–1962), son of Louis and Cecilia Bernstein, was born in Baltimore, Md. In 1929 he received a four-year scholarship at the Maryland Institute of Fine and Applied Arts, then shared a studio in Baltimore with Ben Silbert. From 1936–40 he worked in New York under the W.P.A. project. From 1940–47 he worked in Baltimore, then moved to Washington, D.C. where he continued to paint and teach. In 1952 he met Kenneth Noland, and the next year visited New York with him where seeing the work of Helen Frankenthaler radically affected his style. His earlier more Expressionist style was replaced in 1954 by stained canvas compositions called "veils." In 1960 he experimented with more explosive designs of brighter color called "florals" and in 1961 painted "unfurleds," diagonal bands of color across the ends and bottoms of a bare canvas. Finally he was working with "stripes," precise bands of color arranged first vertically, then diagonally. He died in Washington in 1962.

730.
fig. 611

Theta

Parallel rivulets of color are stained into a field of bare, unsized white canvas and extend diagonally from the sides to the bottom. On the left are strong reds, orange, yellow, and blues. On the right are deeper blues, greens, and magenta.
Acrylic resin paint on unsized canvas. 102 × 168 in. (259.1 × 326.7 cm.)
Painted in 1961.
Collections: Mrs. Marcella Louis Brenner, widow of the artist, Washington, D.C.; Private Collection, Boston, Mass., 1967.
Anonymous Gift. 67.623
Reference: M. Fried, "The Achievement of Morris Louis," *Artforum*, Los Angeles, Vol. V, no. 6, p. 39 (repr.).
Exhibitions: Venice Biennale XXXII, 1964, no. 13./ San Francisco Museum of Art,

Colorists 1950–65, 1965 (repr. color, reversed)./ Los Angeles County Museum of Art, Boston MFA, and St. Louis City Art Museum, *Morris Louis*, 1967, no. 40 (repr. p. 61).

GEORGE BENJAMIN LUKS (1867–1933) was born in Williamsport, Pa. He studied at the Pennsylvania Academy of the Fine Arts and later worked at the Düsseldorf Academy and in Paris and London, where he was interested in the work of Hals, Goya, and Manet. On his return, he became an illustrator for the *Philadelphia Press* and in 1896, for the *Philadelphia Bulletin*, he covered the Spanish-American War in Cuba. In 1902 he committed himself solely to painting and in 1908 became one of "The Eight." He worked in New York until his death, teaching at the Arts Students League, with sojourns to New England, Nova Scotia, and Pennsylvania.

731.
fig. 548

The Wrestlers

The red bodies of the men are shadowed in brown as they wrestle on a gray mat before a black background.
Oil on canvas. 48¼ × 66¼ in. (122.5 × 168.3 cm.)
Signed and dated lower right: *George Luks/ 1905.* Inscribed on back: *The Wrestlers/ 1905/ George Luks.*
Collection: Mrs. George Luks (Mrs. Werner Frankenberg), New York, 1921.
Charles Henry Hayden Fund. 45.9
References: "The Diary of John Sloan," unpublished MS. owned by Mrs. John Sloan, New York, entries Jan. 11, 1908 and April 16, 1910./ E.L. Cary, *Luks*, New York, 1931, p. 44 (repr. p. 45).
Exhibitions: New York, Kraushaar Galleries, *Luks*, 1923, no. 24 (repr.)./ Newark, N.J., Newark Museum, *Luks*, 1934, no. 12 (repr. p. 41)./ New York, Whitney Museum, *New York Realists*, 1937, no. 57./ New York, World's Fair, *Masterpieces of Art*, 1939–1940, no. 319./ Toronto Art Gallery, *Great Paintings*, 1940, no. 119./ Brooklyn Museum, *The Eight*, 1943–1944, no. 75./ New York, Whitney Museum, *Juliana Force and American Art*, 1949, no. 83./ Philadelphia, Pennsylvania Academy of the Fine Arts, *150th Anniversary*, 1955, no. 205 (repr. p. 120)./ Ogunquit Museum, *Luks*, 1956, no. 4./ Cincinnati Art Museum and Dayton Art Institute, *An American Viewpoint*, 1957./ San Diego Fine Arts Gallery, *Modern American Painting: 1915*, 1962–1963, no. 27 (repr. p. 17).

732.

The Joy of Living

An old woman with brown skin sits in three-quarter length, dozing by a table. She wears a dark brown dress, and the background is dark red-brown.
Oil on canvas. 35¼ × 23½ in. (89.5 × 59.7 cm.)
Signed lower right: *George Luks.* Painted about 1905.
Collection: With Frank K.M. Rehn, New York.
Charles Henry Hayden Fund. 34.1458
Exhibition: Boston, Vose Galleries, *Luks*, 1934, no. 4.

733.

White Blackbird

A lady, three-quarter length, sits in left profile before a dark brown background; she wears a black dress with a yellow and orange collar and a brown and yellow feathered hat.
Oil on canvas, mounted on masonite. 30¼ × 25¼ in. (76.8 × 64.1 cm.)
Painted in 1919.
Anonymous loan. 8.62

The date is given by the Newark Museum catalogue (*see* below) on the basis of style. A handwritten label on the frame gives the same date.
Exhibition: Newark, N.J., Newark Museum, *Luks*, 1934, no. 43.

734.
fig. 546

Bulfinch Houses, Beacon Hill

The red and purple houses beyond green and brown trees and grass have gray windows. A woman in black stands with two children dressed in pink and blue.
Oil on canvas. 36¼ × 30¼ in. (92.1 × 76.8 cm.)
Signed lower right: *George Luks.* Painted about 1923.

Collection: Mr. and Mrs. Q.A. Shaw McKean, Boston, about 1923.
Emily L. Ainsley Fund. 60.538
Reference: E.L. Cary, *Luks*, New York, 1931, p. 34 (repr. p. 35).
Exhibition: Newark, N.J., Newark Museum, *Luks*, 1934, no. 55.

735.
King's Chapel, Boston
The black chapel, shadowed in deep blue, is surrounded by a purple street and build-ings. Pedestrians wear black and brown. The trees are green under pink and blue sky.
Oil on canvas. 36 × 30¼ in. (91.4 × 76.8 cm.)
Signed lower center: *George Luks*. Painted about 1923.
Anonymous loan. 197.62

736.
fig. 547
Noontime, St. Botolph Street, Boston
The ochre-brown and red brick houses, with their purple and white striped blinds, are streaked with purple shadows. An iceman, in yellow, walks in the pink and yellow street beside green grass.
Oil on canvas. 30¼ × 25¼ in. (76.8 × 64.1 cm.)
Signed lower right: *George Luks*. Painted about 1923.
Collection: Mr. and Mrs. Q.A. Shaw McKean, Boston, about 1923.
Emily L. Ainsley Fund. 60.537
Luks painted this picture, *Bulfinch Houses, Beacon Hill* (Cat. no. 734) and several others when he was staying with Mr. and Mrs. Q.A. Shaw McKean.
Exhibition: Newark, N.J., Newark Museum, *Luks*, 1934, no. 56.

737.
Jenny
The laughing child is seated full-length, facing front, and wears a white costume shadowed in mauve. The background is purple.
Oil on canvas. 36 × 25 in. (91.4 × 63.5 cm.)
Signed lower right: *George Luks*. Painted by 1925.
Collection: John T. Spaulding, Boston, 1925.
Bequest of John T. Spaulding. 48.573
Exhibitions: Boston, MFA, *The Spaulding Collections*, 1948, no. 52./ —, *Living with Art*, 1957, no. 20.

738.
Jenny
A little girl, standing full-length and facing front, wears a long brown dress patterned in white, green, yellow, and blue. Beside her is a large chair upholstered in purple; the background and floor are brown.
Oil on canvas. 40 × 30 in. (101.6 × 76.2 cm.)
Painted in 1926.
Anonymous loan. 7.62
Dated by the Newark Museum (*see below*), on the basis of style.
Exhibition: Newark, N.J., Newark Museum, *Luks*, 1934, no. 62.

739.
A Clown
Half-length and turned three-quarters right, he leans on green and orange cushions. His face and head are painted white, with red and blue, and his costume is blue and yellow. The background is brown.
Oil on canvas. 24 × 20 in. (61 × 50.8 cm.)
Signed lower left: *George Luks*. Painted in 1929.
Collection: John T. Spaulding, Boston, 1929.
Bequest of John T. Spaulding. 48.574
Both Elizabeth Cary and the Pennsylvania Academy's catalogue (*see below*) give the date.
Reference: E.L. Cary, *Luks*, New York, 1931, p. 19 (repr. p. 20).
Exhibitions: Boston, MFA, *The Spaulding Collections*, 1948, no. 53 (pl. VII)./ Phila-delphia, Pennsylvania Academy of the Fine Arts, *150th Anniversary*, 1955, no. 198 (repr. p. 121)./ Santa Barbara Museum and San Francisco, California Palace of the Legion of Honor, *All about the Circus*, 1959, no. 36.

STANTON MACDONALD-WRIGHT, born in Charlottesville, Va. in 1890, first studied at the Art Students League, New York. From 1907 to 1916 he studied and worked in Paris, successively at the Sorbonne, the Grande Chaumière, the Académie Julian, and the École des Beaux Arts. With Morgan Russell (1886–1953) he established the movement called Synchronism, in essence the solidification of forms and establishment of space by means of color. In 1916, he settled in California. A student of oriental culture, a writer, and a critic, he has taught in Japan and at Scripps College, Claremont, Calif. and is now a Professor of Oriental Art at the University of California at Los Angeles. He lives in Pacific Palisades, Calif., and Kyoto, Japan.

740. **Still Life with Arum Lilies and Fruit**

fig. 572

White and green lilies are in a purple vase, surrounded by red and yellow fruit and flowers, blue drapery, and a pink and white dish. A mat on the white table is red and blue; the background is white.
Oil on canvas. 22 × 18 in. (55.9 × 45.7 cm.)
Signed upper right: *S. Macdonald-Wright*. Painted in 1923.
Bequest of John T. Spaulding. 48.575

Exhibitions: Cleveland Museum, *6th Exhibition of Contemporary American Painting*, 1926, listed in the *Bulletin*, 1926, XIII, no. 6, p. 151./ Boston, MFA, *The Spaulding Collections*, 1948, no. 54.

HENRY LEE McFEE (1886–1953), born in St. Louis, Mo., studied painting in Pittsburgh, Pa. in 1907 and in 1908 joined the Art Students League summer school in Woodstock, N.Y. In 1909 he began independent work and lived in Woodstock as a still-life, portrait, and landscape painter until he moved to California. He then taught painting at Scripps College, Claremont, until his death.

741. **Portrait of a Squash**

fig. 570

A green squash, a purple eggplant, and green apples lie on a blue, green, and white striped cloth over a brown table. A brown curtain, right, is before the white wall.
Oil on canvas. 24½ × 20 in. (62.2 × 50.8 cm.)
Signed lower right: *McFee—*. Painted in 1926–1927.
Collection: John T. Spaulding, Boston, 1927.
Bequest of John T. Spaulding. 48.578
Exhibition: Boston, MFA, *The Spaulding Collections*, 1948, no. 57.

LOREN MacIVER (Mrs. Lloyd Frankenburg) was born in New York in 1909, and apart from brief study at the Art Students League in 1919–1920, she is self-taught. She has lived in New York City, but from 1931 to 1940 worked in North Truro, Mass., and from 1936 to 1939 for the Federal Arts Project. She first visited Europe in 1948 and since then has returned frequently for extended visits.

742. **Fiery Rings**

fig. 599

A composition of elements symbolizing the top of a gas stove, painted in gray, lavender, and blue: burner flames, a kettle, and in the center a black and yellow pilot light. To the left are a vertical band of cooking utensils: measuring spoons, an eggcup, pepper mill, pill bottle, and an iron weight.
Oil on canvas. 26 × 32 in. (66 × 81.3 cm.)
Signed lower right: *MacIver*. Painted in 1946.
Collections: Edwin Hewitt, New York, 1946.
Lent anonymously. 72.64

Fiery Rings appears in a silent color film entitled *Loren MacIver*, made by Mariette Charlton (Radim Films, New York, 1964).

Exhibitions: Vassar College Art Gallery, *MacIver*, 1950, no. 19./ New York, Whitney Museum and circulated in the U.S., *MacIver and I. Rice Pereira*, 1953, p. 35, no. 32./ New York, Wildenstein and Co., *Masters of Seven Centuries*, 1962, no. 83 (repr. p. 56)./ Venice, *XXXI Biennale*, 1962, p. 223, no. 8.

743.   **Morning Cart**
fig. 600

A flower cart, seen from the side, with large and small wheels, is painted atmospherically in shades of blue.
Oil on canvas. 56 × 57 in. (142.2 × 144.8 cm.)
Signed lower right: *MacIver*. Painted in 1960.
Gift of Mr. and Mrs. John McAndrew. 61.605

LEO MANSO   born in New York in 1914, studied at the Educational Art Alliance, New York in 1929 and from 1930 to 1934 at the National Academy of Design. He taught design and drawing at Columbia University from 1950 to 1956 and is an instructor at New York University and the Cooper Union School of Art. He is also cofounder and Director of the Artists' Cooperative Gallery 256, Provincetown, Mass.

744.   **Premonitions**
fig. 605

An abstract composition of horizontal bands of muslin, painted and stained with orange, brown, gray, and green, with areas of thick aluminum paint at top and lower centers.
Collage: oil and aluminum paint, cloth on panel. 29¾ × 22¾ in. (75.5 × 57.7 cm.)
Signed lower right: *Manso*. Painted in 1963.
Ellen Kelleran Gardner Fund. 64.1946

JOHN MARIN   (1870–1953) was born in Rutherford, N.J. After four years' apprenticeship, he worked as a free-lance architect from 1893 to 1899. He then studied until 1901 in Philadelphia at the Pennsylvania Academy of the Fine Arts and in 1904 briefly at the Art Students League, New York. From 1905 to 1909, and again in 1910, he lived in Paris and traveled extensively in Europe. In 1910 he settled in Brooklyn, N.Y. but in 1916 moved permanently to Cliffside, N.J. He spent summers in Maine, Massachusetts, New Hampshire, and once in New Mexico until 1933, after which he went regularly to Cape Split, Me., where he died.

745.   **Movement—Sea or Mountain as You Will**
fig. 589

Brusquely applied areas of blue, green, red-brown, and white accented by angular lines of dark gray, red-brown, and black. A faint wash of pink over a thinly gessoed white canvas.
Oil on canvas. 30 × 36¾ in. (76.2 × 93.3 cm.)
Signed and dated lower right: *Marin 47.*
Collection: Downtown Gallery, New York.
Arthur G. Tompkins Residuary Fund. 63.1527

From about 1945 until his death Marin periodically sustained a series of abstracted, geometric paintings on the theme of "movement," each conceived in terms of the organic nature rather than of the specific physical form of his subject.

Exhibitions: New York, An American Place, *Marin*, 1947–1948, no. 10./ New York, Downtown Gallery, *23rd Anniversary*, 1948, no. 15./ University of Illinois, *Contemporary American Paintings*, 1949, no. 77 (pl. 52)./ New York, Art Students League, *Diamond Jubilee*, 1950, no. 236 (repr. p. 74)./ Baltimore Museum, *Man and His Years*, 1954, no. 119 (repr. p. 37)./ New York, American Academy of Arts and Letters, *Marin*, 1954, no. 13./ University of California at Los Angeles and circulated in the U.S., *Marin Memorial*, 1955, no. 21./ London, Arts Council of Great Britain, *Marin*, 1956, no. 18./ Palm Beach, Fla., Society of the Four Arts, *Marin Memorial*, part II, 1956, no. 18./ University of Georgia Museum, *Marin*, 1956./ New York, Whitney Museum and circulated in the U.S., *Nature in Abstraction*, 1958, pp. 6, 67 (repr. p. 27)./ New York, Downtown Gallery, *Marin*, 1963, no. 21.

WILLIAM SANFORD MASON (1824–1864)

746.   **A Country House**
Oil on canvas. 16¾ × 24 in. (42.5 × 61 cm.)

Signed and dated lower left: *W. Sanford Mason 1852.*
M. and M. Karolik Collection. 48.452
Reference: *Karolik Catalogue*, 1949, no. 188 (repr.).

747. **Venus and Cupid**
Oil on chipboard. Painted oval. 10 × 12 in. (25.4 × 30.5 cm.)
Signed and dated lower left: *W. Sanford Mason 1856.*
M. and M. Karolik Collection. 48.453
Reference: *Karolik Catalogue*, 1949, no. 189 (repr.).

ALFRED HENRY MAURER (1868–1932) was born in New York, son of Louis Maurer, one of the most important illustrators for Currier and Ives. In 1884 he began work in the family lithography business, and except for study at the National Academy and work in commercial art, he was self-taught. From 1897 to 1914 he lived and worked in France, studying briefly at the Académie Julian, and was successively influenced by Impressionism, Post-Impressionism, Fauvism, and Cubism. He then settled in New York, spending summers in Marlboro, N.Y., where he worked until his death by suicide.

748. **Abstract Heads**
fig. 563
Two superimposed heads composed of geometric planes of russet, purple, blue, and white accented by black lines. The angular background planes are purple, mauve, and gray.
Oil on chipboard. 30 × 19¾ in. (76.2 × 50.1 cm.)
Signed upper left: *A.H. Maurer.* Painted about 1931.
Collections: Estate of the artist, New York; Hudson D. Walker, Forest Hills, N.Y., 1941.
Abraham Shuman Fund. 59.254
Maurer painted a series of abstracted double heads between about 1930 and the time of his death in 1932. They have been interpreted as symbolic of the tension caused his sensitive temperament by his aged father, who unlike the son had received acclaim as a painter.
Reference: B.H. Hayes and M.C. Rathbun, *Layman's Guide to Modern Art*, New York, 1949 (repr. part 3).
Exhibitions: Andover, Mass., Addison Gallery, *Seeing the Unseeable*, 1947./ Bloomfield Hills, Mich., Cranbrook Academy Art Galleries, *Light and the Painter*, 1952, no. 54./ New York, Wildenstein and Co., *20th Century American Paintings*, 1952, no. 17./ New York, Bertha Schaefer Gallery, *Hartley-Maurer*, 1956, no. 9.

EDWARD MELCARTH, born in Louisville, Ky. in 1914, first studied painting at the Chelsea Polytechnic Art School, London, then in Boston at the Museum School with Karl Zerbe. He was in Paris until 1939, studying with Bissière at the Académie Ronson, and then returned to settle in New York. A painter and sculptor, in 1951–1952 he taught at the University of Washington, Seattle and is now an instructor at the Art Alliance, New York.

749. **Self-Portrait**
Standing three-quarter length, in a black coat, his back turned, he looks front over his shoulder as he lifts a white cloth from a canvas. Behind is a yellow and gray studio interior.
Oil on canvas. 30¼ × 25¼ in. (76.8 × 64.1 cm.)
Signed upper left: *E. Melcarth.* Painted in 1941.
Charles Henry Hayden Fund. 42.392

GARI MELCHERS (1860–1932) was born in Detroit. From 1877 to 1881 he studied with Von Gebhardt at the Düsseldorf Academy and then attended the École des Beaux Arts, Paris under Boulanger and Lefebvre. He lived in Egmond-aan-Zee, Holland from 1883 to 1909, traveled in Europe and then was professor at the State Academy, Weimar until his return to New York in 1914. Prominent as a figure and portrait painter, he lived in Falmouth, Va. from 1916 until his death.

750.

The Hermit

Seated half-length and in right profile, a man, wearing white and gray robes, leans on a gray table. Beside him are a blue jug and oranges before a yellow background.

Oil on canvas. 22½ × 17½ in. (57.1 × 44.5 cm.)

Signed upper right: *G. Melchers*. Painted about 1900.

Collection: Purchased from the artist by John T. Spaulding, Boston, 1921.

Bequest of John T. Spaulding. 48.579

"This little canvas was painted about twenty or more years ago, and is a study for a large picture, *The Last Supper*" (repr. no. 28 in *Melchers Memorial Exhibition*, Virginia Museum, Richmond, 1938). (Letter from the artist to Mr. Spaulding, May 5, 1921.)

Exhibitions: Boston, Copley Gallery, *Melchers*, 1919, no. 40./ New York, Montross Gallery, *Melchers*, 1919, no. 15./ Boston, MFA, *The Spaulding Collections*, 1948, no. 58.

751.

fig. 530

Mother and Child

A woman, half-length and facing front in a brown dress, carries a baby dressed in white. The background is mauve.

Pastel on paper. 21¼ × 15¼ in. (54 × 38.7 cm.)

Signed upper left: *Gari Melchers*. Drawn about 1904.

Collection: Mrs. Louis Hines.

Charles Henry Hayden Fund. 33.10

According to the artist's wife, the pastel was done about 1904 with Anna, their cook, as the model. A larger version of the picture, in oil, is in the Art Institute of Chicago.

Exhibition: New York, American Academy of Arts and Letters, *A Change of Sky*, 1960, no. 1.

ENRICO MENEGHELLI was born in Italy in 1853. He had come to the United States by 1879 and worked in Boston, New York, and Philadelphia. It is not known when he died.

752.

fig. 421

The Lawrence Room, Museum of Fine Arts, Boston

The dark brown paneling is hung with armor and paintings; fabrics above it are red on a green wall. A couple in gray and black stand amid the brown furnishings before a yellow and gray room beyond.

Oil on canvas mounted on masonite. 16 × 20 in. (40.6 × 50.8 cm.)

Signed and dated lower right: *E. Meneghelli 1879.*

Gift of M. Knoedler and Co. 57.675

Col. T.B. Lawrence bequeathed his collection of arms and armor to the Boston Athenaeum in 1869 together with a $25,000 contribution toward the construction of the new Museum of Fine Arts. The Lawrence armor was destroyed in the great fire of 1872, but with the insurance money Mrs. Lawrence purchased and gave to the MFA a room of rare English paneling, and the collection of carvings and embroideries shown here.

753.

fig. 420

The Picture Gallery in the Old Museum

Paintings in gold frames hang on the green wall; the bench and floor are brown.

Oil on cardboard. 16 × 12 in. (40.6 × 30.5 cm.)

Signed and dated lower right: *E. Meneghelli 1879.*

Gift of Hollis French. Res. 12.2

Part of a wall in a picture gallery when the Boston Museum was in Copley Square (1876–1909); the paintings shown were both owned by and lent to the Museum and include *The Quarry* by Courbet (then lent by Henry Sayles, now owned by the MFA), the *Volunteers of '92* by Couture, and a Diaz landscape.

754.

fig. 419

Gallery of the Museum of Fine Arts, Copley Square

Through a dark brown arch can be seen three large paintings with gold frames; two

hang on a gray wall, the third is seen through another arch. The floor and furniture are brown.
Oil on canvas. 17 × 13¼ in. (43.2 × 33.6 cm.)
Painted after 1890.
Gift of Giovanni Castano. 61.238

The three large paintings owned by the Boston Museum are: upper left, *Summer*, by Gustave Doré; below, Regnault's *Automedon with the Horses of Achilles*; and right, *By the Riverside*, by Henri Lerolle. The last of the three acquired by the MFA was the Regnault, given in 1890.

WILLARD LEROY METCALF (1858–1925), born in Lowell, Mass., was apprenticed to an engraver in 1878, then studied at the Boston Museum School with George Loring Brown. In 1883 he attended the Académie Julian, Paris under Boulanger and Lefebvre but was strongly influenced by the Impressionists. On his return he worked in New York as an illustrator until 1900. He spent the year 1903 in Maine and lived primarily in New England until his death in New York.

755.   **The Birches**
A row of young yellow and white birches with bright yellow-green leaves are on the grassy bank of a stream; the water and sky are blue.
Oil on canvas. 26 × 29 in. (66 × 73.6 cm.)
Signed and dated lower right: *W.L. Metcalf. 1906.*
The John Pickering Lyman Collection. Gift of Miss Theodora Lyman. 19.1330

756.   **The First Snow**
fig. 510
White snow-covered fields are touched with green and brown under a gray sky. Trees by a stone wall and a stream in the foreground are all gray.
Oil on canvas. 26 × 29 in. (66 × 73.6 cm.)
Signed and dated lower right: *W.L. Metcalf. 1906.*
Bequest of Ernest Wadsworth Longfellow. 23.483

757.   **May Pastoral**
fig. 509
Green and yellow trees divide a green field; red-brown hills beyond are under a pale gray sky.
Oil on canvas. 36 × 39 in. (91.4 × 99 cm.)
Signed and dated lower left: *W.L. Metcalf 1907.*
Charles Henry Hayden Fund. 08.325

Exhibition: Philadelphia, Pennsylvania Academy of the Fine Arts, *Ten American Painters*, 1908, no. 51 (repr.).

ALFRED JACOB MILLER (1810–1874)

758.   **Beating a Retreat**
fig. 288
Oil on canvas. 29 × 36 in. (73.6 × 91.4 cm.)
Signed on rock lower right: *A.J. Miller* (A, J, and M in monogram). Painted about 1842.
M. and M. Karolik Collection. 48.454
Reference: Karolik Catalogue, 1949, no. 190 (repr.).

EDWARD MORAN (1829–1901), born in Bolton, Lancashire, England, came to Maryland in 1844. A weaver by trade, he studied painting with James Hamilton and Paul Weber in Philadelphia, where he worked until 1862. He then studied at the Royal Academy, London, and after returning to Philadelphia, in 1872 settled in New York, where he remained except for the year 1879–1880, spent in Paris, until his death.

759.   **Jacques and the Forest of Arden**
fig. 370
Jacques, clothed in brown and green, lies on the bank of a blue stream in the green and brown forest. The rocks about him are gray and the deer beyond is brown; the sky is white and blue.

Oil on canvas. 38½ × 32 in. (97.8 × 81.2 cm.)
Signed lower left: *E. Moran*. Painted in 1860's.
Gift of Harold W. Dana. 41.530

In Act II, Scene 1 of Shakespeare's *As You Like It*, the First Lord says of Jacques: ". . . the melancholy Jacques grieves at that . . . as he lay under an oak, whose antique root peeps out upon the brook that brawls along this wood: To the which place some poor sequester'd stag, that from the hunters' aim had ta'an a hurt, did come to languish. . . ."
Exhibitions: Dallas Museum of Fine Arts, *Famous Families in Art*, 1960, no. 51./ Cambridge, Mass., Busch-Reisinger Museum, *Rivers and Seas—Changing Attitudes Toward Landscape, 1700–1962*, 1962, no. 36.

SAMUEL FINLEY BREESE MORSE (1791–1872), born in Charlestown, Mass., studied painting in London from 1811 to 1815 with Washington Allston and Benjamin West. On his return, he worked in New England and Charleston, S.C. as an itinerant portrait painter. He settled in New York in 1823 and in 1826 became a founder of the National Academy of Design, being, until 1845, its first President. He traveled in France and Italy from 1829 to 1832, returned to settle in New York, and became Professor of Painting and Sculpture at New York University. About 1837 he abandoned painting in order to perfect his invention, the electric telegraph (and Morse code). He died in New York.

760. **Mrs. Griffiths**
fig. 162
Seated in half-length, turned three-quarters left, she wears a black dress with a white shawl and bonnet and holds a red and gray stole. Behind, left, a red curtain is before a blue sky with pink and gray clouds.
Oil on canvas. 30¼ × 25¼ in. (76.8 × 64.1 cm.)
Painted about 1820.
Collection: Mrs. G.O. Wales, Braintree, Mass., by 1913.
Bequest of Mrs. George Oliver Wales. 28.316
Reference: H.B. Wehle, *Morse*, New York, 1932, p. 35.

761. **Little Miss Hone**
Oil on panel. 30 × 25 in. (76.2 × 63.5 cm.)
Painted in 1824.
M. and M. Karolik Collection. 48.455
Reference: *Karolik Catalogue*, 1949, no. 191 (repr.).

762. **Dr. Thomas Fuller**
fig. 165
Turned slightly left, the elderly man, seated half-length, wears a black suit with a white neckcloth. The background is of varied browns. The arm of a black horsehair sofa is at the lower right.
Oil on canvas. 29½ × 24½ in. (74.9 × 62.2 cm.)
Signed and dated on back, center left: *AEtat.63./ June. 1829./ SFBM.*
Collections: Dr. and Mrs. Thomas Fuller, Cooperstown, N.Y.; Mary Fuller (Mrs. Theodore Pomeroy), their daughter, Utica, N.Y.; Dr. Thomas Pomeroy, her son, Detroit; Mrs. Mary Fuller Chase, his daughter, Hanover, N.H.; Mary Fuller Chase (Mrs. Maxey N. Morrison), her granddaughter, Philadelphia; Frederick Chase, her uncle, Milton, Mass., 1948.
Gift of Frederick Chase. 57.767

Thomas Fuller (1765–1837), son of Thomas and Sarah Griffin Fuller, was born in Windham, Conn. He was a general physician in Cooperstown, N.Y. from 1791 until his death. The portrait of his wife (Cat. no. 763) is a pendant portrait.
Reference: H.B. Wehle, *Morse*, New York, 1932, p. 35.

763. **Mrs. Thomas Fuller (Mary Fuller)**
fig. 164
Half-length, she is seated and turned three-quarters right before a brown background. Over a black dress she wears a gray shawl embroidered with blue and red, and mauve

ribbons adorn her white bonnet and ruff. The arm of a black horsehair sofa is at the lower right.
Oil on canvas. 29½ × 24½ in. (74.9 × 62.2 cm.)
Signed and dated on back, left center: *AEtat. 57.| June. 1829.| SFBM.*
Collections: Same as Cat. no. 762.
Gift of Frederick Chase. 57.768

Mary Fuller, born in Hampton, Conn. in 1772, was the daughter of Joseph and Mary Holt Fuller. She was married in 1793 to Dr. Thomas Fuller, and lived in Cooperstown, N.Y., until she died in 1851. Pendant to the preceding.
Reference: H.B. Wehle, *Morse*, New York, 1932, p. 35.

764.   **Miracle of Saint Mark**
People in dark red, green, and blue oriental dress are gathered in amazement about a prostrate naked slave. To the right, a judge is seated on a dais, and suspended above is the figure of St. Mark. The sky behind is blue-green.
Oil on canvas. 27½ × 38½ in. (69.8 × 97.8 cm.)
Painted about 1829–1832.
Gift of Edward L. Morse, the artist's son. 18.653

A copy of the painting by Tintoretto, now in the Accademia, Venice. A slave of Alexandria had incurred his master's anger by frequently worshiping at the nearby temple holding the remains of St. Mark and had been condemned to torture and death. The painting shows St. Mark himself preventing the punishment by shattering the instruments of torture. Morse traveled and worked in Italy from 1829 to 1832.
Reference: H.B. Wehle, *Morse*, New York, 1932, p. 46.
Exhibition: Boston Athenaeum, *Exhibition*, 1835, no. 39 (as *Miracle of the Slave*).

765.   **Niagara Falls from Table Rock**
fig. 163
Oil on canvas. 24 × 30 in. (61 × 76.2 cm.)
Inscribed on back of canvas before relining: *To Nathl Jocelyn Saml F.B. Morse New Haven 1835.*
M. and M. Karolik Collection. 48.456
Reference: *Karolik Catalogue*, 1949, no. 192 (repr.).

766.   **The Reverend Thomas Harvey Skinner**
Oil on chipboard. 29½ × 24½ in. (74.9 × 62.2 cm.)
Inscribed on back in ink: *This portrait of the Revd Dr. Skinner was painted by me| about the year 1836 or 1837 in the N. York city University| and presented to my friends Mr. & Mrs. Wainwright| Saml F B Morse| New York, March 1860.*
M. and M. Karolik Collection. 48.457
Reference: *Karolik Catalogue*, 1949, no. 193 (repr.).

WILLIAM SIDNEY MOUNT (1807–1868), born in Setauket, N.Y., grew up in nearby Stony Brook. In 1824 he was apprenticed to his brother Henry, a sign and ornamental painter in New York, and in 1826 began study at the National Academy of Design. From 1829 to 1836 he worked in New York, partly as a portrait painter, but chiefly doing detailed and objective genre subjects. He settled in Stony Brook in 1837 and lived there, except for short excursions, until his death.

767.   **Rustic Dance after a Sleigh Ride**
fig. 240
Oil on canvas. 22 × 27¼ in. (55.9 × 69.2 cm.)
Signed and dated lower right: *William. S. Mount. 1830.*
M. and M. Karolik Collection. 48.458
Reference: *Karolik Catalogue*, 1949, no. 194 (repr.).

768.   **Julia Parish Raymond**
Seated in over half-length before a gray background, she is turned slightly right. White flowers adorn her hair and white dress. She rests her left arm on a red-covered table on

which lie brown books and a pink rose.
Oil on panel. 9 × 7 in. (22.9 × 17.8 cm.)
Painted about 1847.
Collection: Roswell Parish, the sitter's nephew, Boston.
Bequest of Roswell Parish. 56.879

Julia Parish (1823–1850), born in Smithtown, N.Y., was the daughter of Roswell and Desire Smith Parish. She married Simeon T. Raymond, Jr., of New York in 1847 and probably lived there until her death in Nissequogue, N.Y. The portrait is dated according to her apparent age.

769. **The Barn by the Pool**
Oil on chipboard. 10 × 13¼ in. (25.4 × 33.6 cm.)
Painted about 1850.
M. and M. Karolik Collection. 48.459
Reference: Karolik Catalogue, 1949, no. 195 (repr.).

770. **The Fence on the Hill**
Oil on chipboard. 8¼ × 13¼ in. (21 × 33.6 cm.)
Painted about 1850.
M. and M. Karlolik Colection. 48.460
Reference: Karolik Catalogue, 1949, no. 196 (repr.).

771. **The Bone Player**
fig. 238
Oil on canvas. 36 × 29 in. (91.4 × 73.6 cm.)
Signed and dated lower right: *Wm.S.Mount 1856*. Inscribed on back: *The Bone Player/ Painted by Wm S. Mount/ 1856.*
M. and M. Karolik Collection. 48.461
Reference: Karolik Catalogue, 1949, no. 197 (repr.).

JOHN FRANCIS MURPHY (1853–1921), born in Oswego, N.Y., worked as a sign painter in Chicago until 1870. A self-taught landscape painter, he moved in 1875 to New York City, where he worked until 1887, the year of his election to the National Academy. He then lived in Arkville, N.Y., until his death in New York City. His style is a mixture of influences from the Romantic Hudson River School and from Corot.

772. **Rocky Fields**
Gray rocks lie in a green pasture beside scattered brown trees in autumn foliage. The pale gray sky is cloudy.
Oil on canvas. 8 × 10 in. (20.3 × 25.4 cm.)
Signed lower left: *J. Francis Murphy*. Painted in 1886.
Collection: Bradley Gilman, Boston.
Charles Henry Hayden Fund. 21.145

773. **Landscape Study**
fig. 512
A grisaille study of a broad open field with a shallow pond foreground and a stand of trees in the right background. The sky is cloudy.
Oil on canvas. 16 × 21½ in. (40.6 × 54.6 cm.)
Signed lower right: *J.F. Murphy*. Painted about 1905.
Bequest of Mrs. Edward Jackson Holmes. 65.600

774. **Sunset**
An orange and yellow sky rises over a green landscape, broken only by trees with red fall foliage.
Oil on canvas. 5 × 7 in. (12.7 × 17.8 cm.)
Signed lower left: *J.F. Murphy*.
Bequest of Hiram Hyde Logan. 22.831

JOHN NEAGLE (1796–1860), although born in Boston, was of a Philadelphia family and was raised there. He studied drawing and painting under Pietro Ancora and Bass Otis, but in 1812 he was apprenticed to the coach and ornamental painter Thomas Wilson. However, Thomas Sully, whose stepdaughter Neagle married, markedly influenced his style of painting. He began to paint professionally in 1818. Except for visits to Kentucky, New Orleans, Baltimore, and Boston, he lived in Philadelphia all his life. His portrait of *Pat Lyon at the Forge* (Cat. no. 777), of 1826, helped establish his considerable reputation. He was Director of the Pennsylvania Academy of the Fine Arts in 1830–1831 and from 1835 to 1843 was President of the Artists' Fund Society, of which he had been a founder.

775.
fig. 167

George Peabody

Oil on canvas. 30 × 25 in. (76.2 × 63.5 cm.)
Signed and dated lower left: *Painted by/ John Neagle/ Decr 17 1822/ Baltimore.*
M. and M. Karolik Collection. 48.462
Reference: Karolik Catalogue, 1949, no. 198 (repr.).

776.
fig. 166

Gilbert Stuart

Half-length and turned three-quarters left, the elderly man wears a black coat and white neckcloth. The background is brown.
Oil on canvas. 26½ × 21½ in. (67.3 × 54.6 cm.)
Signed and dated upper left: *J. Neagle 1825.*
Collections: Presented by the artist to Isaac P. Davis, Boston; Boston Athenaeum, 1853.
Deposited by the Boston Athenaeum, 1876. Ath. 35

A replica of this portrait of Gilbert Stuart (1755–1828) is owned by the Historical Society of Pennsylvania, and another by the Rhode Island School of Design. In his *Diary* (*see below*), Neagle recorded on May 9, 1826, "Finished the coat and cravat and background of Gilbert Stuart's portrait," and on Jan. 8, 1827, "Painted on the head of Stuart for Davis." His work on the portrait was therefore spread over at least two years.

References: H.T. Tuckerman, *Book of the Artists,* New York, 1870, p. 627./ J. Winsor, *Memorial History of Boston,* Boston, 1881, IV, p. 390./ J. Stuart, *Scribner's Monthly,* Oct. 7, 1887, p. 397./ S. Isham, *American Painting,* New York, 1905, p. 179./ W. Dunlap, *History of the Arts of Design,* Boston, 1918, I, pp. 254–255./ V. Barker, "Neagle," *The Arts,* 1925, VIII, no. 1, p. 7./ F.F. Sherman, *Early American Painting,* New York, 1932, p. 138./ W.T. Whitley, *Stuart,* Cambridge, Mass., 1932, pp. 188–189./ J.H. Morgan, *Stuart and His Pupils,* New York, 1939, pp. 67–69./ E.P. Richardson, *American Romantic Painting,* New York, 1945, no. 72 (repr.)./ M. Lynch, "Neagle's Diary," *Art in America,* 1949, XXXVII, no. 2, p. 83.

Exhibitions: Boston Athenaeum, *Exhibitions,* 1853–1876, excepting 1857 and 1858./ Boston, MFA, *Contemporary Art,* 1879, no. 98./ Boston, Art Club, *Early American Portraits,* 1911, no. 30./ Philadelphia, Pennsylvania Academy of the Fine Arts, *Portraits by Neagle,* 1925, pp. 7–9./ New York, Metropolitan Museum, *Life in America,* 1939, no. 76 (repr. p. 53)./ Washington, D.C., National Gallery, *Makers of History in Washington, 1800–1950,* 1950 (repr. p. 19).

777.
fig. 171

Pat Lyon at the Forge

Wearing a white shirt and leather apron, Lyon, with a boy assistant, stands full-length in the brown smithy, surrounded by tools, and rests a hammer on a gray anvil before him. Through a window, left, appears a gray tower against gray-clouded blue sky.
Oil on canvas. 93 × 68 in. (236.1 × 172.6 cm.)
Signed and dated lower left: *J. Neagle 1826 & 7.*
Collection: Purchased from the sitter by the Boston Athenaeum, 1828.
Deposited by the Boston Athenaeum. 16.40

Patrick Lyon (1779–1829), born in London, was a blacksmith, locksmith, designer, and hydraulic engineer who, in 1803, had built America's first fire engine. He commissioned this portrait in 1825, and retired the next year, a wealthy and prominent citizen of Philadelphia. His wish to be portrayed as a blacksmith rather than as a gentleman is explained by the story of his imprisonment, and subsequent disgrace and poverty, due to a false accusation of theft by the officers of a bank. The tower of Walnut Street Jail, Philadelphia, where he was imprisoned, can be seen in the portrait. The Boston Athenaeum has a wash drawing, 7¾ × 6½ in., of the composition; the Pennsylvania Academy of the Fine Arts owns the replica, 94½ × 68½ in., signed and dated 1829, and an oil study, 9¾ × 8 in.; the Historical Society of Pennsylvania also has an oil sketch, 18½ × 13½ in.

References: T. Fitzgerald, "Neagle," *Lippincott's Magazine*, 1868, 1, p. 480./ H.T. Tuckerman, *Book of the Artists*, New York, 1870, p. 627./ W.H. Downes, "Boston Painters and Paintings," *Atlantic Monthly*, 1888, LXII, no. 371, p. 383./ J. Sartain, *Reminiscences of a Very Old Man*, New York, 1899, pp. 191–193./ W. Dunlap, *History of the Arts of Design*, Boston, 1918, III, pp. 168–170./ M.M. Swan, *The Athenaeum Gallery*, Boston, 1940, pp. 37–38./ R.R. Patrick, "Neagle and Lyon," *Art Bulletin*, 1951, XXXIII, no. 3, pp. 187–192 (fig. 1)./ J.T. Flexner, "Early Nineteenth Century American Genre," *Antiques*, 1954, LXVI, no. 3, p. 196 (repr.)./ —, *Light of Distant Skies*, New York, 1954, p. 192 (fig. 87)./ B. Hogarth, "Outline of American Painting," *American Artist*, 1962, XXVI, no. 2, p. 58 (repr.).

Exhibitions: Boston Athenaeum, *Exhibitions*, 1828–1874, excepting 1829, 1833, and 1834./ London, American Exhibition Company, 1887./ Philadelphia, Pennsylvania Academy of the Fine Arts, *Portraits by Neagle*, 1925, pp. 9–10./ New York, Metropolitan Museum, *Life in America*, 1939, no. 89 (repr. p. 65)./ Baltimore Museum, *Souvenir of Romanticism in America*, 1940 (repr.)./ Pittsburgh, Pa., Carnegie Institute, *Survey of American Painting*, 1940, no. 88 (pl. 29).

GILBERT STUART NEWTON (1794–1835), born in Halifax, N.S., was brought to Cambridge, Mass. in 1803. He studied with his uncle, Gilbert Stuart, in Boston and in 1817 left to travel in Italy. He then studied at the Royal Academy in London and settled there permanently. He was a popular painter of literary, genre, and historical subjects but did portraits as well. Shortly after a visit to Boston in 1832 to be married, he became insane and died in Chelsea, England.

778.

fig. 197

Self-Portrait

A young man, half-length, turns slightly left before a brown background. He wears a dark brown greatcoat over a black jacket and red tie.

Oil on canvas. 20 × 17¼ in. (50.8 × 43.8 cm.)

Painted in 1818.

Turner-Sargent Fund. 96.693

Probably painted in the year of its exhibition at the Royal Academy.

Exhibitions: London, Royal Academy, 1818, no. 175./ Halifax, Nova Scotia Society of Artists, *200 Years of Art in Halifax*, 1949, no. 91.

779.

fig. 198

The Farewell

A girl, three-quarter length, leans on a brown balustrade and holds a white handkerchief; her dress is gray with white sleeves, and a gold chain is attached to a ruby on her bodice. The foliage to the right is green under a cloudy blue sky.

Oil on chipboard. 10¼ × 8¼ in. (26 × 21 cm.)

Painted by 1826.

Collections: *Viscount Cliefden Sale*, London, 1893; Samuel P. Avery, New York, 1893.

Gift of Samuel Putnam Avery. 97.227

A variation of this painting was done for Lord Dover and was engraved by Charles Heath in the *Literary Souvenir*, London, in 1826. A label on the back of the painting indicates that I.H. Phillips made a mezzotint in 1836.

780.

A Young Lady in Cauchoise Dress

Three-quarter length, she stands at an open window wearing a black bodice over a yellow skirt, yellow and white sleeves, and a shawl and white cap. The interior is brown.

Oil on chipboard. 15 × 9 in. (38.1 × 22.9 cm.)

Painted about 1829.

Collection: Anna G. Grey, Boston, by 1892.
William Wilkins Warren Fund. 95.1374

The portrait was once called *A Spanish Girl*; her costume, however, is typical of those worn by the women of Caux, Normandy, in the early nineteenth century. In a sketchbook, George P.A. Healy had made a drawing after this painting and had inscribed it: *after G.S. Newton—at Mr. Wills's—July 6th, 1838.* The portrait was probably painted the year of its exhibition in London.

Exhibition: London, Royal Academy, 1829, no. 114.

781. **Forsaken**

A girl in white sits on a red sofa, weeping. Letters are scattered on the floor of a brown interior with blue curtains.
Oil on canvas. 24 × 20 in. (61 × 50.8 cm.)
Collection: Thomas G. Appleton, Boston, by 1880.
Bequest of Thomas Gold Appleton. 84.280

According to an old label on the back, this painting was given to a Dr. R. Ferguson by the artist. The painter John Constable said of it: "I knew that Newton could paint most things, but I did not know he could paint a sob." MFA records of 1884 state that it was painted for Lord Chesterfield and that a replica was made for Lord Francis Leveson Gower.

Reference: W.H. Downes, "Boston Painters and Paintings," *Atlantic Monthly*, 1888, LXII, no. 370, p. 263.

YUTAKA OHASHI was born in Hiroshima, Japan in 1923. From 1941 to 1946 he studied in the Metal Craft Department of the Tokyo Academy of Fine Arts and studied painting on his own, with criticism from Genichiro Inokuma. On his arrival in the U.S. in 1950, he studied with Karl Zerbe at the Boston Museum School until 1955, then worked in Europe until 1958 under a Traveling Scholarship. He returned to Japan on a Guggenheim Fellowship in 1959–1960, and he now lives in New York City.

782.
fig. 597

Horse

A collage of overlapping geometric pieces of black, ochre, and white rice paper which take the shape of a horse seen in right profile.
Casein and rice paper on canvas. 65 × 45 in. (165.1 × 114.3 cm.)
Signed upper left: *Ohashi.* Inscribed on back, lower right: *Horse/ Y Ohashi/ 1962.*
Abraham Shuman Fund. 64.305

"My objective is to create a strong movement of dark form cutting through into white and gray area without particular realistic form. . . . The image of horse or animal form in this painting came only in the last stage. While I was concerned with the force of movement in abstract form somehow the painting acquired this image. That is the only reason of this title." (Letter from the artist, April 5, 1964.)

Reference: T.N. Maytham, "Some Recent Accessions," *MFA Bulletin*, 1964, LXII, p. 150 (repr.).

KENZO OKADA Born in Yokahama, Japan in 1902, studied at the Tokyo Academy of Art and in Paris from 1924 to 1927. He returned to Japan in 1938 and taught at the Nippon University School of Fine Arts from 1940 to 1942, the Musashino Art Institute from 1947 to 1950, and the Tama Fine Arts College in 1949–1950, all in Tokyo. He came to New York in 1950 and has lived there since, except for a trip to Japan in 1957–1958.

783.
fig. 595

Earth Glow

Geometric planes of brown, light brown, white, and yellow, upon which are curved shapes of white, gray, green, and yellow.
Oil on canvas. 71½ × 59¾ in. (181.5 × 151.8 cm.)

Signed lower right: *Kenzo Okada*. Painted in 1956.
Charles Henry Hayden Fund. 62.222

Exhibitions: New York, Betty Parsons Gallery, *Okada*, 1956, no. 11./ Buffalo, Albright-Knox Art Gallery, *Okada*, 1965, no. 25.

784. **A Story**

fig. 596

A diptych on one canvas: in the left half a conglomerate mass of planes of soft grays, greens, ochres, and lavenders extends across the middle of an off-white field. In the right half, a portion of a beige torii dominates an implied landscape of pale gray, gray-blue, and yellowish gray rocks with a few shafts of spiky gray-brown grass. Mountains behind are suggested by a gray-brown triangular cleft at the top of a near white background.

Oil on canvas. 81 × 106 in. (205.9 × 269.4 cm.)
Signed lower left: *Kenzo Okada*. Painted in 1966.
Gift of Mrs. Susan Morse Hilles. 67.648

Exhibition: New York, Betty Parsons Gallery, *Okada*, 1967, no. 1 (repr.).

SAMUEL STILLMAN OSGOOD (1808–1885), born possibly in New Haven, Conn., grew up in Boston and studied painting there until 1829. He visited Charleston, S.C. in 1829–1830; after study and travel in Europe from 1835 to 1839, he again visited Charleston and Boston, then settled in New York City until 1851, except for two years in Philadelphia, 1847 to 1849. He again visited Europe, visited New Orleans several times, and lived in New York until 1869, when he moved to California, where he died.

785. **Miss Anna Quincy Thaxter Parsons**

Seated in half-length, the young woman turns three-quarters left and rests her right arm on a green-covered table; she wears a white dress with gold belt and edge and a purple robe over one shoulder. The background and spandrels are black.

Oil on canvas. Painted oval. 30 × 25 in. (76.2 × 63.5 cm.)
Painted about 1830.
Gift of Lucia R. Peabody. 21.1647

786. **Miss Stebbins of New York**

fig. 243

Three-quarter length, she stands turned three-quarters left, but looking to the right, before a gray wall. She holds a black fan in her crossed hands and wears a white dress and black lace shawl.

Oil on canvas. 12 × 10 in. (30.5 × 25.4 cm.)
Painted about 1840–1850.
Collection: Maxim Karolik, Newport, R.I., 1944.
Bequest of Maxim Karolik. 64.439

An inscription on the reverse of the painting has identified the subject only as "Miss Stebbins . . . 7th St."; she may be Miss Angelina Stebbins (born 1818) or Miss Caroline Stebbins (born 1824), the daughters of John (died 1834) and Mary Largin Stebbins. Henry G. and Russell Stebbins were brothers of these girls. After 1840, Henry G. Stebbins lived at "7 Ave. 5th." After their father's death, Angelina and Caroline may have lived with their brother Henry. The address on the stretcher is possibly a confused version of "7 Ave. 5th." It is perhaps only coincidence that about 1840 Osgood painted a portrait similar in style and pose of Mrs. Mary Elizabeth Hewett (New-York Historical Society), who in 1854 became the wife of Russell Stebbins.

BASS OTIS (1784–1861) was born in Bridgewater, Mass. While apprenticed to a scythe-maker, he learned painting from a coach-maker and by 1808 was working as a portrait painter in New York. Three years after moving to Philadelphia in 1812, he invented the perspective protractor, and in 1818/19 he made America's first lithograph. He returned to New York in 1845, then moved to Boston, where he worked until 1858. From then until his death he lived in Philadelphia.

787.

fig. 223

Virginia A. and George Simmons

A young girl and boy, full-length and facing front, stand before a gray funerary urn surrounded by green and brown trees. She wears a white lace dress and pantaloons and has her left arm around her brother, who holds an open book and wears a red dress over white trousers. A distant city is under blue sky and gray clouds in the right background.

Oil on canvas. 56¾ × 39½ in. (144.1 × 100.3 cm.)

Signed and dated lower left: *B. Otis/ pinxt. 1844.*

Collection: Virginia Wainwright, granddaughter and great-niece of the sitters, Allston, Mass.

Bequest of Virginia Wainwright. 62.1102

George Simmons never married, but his sister Virginia married John Whitney Beals and had five children by him. While the children are presumably from Philadelphia, where Otis was reputedly living in 1844, the city shown seems to be Boston, with the dome of Bulfinch's State House atop Beacon Hill. The inscription on the funerary urn, dedicated to a deceased brother and sister, reads, "In memory of Mary Isabell Simmo—/ died Novr. 27 1834/ aged 3 months/ Frank Simmons/ born March 4th, 1843/ died Feby, the 3rd/ 1844."

WILLIAM PAGE

(1811–1885), born in Albany, N.Y., studied painting in New York City with James Herring and Samuel F.B. Morse. From 1828 to 1849 he painted portraits and historical subjects, primarily in New York but also in Northampton, Mass., Albany and Rochester, N.Y., and from 1843 to 1847, in Boston. From 1850 to 1860 he worked in Rome copying old masters and painting historical and religious subjects. On his return he settled in Eagleswood, N.J. near George Inness, but after 1860 he lived in Tottenville, Staten Island, N.Y., until his death. He was President of the National Academy of Design from 1871 to 1873.

788.

fig. 295

John Quincy Adams

Three-quarter length, seated in a red upholstered armchair, slightly right, he holds a cane and wears a black suit and tie, white waistcoat, and high white collar.

Oil on canvas. 46½ × 35½ in. (118.1 × 90.2 cm.)

Signed lower right, on the paper: *Page.* Painted in 1838.

Collection: City of Boston, 1838.

Deposited by the City of Boston. 30.76e

John Quincy Adams (1767–1848), son of John and Abigail Smith Adams, was Secretary of State in 1817 and sixth President of the U.S. in 1825. Adams noted in his diary (C.F. Adams, ed., *Memoirs of John Quincy Adams*, Philadelphia, 1876, x, p. 42) that his portrait was painted by Page in 1838.

References: H.T. Tuckerman, *Book of the Artists*, New York, 1870, p. 297./ W.H. Downes, "Boston Painters and Paintings," *Atlantic Monthly*, 1888, LXII, no. 371, p. 384./ J.C. Taylor, *Page*, Chicago, 1957, pp. 20–22, 66, 258 (fig. 7).

Exhibitions: Boston, MFA, *Contemporary Art*, 1879, no. 92./ Detroit Institute of Arts, *World of the Romantic Artist*, 1944–1945, no. 3.

789.

fig. 294

William Lloyd Garrison

Seated half-length, turned three-quarters right, before a brown background, the bald gentleman wears a black suit and tie.

Oil on canvas. 30 × 25 in. (76.2 × 63.5 cm.)

Painted about 1844–1847.

Collections: Mr. Thompson, England; Francis G. Shaw, Boston, 1859; Mrs. Francis G. Shaw, Boston.

Gift of Mrs. Francis George Shaw. 87.420

William Lloyd Garrison (1805–1879) was a Boston abolitionist and reformer whose antislavery newspaper, *The Liberator* (founded in 1831) was a powerful and influential support to the American abolitionist movement. The apparent age of the sitter concurs with the presence of Page in Boston between 1844 and 1847.

References: E.P. Richardson, *American Romantic Painting*, New York, 1945, no. 124 (repr.)./ J.C. Taylor, *Page*, Chicago, 1957, pp. 69, 263 (fig. 22).

Exhibition: Detroit Institute of Arts, *World of the Romantic Artist*, 1944–1945, no. 12 (repr. p. 10).

790. **Sargent Smith Littlehale**

Bust-length, turned three-quarters left, he wears a white stock with a black jacket. The background is brown to the left, red to the right.
Oil on canvas. 24¼ × 20 in. (61.6 × 50.8 cm.)
Painted in 1846.
Collection: Mary Frances Littlehale, daughter of the sitter, Boston.
Bequest of Mary Frances Littlehale. 05.48

Sargent Smith Littlehale (1787–1851) was born in Gloucester, Mass. the son of Richard and Sarah Byles Littlehale. Partner in a prosperous wholesale grocery business in Boston, he held positions as Assessor, Councilman, Overseer to the Poor, and director of a bank, and was a promoter of the Boston and Albany railroad. He died in Boston. The date for the painting is given in his daughter's *Reminiscences (see below)*.

References: E.D. Cheney, *Reminiscences*, Boston, 1902, pp. 33–35 (repr. opp. p. 22)./ J.C. Taylor, *Page*, Chicago, 1957, pp. 68, 265 (fig. 20).

791. **Mrs. Sargent Smith Littlehale (Ednah Dow)**

Seated bust-length before a brown and gray background, turned three-quarters left, she wears a brown and red dress with a white lace collar.
Oil on canvas. 24½ × 20 in. (62.2 × 50.8 cm.)
Painted in 1846.
Collection: Same as Cat. no. 790.
Bequest of Mary Frances Littlehale. 05.49

Ednah Dow (1797–1876), born in Exeter, N.H., was the eldest daughter of Jeremiah and Ednah Parker Dow, owners of a large tannery in Exeter. She married Sargent Littlehale in 1819 and died in Boston. Pendant to the preceding (Cat. no. 790).

References: E.D. Cheney, *Reminiscences*, Boston, 1902, pp. 33–35 (repr. opp. p. 22)./ A. Burroughs, *Limners and Likenesses*, Cambridge, Mass., 1936, p. 164./ E.P. Richardson, "Two Portraits by Page," *Art Quarterly*, 1938, I, no. 2, pp. 90–103./ —, *American Romantic Painting*, New York, 1945, no. 125 (repr.).

792.
fig. 293 **Harriet Hosmer**

Bust-length, facing front before a brown background, the young woman wears a brown jacket and red tie with a white blouse. The spandrels are brown.
Oil on canvas. Painted oval. 21½ × 16¾ in. (54.6 × 42.5 cm.)
Painted about 1854–1857.
Collection: Given by the sitter to Mrs. Lucien Carr.
Gift of the Estate of Mrs. Lucien Carr. 22.703

Harriet Hosmer (1830–1908), born in Watertown, Mass., was the leading sculptress of her time. From 1852 she studied with John Gibson in Rome and lived in Rome and England until 1900, becoming an intimate friend of the Robert Brownings, among other intellectual figures. She died in Massachusetts. The portrait was painted in Rome between 1854 and 1857 according to letters from Robert Browning (*see* Carr, *below*).

References: C. Carr, ed., *Harriet Hosmer*, New York, 1912, pp. 47, 81./ E.P. Richardson, "Two Portraits by Page," *Art Quarterly*, 1938, I, no. 2, pp. 90–103./ S. van Rensselaer, "Hosmer," *Antiques*, 1963, LXXIV, no. 4 (repr. p. 426).

Exhibitions: Detroit Institute of Arts and Toledo Museum, *Travelers in Arcadia*, 1951, no. 80./ New York, American Academy of Arts and Letters, *The Great Decade in American Writing, 1850–1860*, 1954, no. 118./ New York, Grolier Club, *The Italian Influence on American Literature*, 1961, no. 272.

DAVID PARK (1911–1960) was born in Boston and in 1928 studied at the Otis Art Institute, Los Angeles. In 1929 he settled permanently in San Francisco and first worked as a stonecutter. From 1931 to 1936 he taught at various private schools and at the University of California Extension Division. From 1936 to 1941 he taught at the Winsor School, Boston; then on his return to California, he was an instructor from 1943 to 1952 at the California School of Fine Arts, San Francisco. From 1955 until his death, he taught at the University of California, Berkeley. With Elmer Bischoff and Richard Diebenkorn, Park was an important member of an informal group of painters called the "Bay School," which showed renewed interest in figurative subjects, often expressionistically handled.

793. **Rowboat**
fig. 609
Two men seated in a yellow and white boat with yellow and orange oars. They are painted with broad strokes of pink, brown, red, and blue. The water is blue and green touched with red, brown, and yellow.
Oil on canvas. 56¾ × 61 in. (144.1 × 154.9 cm.)
Signed and dated lower right: *Park 58.*
Collections: Institute of Contemporary Art, Boston, Provisional Collection; Private Collection, Boston.
Anonymous gift. 63.2667

Exhibitions: New York, Staempfli Gallery, *Park*, 1959, no. 19 (repr.)./ Boston, Institute of Contemporary Art, *Provisional Collection*, 1961, no. 39 (repr. cover)./ New York, Staempfli Gallery and circulated in the U.S., *Park*, 1961, no. 44 (repr.).

WILLIAM McGREGOR PAXTON (1869–1941) was born in Baltimore and taken to Newton, Mass. in 1870. He studied painting in Boston with Dennis Bunker, then in Paris with Gérôme and at the École des Beaux Arts. On his return, he taught at the Boston Museum School and worked in Boston as a portrait, genre, and mural painter until his death in Newton. A member of the "Boston School" with Tarbell, Benson, and others, his polished, often idealized and sentimental style reflected the thinking of Gérôme and current practice in French academic circles.

794. **The New Necklace**
fig. 489
A girl, seated at a brown desk and wearing a pink and blue kimono over a pink skirt, shows a necklace to another, dressed in blue, who stands behind her. A green and gold Japanese screen is before a brown painting and green and brown patterned wallpaper. In the foreground a brown and blue hat is on a chair.
Oil on canvas. 35½ × 28½ in. (90.2 × 72.3 cm.)
Signed and dated lower left: *Paxton/ 1910.*
Collection: Zoe O. Sherman, Boston, 1912.
Zoe Oliver Sherman Collection. 22.644

Exhibitions: Boston, St. Botolph Club, *Paxton*, 1913, no. 2./ Maryhill, Md., Maryhill Museum, *Paxton*, 1946, no. 8.

795. **Nude**
fig. 488
Seated full-length and in right profile, a girl reaches across green and blue bedcovers. Beyond her are a brown chair and white sheets piled against the brown wall.
Oil on canvas. 24 × 33 in. (61 × 83.8 cm.)
Signed upper right: *Paxton.*
Charles Henry Hayden Fund. 16.98

Reference: R.H.I. Gammell, *Twilight in Painting*, New York, 1946 (pl. 55).
Exhibition: Hartford, Conn., Wadsworth Atheneum, *Nude in Art*, 1946, no. 40.

CHARLES WILLSON PEALE (1741–1827), born in Queen Anne's County, Md., was a professional saddler in Annapolis when he first took lessons from John Hesselius in Philadelphia. In 1765 he visited Boston where he saw some of the work of Smibert and met Copley. From 1767 to 1769 he studied with Benjamin West in London, then worked in the vicinity of Annapolis and Philadelphia until 1776, when he entered the Revolutionary Army. In 1778 he settled permanently in Philadelphia. In addition to his portrait, historical, and miniature painting, Peale was a scientist, naturalist, and inventor. In 1872 he established his picture gallery, which in 1786 became the Peale Museum. It contained many of his paintings and thousands of botanical, geological, and zoological specimens and curiosities. He was, in 1795, an organizer of the Columbianum, or American Academy of Fine Arts in Philadelphia, and was also a founder of the Pennsylvania Academy of the Fine Arts.

796.
fig. 106

Thomas and Henry Sergeant

Identically dressed in dark green suits and white shirts, the twins stand three-quarter length, facing front, with an arm about each other. The boy on the left holds a plumed light brown hat; the boy on the right pats a black and white setter. The background is brown.
Oil on canvas. 35½ × 29 in. (90.2 × 73.6 cm.)
Painted about 1787.
Collections: Thomas Sergeant Perry; Miss Margaret Perry, his daughter and great-granddaughter of Thomas, great-great-niece of Henry Sergeant, Boston; Jay Pierrepont Moffat, her great-nephew.
Lent by Jay Pierrepont Moffat. 110.60
Thomas and Henry Sergeant, born in 1782, were the twin sons of Jonathan Dickinson and Margaret Spencer Sergeant, who were painted by Peale in 1786. These portraits are now owned by Princeton University and by Mrs. Thomas Mabry, Stockbridge, Mass., respectively (Sellers, *Peale*, Philadelphia, 1952, pp. 192–193 (repr. p. 311).

797.
fig. 104

Nathaniel Gorham

Bust-length, turned three-quarters right, he wears a gray coat over a red waistcoat and white stock. The background is gray within four brown spandrels.
Oil on canvas, mounted on masonite. Painted oval. 26 × 22 in. (66 × 55.9 cm.)
Painted about 1793–1794.
Collections: Peter Chardon Brooks, son-in-law of the sitter, West Medford, Mass.; Francis Brooks, his grandson, West Medford; Mrs. Edmund Wheelwright (Elizabeth Brooks), his daughter, Boston, by 1907; Edwin H. Abbot Jr., Cambridge, Mass., 1948.
Gift of Edwin H. Abbot Jr., in memory of his brother, Philip Stanley Abbot. 48.1356
Nathaniel Gorham (1738–1796), born in Charlestown, Mass., was President of the Congress of the Confederation in 1780, Chairman of the Constitutional Convention in the Committee of the Whole, 1787, and signer of the Constitution. His unsuccessful venture in the Phelps-Gorham purchase during the boundary dispute between New York State and Massachusetts ruined him financially; he died in Boston. A replica of this portrait, once owned by Brooks Adams, is now in the Adams Mansion (National Park Service), Quincy, Mass. A portrait of Gorham was listed in the Peale Museum catalogue of 1795, and it is not certain which of the two portraits was painted for the Museum. Our portrait was probably the one done for Peter C. Brooks after his marriage in 1792 to Anne, Gorham's daughter. A third version is owned by Nathaniel Gorham, Buffalo, N.Y.
Reference: C.C. Sellers, *Portraits and Miniatures by C.W. Peale*, Philadelphia, 1952, no. 312, p. 91 (repr. p. 311).

798.

George Washington

Bust-length and turned three-quarters left on a brown background, he wears a black suit over a white stock and ruffled shirt.
Oil on panel. 7½ × 6 in. (19 × 15.2 cm.)
Painted after 1795.
Collections: Gift of the artist to Mrs. Calahan, Annapolis, Md.; Mrs. Ridgeley, her granddaughter, Washington, D.C.; Charles Sumner, Boston.

Bequest of Charles Sumner. 74.29

A replica of Peale's portrait of George Washington, painted from life in 1795, which is now in the New-York Historical Society.

References: J.H. Morgan and M. Fielding, *Life Portraits of Washington*, Philadelphia, 1931, p. 41, no. 46./ C.C. Sellers, *Portraits and Miniatures by C.W. Peale*, Philadelphia, 1952, no. 948.

799.
fig. 105

Mrs. Charles Willson Peale (Hannah Moore)

Nearly half-length and facing front, she sits in a brown chair before an olive-brown background. She wears a yellow-brown dress with a wide white fichu and white bonnet.
Oil on canvas. 24⅛ × 20⅛ in. (61.3 × 51 cm.)
Signed and dated center right: *C.W. Peale/ painted 1816* (W and P in monogram). Inscribed in ink on back of canvas: *Hannah Peale aged 61 yrs 10th July 1816/ painted by Chas. W. Peale in his 76 year.*
Collections: Hannah Moore Peale, the artist's wife, Philadelphia; Deborah Moore Jackson, her sister, Philadelphia, 1821; Harriet Jackson Iddings, 1832; Mary Iddings Parker, her daughter; the Rev. Henry Ainsworth Parker, by 1902; Reginald Seabury Parker, his son, Cambridge, Mass., 1919; Mrs. Reginald S. Parker, 1965.
Gift of Mrs. Reginald Seabury Parker in memory of her husband. 65.611

Hannah Moore (1755–1821), the third wife of Charles Willson Peale, was painted three times by her husband: a miniature in 1805 at the time of their marriage (Sellers, no. 651); an oil portrait with his daughter by an earlier marriage, Elizabeth, about the same time (Sellers, no. 652); and the present picture. Peale wrote (Sellers, p. 165) of the painting to his son Rembrandt that he was trying a "new method," using Mrs. Peale as a subject and placing her in the most difficult pose to render. The method was one of the mechanical devices, using a lens, which was to aid with the accuracy of details. He added ". . . and I believe it is the best portrait I have ever executed." The heavy crackle suggests that Peale may have experimented with his pigments as well.

Reference: C.C. Sellers, *Portraits and Miniatures by C.W. Peale*, Philadelphia, 1952, no. 653 (repr. p. 341).

JAMES PEALE

(1749–1831), born in Chestertown, Md., was first trained as a saddler and cabinet-maker in Annapolis. His elder brother, Charles Willson Peale, on his return from London in 1769, taught him to paint, and after the Revolution they became established portrait painters in Philadelphia. James specialized in minatures until 1818, when his eyes began to fail, and thereafter he painted still life and landscapes until his death in Philadelphia.

800.

Watermelon and Fruit
Oil on canvas. 16¾ × 21 in. (42.5 × 53.3 cm.)
Painted in the 1820's.
M. and M. Karolik Collection. 48.464
Reference: *Karolik Catalogue*, 1949, no. 199 (repr.).

801.
fig. 161

Still Life with Fruit in a Bowl

Green and purple grapes, red and green apples, and yellow and red peaches fill and surround a white lustreware bowl. A silver knife lies on two blue and red napkins. The tablecloth is white; the background, brown.
Oil on canvas. 22 × 27 in. (55.9 × 68.6 cm.)
Painted about 1825.
Collection: Anonymous Philadelphia family since about 1825.
Ellen Kelleran Gardner Fund. 42.116

The relatively few signed and dated still-life paintings by James Peale are from the last years of his life.

Reference: W. Born, *Still Life Painting in America*, New York, 1947, p. 14 (pl. 30).
Exhibition: Cincinnati Art Museum, *The Peale Family*, 1954, no. 97.

REMBRANDT PEALE (1778–1860), born in Bucks County, Pa. after about 1790, took lessons in painting from his father, Charles Willson Peale. In 1797 he and his older brother Raphaelle opened a museum in Baltimore, and in 1802–1803, while in London to exhibit a mastodon skeleton, he studied at the Royal Academy under West. He painted portraits and historical pictures in Philadelphia, with trips to Paris in 1808 and 1809, from 1803 to 1820. He opened Rembrandt's Picture Gallery there in 1811 and reopened the museum in Baltimore in 1814. About 1820 he moved to New York, following the success of his great historical work, *The Court of Death* (Detroit Institute of Arts) and helped to found the National Academy of Design in 1826. He settled again in Philadelphia in 1834, after trips to Europe, and concentrated on his portraits of Washington. He died in Philadelphia.

802.

fig. 108

Samuel Rodman

Turned slightly right, bust-length, on a blue and brown background, he wears a brown coat over a green waistcoat and white neckcloth.
Oil on paper, mounted on canvas. 21¼ × 17 in. (54 × 43.2 cm.)
Painted about 1800.
Collection: Mrs. Andrew Robeson, grandmother of the donor, Providence, R.I.
Gift of Miss Harriet A. Robeson. 49.1146

Samuel Rodman (1753–1835), son of Thomas and Mary Borden Rodman, was born in Newport, R.I. His marriage to the daughter of a prosperous whaling merchant soon associated him with his father-in-law's firm, and he lived in New Bedford, Mass. as merchant and banker from 1798 until his death. This portrait, dated on the basis of style, is a replica of the probable original, 30 × 25 in., owned by Mary G. Snelling, Columbia, S.C. Another replica, 32 × 27 in., is in the possession of Mrs. Thomas Goethals, Brookline, Mass. The portrait of his wife (Cat. no. 803) is pendant to this portrait.

803.

fig. 107

Mrs. Samuel Rodman (Elizabeth Rotch)

Bust-length before a blue and brown background, she turns slightly left and wears a white shawl over a gray dress and a gray bonnet.
Oil on paper, mounted on canvas. 21¼ × 17 in. (54 × 43.2 cm.)
Painted about 1800.
Collection: Same as Cat. no. 802.
Gift of Miss Harriet A. Robeson. 49.1147

Elizabeth Rotch, born in Nantucket, Mass. in 1757 was the daughter of William Rotch of Nantucket and New Bedford. She married Samuel Rodman in 1780 and had nine children by him, all born in Nantucket. She died in New Bedford in 1856. Pendant to the preceding.

804.

Dr. John Davidson Godman

Seated on a red chair, bust-length, the young man faces front; his jacket is blue over a buff waistcoat and white neckcloth. The background is olive.
Oil on canvas. Painted oval. 22 × 18 in. (55.9 × 45.7 cm.)
Painted about 1821.
Bequest of Nellie G. Taylor. 43.136

John Godman (1794–1830), son of Capt. Samuel and Anna Henderson Godman, was born in Annapolis, Md. Anatomist and naturalist, author of the first *American Natural History*, 1826 to 1828, he was Professor of Surgery at the Cincinnati Medical College in 1821, and in 1822 edited the first medical journal published west of the Alleghenies. From 1822 to 1826 he was lecturer at the Philadelphia School of Anatomy. He died in Germantown, Pa. From his apparent age, he was probably painted in 1821, at the time of his marriage to the artist's daughter, Angelica Kauffman Peale. The canvas appears to have been cut down from a larger size.

805.

George Washington

Bust-length before a dark brown background, he turns three-quarters left and wears a black coat over a white stock and ruffled shirt.

Oil on canvas. 28¾ × 23¾ in. (73 × 60.3 cm.)
Painted after 1824.
Collections: Dr. David Gilbert, Philadelphia; W. Kent Gilbert, his son; S.P. Avery Jr., Boston, by 1845; Mary Appleton, Boston, 1904.
Maria Antoinette Evans Fund. 30.474

One of nearly eighty of the "Porthole" portraits of Washington; the prototype, painted about 1823–1824, is now in the Capitol, Washington, D.C. The painting listed as no. 244 in the catalogue of the *Charles Willson, James and Rembrandt Peale* exhibition at the Pennsylvania Academy of the Fine Arts, 1923, as a *Portrait of Washington* by Rembrandt Peale, lent by the Boston Museum, is in fact our *Washington* by Charles Willson Peale (Cat. no. 798).

Reference: J.H. Morgan and M. Fielding, *Life Portraits of Washington*, Philadelphia, 1931, p. 376, no. 4.

806.

The Duke of Wellington (copy after Sir Thomas Lawrence)

Half-length and turned slightly right, his arms folded, he wears a red uniform coat, with epaulets, cuffs, and lacings of gold and a blue ribbon across his chest. The background is gray and green.

Oil on canvas. 35½ × 26¾ in. (90.2 × 67.9 cm.)
Painted about 1829–1831.
Collection: Boston Museum and Gallery of Fine Arts, about 1841.
Gift of the Owners of the Boston Museum. 03.1078

Arthur Wellesley (1769–1852), First Duke of Wellington, was a politician and soldier nicknamed the "Iron Duke" and victor at the Battle of Waterloo. Sir Thomas Lawrence made nine portraits of the Duke: this copy is after that in the Victoria and Albert Museum, London, painted about 1814. After that date, Peale visited Europe only twice, in 1829–1830 and in 1831.

Reference: *Catalogue of Paintings . . . in the Collection of the Boston Museum and Gallery of Fine Arts*, Boston, 1844, no. 75.

807.

Rajah Rammohun Roy

Turned three-quarters left, half-length, he wears a red and green striped turban and a red neckcloth under his dark blue coat. The background is brown.

Oil on canvas. 30 × 25 in. (76.2 × 63.5 cm.)
Inscribed on back, upper right: *The Rajah Rammohun Roy/ Painted from life at London/ August 1833/ by Rembrandt Peale.*
Collection: Purchased from the artist by the Boston Athenaeum, 1838.
Deposited by the Boston Athenaeum, 1876. Ath. 38

Rammohun Roy (1774–1833), born in Bengal, India, was a religious reformer who founded the Brahma Samaj, or Theistic Church, in India. In 1830 he was created Rajah by the Emperor of Delhi and was sent as his Agent to England, where he died.

Exhibition: New York, National Academy of Design, *10th Exhibition*, 1835, no. 30.

RUBENS PEALE (1784–1865)

808.

Basket of Fruit

Oil on canvas. 14 × 22 in. (35.5 × 55.9 cm.)
Signed lower right on the table edge: *Rubens Peale.*
M. and M. Karolik Collection. 48.464
Reference: Karolik Catalogue, 1949, no. 200 (repr.).

JOHN FREDERICK PETO (1854–1907) was born in Philadelphia and was painting there by 1876. Primarily self-taught, he studied briefly at the Pennsylvania Academy of the Fine Arts in 1878 and there became a good friend of William Harnett. In 1889 he settled in Island Heights, N.J. and except for a visit in 1894 to Lerado, O. worked there until his death. With Harnett he was one of the leading *trompe l'oeil* painters of the nineteenth century.

809.
fig. 445

Pots and Pans

Before a yellow copper bucket and a gray tankard are a copper pot, a blue and white pitcher, and a green candlestick on a brown tray. With red drapery, all are on a brown table against a dark gray background.
Oil on canvas. 22 × 16 in. (55.9 × 40.6 cm.)
Painted about 1880.
Collections: Mrs. George Smiley, the artist's daughter, Island Heights, N.J., 1907; Maxim Karolik, Newport, R.I., 1954.
Bequest of Maxim Karolik. 64.410
Large-scale simple forms, dark palette, and textural handling of paint indicate an early date.

810.
fig. 448

The Poor Man's Store

A green wooden wall and shutter with black and white plaques below a raised window sash. Two shelves, one lined with mauve paper, carry variously colored candies, a ginger-bread horse, apples, peanuts, cookies, etc. in bright colors. The interior is black.
Oil on canvas and wood. 36 × 25½ in. (91.4 × 64.8 cm.)
Signed and dated upper left, on the canvas: *J. F. Peto/—85.*
Collections: Private collection, East Orange, N.J.; Mrs. Raymond Dey, Preakness, N.J., about 1940; Miss Mary Allis, Southport, Conn., about 1943; Maxim Karolik, Newport, R.I., 1951.
M. and M. Karolik Collection. 62.278
A similar work, also entitled *Poor Man's Store*, was shown in the 1880 annual exhibition at the Pennsylvania Academy of the Fine Arts, Philadelphia.
References: A. Frankenstein, *After the Hunt*, Berkeley, Calif., 1953, pp. 101–102 (pl. 84)./ E.P. Richardson, *Painting in America*, New York, 1956, pp. 322–323 (fig. 136)./ T.N. Maytham, "Some Recent Accessions," *MFA Bulletin*, 1962, LX, no. 322, pp. 137–138 (repr. p. 137).
Exhibitions: Smith College Museum, Brooklyn Museum, and San Francisco, California Palace of the Legion of Honor, *Peto*, 1950, no. 4 (fig. 7)./ New York, Wildenstein and Co., *Landmarks in American Art 1679–1950*, 1953, no. 32 (repr.)./ New York, American Federation of Arts, circulated in the U.S., *Harnett and His School*, 1953–1954./ Detroit Institute of Arts and San Francisco, M.H. de Young Memorial Museum, *Painting in America, the Story of 450 Years*, 1957, no. 140./ Toronto Art Gallery and circulated in Canada, and New York, Whitney Museum, *American Painting from 1865–1905*, 1961, no. 51 (pl. XXVI)./ New York, World's Fair, Gallery of Better Living Center, *Four Centuries of American Masterpieces*, 1964, no. 22 (repr.).

811.
fig. 446

Student's Materials

Brown, red, green, and blue books are stacked on a brown table with a green candlestick and cloth and a brown pipe and inkpot. The background is black.
Oil on canvas. 20¼ × 16¼ in. (51.4 × 41.2 cm.)
Signed upper right: *JF Peto*. Painted about 1890–1900.
Collections: Probably Mrs. George Smiley, the artist's daughter, Island Heights, N.J., 1907; Maxim Karolik, Newport, R.I., 1953.
Bequest of Maxim Karolik. 64.412

812.
fig. 447

Old Time Letter Rack

The pink ribbon rack holds envelopes, cards, a book, a picture of Lincoln, and a pipe, all of blue, yellow, brown, or green. Also tacked to the green board are paper scraps and some string, of blue, gray, or yellow.
Oil on canvas. 30 × 25 in. (76.2 × 63.5 cm.)
Signed and dated lower right: *John F. Peto/ 94*. Inscribed on back, lower center: *Old Time Letter Rack/ by/ John F. Peto/ Island Heights/ New Jersey/ 1894*,
Collections: Dr. Ill, New Jersey, about 1894; Edward Ill, his grandson.

Southampton, N.Y.; Maxim Karolik, Newport, R.I., 1952.
Bequest of Maxim Karolik. 64.411

Reference: A. Frankenstein, *After the Hunt*, Berkeley, Cal., 1953, pp. 17 (footnote), 108 (pl. 7, as *Letter Rack with Lerado Postmark*).

Exhibitions: American Federation of Arts, circulated in the U.S., *Harnett and His School*, 1953–1954./ Philadelphia, Pennsylvania Academy of the Fine Arts, *150th Anniversary*, 1955, no. 177 (as *Letter Rack with Lerado Postmark*)./ Ogunquit Museum, *8th Annual—Luminist and Trompe l'Oeil Painters*, 1960, no. 21.

HENRY CHEEVER PRATT (1803–1880)

813. **On the Ammonoosuc River**
Oil on canvas. 25¼ × 30¼ in. (64.1 × 76.8 cm.)
Painted in 1828.
M. and M. Karolik Collection. 48.465
Reference: *Karolik Catalogue*, 1949, no. 201 (repr.).

CHARLES PRENDERGAST (1863–1948), born in Boston, lived with his older brother Maurice in Winchester, Mass. until 1914 when they moved to New York City. A frame-maker by profession, Charles Prendergast substituted for the then popular ornate gilt frames a simple carved frame finished with gilt and raw gesso. Also a painter, he worked in watercolor and began to make incised and painted gesso panels by 1906, as well as decorated screens and carved and decorated chests. His work displays a profound near-eastern and oriental influence in style and subject, much of it drawn from visits to the Chinese and Persian collections of the MFA. In 1925 he traveled in Europe and there married Eugenie van Kemmel. Except for several more European trips, he worked principally in Westport, Conn. until his death.

814. **The Fountain**
fig. 537
Figures, mostly women, robed in pink, white, gold, or green, are occupied with flowers or musical instruments. Behind, a small fountain and gold trees are before a gray, red, and brown town on green and yellow hills; left are a blue lake and gold trees. In the foreground, exotic birds and animals of gold, gray blue, and yellow gambol among green, blue, yellow, and red flowers and fruit. The sky is pale blue-gray.
Watercolor and gold leaf on incised gesso. 31¼ × 61¾ in. (79.4 × 156.8 cm.)
Painted about 1932–1934.
Gift of Mrs. Charles Prendergast. 62.811

References: "The Brothers Prendergast in Review," *Art News*, 1938, XXXVIII, no. 2, p. 15./ M. Breuning, "Decorative Art of Charles Prendergast," *Art Digest*, 1947, XXI, no. 13, p. 18./ "Charles Prendergast," *Art News*, 1947, XXVI, no. 2, p. 44./ T.N. Maytham, "Some Recent Accessions," *MFA Bulletin*, 1962, LX, no. 322, pp. 138–139 (repr. p. 138).

Exhibitions: New York, Kraushaar Galleries, *Charles Prendergast*, 1935, no. 12./ Andover, Mass., Addison Gallery, *The Prendergasts*, 1938, no. 7./ Washington, D.C., Corcoran Gallery, *16th Biennial*, 1939, p. 48./ New York, Kraushaar Galleries, *Charles Prendergast*, 1947, no. 6./ —, *Charles Prendergast Memorial*, 1954, no. 17./ New York, Roy Davis Gallery, *Charles Prendergast*, 1963, no. 31 (repr.).

MAURICE BRAZIL PRENDERGAST (1859–1924) was born in St. John's, Newfoundland and in 1861 was taken to Boston. He began sketching and painting in Massachusetts and Maine from 1887 to 1889; his trip in 1886 to England, and perhaps Paris, was the first of six visits to Europe. In 1891 he studied at the Académie Julian with Laurens, at the Colarossi School, and in London. In 1894 he settled in Winchester, Mass. Between 1905 and 1908, when he joined "The Eight," he moved into Boston; in 1912 he worked in New Hampshire, and in 1914 he finally settled in New York, where he died. Despite his association with the Realist artists of "The Eight," his artistic affinities lay with his French contemporaries, Boudin and the Nabis, Bonnard and Vuillard.

815.

fig. 533

Lady with a Red Sash

A lady, her back turned, wears a red sash with her white dress and carries a red parasol. Behind her people in gray, white, and mauve stand under yellow street lights before purple buildings. The sky and ground are gray.

Oil on canvas. 24 × 8¼ in. (61 × 21 cm.)

Signed lower right: *Prendergast.* Painted about 1900.

Collection: Mrs. Charles Prendergast, the artist's sister-in-law, Westport, Conn.

Emily L. Ainsley Fund. 62.322

Reference: T.N. Maytham, "Some Recent Accessions," *MFA Bulletin*, 1962, LX, no. 322, p. 140 (repr. p. 139).

Exhibition: Boston, MFA and circulated in the U.S., *Maurice Prendergast*, 1960–1961, no. 10 (repr. p. 24).

816.

fig. 532

Race Track

People in white, gray, red, and brown gather by the green track before the carriages and brown and white horses. A distant crowd is brown on the bare canvas, with red touches throughout.

Oil on canvas. 23 × 20½ in. (58.4 × 52 cm.)

Signed lower right: *Prendergast.* Painted about 1900.

Collection: Mrs. Charles Prendergast, the artist's sister-in-law, Westport, Conn.

Emily L. Ainsley Fund. 62.321

817.

fig. 534

Flowers in a Blue Vase

The vase, filled with red, yellow, and orange flowers with green leaves, stands on a red and white patterned cloth before a green background.

Oil on canvas. 19 × 16 in. (48.2 × 40.6 cm.)

Signed lower left: *Prendergast.* Painted about 1915.

Bequest of John T. Spaulding. 48.589

A similar work, *Old Fashioned Flowers*, 1914, is in the Addison Gallery, Andover, Mass.

Exhibition: Boston, MFA, *The Spaulding Collections*, 1948, no. 66.

818.

fig. 536

Eight Bathers

Eight women, nude or robed in green, yellow, or red, stand and sit by white and mauve rocks. The sea behind appears gray before blue and white sky.

Oil on canvas. 28¼ × 24 in. (71.7 × 61 cm.)

Signed lower center: *Prendergast.* Painted about 1916–1918.

Collection: Mrs. Charles Prendergast, the artist's sister-in-law, Westport, Conn.

Abraham Shuman Fund. 61.663

Exhibition: Boston, MFA and circulated in the U.S., *Maurice Prendergast*, 1960–1961, no. 38 (repr. p. 14).

819.

fig. 535

Picnic Grove

People in blue and white, red, yellow, green, or purple stand in the green and brown grove.

Oil on canvas. 19¼ × 27¼ in. (48.9 × 69.2 cm.)

Signed lower center: *Prendergast.* Painted about 1918.

Collection: Mrs. Charles Prendergast, the artist's sister-in-law, Westport, Conn.

Charles Henry Hayden Fund. 58.327

Exhibitions: Cleveland Museum, *Maurice Prendergast*, 1926./ New York, Kraushaar Galleries, *William Glackens and His Friends*, 1957, no. 30./ Boston, MFA and circulated in the U.S., *Maurice Prendergast*, 1960–1961, no. 46 (repr. p. 61).

WILLIAM MATTHEW PRIOR (1806–1873), born in Bath, Me., was painting portraits by 1824 and lived in Portland, Me. from about 1831 to 1840. He then settled in Boston, later in East Boston, and as an itinerant artist traveled to New Bedford, Mass., Newport, R.I., and Baltimore. He worked in Boston as a portrait and landscape painter, and author of several religious books, until his death.

820.
fig. 253

William Allen
Oil on canvas. 32¼ × 40 in. (81.9 × 101.6 cm.)
Inscribed on back: *W. Allen/ By Wm. M. Prior/ 1843.*
M. and M. Karolik Collection. 48.466
Reference: Karolik Catalogue, 1949, no. 202 (repr.).

821.

Mother and Daughter
Seated, half-length and turned three-quarters left, the mother places her hand on the shoulder of a child, dressed in blue, who holds a white fan and pink flowers. The mother wears black with a plaid ribbon held at the neck by a gold pin. The background is brown.
Oil on canvas. 31½ × 27 in. (80 × 68.8 cm.)
Inscribed on back: *By W.M. Prior/ Mr Turner Paid/ $4.00/ Mr. Sawin 4 00/ May 1851.*
Collections: Mrs. Nina Fletcher Little, Brookline, Mass., 1947; Maxim Karolik, Newport, R.I., by 1952.
Bequest of Maxim Karolik. 64.461
Reference: N.F. Little, "Prior, Traveling Artist," *Antiques,* 1948, LIII, no. 1 (repr. p. 48 as *Lady and Child*).
Exhibition: Worcester, Mass., Art Museum, *The Private Collection of Maxim Karolik,* 1952, no. 35.

822.
fig. 252

Three Sisters of the Coplan Family
Oil on canvas. 26¾ × 36¼ in. (67.9 × 92.1 cm.)
Inscribed on the back: *W.M. Prior/ 36 Trenton Street (third Section)/ East Boston/ Sep. 1854.*
M. and M. Karolik Collection. 48.467
Reference: Karolik Catalogue, 1949, no. 203 (repr.).

823.

Winter Scene
Snow covers the brown and black cottages, bare trees, and brown banks of a lake, where people in brown, blue, red, and black skate on gray ice. The sky is blue and gray.
Oil on canvas. 19¼ × 26 in. (48.9 × 66 cm.)
Signed on back, lower center: *By WM. Prior Artist.*
Collections: Stanley Silversweig, Worcester, Mass.; Maxim Karolik, Newport, R.I., 1960.
Bequest of Maxim Karolik. 64.454
Exhibition: Southampton, N.Y., Parrish Art Museum, *American Paintings, 1815–1865,* 1961, no. 31 (repr.).

JOHN QUIDOR (1801–1881)

824.

A Battle Scene from Knickerbocker's History of New York
Oil on canvas. 27 × 34½ in. (68.6 × 87.7 cm.)
Signed and dated lower center on fallen branch: *J.Quidor, N.Y. 1838.* Inscribed on back before relining: *The Original Painting by John Quidor N.York 1838.*
M. and M. Karolik Collection. 48.468
Reference: Karolik Catalogue, 1949, no. 204 (repr.).

825.
fig. 218

Rip Van Winkle at Nicholas Vedder's Tavern
Oil on canvas. 27 × 34 in. (68.6 × 86.3 cm.)
Signed and dated on portrait of King George: *The Original by John Quidor/ 1839.* Inscribed on back before relining: *John Quidor pinst New York 1839.*
M. and M. Karolik Collection. 48.469
Reference: Karolik Catalogue, 1949, no. 205 (repr.).

WILLIAM TYLEE RANNEY (1813–1857)

826.   **Duck Hunters on the Hoboken Marshes**
fig. 283   Oil on canvas. 26 × 40 in. (66 × 101.6 cm.)
Signed and dated on side of boat: *W. Ranney/ 49.*
M. and M. Karolik Collection. 48.470
Reference: Karolik Catalogue, 1949, no. 206 (repr.).

EDWARD WILLIS REDFIELD, born in Bridgeville, Del. in 1869, studied for five years at the Pennsylvania Academy of the Fine Arts with Thomas Anshutz and James Kelly. Then, intent on becoming a portraitist, he attended the Académie Julian, Paris, under Bouguereau and Robert Fleury. He painted in and about Fontainebleau, then returned to America as a landscape painter. In 1898 he settled in New Hope, Pa., where he still lives.

827.   **The Ravine**
fig. 522   *A brown valley, partially covered with snow and brown or green trees, lies under blue sky. A gray bridge crosses the foreground stream before brown and white farm buildings.*
Oil on canvas. 38¼ × 50¼ in. (97.1 × 127.6 cm.)
Signed lower right: *E.W. Redfield.* Painted in 1909.
Charles Henry Hayden Fund. 10.158
"Painted in Feb. 1909 on Goat Hill, behind Lambertville, N.J." (Letter from the artist, Nov. 13, 1949.)
Exhibition: Boston, St. Botolph Club, Redfield, 1910, no. 8.

828.   **Mountain Brook**
A soft blue brook, flecked with brown, flows between white snow-covered ground, shadowed blue; the tree trunks are brown and the buildings in the distance are pale yellow under a pale blue sky.
Oil on canvas. 26 × 32 in. (66 × 81.2 cm.)
Signed lower right: *E.W. Redfield.* Painted about 1912.
The John Pickering Lyman Collection. Gift of Miss Theodora Lyman. 19.1332
"Painted about 1912 at Johnson's Creek, near New Hope, Pa." (Letter from the artist, Nov. 13, 1949.)

WILLIAM RIMMER (1816–1879), born in Liverpool, England, was brought to Nova Scotia at two years of age, and to Boston in 1826. By 1831 he was helping to supplement the family income by painting portraits and signs; after 1840 he was an itinerant portrait painter around Boston. From 1845 to 1855 he worked in Randolph, Mass., making shoes and painting portraits and religious and other subjects. He had also studied medicine, and practiced from about 1855 to 1863 in East Milton, Mass. He began to sculpt and to lecture on art anatomy in Boston and Lowell. From 1866 to 1870 Rimmer was Director of the School for Design for Women at the Cooper Union, New York. In 1870 he reopened his art school in Boston, and from 1876 until his death he taught at the Boston Museum School. He wrote *Elements of Design*, 1864, and *Art Anatomy*, 1877.

829.   **Mrs. Robert Restiaux Kent (Eliza Watson)**
fig. 335   *Half-length and in left profile, she is seated before a brown piano with an open music book and wears a red dress with a white ruffled collar. The background is brown, touched with blue and gold.*
Oil on canvas. 30 × 25 in. (76.2 × 63.5 cm.)
Painted in 1867.
Collection: Henry Watson Kent, the sitter's son, New York.
Gift of Mrs. Richard B. Kent in the name of Henry Watson Kent. 49.27
Eliza F. Watson, daughter of Captain Horace Watson of Hingham, Mass., was the wife of Robert Restiaux Kent.
Exhibition: New York, Whitney Museum and Boston, MFA, Rimmer, 1946–1947, no. 11 (repr.).

830.

fig. 332

Evening: Fall of Day

A winged, nude male figure, symbolizing Day, is modeled in dark gray and yellow-brown against a gray ground. The sea and hills below are in pale gray and brown.
Oil on canvas. 40 × 50 in. (101.6 × 127 cm.)
Signed lower right: *W. Rimmer.* Painted in 1869.
Purchased. 81.110

The date is given by Lincoln Kirstein (*see below*) and in the exhibition catalogue of 1946–1947 (*see below*).

References: T.H. Bartlett, "Rimmer," *American Art Review*, 1879–1880, I, no. 2, p. 510./ —, *Rimmer*, Boston, 1882, p. 125 (pl. XIX)./ L. Kirstein, "Rimmer," *Massachusetts Review*, Summer 1961 (fig. 8).

Exhibitions: New York, Whitney Museum and Boston, MFA, *Rimmer*, 1946–1947, no. 15 (repr.)./ Brooklyn Museum, *Nude Painting from the 18th, 19th and 20th Centuries*, 1961, no. 6.

831.

fig. 333

Flight and Pursuit

A man in a white tunic, headband, and blue cape flees through an elaborate pale gray, brown, and yellow Moorish interior. In the background runs a ghostlike figure, muffled in a white robe, with sword drawn.
Oil on canvas. 18 × 26¼ in. (45.7 × 66.7 cm.)
Signed and dated lower left: *W. Rimmer/ 1872.*
Collections: Given by the artist to Col. Charles B. Nichols, Providence, R.I.; Mrs. Charles B. Nichols, Providence; Miss Edith Nichols, Providence.
Bequest of Miss Edith Nichols. 56.119

Also known as *Pursuer and Pursued*, an early, now lost pencil sketch for the painting was entitled *Oh for the Horns of the Altar!* It is an allegory, in the Transcendentalist spirit, of Man and his attempt to escape from his conscience (Exhibition catalogue of 1946–1947, *see below*).

References: T.H. Bartlett, *Rimmer*, Boston, 1882, p. 127 (pl. XVI, reversed)./ L. Kirstein, "Rediscovery of Rimmer," *Magazine of Art*, 1947, XL, no. 3, p. 95 (repr. p. 94)./ E.P. Richardson, *Painting in America*, New York, 1956, p. 262 (fig. 111)./ L. Kirstein, "Rimmer," *Massachusetts Review*, Summer 1961 (fig. 16)./ S. Preston, "New York," *Burlington Magazine*, 1961, CIII, no. 700 (fig. 43).

Exhibitions: Boston, MFA, *Rimmer*, 1880, no. 22./ New York, Whitney Museum and Boston, MFA, *Rimmer*, 1946–1947, no. 18 (repr.)./ Detroit Institute of Arts and San Francisco, M.H. de Young Memorial Museum, *Painting in America, the Story of 450 Years*, 1957, no. 117./ New York, American Federation of Arts, circulated in the U.S., *A Rationale for Modern Art*, 1959–1960./ Toronto Art Gallery and circulated in Canada, and New York, Whitney Museum, *American Painting from 1865–1905*, 1961, no. 52 (pl. XXVI).

832.

The Sentinel

A brown-skinned soldier, standing full-length and leaning on a halberd, wears a gold breastplate, a brown headdress, and short trousers. Behind him are a yellow wall and blue sky with white and gray clouds.
Oil on cardboard. 18½ × 12¼ in. (47 × 31.1 cm.)
Signed lower left: *W.R.*
Collection: Miss Caroline H. Rimmer, the artist's daughter, Boston.
Gift of Mrs. Henry Simonds. 23.183

A three-line inscription at the lower left of the painting appears to be Hebrew, Greek, and Punic script.

Reference: T.H. Bartlett, "Rimmer," *American Art Review*, 1879–1880, I, no. 2, p. 511.
Exhibitions: Boston, MFA, *Rimmer*, 1880, no. 10./ New York, Whitney Museum and Boston, MFA, *Rimmer*, 1946–1947, no. 25.

THEODORE ROBINSON (1852–1896), born in Irasburg, Vt., settled with his family in Evansville, Wisconsin in 1856. In 1874 he studied at the National Academy of Design, but two years later moved to Paris where he studied under Carolus-Duran and then Gérôme. He returned to New York in 1881 but was again in France in 1884 working largely at Barbizon and in association with Monet at Giverny where he actively absorbed the Impressionist style. He frequently traveled between New York and Europe until 1893, after which he worked in New York and New England. He was a founder and leader with Twachtman and Chase of the Impressionist-oriented Ten American Painters. He died in New York.

833.　　　　**Branch of the Seine, Giverny**

fig. 478

A view on the river Epte with lush growths of blue and blue-green shrubbery and trees overhanging and reflected in the blue and silvery water. A pale blue sky appears through the leaves beyond, and to the right stands the red-brown trunk of a tree.
Oil on canvas. 21¼ × 25½ in. (55 × 64.7 cm.)
Painted about 1888.
Collections: Discovered in loft of Hôtel Baudy, Giverny; Waldo Peirce, Newburyport, Mass.
Gift of Waldo Peirce. 67.345

THOMAS PRICHARD ROSSITER (1818–1871)

834.　　　　**Opening of the Wilderness**

fig. 286

Oil on canvas. 17¾ × 32½ in. (45.1 × 82.5 cm.)
Signed lower right: *T.P. Rossiter.* Inscribed in pencil on stretcher: *Opening of the Wilderness/ T.P. Rossiter.* Painted possibly about 1846–1850.
M. and M. Karolik Collection. 48.471
Reference: Karolik Catalogue, 1949, no. 207 (repr.).

ALBERT PINKHAM RYDER (1847–1917) was born in New Bedford, Mass., and although self-taught began to paint landscapes at an early age. About 1870 he moved permanently to New York, where he studied briefly at the National Academy of Design and informally with the portrait painter and engraver William E. Marshall. In 1877 he spent a month in London and toured England and western Europe in the summer of 1882. He again briefly visited London in 1887 and 1896. He was a founder of the Society of American Artists in 1877. He died in Elmhurst, L.I., N.Y. Ryder was the most important American Romantic painter of the late nineteenth century; his work was a foil to the Realist paintings of the other major figures of the period, Homer and Eakins.

835.　　　　**The Golden Hour**

fig. 431

The lake and sky are yellow-brown, with a white sailboat and some buildings to the left. In the foreground a woman, in red and blue, gathers herbs on the brown wooded bank.
Oil on canvas. 7½ × 12½ in. (19 × 31.7 cm.)
Signed lower right: *Ryder.* Painted before 1880.
Collections: C.B. Smith, the artist's nephew; Hiram Hyde Logan, Boston.
Bequest of Hiram Hyde Logan. 22.841

The detail, relative clarity of drawing, and placidity indicate an early date.
Reference: F.N. Price, Ryder, New York, 1932, no. 54.
Exhibition: Buffalo, Albright Art Gallery, American Artists, 1918, no. 77.

836.　　　　**Constance**

fig. 432

Constance and her son lie in a brown boat, adrift on a dark green sea. A yellow light surrounds them and touches the clouds in the green sky.
Oil on canvas. 28¼ × 36 in. (71.7 × 91.7 cm.)
Finished in 1896.
Collections: Sir William Van Horne, Montreal, before 1905; Lady Van Horne, Montreal, by 1918; Art Association of Montreal.
Abraham Shuman Fund. 45.770

Constance was the daughter of the Emperor of Rome and wife of the King of Northumberland. Through the jealousy of her mother-in-law, she and her baby son were treacherously abandoned at sea in a boat with neither rudder nor sail. However, miraculously safeguarded, after five years they reached Rome and future happiness. (Geoffrey Chaucer, *Canterbury Tales*, The Man of Law's Tale.) In a letter of 1896 to J. Alden Weir, Ryder said, "I have finished . . . Constance . . ." The Addison Gallery, Andover, Mass. owns an unfinished version, 27½ × 36 in.

References: S. Hartmann, *American Painting*, Boston, 1901, I, pp. 315–316./ J.L. French, "A Painter of Dreams," *Broadway Magazine*, Sept. 1905 (repr.)./ R.E. Fry, "The Art of Ryder," *Burlington Magazine*, 1908, XIII, no. LXI, p. 63 (pl. I)./ F.N. Price, *Ryder*, New York, 1932, p. xxi, no. 20 (repr.)./ L. Goodrich, *Ryder*, New York, 1959, pp. 19, 115, 121 (pls. 65–67)./ H. Dorra, "Ryder and Romantic Painting," *Art in America*, 1960, XLVIII, no. 4, p. 31 (repr.)./ L. Katz, "Emblems of Ryder," *Arts*, 1961, XXXV, no. 10, p. 52.

Exhibitions: Worcester, Mass., Art Museum, *15th Annual*, 1912, no. 43 (repr.)./ New York, Metropolitan Museum, *Ryder Memorial*, 1918, no. 43 (repr.)./ New York, Whitney Museum, *Ryder*, 1947, no. 5 (repr. p. 26)./ Boston, MFA, *American Marine Paintings*, 1955, no. 21 (repr.)./ Washington, D.C., Corcoran Gallery, *The American Muse*, 1959, no. 65./ New Bedford, Mass., Swain School of Design, W. Crapo Gallery, *Ryder-Bierstadt*, 1960, no. 4 (repr.)./ Washington, D.C., Corcoran Gallery, *Ryder Retrospective*, 1961, no. 56 (repr. p. 42).

ROBERT SALMON (1775–about 1845), son of Francis Salomon, was born in Whitehaven, Cumberland, England. He exhibited at the Royal Academy, London under the name of Salomon in 1802 and again at the Liverpool Academy in 1824. He worked in Liverpool from 1806 to 1811 and from 1822 to 1825; in Greenock, Scotland from 1811 to 1822 and in 1825–1826; and in North Shields, London, and Southampton from 1826 to 1828. He settled in Boston, as Robert Salmon, in 1828 and flourished there as a marine and ship painter, but returned to England in 1842. His last dated painting is of the Northumberland coast, in 1843. He died in England sometime before 1851 (a Boston newspaper of that time mentioned that he was no longer living).

837.
fig. 183

"Ceres," Privateer of Liverpool

A three-masted ship with a dark brown hull and white sails, flying the Union Jack and Red Ensign, sails broadside across the green water of a bay. About her are other similar vessels and rowboats; the shoreline is green under blue sky and white clouds.
Oil on canvas. 33¼ × 52½ in. (84.4 × 133.3 cm.)
Signed and dated lower right: *R.S. 1808.*
Gift of Henry R. Dalton. 43.28

The setting is probably the Mersey River, on which Liverpool is built. To the left, Bidston Hill appears on the horizon, sloping down to the Birkenhead Pool, now the Birkenhead Docks. On its top are the Signal Tower and a row of flagpoles, each pole representing, in those days, a ship owner or company. When the signalman on duty saw a ship crossing the bar, he hoisted the appropriate flag. The land to the right is now covered by New Brighton.

838.
fig. 184

Ship Aground

The black and red hull of a ship, masts broken and sails ripped, lies on a brown rocky beach before brown and green cliffs. The sea and sky are gray, and the men wear green, brown, and red.
Oil on panel. 10¼ × 14¼ in. (26 × 36.2 cm.)
Inscribed on back: *No. 557 Painted by Robert Salmon*. Painted in 1827.
Collection: Purchased from the artist by Francis Alexander, Boston.
Gift of Miss E.F.P. Holland. 11.3959

In his catalogue (*see below*) Salmon listed all the pictures from no. 426 to no. 574 as having been painted in London in 1827. The entry for *Ship Aground* reads: "No. 557. 1 day. 15 × 10. Ship aground, sold in Boston auction to Alexander, the painter 3¼ doll."

References: R. Salmon, "Catalogue of Pictures, 1806–1840" no. 557 (MS copied by Miss Daracott, 1881, after lost original, Boston Public Library)./ E.P. Richardson, *American Romantic Painting*, New York, 1945, no. 45 (repr.).

Exhibitions: Cambridge, Mass., Fogg Art Museum, *New England Genre*, 1939, no. 26./ Detroit Institute of Arts, *World of the Romantic Artist*, 1944–1945, no. 48.

839.   **The British Fleet Forming a Line off Algiers**

fig. 185

British men-of-war, brown and black with gray, white, and brown sails, maneuver on the gray-green water, with various ships and boats sailing among them. White and gray clouds are in the blue sky, and the distant shoreline is green.

Distemper on canvas. 99 × 190¼ in. (251.4 × 483.2 cm.)

Signed and dated lower right: *R.S. 1829.*

Collection: Dr. Charles Eliot Ware, Boston.

Bequest of Miss Mary Lee Ware. 37.500

Recorded in Salmon's catalogue (*see below*) as: "Commenced 1829 no. 630. The second sean for sellf begun the first Janewary, finished 30. View of the British fleet forming the line in the vicinity of Algears. 30 Days in Boston." He painted five of these huge canvases during his first year in Boston: the first, a *View of the Market Row*, was commissioned by the Boston Theatre as a "Drop Scene." Another, *View of Boston from Pemberton Hall* (Harrison Gray Otis House, Boston) may have been a drop scene. The three others: this one, a *View of Allgears* (list no. 629) and a *Nite Battell at Algears and the Algerean Fleet on Fire* (list no. 623), both unlocated, were probably intended to form a panorama. The bombardment of Algiers in 1816, during the suppression of the Barbary States by the British Fleet, was under Sir Edward Pellew, Lord Exmouth, with the aid of a Dutch squadron.

References: R. Salmon, "Catalogue of Pictures, 1806–1840" no. 630 (MS copied by Miss Daracott, 1881, after lost original, Boston Public Library)./ W.G. Constable, "The British Fleet at Algiers, 1816," *MFA Bulletin*, 1943, XLI, no. 243, pp. 2–7 (fig. 1).

840.   **South Sea Whale Fishing**

fig. 186

Several whaling vessels, flying the American flag, have reached whaling grounds in midocean. The small open boats have been lowered, filled with sailors who have harpooned their whales and are towing them back to the ship. The water is green, the sky clouded.

Oil on panel. 16½ × 23¾ in. (41.9 × 60.3 cm.)

Signed and dated lower right: *R.S. 1831.* Inscribed on back: *No. 718/ Painted by/ R. Salmon/ 1831.*

Collections: Commissioned from the artist by Josiah Putnam Bradlee, Boston, 1831; Joseph P.B. Henshaw, his nephew, Boston.

Gift of Joseph P.B. Henshaw. 27.356

The entry in Salmon's catalogue (*see below*) reads: "No. 718—13 Day. 24 × 16½ South Sea Whale fishing for Mr. Bradlee. $50." Salmon is not known to have sailed with the whaling fleet.

References: R. Salmon, "Catalogue of Pictures, 1806–1840" no. 718 (MS copied by Miss Daracott, 1881, after lost original, Boston Public Library)./ C.D. Childs, "Salmon," *Old Time New England*, 1938, XXVIII, no. 3, p. 97 (fig. 3)./ E.P. Richardson, *American Romantic Painting*, New York, 1945, no. 46 (repr.)./ C.D. Childs, "Marine Painting—Flood Tide," *Antiques*, 1954, LXVI, no. 1 (repr. p. 54).

Exhibitions: Detroit Institute of Arts, *Five Centuries of Marine Painting*, 1942, no. 94 (pl. 12, incorrectly dated 1835)./ —, *World of the Romantic Artist*, 1944–1945, no. 49 (incorrectly dated 1835)./ Brooklyn Museum, *The Coast and The Sea*, 1948–1949, no. 104./ Williamstown, Mass., Lawrence Art Museum, *American Art*, 1960, checklist p. 5.

841.   **South Sea Whale Fishing II**

Four three-masted vessels, brown and black with gray sails, lie on a green and gray sea under gray sky. In the foreground, men in two dorys, wearing brown, gray, red, and black, battle a black whale.

Oil on panel. 16½ × 24 in. (41.9 × 61 cm.)
Signed and dated lower right: *R S 1831.* Inscribed on back: *No. 719/ Painted by R. Salmon/ 1831.*
Collections: Commissioned from the artist by Josiah Putnam Bradlee, Boston, 1831; Samuel Henshaw, his nephew, Boston; Miss Gertrude Thurston, Cambridge.
Gift of Miss Gertrude Thurston in memory of Samuel Henshaw. 45.233
The entry in Salmon's catalogue (*see below*) reads: "No. 719. 18 Day. 24 by 16½. South Sea Whale Fishing for Mr. Bradlee. $50."
References: R. Salmon, "Catalogue of Pictures, 1806–1840" no. 719 (MS copied by Miss Daracott, 1881, after lost original, Boston Public Library)./ J. Wilmerding, "A New Look at Robert Salmon," *Antiques*, New York, 1965, LXXXVII, no. 1, p. 91 (fig. 3).
Exhibition: Vancouver Art Gallery, *Of Ships and the Sea*, 1963, no. 25.

842.

fig. 187

The New Ship "Duncan"

A three-masted vessel with a black hull and white sails lies anchored broadside in green water and flies the American flag. Other brown boats and vessels with gray sails are about her, before a green coast and under blue sky with gray clouds.
Oil on panel. 16¼ × 24 in. (41.2 × 61 cm.)
Signed and dated lower right: *R S 1832.* Inscribed on back: *No. 725/ Painted by R. Salmon/ 1832.*
Gift of William R. Langdon. 48.1164
The entry in Salmon's catalogue (*see below*) is: "No. 725. 12 Day 24 × 16½. The New Ship Duncan on specu. Solld and paid. $30.00." The *Duncan* was built at Hingham, Mass. in 1832 by Leavitt Souther. The original owners were Benjamin L. Reed and William B. Reynolds *et al.* of Boston. She was sold in New York and on Sept. 18, 1846 left New York for Glasgow, but was never heard from again.
Reference: R. Salmon, "Catalogue of Pictures, 1806–1840" no. 725 (MS copied by Miss Daracott, 1881, after lost original, Boston Public Library).

843.

Plymouth Sound, England

Oil on panel. 9½ × 12¼ in. (24.1 × 31.1 cm.)
Signed and dated on back: *Painted by R. Salmon/ 1837.*
M. and M. Karolik Collection. 48.472
Reference: Karolik Catalogue, 1949, no. 208 (repr.).

844.

Rocks at Nahant: Swallow's Cove

A small green cove, surrounded by brown and black cliffs, lies under a blue sky with white and gray clouds. In the foreground, brightly clothed people are in a boat with a white sail; others fish from the rocks.
Oil on panel. 7½ × 9½ in. (19 × 24.1 cm.)
Inscribed on back of panel: *No. 23/ Painted by R. Salmon/ 1839.*
Bequest of Mrs. Arthur Croft. 01.6219
In his catalogue (*see below*), Salmon recorded: "No. 23. November 1839. 10 × 8. 2 day. Rocks at Nahant, Swallow's Cove." No. 23 actually is no. 1023; when Salmon reached one thousand he simply began again with number one. Swallow's Cove is within a few miles of Boston on the North Shore.
References: R. Salmon, "Catalogue of Pictures, 1806–1840" no. 23 (MS copied by Miss Daracott, 1881, after lost original, Boston Public Library)./ J. Wilmerding, "A New Look at Robert Salmon," *Antiques*, New York, 1965, LXXXVII, no. 1, p. 91 (fig. 4).

845.

Storm at Sea

Oil on panel. 16½ × 24¼ in. (41.9 × 61.6 cm.)
Signed and dated on the back: *No. 44/ Painted by R. Salmon/ 1840.*
M. and M. Karolik Collection. 48.473
Reference: Karolik Catalogue, 1949, no. 209 (repr.).

846.

fig. 188

Rainsford's Island, Boston Harbor

Oil on panel. 16 × 24 in. (40.6 × 61 cm.)
Painted about 1840.
M. and M. Karolik Collection. 48.474
Reference: *Karolik Catalogue*, 1949, no. 210 (repr.).

HENRY SARGENT (1770–1845), born in Gloucester, Mass., was taken to Boston in 1779 and trained there for a mercantile career. He chose to paint, however, and from 1793 to 1799 studied with Benjamin West in London. On his return he settled permanently in Boston and worked as a painter of portraits, religious, and genre scenes. He was also active as a militia officer, politician, and inventor.

847.

Watson and the Shark

A gray shark in the foreground attacks the nude boy, while men, clothed in white, gray, brown, or black defend him from a brown boat. The sea is green and gray, the ships and harbor buildings are brown and gray under pink and gray clouds.
Oil on canvas. 18¾ × 23½ in. (47.6 × 59.7 cm.)
Painted about 1789.
Collection: Winthrop Henry Sargent, grandson of the artist, Boston.
Gift of Mrs. Winthrop Sargent. 16.346

The painting was copied from Valentine Green's mezzotint engraving (1779) after Copley's *Watson and the Shark* (Cat. no. 299) when Sargent was studying in Boston about 1789.
Reference: W. Dunlap, *History of the Arts of Design*, Boston, 1918, II, p. 191.

848.

fig. 151

Self-Portrait

Seated in three-quarter length and left profile, the young man faces front and wears a black coat and white neckcloth; he holds a pen and an open brown book. The armchair is upholstered in green before a brown background.
Oil on canvas. 33¾ × 27¼ in. (85.7 × 69.2 cm.)
Painted about 1795.
Collections: Winthrop Henry Sargent, the artist's grandson, Boston; Mrs. Horatio A. Lamb, his sister-in-law, Milton, Mass.; Aimée Lamb, her daughter, Boston.
Gift of Miss Aimée Lamb in memory of Winthrop Sargent. 52.357
Reference: J. DeW. Addison, "Henry Sargent, A Boston Painter," *Art in America*, 1929, XLII, no. 6.

849.

fig. 152

Boy on a Hobby Horse

The child wears a blue suit with a white ruffled collar, a brown hat adorned with a white feather, and rides on a rearing brown horse with red trappings. Below, a brown stool overturned on the brown, red, and gray oriental rug, and behind right, red drapery before a brown wall. Through a window and beyond a gray-brown urn and green leaves is a blue sky with yellow clouds.
Oil on panel. 63 × 50½ in. (160.6 × 128.2 cm.)
Painted about 1817–1818.
Collections: Winthrop Henry Sargent, the artist's grandson, Boston; Mrs. Horatio A. Lamb, his sister-in-law, Milton, Mass., 1918; Aimée Lamb, her daughter, Boston.
Gift of Miss Aimée Lamb in memory of Winthrop Sargent. 58.1364

The boy is perhaps Henry Winthrop Sargent (1810–1881), son of the artist and his wife Hannah Welles Sargent: He strongly resembles his younger brother John (Cat. no. 850) and wears a similar costume. The portrait is dated from his apparent age.
Exhibition: Boston, Harding's Gallery, *1st Exhibition*, 1842, no. 39.

850.

fig. 155

John Turner Welles Sargent

Half-length, the child turns three-quarters right, and wears a dark blue jacket and waistcoat with a large white ruffled collar. The background is red.

Oil on panel. 23¼ × 19¼ in. (59 × 48.9 cm.)
Painted about 1819.

Collections: Winthrop Henry Sargent, the artist's grandson, Boston; Mrs. Horatio A. Lamb, his sister-in-law, Milton, Mass.

Gift of Mrs. Horatio A. Lamb in memory of Mr. and Mrs. Winthrop Sargent. 19.14

John Turner Welles Sargent, born in Dorchester, Mass. in 1813, was the son of the artist and his wife Hannah Welles Sargent. He married Harriet Lydia Boardman in 1841 and died in Boston in 1877. According to a label on the back of the portrait it was painted about 1819, which agrees with his apparent age. His brother is portrayed in Cat. no. 849.

References: F.W. Bayley, "Sargent," *Little Known Early American Portrait Painters*, Boston, 1916–1919, no. 2 (repr.)./ J.DeW. Addison, "Henry Sargent, a Boston Painter," *Art in America*, 1929, XVII, no. 6, p. 279.

851.

fig. 153

The Dinner Party

Beyond a brown arched doorway is a light brown interior with red curtains, brown paintings in gold frames, brass ornaments, and two carpets, one patterned in red, blue, and brown lying under a blue one. Eighteen gentlemen, wearing brown or blue, with two servants attending, sit at a table laden with bowls of fruit, wine bottles, and glasses.

Oil on canvas. 59½ × 48 in. (151.1 × 121.9 cm.)
Painted about 1821.

Collections: D.L. Brown, Boston, 1821; Winthrop Henry Sargent, the artist's grandson, Boston; Mrs. Winthrop Sargent, Boston; Mrs. Horatio A. Lamb, her sister, Milton, Mass.

Gift of Mrs. Horatio A. Lamb in memory of Mr. and Mrs. Winthrop Sargent. 19.13

Said to represent the dining room of the artist's house at 10 Franklin Place, Boston, during a gathering of the Wednesday Evening Club. A letter dated Sept. 17, 1821 (Archives of American Art, Detroit) from the artist to John Trumbull, indicates that the painting was done shortly before the letter was written.

References: W. Dunlap, *History of the Arts of Design*, Boston, 1918, II, pp. 195–196./ J.DeW. Addison, "Henry Sargent, a Boston Painter," *Art in America*, 1929, XVII, no. 6, pp. 280–284 (repr. p. 281)./ A. Burroughs, *Limners and Likenesses*, Cambridge, Mass., 1936, p. 116 (fig. 96)./ J.W. Lane, "Survey of 160 Years of American Painting," *Art News*, 1940, XXXIX, no. 4, p. 15 (repr. p. 13)./ R. Ralston, "19th Century New York Interiors," *Antiques*, 1943, XLIII, no. 6 (repr. p. 266)./ E.P. Richardson, *American Romantic Painting*, New York, 1945, no. 2 (repr.)./ V. Barker, *American Painting*, New York, 1950, p. 296./ M.B. Cowdrey, "Paintings as Documents," *Antiques*, 1950, LVIII, no. 5, p. 373 (repr. p. 372)./ J.T. Flexner, "Early Nineteenth Century American Genre," *Antiques*, 1954, LXVI, no. 3, p. 198./ —, *Light of Distant Skies*, New York, 1954, p. 198 (fig. 81)./ E.P. Richardson, *Painting in America*, New York, 1956, p. 129 (fig. 50)./ H. Sprackling, "The Artist Sets the Table," *Art in America*, 1959, XLVII, no. 3, pp. 69–70 (repr. p. 68).

Exhibitions: Boston, Harding's Gallery, *1st Exhibition*, 1842, no. 38./ New York, Whitney Museum, *American Genre*, 1925, no. 91./ New York, Rochester Memorial Art Gallery, *American Life*, 1935, no. 31./ Pittsburgh, Pa., Carnegie Institute, *Survey of American Painting*, 1940, no. 108 (pl. 37)./ Washington, D.C., Corcoran Gallery, *American Processional*, 1950, no. 120 (repr. p. 106)./ New York, American Federation of Arts, circulated in Germany and Italy, and Whitney Museum, *American Painting in the Nineteenth Century*, 1953–1954, no. 81 (repr.)./ Detroit Institute of Arts and San Francisco, M.H. de Young Memorial Museum, *Painting in America, the Story of 450 Years*, 1957, no. 59./ Washington, D.C., Corcoran Gallery, *The American Muse*, 1959, no. 103.

852.

fig. 154

The Tea Party

Framed by green drapery, a brown candlelit drawing room, hung with gold-framed paintings, contains gilded Empire furniture and a rug patterned in green and yellow. The men, wearing black coats and yellow breeches, converse with ladies who wear predominantly blue gowns with red or pink shawls.

Oil on canvas. 64¼ × 52¼ in. (163.8 × 132.7 cm.)
Painted about 1821–1825.
Collections: D.L. Brown, Boston, in 1828 and 1834; Winthrop
Sargent. the artist's grandson, Boston; Mrs. Horatio A. Lamb, his
in-law, Milton, Mass.
Gift of Mrs. Horatio A. Lamb in memory of Mr. and Mrs. Winthrop Sargent.

Although the scene is said to be the fashionable home of Henry Sargen
10 Franklin Place, Boston, the style of the furnishings, which is Emp
is quite unlike the Hepplewhite furnishings in the Federal interior seen
the *Dinner Party* (Cat. no. 851). The great success of that painting ma
have prompted Sargent to paint this work as a sequel presented in term
of the latest fashion, but not necessarily drawn from a specific setting.

References: W. Dunlap, *History of the Arts of Design*, Boston, 1918, II, p. 196./ J.DeW.
Addison, "Henry Sargent, a Boston Painter," *Art in America*, 1929, XVII, no. 6, pp.
280–284 (repr. p. 281)./ V. Barker, "Painting of the Middle Range," *Magazine of
Art*, 1934, XXVII, no. 5 (repr. p. 239)./ A. Burroughs, *Limners and Likenesses*, Cambridge, Mass., 1936, p. 116./ D. Adlow, "Boston, 1630–1872," *Magazine of Art*,
1943, XXXVI, no. 7 (repr. cover)./ R. Ralston, "19th Century New York Interiors,"
Antiques, 1943, XLIII, no. 6 (repr. p. 266)./ E.P. Richardson, *American Romantic Painting*, New York, 1945, no. 3 (repr.)./ V. Barker, *American Painting*, New York, 1950,
p. 297 (pl. 37)./ J.T. Flexner, "Early Nineteenth Century American Genre,"
Antiques, 1954, LXVI, no. 3, p. 198 (repr.)./ —, *Light of Distant Skies*, New York, 1954,
p. 198 (fig. 81)./ E.P. Richardson, *Painting in America*, New York, 1956, p. 129.
Exhibitions: Boston Athenaeum, *Exhibition*, 1828, no. 161./ New York, Rochester
Memorial Art Gallery, *American Life*, 1935, no. 32./ New York, Whitney Museum,
American Genre, 1935, no. 92./ Columbus, O., Columbus Gallery, *The Colonial
Americas*, 1947, no. 11./ Newark, N.J., Newark Museum, *American Portraits and
Landscape Painting*, 1957, no. 31./ —, *Classical America, 1815–1845*, 1963, no. 286
(repr. frontispiece).

JOHN SINGER SARGENT (1856–1925) was born in Florence of American parents. After
early travels with them to Nice, London, Madrid, and Rome, he was a
student of the Academy of Fine Arts in Florence in 1870. The year 1871–
1872 he spent in Dresden and in 1874 he visited Venice, where he received
encouragement from Whistler. His parents settled in Paris that year and
he attended the École des Beaux Arts and entered the studio of Carolus-
Duran. In 1876 he traveled in the eastern United States, the first of many
visits. He later traveled in Italy, Spain, and Holland, studying the work of
Hals and Velasquez, and in 1885 he settled in London. By 1916 he had completed his murals for the Boston Public Library and received a commission
for murals for the Rotunda of the MFA. When he completed these murals
in 1921, more were commenced for the stairway. He died in London. He
was one of the most fashionable portrait painters of Boston, New York, and
London at the time; his watercolors and paintings of genre and landscape
received high acclaim then as well as now.

853.
fig. 450

Rehearsal of the Pasdeloup Orchestra at the Cirque d'Hiver
*Seen from above, the musicians, wearing black tailcoats and top hats, and gathered
in a semicircle, play instruments of brown, white, and black. The stage is gray and
brown.*
Oil on canvas. 21¾ × 18¼ in. (55.2 × 46.3 cm.)
Inscribed lower right: *rehearsal at the Cirque/ d'Hiver/ John S. Sargent*. Painted
in 1876.
Collections: Acquired from the artist by Henry Bacon, London; Mrs. Henry
Bacon, London, 1912.
Charles Henry Hayden Fund. 22.598
The date for the painting is given by Charteris (*see below*). The conductor
Jules Étienne Pasdeloup's orchestra held rehearsals in the Cirque d'Hiver
for the popular concerts given at the Théâtre des Champs Elysées, Paris.

The MFA has a small pencil drawing for the silk hats and bass viols. An oil version, of the same year, signed and inscribed *to G. Henschel*, is in a private collection, Chicago. Several other drawings (unlocated) were in the Grand Central Art Galleries exhibition in 1928.

References: H. Bacon, *Parisian Art*, Boston, 1883 (repr. p. 202)./ W.H. Downes, *Sargent*, Boston, 1925, p. 119./ E. Charteris, *Sargent*, New York, 1927, pp. 43, 223, 280 (repr. opp. p. 32)./ J.P. Leeper, "Sargent—A Revaluation," *Magazine of Art*, 1951, XLIV, no. 1 (repr. p. 13)./ C.M. Mount, *Sargent*, New York, 1955, p. 442./ J. Simon, "Too Many Sargents?" *Arts*, 1964, XXXVIII, no. 10, p. 21 (repr. p. 20).

Exhibitions: Boston, Copley Hall, *Sargent*, 1899, no. 92./ Boston, MFA, *Sargent Memorial*, 1925, no. 3./ New York, Metropolitan Museum, *Sargent Memorial*, 1926, no. 1 (repr.)./ Hartford, Conn., Wadsworth Atheneum, *American Painting and Sculpture of the 18th, 19th and 20th Centuries*, 1935, no. 33 (repr.)./ —, *Off for the Holidays*, 1955, no. 73./ San Francisco, M.H. de Young Memorial Museum and California Palace of the Legion of Honor, *American Painting*, 1935, no. 119./ Washington, D.C., Corcoran Gallery, *The American Muse*, 1959, no. 13./ New York, American Academy of Arts and Letters, *Impressionist Mood in American Painting*, 1959, no. 24./ Paris, Centre Culturel Americain, *Sargent*, 1963, no. 1 (pl. 1)./ Washington, D.C., Corcoran Gallery and circulated in the U.S., *Private World of John Singer Sargent*, 1964–1965, no. 1 (repr.).

854.

fig. 453

Low Tide at Cancale Harbor

Painted in brown, gray, and white, in the foreground a boy lies on the quay beside a sailboat. Beyond the beach, sailboats are gathered under cloudy sky.

Oil on canvas. 18¾ × 11 in. (47.6 × 27.9 cm.)

Signed and dated lower right: *John S. Sargent/ 1878*. Painted in 1877.

Collection: Mr. and Mrs. Henry Hall Sherman, Boston, before 1916.

Zoe Oliver Sherman Collection. 22.646

References: W.H. Downes, *Sargent*, Boston, 1925, pp. 8, 121./ E. Charteris, *Sargent*, New York, 1927, p. 280./ C.M. Mount, *Sargent*, New York, 1955, p. 442.

Exhibitions: Boston, MFA, *Sargent Memorial*, 1925, no. 5./ Washington, D.C., Corcoran Gallery and circulated in the U.S., *Private World of John Singer Sargent*, 1964–1965, no. 3.

855.

fig. 451

Capri

The olive grove is a soft gray-green, the foliage touched with brown, and there are yellow flowers in the green grass. A girl, wearing a pink skirt with a blue bodice and white blouse, leans against a tree beside a stone wall under a white sky.

Oil on canvas. 30¼ × 25 in. (76.8 × 63.5 cm.)

Signed and dated lower right: *John S. Sargent/ Capri. 1878.*

Collections: Ichabod T. Williams, New York; *E.M. Anderson Collection Sale*, The Plaza, New York, Feb. 16, 1922, no. 6; Mrs. Francis A. Neilson, New York, 1922.

Bequest of Helen Swift Neilson. 46.10

Sargent worked for some weeks in the fall of 1878 in the monastery of Santa Teresa, Capri, and had as a model the noted beauty Rosina, a girl from Anacapri. A study for the head was owned by Mrs. Francis Ormond, the artist's sister, in London, and a version of the subject entitled *A Capri Girl*, 1878, exhibited as *Dans les Oliviers—à Capri* at the Paris Salon of 1879, is owned by Mrs. Walter Binger, New York.

References: W.H. Downes, *Sargent*, Boston, 1925, pp. 122, 261./ E. Charteris, *Sargent*, New York, 1927, pp. 48, 280./ C.M. Mount, *Sargent*, New York, 1955, p. 442.

Exhibitions: Utica, N.Y., Munson-Williams-Proctor Institute, *Expatriates*, 1953, no. 28./ Palm Beach, Fla., Society of the Four Arts, *Sargent-Cassatt*, 1959, no. 2.

856.

fig. 452

Oyster Gatherers of Cancale

Women and children, clothed in gray, brown, white, blue, or black, walk across a light brown beach with puddles reflecting the blue sky. Behind, left, the sea and sky are blue; the lighthouse to the right and clouds are gray and white.

Oil on canvas. 16¼ × 23¾ in. (41.2 × 60.3 cm.)

Signed lower right: *J.S. Sargent/ Paris*. Painted about 1878.
Collections: Purchased from the artist by Samuel Colman, Newport, R.I., and New York; Mary Appleton, Boston, before 1905.
Gift of Mary Appleton. 35.708
A larger, finished version of *Oyster Gatherers* (Corcoran Gallery, Washington, D.C.) signed and dated 1878, was exhibited in the Paris Salon of 1878 as *En Route pour le Pêche*. Our painting was probably painted the same year. The histories of these two paintings and that of the *Mussel Gatherers* (Mrs. John E. Jenkins), belonging in 1924 to Mrs. Carroll Beckwith, have been confused by both Downes and Charteris.
References: "Young Painters of America," *Scribner's Monthly*, 1880, XX, no. 1, p. 12 (engr. p. 7)./ W.H. Downes, *Sargent*, Boston, 1925, pp. 8, 120./ E. Charteris, *Sargent*, New York, 1927, p. 281./ C.M. Mount, *Sargent*, New York, 1955, p. 442.
Exhibitions: Boston, MFA, *Sargent Memorial*, 1925, no. 13./ Palm Beach, Fla., Society of the Four Arts, *Sargent-Cassatt*, 1959, no. 3 (repr.).

857.
fig. 460

Robert de Cévrieux

Full-length and facing front, a small boy stands holding a black and brown dog; his black suit has white cuffs and collar, with a red necktie and socks. The carpet is red and blue; the curtain behind, green.
Oil on canvas. 33½ × 19¼ in. (85.1 × 48.9 cm.)
Signed and dated lower left: *John S. Sargent. 1879.*
Charles Henry Hayden Fund. 22.372

The portrait was painted in Paris, where Sargent was studying, and remained in the sitter's possession until shortly before its purchase by the MFA.
References: W.H. Downes, *Sargent*, Boston, 1925, p. 123./ E. Charteris, *Sargent*, New York, 1927, p. 49./ C.M. Mount, *Sargent*, New York, 1955, p. 428./ —, "Carolus-Duran and the Development of Sargent," *Art Quarterly*, 1963, XXVI, no. 4, p. 393 (fig. 9).
Exhibition: Boston, MFA, *Sargent Memorial*, 1925, no. 6.

858.
fig. 454

The Daughters of Edward D. Boit

Three young girls in black stockings and dark red dresses, all with white pinafores, stand in a brown room; the two eldest are in the background between huge blue and white vases and a red screen. A fourth child, in white, sits in the foreground on the gray-green patterned rug and holds a doll dressed in pink.
Oil on canvas. 87 × 87 in. (221 × 221 cm.)
Signed and dated lower right: *John S. Sargent. 1882.*
Collection: Edward Darley Boit, Paris, 1882.
Gift of Mary Louisa Boit, Florence D. Boit, Jane Hubbard Boit, and Julia Overing Boit, in memory of their father. 19.124

The names of the four daughters are listed above in the order in which they appear in the painting, from left to right: Mary, born in Paris in 1874, died unmarried in Newport, R.I. in 1945; Florence, born in Newport in 1868, unmarried, died in Paris in 1919; Jane (1870–1955) was born in Newport, and unmarried, died in Greenwich, Conn.; Julia, born in Enghien, France in 1878, now lives in Newport. Edward Boit of Boston was a painter and close friend of Sargent; his children were portrayed in the drawing room of his Paris residence.
References: *Art Amateur*, 1883, IX, no. 3, p. 46./ H. James, "Sargent," *Harper's New Monthly Magazine*, 1887, LXXV, no. 49, pp. 684, 688–689 (engr. p. 690)./ —, *Picture and Text*, New York, 1893, pp. 97, 104–106./ W.A. Coffin, "Sargent," *Century Magazine*, 1895, LII, no. 2, p. 175 (as *Portraits of Children*)./ A.L. Baldry, "Sargent," *International Studio*, 1900, X, no. 37, pp. 18–19./ W.H. Downes, *Twelve Great Artists*, Boston, 1900, p. 172./ R. Cortissoz, "Sargent," *Scribner's Magazine*, 1903, XXXIV, no. 5, p. 528./ A.C. Meynell, *Sargent*, London, 1903 (repr.)./ J.W. McSpadden, *Famous Painters of America*, New York, 1907, p. 291 (as *The Hall of Children*)./ *MFA Bulletin*, 1912, X, no. 57, p. 21./ L.M. Bryant, *American Pictures and Their Painters*,

New York, 1917, pp. 158–159 (fig. 114)./ *MFA Bulletin*, 1919, XVII, no. 103, p. 49 (repr.)./ N. Pousette-Dart, *Sargent*, New York, 1924 (repr.)./ W.H. Downes, *Sargent*, Boston, 1925, pp. 10, 11, 103 (repr. p. 40)./ E. Charteris, *Sargent*, New York, 1927, pp. 57–58, 258./ J.B. Mason and A.C. Meynell, *Sargent*, London, 1927 (repr.)./ F.W. Paris, *Hall of American Artists*, New York, 1944, III, p. 70./ R.H.I. Gammell, *Twilight in Painting*, New York, 1946 (pls. 48, 49)./ E.P. Richardson, "Sophisticates and Innocents Abroad," *Art News*, 1954, LIII, no. 2 (repr. p. 61)./ C.M. Mount, *Sargent*, New York, 1955, p. 429./ E.P. Richardson, *Painting in America*, New York, 1956, p. 282./ P. Jeannerat, "A Viewing from the Thames," *Art in America*, 1960, XLVIII, no. 2 (repr. p. 25)./ C.M. Mount, "Carolus-Duran and the Development of Sargent," *Art Quarterly*, 1963, XXVI, no. 4, p. 401 (fig. 14).

Exhibitions: Paris, Salon, 1883, no. 2165./ Boston, St. Botolph Club, *Sargent*, 1888./ Boston, MFA, *Sargent Memorial*, 1925, no. 20 (repr.)./ New York, Metropolitan Museum, *Sargent Memorial*, 1926, no. 7 (repr.)./ Chicago Art Institute and New York, Metropolitan Museum, *Sargent, Whistler and Mary Cassatt*, 1954, no. 47 (repr. p. 50)./ Boston, MFA, *Sargent's Boston*, 1956, no. 14 (repr. cover and p. 30)./ New York, Wildenstein and Co., *The American Vision*, 1957, no. 17 (repr.).

859.

fig. 455

Edith, Lady Playfair (Edith Russell)

Three-quarter length, she stands turned three-quarters right and holds a blue and gray vase full of orange and yellow chrysanthemums on a brown table beside her. Yellow bows adorn her full black skirt and yellow bodice, and she wears a black choker. The background is patterned brown and yellow.

Oil on canvas. 60 × 39 in. (152.4 × 99 cm.)

Signed and dated upper left: *John S. Sargent. 1884.*

Bequest of Edith, Lady Playfair. 33.530

Edith Russell was the daughter of Samuel Hammond Russell, whose portrait by Frederic Vinton (Cat. no. 997) is also in the MFA, and in 1878 married Sir Lyon Playfair. He was Professor of Chemistry at the University of Edinburgh, later Postmaster General, Chairman of the Ways and Means Committee, and Deputy Speaker in the House of Commons. He died in 1898, and in 1901 Lady Playfair married Robert Fleming Crooks of London and St. Andrews, Scotland. She died in 1932. A smaller portrait of her, painted by Sargent in 1886, is owned by Mason Hammond, Cambridge, Mass.

References: H. James, "Sargent," *Harper's New Monthly Magazine*, 1887, LXXV, no. 49, p. 691./ —, *Picture and Text*, New York, 1893, p. 104./ A.L. Baldry, "Sargent," *International Studio*, 1900, X, no. 37, p. 21./ W.H. Downes, *Sargent*, Boston, 1925, pp. 23, 139./ E. Charteris, *Sargent*, New York, 1927, pp. 73, 96, 259./ "Notable Sargent Goes to Boston," *Art News*, 1933, XXXI, no. 40, p. 6./ "An Early Sargent for Boston," *Art Digest*, 1933, VIII, no. 2, p. 15./ G. Pène du Bois, "Art and the Decline of the Bourgeoisie," *Magazine of Art*, 1944, XXXVII, no. 6, p. 221 (repr.)./ C.M. Mount, *Sargent*, New York, 1955, p. 430.

Exhibitions: London, Royal Academy, 1885, no. 586./ Boston, St. Botolph Club, *Sargent*, 1888./ Boston, Copley Hall, *Sargent*, 1899, no. 33./ London, Royal Academy, *Sargent*, 1926, no. 337 (repr. p. 91)./ San Francisco, California Palace of the Legion of Honor, *Sargent and Boldini*, 1959, no. 3 (repr.)./ Palm Beach, Fla., Society of the Four Arts, *Sargent-Cassatt*, 1959, no. 4.

860.

fig. 461

Mrs. Edward D. Boit (Mary Louisa Cushing)

Full-length, seated on a gilt settee, she turns three-quarters left before a dark brown background. Her dress is pink with black dots. She wears a black jacket with a dark blue shawl and a pink feather hat.

Oil on canvas. 60¼ × 42 in. (153 × 106.7 cm.)

Signed lower right: *John S. Sargent.* Painted in 1888.

Collection: Daughters of the sitter, 1894.

Gift of Miss Julia Overing Boit. 63.2688

Mary Louisa Cushing (1845–1894), daughter of John and Mary Gardiner Cushing, was born in Boston. She married the artist Edward Darley Boit in 1864, lived in Newport, R.I. until 1871, then in Paris and Biarritz, until her death in Dinard, France. She was portrayed early in 1888, when Sargent stayed with her family during a winter visit to Boston. Her four children are represented in the painting by Sargent, *The Daughters of Edward D. Boit* (Cat. no. 858).

References: A.C. Meynell, *Sargent*, London, 1903 (repr.)./ W.H. Downes, *Sargent*, Boston, 1925, pp. 24, 148./ E. Charteris, *Sargent*, New York, 1927, pp. 97, 174./ C.M. Mount, *Sargent*, New York, 1955, pp. 115, 431.

Exhibitions: Boston, St. Botolph Club, *Sargent*, 1888./ London, Royal Academy, 1888, no. 432./ —, *Sargent*, 1926, no. 280./ Boston, MFA, *Sargent's Boston*, 1956, no. 13 (fig. 11).

861.   **Pagan Deities**

On a blue background is a composition of pagan symbols in yellow and brown, green, white, gray, and blue.
Oil on canvas. 52 × 12½ in. (132.1 × 31.7 cm.)
Painted between 1890 and 1919.
Gift of Mrs. Francis Ormond, the artist's sister. 37.46

This painting and *Frieze of the Prophets* (Cat. no. 866) are preliminary sketches for the Boston Public Library murals. "In 1891 Sargent made a journey to Egypt and Greece for the purpose of studying the ancient pictorial and plastic conceptions of the gods and goddesses of idolatry and polytheism—Neith, Pharoah, the Assyrian King, Pasht, the Sphinx, Thammuz, Astarte, Moloch, Isis, Isiris, and Horus—that were to be introduced in the lunette and ceiling at the north end of the hall in the Boston Library . . ." (W.H. Downes, *Sargent*, Boston, 1925, pp. 34–35.)

Exhibition: Boston, MFA, *Sargent's Boston*, 1956, no. 70.

862.   **Door of a Mosque**
fig. 457

Arab women, in brown and white robes, walk on a gray paving before the yellow and gray facade of a mosque with its black doorway.
Oil on canvas. 25 × 31½ in. (63.5 × 80 cm.)
Painted about 1891.
Gift of Mrs. Francis Ormond, the artist's sister. 37.50

This study, *Head of an Arab* (Cat. no. 863), and *Two Architectural Views* (Cat. no. 864) were probably painted during Sargent's visit to Egypt and adjacent countries in 1890 and 1891.

Exhibition: Palm Beach, Fla., Society of the Four Arts, *Sargent-Cassatt*, 1959, no. 8.

863.   **Head of an Arab**

A bearded, brown-skinned man, half-length and facing front, wears a gray and white turban with a yellow robe. The background is gray.
Oil on canvas. 31½ × 23¼ in. (80 × 59 cm.)
Painted about 1891.
Gift of Mrs. Francis Ormond, the artist's sister. 37.49

Reference: W.H. Downes, *Sargent*, Boston, 1925, pp. 35, 166 (as *Bedouin Arab*).

Exhibitions: Boston, Copley Hall, *Sargent*, 1899, no. 68 (as *Sketch of a Bedouin Arab*)./ Palm Beach, Fla., Society of the Four Arts, *Sargent-Cassatt*, 1959, no. 9./ Washington, D.C., Corcoran Gallery and circulated in the U.S., *Private World of John Singer Sargent*, 1964–1965, no. 54.

864.   **Two Architectural Views**

Painted in blue, green, and brown, the interior and exterior views are adjacent. The former has arched windows and doorway; the latter, steps leading to an arched and columned facade standing by trees and before mountains.
Oil on canvas. 31½ × 25½ in. (80 × 64.8 cm.)
Painted about 1891.
Gift of Mrs. Francis Ormond, the artist's sister. 37.48

Exhibition: Palm Beach, Fla., Society of the Four Arts, *Sargent-Cassatt*, 1959, no. 23.

865.

fig. 456

Miss Helen Sears (Mrs. J. D. Cameron Bradley)

A small girl, dressed all in white, stands full-length before a copper bowl of blue, lavender, and white hydrangeas. The carpet is dark red, and behind her is a blue and yellow curtain before a brown background.

Oil on canvas. 65¾ × 35¾ in. (167 × 90.8 cm.)
Signed and dated upper right: *John S. Sargent. 1895.*
Gift of Mrs. J.D. Cameron Bradley. 55.1116

Helen Sears (died 1966), daughter of J. Montgomery and Sarah Choate Sears, was an artist herself and a friend of Sargent. She married J.D. Cameron Bradley in 1913 and lived in Southboro, Mass. until her death.

References: W.H. Downes, *Sargent*, Boston, 1925, pp. 174–175./ E. Charteris, *Sargent*, New York, 1927, p. 265./ C.M. Mount, *Sargent*, New York, 1955, p. 435.

Exhibitions: Boston, Copley Hall, *Sargent*, 1899, no. 35 (as *Portrait of a Child*)./ Boston, MFA, *Sargent Memorial*, 1925, no. 59 (repr.)./ New York, Metropolitan Museum, *Sargent Memorial*, 1926, no. 28 (repr.)./ Boston, MFA, *Sargent's Boston*, 1956, p. 122, no. 30./ Palm Beach, Fla., Society of the Four Arts, *Sargent-Cassatt*, 1959, no. 12./ San Francisco, California Palace of the Legion of Honor, *Sargent and Boldini*, 1959, no. 11.

866.

fig. 458

Frieze of the Prophets

Five figures, in white, gray, dark brown, or black, stand and gesture before a brown background.

Oil on canvas. 22 × 28 in. (55.9 × 71.1 cm.)
Painted about 1896–1900.
Gift of Mrs. Francis Ormond, the artist's sister. 37.45

This painting and *Pagan Dieties* (Cat. no. 861) are preliminary sketches for the murals at the Boston Public Library, commenced in 1895 and finished in 1919. For a full description of the murals, see *Handbook of the Boston Public Library*, 1921. A study (charcoal with white chalk, 23 × 17 in.) of drapery for the figures in the mural is in the Corcoran Gallery, Washington, D.C.

Exhibitions: Boston, MFA, *Sargent's Boston*, 1956, no. 73 (fig. 25)./ Palm Beach, Fla., Society of the Four Arts, *Sargent-Cassatt*, 1959, no. 11 (repr.)./ Washington, D.C., Corcoran Gallery and circulated in the U.S., *Private World of John Singer Sargent*, 1964–1965, no. 58 (repr.).

867.

Head of Christ

Half-length and facing front, he is holding a book. His robes are yellow, brown, and blue; his halo and the background are yellow.

Oil on canvas. 28¼ × 18 in. (71.7 × 45.7 cm.)
Painted about 1897.
Gift of Edward Jackson Holmes. 25.521

Copies from the twelfth-century mosaic figure of the Saviour in the apse of the Cathedral at Cefalù, Sicily.

References: *MFA Bulletin*, 1925, XXIII, no. 140, pp. 69–70 (repr. p. 69)./ E. Charteris, *Sargent*, New York, 1927, p. 295.

Exhibition: Boston, MFA, *Sargent Memorial*, 1925, no. 135.

868.

fig. 459

Mrs. Fiske Warren (Gretchen Osgood) and Her Daughter

Three-quarter length, she is seated in a carved armchair, and turned three-quarters right. The daughter, Rachel, leans her chin on her mother's left shoulder; they wear pink, Mrs. Warren's dress touched with gray and white. Behind them are brown and gold objects before a green and brown background.

Oil on canvas. 60 × 40¼ in. (152.4 × 102.2 cm.)
Signed and dated lower left: *John S. Sargent. 1903.*
Collections: Fiske Warren, Brookline, Mass., 1903; Mrs. Fiske Warren, Boston, 1938; Mrs. Rachel Warren Barton and Hamilton Warren, the sitter's children, 1961.
Gift of Mrs. Rachel Warren Barton and the Emily L. Ainsley Fund. 64.693

Gretchen Osgood (1871–1961) was born in Chelsea, Mass. the daughter of Dr. Hamilton and Margaret Pearmain Osgood. In 1891 she married Fiske Warren. She was known for her intellectual and artistic abilities, and for the founding of the Verde Valley School in Arizona; she was President of the New England Poetry Society and promoter of a 1st World War Belgian Refugees Committee. She died in Boston. Her eldest daughter Rachel was born in 1892. In 1914 she married Samuel K. Lothrop, a Boston archeologist, and they worked often in Central and South America and the West Indies. In 1950 she married Robert Childers Barton, and has since lived in County Wicklow, Ireland. The portrait was painted in the Gothic Room of Fenway Court, Boston, in April, 1903. On the mantel is the painted terracotta *Madonna and Child* by Jacopo della Quercia.

References: "15th Annual Exhibiton," *Worcester Art Museum Bulletin*, 1912, III, no. 2, p. 5 (repr. pp. 4, 7)./ R.V.S. Berry, "Sargent," *Art and Archaeology*, 1924, XVIII, no. 3, p. 103 (repr. p. 102)./ W.H. Downes, *Sargent*, Boston, 1925, p. 210 (repr. opp. p. 248)./ W. Mechlin, "Sargent," *Magazine of Art*, 1925, XVI, no. 6 (repr. p. 284)./ W.M. Milliken, "American Painting from 1860 until Today," *Cleveland Museum Bulletin*, 1937, XXVI, no. 6, p. 97 (repr. cover)./ D.W. Warner, "Cleveland Brings American Artists to the Forefront," *Art News*, 1937, XXXV, no. 39 (repr. p. 14)./ F.A. Sweet, "Half a Century of American Art," *Chicago Art Institute Bulletin*, 1939, XXXIII, no. 6 (repr. p. 96)./ C.M. Mount, *Sargent*, New York, 1955, pp. 241–245, 329.

Exhibitions: Worcester, Mass., Art Museum, *15th Annual*, 1912, no. 45 (repr.)./ Washington, D.C., Corcoran Gallery, *4th Exhibition of Paintings by Contemporary American Artists*, 1912–1913, no. 33./ Pittsburgh, Pa., Carnegie Institute, *International Exhibition*, 1913, no. 249 (repr.)./ New York, Grand Central Art Galleries, *Sargent*, 1924, no. 11 (repr. p. 17)./ Boston, MFA, *Sargent Memorial*, 1925, no. 80./ New York, Metropolitan Museum, *Sargent Memorial*, 1926, no. 42 (repr.)./ Cleveland Museum, *American Painting from 1860 until Today*, 1937, p. 38, no. 168 (repr. frontispiece)./ Boston, MFA, *Private Collections in New England*, 1939, no. 122./ Chicago Art Institute, *Half Century of American Art*, 1939–1940, no. 141 (pl. 22)./ Boston, MFA, *Sargent's Boston*, 1956, p. 50, no. 38 (figs. 33, 34).

869.

fig. 462

An Artist in His Studio

In a yellow-brown room an artist in gray sits in right profile, holding a palette and brushes, and examines a blue and green landscape. Paintings are propped on a bed, right, strewn with white bedclothes.

Oil on canvas. 21½ × 28¼ in. (54.6 × 71.7 cm.)

Signed upper right: *John S. Sargent*. Painted about 1903.

Charles Henry Hayden Fund. 05.56

Both W.H. Downes (*Boston Transcript*, May 10, 1916), and Sargent's servant Niccola Duverno said that the artist portrayed was an Italian, name unknown; Duverno gave the date of 1903 (letter of Oct. 4, 1905). Sargent's niece believed the artist to be Jean François Raffaelli.

References: N. Pousette-Dart, *Sargent*, New York, 1924 (repr.)./ W.H. Downes, *Sargent*, Boston, 1925, p. 212./ E. Charteris, *Sargent*, New York, 1927, p. 287./ C.M. Mount, *Sargent*, New York, 1955, p. 448.

Exhibitions: London, New English Art Club, 1905 (as *No Nonsense*)./ New York, Grand Central Art Galleries, *Sargent*, 1924, no. 14 (repr. p. 34)./ Boston, MFA, *Sargent Memorial*, 1925, no. 77./ New York, Metropolitan Museum, *Sargent Memorial*, 1926, no. 45 (repr.)./ Boston, American Academy of Arts and Sciences, *The Scientific Methods of Examination of Works of Art*, 1950./ Palm Beach, Fla., Society of the Four Arts, *Sargent-Cassatt*, 1959, no. 13./ Washington, D.C., Corcoran Gallery and circulated in the U.S., *Private World of John Singer Sargent*, 1964–1965, no. 67 (repr.).

870.

fig. 464

General Charles J. Paine

Half-length and facing front before a brown and black background, he is seated, his left arm over the chair back, and wears a black suit and tie.

Oil on canvas. 34 × 28½ in. (86.3 × 72.3 cm.)

Signed and dated upper left: *John S. Sargent. 1904.*

Gift of the Heirs of Charles J. Paine. 54.1410

Charles Jackson Paine (1833–1916), son of Charles Cushing and Fanny Cabot Paine, was born in Boston. Major-General of Volunteers during the Civil War and a wealthy businessman interested especially in railroad development, he was also a skilled and noted yachtsman. He died in Weston, Mass.

References: E. Charteris, *Sargent*, New York, 1927, p. 272./ C.M. Mount, *Sargent*, New York, 1955, p. 439.

Exhibitions: Boston, MFA, *Sargent Memorial*, 1925, no. 94./ New York, Metropolitan Museum, *Sargent Memorial*, 1926, no. 49./ Boston, MFA, *Sargent's Boston*, 1956, no. 39./ Columbus, Ga., Museum of Arts and Crafts, *American Traditionalists of the 20th Century*, 1963, no. 152 (repr. p. 22).

871.

The Countess of Essex (Adela Grant)

Three-quarter length, seated and turned three-quarters right, she looks front, resting her arm on a brown and gray column base, right. Over a white décolleté dress she wears a pale blue stole and scarf. The sky behind is cloudy blue.
Oil on canvas. Painted oval. 47½ × 37¼ in. (120.6 × 94.6 cm.)
Signed upper center: *John S. Sargent*. Painted about 1906–1907.
Collections: George Devereux de Vere Capell, 7th Earl of Essex, Cassiobury, Herts, England; Robert J. Edwards, Boston, 1914.
Juliana Cheney Edwards Collection. Bequest of Robert J. Edwards and gift of the Misses Hannah Marcy and Grace M. Edwards. 25.129

Probably painted in 1906 or 1907, the year of its exhibition at the Royal Academy. Adela Grant, eldest daughter of Beach Grant of New York, became the second wife of George Capell, Seventh Earl of Essex, in 1893; she died in 1922.

References: W.H. Downes, *Sargent*, Boston, 1925, p. 226./ E. Charteris, *Sargent*, New York, 1927, p. 270./ C.M. Mount, *Sargent*, New York, 1955, p. 439.

Exhibitions: London, Royal Academy, 1907, no. 425./ Boston, Copley Gallery, *Sargent*, 1917, no. 3./ Boston, MFA, *Sargent Memorial*, 1925, no. 74./ Palm Beach, Fla., Society of the Four Arts, *Sargent-Cassatt*, 1959, no. 15 (repr.).

872.
fig. 463

The Master and His Pupils

Behind an embankment of gray and brown rocks, surrounded by dark green evergreen trees, three figures in white gather around an artist in gray who works at his easel.
Oil on canvas. 22 × 28 in. (55.9 × 71.1 cm.)
Signed lower left: *John S. Sargent*. Painted in 1914.
Charles Henry Hayden Fund. 22.592
The painting was done in the summer of 1914 on Sargent's trip to the Austrian Tyrol with Adrian Stokes and several other friends, who probably posed for this picture.

References: W.H. Downes, *Sargent*, Boston, 1925, pp. 66, 245 (repr. opp. p. 294)./ E. Charteris, *Sargent*, New York, 1927, p. 293./ C.M. Mount, *Sargent*, New York, 1955, p. 451.

Exhibitions: London, Royal Academy, 1915, no. 28./ New York, Grand Central Art Galleries, *Sargent*, 1924, no. 16./ Boston, MFA, *Sargent Memorial*, 1925, no. 109 (repr.)./ Palm Beach, Fla., Society of the Four Arts, *Sargent-Cassatt*, 1959, no. 19 (repr.)./ Baltimore Museum, *1914*, 1964, no. 209.

873.

The Judgment of Paris

The nude Paris, standing on green ground, offers the apple to Aphrodite, right, who stands on a white cloud with Hera and Athena. All are draped in gray, yellow, or green; the background is blue.
Oil on canvas. 30¼ × 26 in. (76.8 × 66 cm.)
Painted about 1916–1921.
Gift of Mrs. Francis Ormond, the artist's sister. 37.47
This sketch is closely allied in subject and handling to the decorations in the Rotunda of the MFA, but it was not used by Sargent in the completed murals.

Exhibitions: London, National Gallery, *Opening Sargent Gallery*, 1926, p. 9./ Palm Beach, Fla., Society of the Four Arts, *Sargent-Cassatt*, 1959, no. 21 (repr.).

874. **The Road**

Soldiers, in khaki and gray, marching through a battle-scarred gray and brown land-scape. Blue touches their helmets, bayonets, and the sky.

Oil on canvas. 15 × 29¼ in. (38.1 × 74.3 cm.)

Signed and dated lower left: *John S. Sargent 1918.*

Charles Henry Hayden Fund. 19.759

A combat artist for the Allies in June of 1918, Sargent was commissioned to illustrate the cooperation of the British and American troops. He wrote to E. Charteris, Sept. 11, 1918, "The Ministry of Information expects an epic—and how can one do an epic without masses of men. Excepting at night I have only seen three fine subjects with masses of men—one a harrow-ing sight, a field of gassed and blindfolded men—another a train of trucks packed with 'chair à cannon'—and another frequent sight, a big road en-cumbered with troops and traffic; I daresay the latter, combining English and Americans, is the best thing to do, if it can be prevented from looking like going to the Derby."

References: *MFA Bulletin*, 1919, XVII, no. 103, p. 50 (repr.)./ W.H. Downes, *Sargent*, Boston, 1925, pp. 77, 254–255./ E. Charteris, *Sargent*, New York, 1927, p. 294./ L. Kirstein, "American Battle Art, 1588–1944," *Magazine of Art*, 1944, XXXVII, no. 5 (repr. p. 189)./ C.M. Mount, *Sargent*, New York, 1955, p. 452./ J. Simon, "Too Many Sargents?" *Arts*, 1964, XXXVIII, no. 10 (repr. p. 23).

Exhibitions: New York, Grand Central Art Galleries, *Sargent*, 1924, no. 15./ Boston, MFA, *Sargent Memorial*, 1925, no. 119./ New York, Metropolitan Museum, *Sargent Memorial*, 1926, no. 59 (repr.)./ Washington, D.C., National Gallery, *American Battle Painting*, 1944, no. 39./ Palm Beach, Fla., Society of the Four Arts, *Sargent-Cassatt*, 1959, no. 22./ Washington, D.C., Corcoran Gallery and circulated in the U.S., *Private World of John Singer Sargent*, 1964–1965, no. 93 (repr.).

WILLIAM SHARP (active 1819?–1862) was born in Ramsey, England and emigrated to Bos-ton in 1838/39. Engraver and lithographer, he was one of the first to de-velop color lithography in America, having already experimented with it in London as early as 1832. He worked in Boston also as a portrait and landscape painter, but with his various partnerships he was best known for his flower prints, book illustrations, maps, and views.

875. **Fruit and Flower Piece**

fig. 241

A mass of brightly colored flowers, purplish-red and white predominating, and bunches of green grapes are in an ornate blue and gold vase. Before it on a white table are various fruits, some in a glass dish or a brown basket. Beyond a gray-green wall, left, the colors of a green and mauve landscape under blue and pink sky are repeated in a coast scene decoration on the vase.

Oil on canvas. 36 × 29 in. (91.4 × 73.6 cm.)

Signed and dated lower right: *W. Sharp pinxt 1848 Boston.*

Collections: Mrs. Lottie J. Whitney, Jamaica Plain, Mass.; Mrs. Robert W. Swift, Jr., her granddaughter, Milton, Mass.; Maxim Karolik, Newport, R.I., 1959.

Bequest of Maxim Karolik. 64.449

876. **Railroad Jubilee on Boston Common**

fig. 242

Oil on canvas. 39 × 58 in. (99 × 147.3 cm.)

Signed and dated lower right: *W. Sharp pinx^t/ Boston 1851.* On the back is a label inscribed: *No. 1. The Railroad Jubilee/ Representing the three days Celebra-tion/ in Boston 1851./ Designed and painted in Oils by Wm Sharp/ Washington Village Dorchester, Mass.*

M. and M. Karolik Collection. 48.475

Reference: *Karolik Catalogue*, 1949, no. 211 (repr.).

JAMES SHARPLES (1751–1811) was born in Lancashire, England. Said to have been a pupil of George Romney, he painted portraits in Cambridge in 1799, Bath and Bristol in 1781–1782, and London in 1783 and 1785. He lived in Bath and Liverpool until in 1793 he left for America, where he worked in Philadelphia and New York as a portraitist. He was also the inventor of a steam carriage. He settled in Bath, England in 1801, but in 1809 he again moved to New York, where he died.

877.

fig. 103

Joseph Dennie

Half-length and turned three-quarters right before a blue and gray background, he wears a dark brown coat and white stock.
Pastel on paper. 9 × 7 in. (22.9 × 17.8 cm.)
Drawn about 1800.
Bequest of James Dennie. 05.297

Joseph Dennie (1768–1812), born in Boston, graduated from Harvard in 1790. Known as the "American Addison," he became the epitome of a gentleman and soldier of elegance and wit in the Federalist era. In 1799 he took a clerical position in the State Department and lived in Philadelphia, where he edited the successful weekly journal, *Port Folio*, until his death. The date of the portrait is derived from his apparent age.

JOSHUA SHAW (1776–1860)

878.

fig. 268

On the Susquehanna

Oil on canvas. 39 × 55½ in. (99 × 141 cm.)
Signed and dated lower right: *J.Shaw 1839.*
M. and M. Karolik Collection. 48.476
Reference: Karolik Catalogue, 1949, no. 212 (repr.).

CHARLES SHEELER (1883–1965) was born in Philadelphia and first studied there at the School of Industrial Art from 1900 to 1903, then until 1906 at the Pennsylvania Academy with William Merritt Chase. He made study trips to Europe with Chase in 1904 and 1905, and again visited there in 1908 and 1909. From 1910 to 1919 he lived in Philadelphia; he began professional photography in 1912 and exhibited at the Armory Show in 1913. From 1919 to 1927 he lived in New York, then South Salem, N.Y. until 1932, Ridgefield, Conn. until 1942, and Irving-on-Hudson, N.Y. from 1942 until his death. Inspired by the forms of Cubism, if not its theories, which Sheeler first encountered at the Armory Show, he developed a Precisionist style of essentials which remained highly individual and intrinsically American.

879.

fig. 566

View of New York

A black camera and stand covered with a black cloth, a lamp, and a gray canvas chair are before a gray wall and window, through which white clouds in blue sky are visible.
Oil on canvas. 47¾ × 36¼ in. (121.2 × 92.1 cm.)
Signed and dated lower left: *Sheeler—1931.*
Charles Henry Hayden Fund. 35.69

"I know that *View of New York* may be called a cold picture, it is very uncompromising; some might say inhuman. It is the most severe picture I ever painted." (From the artist. Rourke, *see below.*)

References: Cleveland Museum Bulletin, 1931, XVIII, no. 6, p. 119./ —, 1934, XXI, no. 6, p. 100./ C. Rourke, *Sheeler*, New York, 1938, p. 156 (repr. p. 103)./ F.S. Wight, "Sheeler," *Art in America*, 1954, XLI, no. 3 (repr. p. 193)./ A.L. Chanin, "Sheeler," *Art News*, 1955, LIV, no. 4, p. 72./ "Windows," *Art in America*, 1963, LI, no. 2 (repr. p. 112).

Exhibitions: Cleveland Museum, *11th Annual of Contemporary American Oils*, 1931./ Pittsburgh, Pa., Carnegie Institute, *International Exhibition*, 1931, no. 95./ Chicago, Arts Club, *Sheeler*, 1932, no. 4./ Washington, D.C., Corcoran Gallery, *13th Exhibition of Contemporary American Oil Paintings*, 1932–1933, no. 66./ Worcester, Mass., Art Museum, *American Painting of Today*, 1933–1934, no. 112 (repr.)./ Cambridge,

Mass., Fogg Art Museum, *Sheeler*, *1934*./ Cleveland Museum, *14th Annual of Contemporary American Oils*, *1934*./ New York, Rockefeller Center, *1st Municipal Art Exhibit*, *1934*, no. 813./ New York, Museum of Modern Art, *Sheeler*, *1939*, no. 24 (repr.)./ New York, Whitney Museum, *This Is Our City*, *1941*, no. 74./ Andover, Mass., Addison Gallery, *Sheeler*, *1946*./ Philadelphia, Pennsylvania Academy of the Fine Arts, *Sheeler Retrospective*, *1954*, no. 12 (repr. p. 22)./ Worcester, Mass., Art Museum, *Five Painters of America*, *1955*, p. 3./ Minneapolis, Walker Art Center and circulated in the U.S., *The Precisionist View of American Art*, *1960–1961*, p. 58./ Allentown, Pa., Art Museum, *Sheeler Retrospective*, *1961*, no. 13.

880.
fig. 565

Fugue

Pale red, gray, blue, and white factory chimneys stand against a blue sky and white clouds. Below are red, black, and gray buildings and storage tanks. The foreground is brown and gray.

Tempera on canvasboard. 11¼ × 13¼ in. (28.5 × 33.6 cm.)
Signed and dated lower right: *Sheeler—1940.*
Arthur Mason Knapp Fund. 40.780

"I was on a motor trip through New England and in passing through New Bedford in the late afternoon I came upon the subject unexpectedly. It was a breath-taking sight. I walked around it for several hours and later the picture which you now have resulted." (Letter from the artist, Dec. 20, 1940.)

Exhibitions: New York, Downtown Gallery, *Sheeler*, 1946, no. 7 (repr.)./ Minneapolis, Walker Art Center, *Sheeler*, 1952./ Iowa City, University of Iowa, *Sheeler Retrospective*, 1963, no. 46.

EVERETT SHINN (1876–1953) was born in Woodstown, N.J. After studying mechanical engineering in Philadelphia, he studied for five years with Thomas Anshutz at the Pennsylvania Academy. He then worked as a newspaper illustrator in Philadelphia, where he met several of the other future members of the group "The Eight." He lived in New York until his death, working as a painter and illustrator, theatre designer, film director, and playwright.

881.
fig. 540

Alexander Bridge, Paris

People dressed in black, red, and blue walk on the dark gray embankment in the foreground. The distant bridge is white over the black river. Buildings and trees to the side are gray, white, yellow, and green beneath gray and yellow sky.

Pastel on chipboard. 22 × 29½ in. (55.9 × 74.9 cm.)
Signed and dated lower left: *Everett Shinn/ Paris 1900.*
Charles Henry Hayden Fund. 43.125

JOHN SLOAN (1871–1951), born in Lock Haven, Pa., studied at the Pennsylvania Academy and in 1894 started work as a newspaper illustrator in Philadelphia with Robert Henri. In 1904 he moved to New York to become a free-lance illustrator and in 1908 was one of the group "The Eight." Founder and President of the Society of Independent Artists, from 1914 to 1930 and from 1935 to 1938 he taught at the Art Students League and spent summers in Gloucester, Mass. and Santa Fé. He died in New York. With Luks and Henri, Sloan was a leader of the American Realists or "Ash Can School."

882.
fig. 544

Pigeons

Two people, in black and brown, fly pigeons from the roofs of red, brown, and yellow city buildings. The sky is blue with gray clouds.

Oil on canvas. 26 × 32 in. (66 × 81.2 cm.)
Signed and dated lower right: *John Sloan/ 1910.* Inscribed on reverse: *Pigeons John Sloan.*
Charles Henry Hayden Fund. 35.52

"My studio at the time was on West 23rd St. no. 165 . . . My back windows looked out on the roofs of old tenements on 24th St. . . . The pastime of raising pigeons was much in evidence in the tenement districts of those days —The pigeons were flown daily for exercise, and also, incidently, as a lure for strays from neighboring flocks—Such strays were trapped and confined until they became used to their new surroundings. In the background the new station of the Pennsylvania R.R., then under construction, is beginning to show above what was then the 'Tenderloin' section, famous in the police annals." (Letter from the artist, Feb. 9, 1935.)

References: "Diary of John Sloan," MS owned by Mrs. John Sloan, New York, Feb. 7, 14, 18, 22, 24, March 9, and Sept. 6, 1910, and April 17, 1912./ R. Henri, "New York Exhibition of Independent Artists," *The Craftsman*, 1910, XVIII, p.164 (repr.)./ A. Burroughs, *Limners and Likenesses*, Cambridge, Mass., 1936 (fig. 181)./ R. Henri, *The Art Spirit*, Philadelphia, 1939, p. 222./ J. Sloan, *Gist of Art*, New York, 1939 (repr. p. 222)./ V.W. Brooks, *Sloan*, New York, 1955 (repr. pp. 182–183).

Exhibitions: New York, 24–31 West 35th St., *Independent Artists*, 1910, no. 69./ Chicago Art Institute, *Century of Progress*, 1934, no. 682./ New York, Montross Gallery, *Sloan*, 1934, no. 30./ Andover, Mass., Addison Gallery, *Sloan*, 1938, no. 7 (repr.)./ New York, Museum of Modern Art, *Art in Our Time*, 1939, no. 138 (repr.)./ San Francisco, California Palace of the Legion of Honor, *Seven Centuries of Painting*, 1940, no. L-271 (repr.)./ New York, Metropolitan Museum, *Contemporary Painting in the U.S.*, 1941, no. 143./ Philadelphia Museum of Art, *Artists of the* Philadelphia *Press*, 1945, no. 57./ London, Tate Gallery, *American Painting*, 1946, no. 195./ New York, Whitney Museum and circulated in the U.S., *Sloan*, 1952, no. 24./ Wilmington, Del., Society of Fine Arts and New York, James Graham and Sons, *50th Anniversary of the Exhibition of Independent Artists*, 1960, no. 79 (repr. p. 12)./ New Orleans, Isaac Delgado Museum, *World of Art in 1910*, 1960 (repr.).

JOHN SMIBERT (1688–1751) was born in Edinburgh, Scotland and was first apprenticed to a house painter there. In 1709 he left for London, where he began work for a coach painter and studied at the Great Queen Street Academy. From 1717 to 1720 he studied in Florence and Rome, then until 1728 worked in London as a portraitist. That same year he accompanied Dean Berkeley to Newport, R.I., en route to Bermuda, where the Dean had hoped to found a college for the Indians. Smibert, however, left for Boston in 1729, opened an artist's supply shop, and established himself as the leading Colonial portrait painter. He exerted considerable influence on the artists of Boston: Pelham, Feke, Blackburn, and indirectly, Copley. He died in Boston.

883.
fig. 5

The Parting of Hector and Andromache

Hector, in a red cloak over gray armor and white tunic, stands right and receives his son from Andromache, who wears a blue stole over a yellow dress. A servant girl behind her is in brown, and the soldier beyond Hector wears a green cloak over brown armor. The building is brown, the sky blue.

Oil on canvas. 49¼ × 39½ in. (125.7 × 100.3 cm.)

Painted about 1717–1720.

Collections: Estate of the artist, Boston, 1752; Eliza W. Fuller and Mary F. Storer, descendants of the artist; Mrs. Genevieve M. Fuller, their niece, and Henry M. Fuller, her son, Milton, Mass.

Gift of Genevieve Morrill Fuller in memory of Henry Morrill Fuller. 64.2053

The unsophisticated handling of paint and proportions suggest that the picture is an early work probably painted in Italy after an unknown seventeenth-century painting seen in Rome. The muted color indicates the possibility that an engraving may have been the source. The subject itself, from the *Iliad* (Book VI) is of the moment when Hector takes leave of his wife Andromache and their child Astyanax as he sets out to do battle with Achilles outside the walls of Troy.

References: V. Barker, *American Painting*, New York, 1950, p. 174./ H.W. Foote, *Smibert*, Cambridge, Mass., 1950, pp. 109, 231.

884.
fig. 6

Mrs. James MacSparran (Hannah Gardiner)

Half-length and facing front, she wears a blue dress over white. The background, seen through brown spandrels, is gray.

Oil on canvas. Painted oval. 30¼ × 25¼ in. (76.8 × 64.1 cm.)
Painted in 1729.
Collection: Mrs. Margaret Elton, great-grandniece of the sitter, Dorchester, Mass.
Gift of Mrs. Margaret Allen Elton. 88.289

Hannah Gardiner (1704–1755), daughter of William Gardiner of Narragansett, R.I. and commonly known as "handsome Hannah," married in 1722 the Rev. James MacSparran, Anglican minister of the Narragansett Church. In 1729, before her departure for London, where she died of smallpox, Smibert visited the MacSparrans at Narragansett. His portrait of the Rev. MacSparran is in the Bowdoin College Museum, Brunswick, Me.

References: W. Updike, *History of the Episcopal Church in Narragansett, R.I.*, Boston, 1907, I (repr. opp. p. 70)./ M.H. Elliott, "Some Recollections of Newport Artists," *Historical Society Bulletin*, Newport, R.I., 1921, no. 35, p. 2./ F.W. Bayley, *Five Colonial Painters*, Boston, 1929 (repr. p. 407)./ A. Burroughs, "Notes on Smibert's Development," *Art in America*, 1942, xxx, no. 2, p. 119./ H.W. Foote, *Smibert*, Cambridge, Mass., 1950, p. 169.

Exhibitions: Worcester, Mass., Art Museum, *New England Painting, 1700–75*, 1943, no. 14./ New Haven, Yale University Art Gallery, *Smibert*, 1949, no. 19./ Vancouver Art Gallery, *Two Hundred Years of American Painting*, 1955, no. 1.

885.
fig. 4

Judge Samuel Sewall

Half-length, the judge turns three-quarters right and wears a black skullcap and a dark brown coat with a white steenkirk tie. The brown spandrels are before a gray background.

Oil on canvas. Painted oval. 30¼ × 25½ in. (76.8 × 64.8 cm.)
Painted in 1729.
Collections: The Rev. Joseph Sewall, the sitter's son, 1730; Samuel Sewall, 1769; Judge Samuel Sewall, 1776; the Rev. Samuel Sewall, Burlington, Mass., 1814; Samuel Sewall, 1866; Nellie L. Sewall Bennet; Benjamin Flayderman, Boston, 1943.
Bequest of William L. Barnard by exchange and the Emily L. Ainsley Fund. 58.358

Samuel Sewall (1652–1730), the son of Henry and Jane Dummer Sewall of Newbury, Mass., was born in Bishopstoke, Hampshire, England; the family returned to America in 1661. After graduation from Harvard in 1671, Sewall became a resident fellow and tutor there. In 1675 he married Hannah Hull, daughter of the mint-master John Hull, and the first of his three wives; she bore him fourteen children. Active in religious circles, he also ran the only licensed printing press in the colony, between 1681 and 1684. In 1683, he was deputy to the General Court from Westfield and from 1684 to 1686 was, ex officio, a Judge of the Superior Court. From 1691 to 1725 he was a member of the Boston Council. In 1692 he was appointed one of the special judges to try the witches of Salem but was the only member of that tribunal to publicly recant his part in the matter. In 1692 he was appointed a Judge of the Superior Court and its Chief Justice from 1718 to 1728. In 1700 he published a pamphlet, *The Selling of Joseph*, in opposition to Negro slavery. His voluminous diaries (Massachusetts Historical Society), covering the period from 1674 to 1677 and 1685 to 1729, are incomparable documents of life in early Boston. Smibert arrived in Boston in November, 1729; Judge Sewall suffered his final illness during December and died on January 1, 1730.

The painting is recorded in the poem by Mather Byles, "To Mr. Smibert, on Sight of His Pictures," composed in 1730 to mark the exhibition held by Smibert of his work, the first of its kind in America. An inscription, barely visible, in the upper spandrels, reads: *The Honble Samuel Sewall Esq. Chief Justice—of the—of probate for the County of Suffolk Aetatis 78*; and, in the lower spandrels: *Auris mens oculus manus os pes munere fungi dum pergunt praestat* [desist?] *ere velle mori.* A contemporary replica by Smibert (Foote,

Smibert, p. 190) is in the Essex Institute, Salem, Mass. The Massachusetts Historical Society, Boston owns the three-quarter-length seated portrait of Samuel Sewall, painted by Nathaniel Emmons in 1728, of which the head and shoulders are similar to the MFA's painting.

References: J. Winsor, *Memorial History of Boston*, Boston, 1881, II, p. 148 (notes)./ M.E. Sewall Curtis, *Ye Olde Meeting House*, Burlington, Mass., Boston, 1909 (repr. opp. p. 54)./ H.W. Foote, "Mr. Smibert Shows His Pictures," *New England Quarterly*, 1935, VIII, no. 1, p. 18 (incorrectly identified as belonging to the Massachusetts Historical Society)./ —, *Smibert*, Cambridge, Mass., 1950, pp. 189–190./ R.C. Vose, Jr., "Samuel Sewall by Smibert," MS, 1957.

Exhibitions: Boston, Scollay Square, Smibert's studio, 1730./ Yale University Art Gallery, *Smibert*, 1949, no. 28.

886.
fig.7

Judge Charles Chambers

Three-quarter length and turned three-quarters right, he is seated behind a table covered with a green cloth on which rests a pewter inkstand, quill pen, and a letter. He wears a brown velvet suit and white steenkirk tie. Through a window, right, a moored ship is visible.

Oil on canvas. 47¾ × 37¾ in. (121 × 96 cm.)
Painted in the early 1730's.
Collections: Russell Sturgis Codman, Boston; Charles R. Codman, Boston, 1941; Mrs. Charles R. Codman, Boston.
Gift of Mrs. Charles R. Codman, in memory of her husband, Charles R. Codman and her son, Charles R. Codman, Jr.

Charles Chambers (1660–1743), son of Edward and Elizabeth Palmer Chambers of Torksey, Lincolnshire, England, was a sea captain, a merchant of Boston, a Justice of the Peace, and a Judge of the Court of Common Pleas. In 1687 he married Rebecca Patefield and in 1735 or 1736 married Margaret Vaughan, widow of Captain Foye. He died in Charlestown, Mass. The date is established by his apparent age, the strength of style typical of Smibert's earlier American work, and the costume.

References: C.K. Bolton, *Founders*, Boston, 1919, II, p. 536./ F.W. Bayley, *Five Colonial Artists*, Boston, 1929, p. 365./ H.W. Foote, *Smibert*, Cambridge, Mass., 1950, pp. 142–143.

Exhibition: Boston, MFA, *One Hundred Colonial Portraits*, 1930, p. 18 (repr.).

887.
fig. 9

Thomas Hancock

Half-length, turned half right, he wears a long gray wig, a white stock with a ruffled shirt, and a brown coat and partially buttoned waistcoat. The background is olive brown.

Oil on canvas. Painted oval. 30 × 25 in. (76.2 × 63.5 cm.)
Painted about 1730.
Collections: Lydia Hancock, wife of the sitter, 1764; John Hancock, nephew of the sitter, 1776; Dorothy Quincy Hancock, his wife, 1793–1830; Mrs. Lydia B. Taft, Milton, Mass., by 1919; Ray Baker Taft, Hingham, Mass., by 1935; Miss Ellyn L. Edwards, York, Me., 1938; Miss Amelia Peabody, Boston, 1964.
Gift of Miss Amelia Peabody. 65.1712

Thomas Hancock (1703–1764) was born in Lexington, Mass., the son of the Rev. John and Elizabeth Hancock. As a youth he was apprenticed to Daniel Henchman, a wealthy bookseller of Boston, whose daughter, Lydia, he married in 1730. In the years following he became one of the city's most prosperous merchants and a member of the Boston Council. In 1737 he built the famed Hancock House on Beacon Street, later occupied by his nephew and heir, John Hancock.

Reference: H.W. Foote, *Smibert*, Cambridge, Mass., 1950, p. 162.

888.
fig. 8

Daniel, Peter, and Andrew Oliver

Three boys, half-length, are seated around a table upon which are a blue cloth and a brown volume; all wear white shirts and stocks. Daniel, on the left, wears a red suit;

Peter, in the center, blue; and Andrew, to the right, brown. The background is brown.
Oil on canvas. 40 × 57½ in. (101.6 × 146 cm.)
Painted about 1730.
Collections: Andrew Oliver, Boston; Andrew Oliver, his son, Boston, 1774; descended in the family to Dr. Fitch Edward Oliver, Boston; Dr. Andrew, Dr. Edward P., E. Lawrence, and Susan L. Oliver, his children, Boston.
Emily L. Ainsley Fund. 53.952

The sons of Daniel and Elizabeth Belcher Oliver from left to right are: Daniel, Jr. (1704–1727), a graduate of Harvard in 1722, who was born in Boston and died of smallpox in London; Peter (1713–1791) who graduated from Harvard in 1730, became Chief Justice of the Superior Court of Massachusetts and died in Birmingham, England; and Andrew (1706–1774), a graduate of Harvard in 1726 who later became Lieutenant Governor of Massachusetts. On the back of the canvas is inscribed: *Andrew Oliver/ Lt.Gov., Mass. Peter Oliver/ Chief Justice, Mass. Daniel Oliver/ d. 1727.* The date of the portrait is determined by the apparent age of Peter. Although Daniel died in 1727, a miniature of him (Seabury Oliver, Morristown, N.J.) sent from London enabled Smibert to include him in the painting.

References: A.T. Perkins, "Blackburn and Smibert," *Massachusetts Historical Society Proceedings*, 1878, XVI, p. 397./ F.W. Bayley, *Five Colonial Artists*, Boston, 1929 (repr. p. 409)./ F.W. Coburn, "Smibert," *Art in America*, 1929, XVII, no. 4, p. 177 (repr. p. 179)./ H.W. Foote, *Smibert*, Cambridge, Mass., 1950, pp. 176–177./ A. Oliver, *Faces of a Family*, 1960, p. 4, no. 3 (repr.).

Exhibitions: Boston, MFA, *One Hundred Colonial Portraits*, 1930 (repr. p. 59)./ Yale University Art Gallery, *Smibert*, 1949, no. 21./ Boston, Massachusetts Historical Society, *The Olivers and Their Friends*, 1960.

889. **Judge Edmund Quincy**

Half-length and turned three-quarters right before a brown background, he wears a red brown coat with a white steenkirk tie and a full gray wig.
Oil on canvas. Painted oval. 30½ × 24½ in. (77.5 × 62.2 cm.)
Painted in 1733.
Collection: Josiah Quincy, great-grandson of the sitter, Boston.
Gift of the Children of Josiah Quincy. 76.348

Edmund Quincy (1681–1738) was the son of Edmund and Elizabeth Gookin Quincy of Braintree, Mass. A graduate of Harvard in 1699, in 1718 he was appointed Judge of the Superior Court of Massachusetts, a position he held until 1737. That year he was sent to London as the agent for the Bay Colony to settle a quarrel over the Massachusetts-New Hampshire border. There he died of smallpox. Before the canvas was relined, an inscription on the back read: *Painted by Smibert 1733—Boston Massachusetts Bay.* Mrs. Dunn Ross of Portsmouth, R.I. owns a replica by Smibert.

References: A.T. Perkins, "Blackburn and Smibert," *Massachusetts Historical Society Proceedings*, 1878, XVI, pp. 398–399./ W.H. Downes, "Boston Painters and Paintings," *Atlantic Monthly*, 1888, LXII, no. 369, p. 91./ A. Burroughs, *Limners and Likenesses*, Cambridge, Mass., 1936, p. 37 (fig. 27)./ H.W. Foote, *Smibert*, Cambridge, Mass., 1950, p. 184.

Exhibition: Boston, MFA, *Contemporary Art*, 1879, no. 94.

890.
fig. 10 **John Turner**

Half-length, he turns three-quarters right in a green coat over a white shirt and stock. A gray and blue seascape, right, is beyond the gray wall.
Oil on canvas. 35¼ × 27¾ in. (89.5 × 70.5 cm.)
Painted about 1735.
Collections: Winthrop Sargent, descendant of the sitter, Boston; Mrs. Horatio A. Lamb, his sister-in-law, Boston.
Gift of Mrs. Horatio A. Lamb, in memory of Mr. and Mrs. Winthrop Sargent. 18.663

John Turner (1709–1786), born in Salem, Mass., was the son of that John

Turner without whom, it was said, nothing of importance, civil or military, could be done in Salem, and of Mary Kitchen Turner. In 1772 he was Collector for the port of Salem and in 1757–1758 served in the House of Deputies. The Turner house, owned by the family for many generations, was made famous by Hawthorne as *The House of the Seven Gables*.

References: F.W. Bayley, *Five Colonial Artists*, Boston, 1929 (repr. p. 431)./ A. Burroughs, *Limners and Likenesses*, Cambridge, Mass., 1936, p. 36./ —, "Notes on Smibert's Development," *Art in America*, 1942, xxx, no. 2, p. 119./ H.W. Foote, *Smibert*, Cambridge, Mass. 1950, p. 193.

Exhibitions: Pittsburgh, Pa., Carnegie Institute, *Survey of American Painting*, 1940, no. 19./ Yale University Art Gallery, *Smibert*, 1949, no. 32.

891.
fig. 11

Lady in a Blue Dress

More than half-length, she faces front in a blue satin dress and a red stole and leans her left elbow upon a brown pedestal. The background is brown and gray.
Oil on canvas. 35¾ × 28½ in. (90.8 × 72.3 cm.)
Painted about 1740–1745.
Collections: W.B.T. Smith, 1912; George Nixon Black, Boston, by 1922.
Bequest of George Nixon Black. 29.792

Although given to the MFA as a portrait of Anne Waldo Tyng, wife of Edward Tyng, the identity of the sitter had not been established when the picture belonged to W.B.T. Smith, a collateral descendant of the Tyng family. However, a well-documented portrait of Anne Waldo Tyng by Smibert (Yale University Art Gallery, New Haven) shows a lady of entirely different features. Probably shown here is another member of the Tyng family.

References: F.W. Bayley, *Five Colonial Artists*, Boston, 1929 (repr. pl. 433)./ Robie, "Waldo Portraits by Smibert and Blackburn," *The American Society of the Legion of Honor Magazine*, New York, Spring, 1949, p. 49./ H.W. Foote, *Smibert*, Cambridge, Mass., 1950, p. 195.

Exhibition: Boston, Art Club, *American Painters Before the Revolution*, 1922, no. 17.

RAPHAEL SOYER was born in Tombov, Russia, in 1899 and came to New York in 1912. In 1915–1916, he studied at night at the Cooper Union, from 1917 to 1920 at the National Academy of Design, and briefly in the 1920's with Guy Pène du Bois at the Art Students League. Then for five years he worked in factories, painting in spare moments, and in 1935 made the first of four short visits to Europe. He has always lived in New York.

892.

Furnished Room

A woman in black and a man in a brown vest and blue shirt, both half-length, sit apart in a red interior. A brown wine bottle with blue labels stands on a gray table.
Oil on canvas. 27 × 26¼ in. (68.6 × 66.7 cm.)
Signed lower left: *Raphael Soyer*. Painted about 1935.
Gift of Mr. and Mrs. James N. Rosenberg in memory of Joseph M. Herman. 46.455
"Painted in the middle thirties . . . it depicts lonely, transient, furnished room life." (Letter from the artist, June 18, 1951.)
Exhibition: New York, Valentine Gallery, *Soyer*, 1938, no. 9.

EUGENE EDWARD SPEICHER (1883–1962), born in Buffalo, N.Y., first studied there at the Albright Art Gallery School. In New York he studied for two years at the Art Students League with F.V. Du Mond and Chase, and at the Lincoln Arcade with Robert Henri. In 1910, after extensive travel in Europe, he settled in New York City, and about 1918 moved to Woodstock, N.Y. He thereafter alternated between the two until his death in Woodstock.

893.
fig. 559

Katharine

Three-quarter length and facing front, seated in a blue and yellow upholstered chair, she wears a pink sweater and brown skirt. Behind are a purple chair and a table on

which are a brown clock and green, pink, and white flowers. The background is a green wall.
Oil on canvas. 50 × 40 in. (127 × 101.6 cm.)
Signed lower left: *Eugene Speicher*. Painted about 1923.
Collection: John T. Spaulding, Boston, 1925.
Bequest of John T. Spaulding. 48.603
A portrait of Katharine Rosen.

Exhibitions: New York, Whitney Studio, *Group Exhibition*, 1924./ Boston, MFA, *The Spaulding Collections*, 1948, no. 79./ New York, Whitney Museum, *Juliana Force and American Art*, 1949, no. 117 (repr. p. 23)./ Buffalo, Albright Art Gallery, *Speicher*, 1950, no. 5 (pl. 2).

894. **Bouquet**

Red and blue, purple, yellow, green, and orange flowers stand in a white and black vase on a red table. A blue and white curtain hangs, right, before a brown background.
Oil on canvas. 16½ × 14¼ in. (41.9 × 36.2 cm.)
Signed lower left: *Eugene Speicher*. Painted about 1925.
Collection: John T. Spaulding, Boston, 1925.
Bequest of John T. Spaulding. 48.602
Exhibition: Boston, MFA, *The Spaulding Collections*, 1948, no. 78.

895. **Anna**

Seated in three-quarter length, facing front and wearing a brown skirt and yellow sweater, she leans on the back of the brown upholstered chair. The background is gray, brown, and green.
Oil on canvas. 39¾ × 32 in. (100.9 × 81.2 cm.)
Signed center left: *Eugene Speicher*. Painted in 1934.
Charles Henry Hayden Fund. 35.736
"Painted in my studio last winter . . . The model was a dancer in the 'New Group,' and a Russian by birth I believe." (Letter from the artist, May 20, 1935.)

Exhibitions: Pittsburgh, Pa., Carnegie Institute, *International Exhibition*, 1935, no. 17 (pl. 15)./ New York, American Academy of Arts and Letters, *Speicher Memorial*, 1963, no. 14.

MAURICE STERNE (1878–1957) was born in Libau, Latvia. From 1889 to 1892 he was a map engraver in New York, then studied mechanical drawing at the Cooper Union and anatomy with Thomas Eakins at the National Academy of Design. He traveled through Europe and the Far East from 1904 to 1919, then until 1933 returned to work part of every year in Anticoli-Corrado, Italy. He lived in New York, spent summers in Provincetown, Mass., and died in Mount Kisco, N.Y.

896. **Breadmakers**

Two women are at the arched entrance of a black interior. One, seated and kneading dough, wears a black and gray costume; the other wears black and yellow with a green kerchief.
Oil on masonite. 48 × 32¼ in. (121.9 × 81.9 cm.)
Signed and dated lower left: *Maurice Sterne/ 1923*.
Collections: Carl Hamilton, Paris; Harry C. Bentley, Boston.
Charles Henry Hayden Fund. 44.581
Reference: J.I.H. Baur, *Revolution and Tradition in Modern American Art*, Cambridge, Mass., 1951 (pl. 131).
Exhibition: New York, Museum of Modern Art, *Sterne*, 1933, no. 57 (repr.).

897.
fig. 571 **Green Apples**

Green apples, touched with red, lie on a gray and white cloth on the floor. Behind, the chair legs and the background are brown and gray.
Oil on canvas. 27½ × 34¾ in. (69.8 × 88.2 cm.)
Signed lower left: *Sterne*. Painted in 1924.

Gift of Edward Jackson Holmes. 41.111

The date is given in the Museum of Modern Art catalogue (*see below*).

Exhibitions: New York, Museum of Modern Art, *Sterne*, 1933, no. 60./ New York, Hirschl & Adler Galleries, *Sterne*, 1962, no. 60.

898.   **Vase of Flowers**

Orange nasturtiums and purple and yellow pansies are in a bright green vase which rests on a light brown table. Tones of rose, blue-green, and purple are in the background.
Oil on canvasboard. 18½ × 14¼ in. (47 × 36 cm.)
Signed lower left: *Sterne*.
Bequest of Mrs. Edward Jackson Holmes. 65.433

FLORINE STETTHEIMER (1871–1944) was born in Rochester, N.Y. and studied at the Art Students League, New York, under Kenyon Cox in the mid-1880's. After further training in Germany, the artist-poetess traveled in Italy and to Paris until 1914. In 1915 she established a salon with her two sisters at Alwyn Court, her mother's home in New York. She also traveled throughout New England and Canada. She died in New York.

899.   **Lake Placid**
fig. 569

Figures in blue and red, yellow, brown, and black bathing suits swim in pale green and gray water or relax on the red float and in red and yellow boats. A red porch is in the left foreground; in the background are distant pink hills and sky.
Oil on canvas. 40 × 50 in. (101.6 × 127 cm.)
Signed and dated lower left: *FS/ 1919*.
Gift of Miss Ettie Stettheimer, the artist's sister. 47.1541

The figures represented are: the artist's mother on the balcony; the artist descending the steps; right, the Marquis de Buenavista stands on a raft; Marie Sterner is lying down; the artist's sisters Ettie and Carrie are seated, the latter with a sunshade; Elie Nadelman is half in the water; left, in the canoe are Maurice Sterne and Elizabeth Duncan; right, swimming toward the raft, are Rabbi Stephan S. Wise and the artist's sister Ettie (again); in the launch is Professor E.R.A. Seligmann, and on the surfboard, his daughter Hazel.

Reference: P. Tyler, *Florine Stettheimer*, New York, 1963, pp. 22, 97, 129, 131, 152, 159 (repr.).

Exhibitions: New York, Museum of Modern Art, *Stettheimer*, 1946, p. 54 (repr. p. 19)./ Smith College Museum, *Stettheimer*, 1952./ New York, Durlacher Brothers, *Stettheimer*, 1963.

DONALD STOLTENBERG, born in Milwaukee, Wisc. in 1927, studied at the Chicago Institute of Design from 1948 to 1953 and taught there for one semester. In 1953 and 1955 he traveled and worked in Europe and since then has lived in Boston, teaching at the DeCordova Museum, Lincoln, and as a visiting critic to the Rhode Island School of Design. He has also worked as a commercial designer.

900.   **Third Avenue**
fig. 592

Composition of geometric planes of gray, white, black, red, and gold, form a perspective view of the structure of an elevated railway. Above are planes of black with gray touched with gold, green, and brown.
Oil on canvas. 47¾ × 72¼ in. (121.2 × 184.1 cm.)
Signed and dated lower right: *Stoltenberg '55*.
Charles Henry Hayden Fund. 56.509

" 'Third Avenue' was painted...in the knowledge that its subject matter as it then appeared was doomed and would soon lose its special character with the destruction of the elevated ... the fantastic patterns of light striking the pavement, the black mysterious monumentality of the structure, the rich darks set off by piercing shafts of white light, the flashes of colored traffic lights and neon underneath, the elaborate sculpture above ... The picture represents the culmination of a long series of drawings and paintings devoted to the same subject." (Letter from the artist, Oct. 29, 1956.)

Exhibitions: Chicago Art Institute, *62nd Exhibition of American Painting and Sculpture*, 1957, no. 117./ Lincoln, Mass., De Cordova Museum, *Margaret Brown Memorial*, 1957, p. 35./ Birmingham, Ala., Birmingham Museum, *Contemporary American Painting*, 1962.

JULIAN RUSSELL STORY (1857–1919) was born in Walton-on-Thames, England and studied at Oxford University before becoming a pupil of Frank Duveneck in Florence and of Gustave, Rodolph, and Lefebvre in Paris. He worked in Vallambrosa, Italy, and lived in Paris and then Philadelphia, where he died.

901.
fig. 418

Ernest Wadsworth Longfellow

Standing in three-quarter length before a brown background, turned three-quarters right, he wears a black topcoat with brown fur over a black suit with a white tie.
Oil on canvas. 22 × 18 in. (55.9 × 45.7 cm.)
Signed and dated upper right: *Julian Story 1892*.
Bequest of Ernest Wadsworth Longfellow. 23.503

Ernest Wadsworth Longfellow (1845–1921), artist, was the son of Henry Wadsworth and Frances Appleton Longfellow. A landscape and marine painter, he lived in New York City and Boston where he died.

ROBERT STREET (1796–1865)

902.

Likeness of Himself
Oil on canvas. 19 × 16 in. (48.2 × 40.6 cm.)
Signed lower left: *Sketch by R Street. Likeness of Himself.*
M. and M. Karolik Collection. 48.477
Reference: Karolik Catalogue, 1949, no. 213 (repr.).

GILBERT STUART (1755–1828), born in North Kingston, R.I., after 1761 lived in Newport where he met the Scottish painter Cosmo Alexander, his first teacher. In 1772 he accompanied Alexander, who died the same year, to Edinburgh but quickly returned; in 1775 he went to London, where he worked, at first unsuccessfully, as a portrait painter. From 1777 to 1782 he worked in the studio of Benjamin West, and from 1782 to 1787 he was active as one of the more fashionable portrait painters, competing with Romney and Reynolds. However, indebtedness drove him to Dublin, and in 1792 again forced him to flee to New York. He again became successful, in good part due to his portraits of Washington, and worked in New York until 1794, in Philadelphia and Germantown until 1803, and in Washington until 1805, when he settled permanently in Boston. Among the artists he had numerous followers, and through informal instruction and advice he influenced many more. A portrait of Stuart by John Neagle (Cat. no. 776) is also in the MFA collection.

903.
fig. 109

John Park

Half-length and turned three-quarters right, he stands before a background of green trees against blue and white sky and holds a black and white spaniel. He wears a blue-gray coat with gilt buttons over a yellow waistcoat and white neckcloth.
Oil on canvas. 30 × 25 in. (76.2 × 63.5 cm.)
Painted in 1780.
Collections: Thomas Inglis, London, brought to Boston in 1887; George H. Story, New York; Eben D. Jordan, Boston, about 1896.
Gift of Robert Jordan from the collection of Eben D. Jordan. 24.211

Inscribed on the stretcher is: *Portrait of my dear Father John Park/ 1780 aged 57/ painted by G. Stewart.* The sitter has not yet been identified. In 1887, Mr. Inglis wrote from London that "a Mr. Park, who wrote the history of Hamstead" is represented; that John James Park was not born until 1785.

Possibly shown is John Parke, the famous oboist of London, born about 1745. However, that Parke would have been but about thirty-five in 1780, a date which closely concurs with the style of costume and Stuart's painting. To support the identification as the oboist, Mount (*see below*) has suggested, in itself plausible, that the dog is by Trumbull, who was also in West's studio in 1780. The painting style and coarse crackle pattern do vary from the rest, and x-rays have revealed that the hand once held a horizontal, rectangular object, perhaps a book or musical manuscript. However, if the painting was by Stuart in 1780, the need for a change by Trumbull at about that time remains unexplained.

References: *Collection of Eben D. Jordan—Catalogue of Pictures*, Boston, 1903, no. 96./ L. Park, *Stuart*, New York, 1926, II, p. 902./ C.M. Mount, *Stuart*, New York, 1964, pp. 117, 361.

Exhibitions: New York, Metropolitan Museum, *American Artists*, 1895, no. 132./ Brookline, Mass., Town Hall, *Loan Exhibition*, 1897, no. 97 (as John Parr).

904.
fig. 110

John Richardson

Dressed in a high-collared blue coat with gold buttons, a frilled shirt and white stock, the young man, half-length, turns three-quarters right. The background is of blue sky and brown clouds within brown spandrels.

Oil on canvas. Painted oval. 29¾ × 24¾ in. (75.5 × 62.8 cm.)
Painted about 1788.

Collections: The Rev. Gardiner Richardson Young, Culduff, County Donegal, Ireland; Miss Katherine Mary Gervais, his niece, County Tyrone, Ireland; Percy R. Pyne II, probably New York; William K. Richardson, Boston; Mrs. Louis Curtis, Sr., his sister, Brookline, Mass., 1951; Louis Curtis, her son, Brookline.

Gift of Louis Curtis, in memory of his uncle, William K. Richardson. 55.1001

John Richardson, a landowner near Colraim, County Londonderry, Ireland, married a Mrs. Whalley (née Ward); he was a member of the Irish Parliament for Newton Lemavady in 1790, and died childless. Painted in Dublin soon after Stuart's arrival from London.

References: L. Park, *Stuart*, New York, 1926, II, no. 707 (repr. IV, p. 434)./ C.M. Mount, *Stuart*, New York, 1964, p. 362.

Exhibition: Allentown, Pa., Allentown Museum, *World of Benjamin West*, 1962, no. 69 (repr.).

905.
fig. 111

Dorcas, Lady Blackwood (Dorcas Stevenson), later Baroness Dufferin

An elderly lady, half-length, sits, facing front, wearing a blue sash and black shawl and choker with her pale gray dress and cap. The background is nearly black.

Oil on canvas. 30¼ × 25 in. (76.8 × 63.5 cm.)
Painted about 1788–1793.

Collections: Descendants of the sitter; Herbert C. Labey, London, before 1922.

Helen and Alice Colburn Fund. 22.737

Dorcas Stevenson (1726–1807), daughter of James Stevenson of Killyleagh, County Down, Ireland, in 1751 married Sir John Blackwood, M.P. for Killyleagh and Bangor, a strong opponent of the union between Ireland and England. In 1800 she was created Baroness Dufferin and Claneboye of Ballyleidy and Killyleagh at the request of her son James; she died in London. The portrait was painted during Stuart's sojourn in Ireland from 1788 to 1793; an x-ray has revealed another portrait, of a man, by Stuart underneath that of the Baroness.

References: "Two Drawings and Two Paintings," *MFA Bulletin*, 1923, XXI, no. 123, p. 6 (repr. p. 5)./ L. Park, *Stuart*, New York, 1926, I, no. 255 (repr. III, p. 156)./ V. Barker, *American Painting*, New York, 1950, p. 245./ C.M. Mount, *Stuart*, New York, 1964, p. 359.

Exhibitions: Boston, MFA, *Stuart*, 1928, no. 21./ Indianapolis, Herron Museum of Art, *Stuart*, 1942, no. 6 (repr.).

906.
fig. 112

Colonel James Swan

Turned three-quarters left, bust-length, the young man wears a blue coat with gilt buttons over a white neckcloth tied in an elaborate bow. Behind is a brown and red drapery before blue sky with white clouds.

Oil on canvas. 28¾ × 23½ in. (73 × 59.7 cm.)
Painted about 1793–1798.

Collections: Mrs. John Clarke Howard, the sitter's daughter, Boston, about 1830; Hepzibah Howard Wayland, her daughter, Providence, R.I., 1833; Howard Wayland, her son, Providence; Mrs. Charles Stafford, his widow, remarried, Providence; Miss Elizabeth Howard Bartol, the sitter's great-granddaughter, Boston.

Swan Collection. Bequest of Elizabeth Howard Bartol. 27.538

James Swan (about 1750–1831), born in Fifeshire, Scotland, came to America at eleven and at eighteen was a clerk in a Boston counting house. During the American Revolution he was a Major of Artillery, later promoted to Colonel; in 1784–1785 he was Representative from Dorchester to the General Court. By the end of the Revolution he held considerable land in Virginia and Maine; in 1785 his wife, Hepzibah Clark (*Mrs. James Swan* [*Hepzibah Clarke*], Cat. no. 920) inherited most of the estate of William Dennie. Noted for their extravagance, by 1787 Swan was forced to move to Paris; but Lafayette and others made possible his return to New England a rich man. At the time of the French Revolution he was able to acquire an extensive collection of French art and furniture from fleeing aristocrats; many are now in the MFA as part of the Swan Collection. He returned to France in 1798, again went bankrupt, and remained for twenty-two years in semivoluntary, but comfortable, confinement in the French debtor's prison at Ste.-Pélagie. The portrait was painted in New York or Philadelphia between Stuart's return in 1793 and Swan's departure for France in 1798.

References: G.C. Mason, *Stuart*, New York, 1879, p. 263./ L. Park, *Stuart*, New York, 1926, II, no. 813 (repr. IV, p. 504)./ L. Dresser, "Eighteenth Century Portraits," *Maine and Its Role in American Art*, New York, 1963, pp. 22, 28 (repr. p. 22).

Exhibitions: Boston Athenaeum, *Stuart*, 1828, no. 191./ Boston, MFA, *Stuart*, 1880, no. 222./ Boston, Copley Hall, *Portraits*, 1896, no. 241./ San Francisco, M.H. de Young Memorial Museum and California Palace of the Legion of Honor, *American Painting*, 1935, no. 35.

907.
fig. 118

George Washington

An unfinished bust-length portrait, his head, with ruddy complexion and blue eyes, is turned three-quarters left; he wears a white stock and black jacket. Behind him the background is sketched in brown.

Oil on canvas. 48 × 37 in. (121.9 × 94 cm.)
Painted in 1796.

Collections: Purchased from the artist's estate by the Washington Association, Boston, and twenty-two subscribers, and given by them to the Boston Athenaeum, 1831.

Deposited by the Boston Athenaeum, 1876. Ath. 1

General George Washington (1732–1799) was the first President of the U.S., from 1789 to 1797. Conflicting traditions and records have caused some confusion concerning the origin of the "Athenaeum Head," so called because of its purchase for the Boston Athenaeum. Stuart's first portrait of Washington from life, the so-called "Vaughan portrait" (National Gallery, Washington) was painted in March, 1795. Lawrence Park (*Stuart*, II, p. 854, no. 18) considered the full-length "Lansdowne portrait" commissioned by William Bingham of Philadelphia, the second, citing a letter of April, 1796 by Washington to Stuart which mentions a promise of a portrait for Mrs. Bingham. The "Athenaeum Head" has been considered traditionally the third and last life portrait, painted also in Philadelphia or the Germantown studio, in 1796 with its pendant of Martha Washington (Cat. no. 908). This unfinished pair is known to have remained in Stuart's possession until his death, the one serving as the model for scores of replicas (for example, Cat. nos. 914 and 926). C.M. Mount (*see below*) contends that but two life portraits were made, the "Athenaeum Head" being the Bingham commission uncompleted. However, this theory provides no satisfactory explanation for the fact that they are unfinished or for the existence of the pendant of Mrs. Washington; Stuart compounded the problem by his statement appended to the April, 1796 letter from Washington that he painted three portraits of Washington from life, one the "Athenaeum Head," one owned that year (1823) by Samuel Williams of London (a version of the Lansdowne type), and one rubbed out. The "Athenaeum Head" is the best known representation of Washington, in large part due to the replicas and to the copies by Stuart's own daughter, Jane, and innumerable others.

References: T.G. Cary, *Thomas Handasyd Perkins Memoir*, Boston, 1856, pp. 197–201./ H.T. Tuckerman, *Book of the Artists*, New York, 1870, pp. 118–119, 627./ Jane Stuart, "Stuart Portraits of Washington," *Scribner's Monthly*, 1876, XII, no. 3, pp. 370, 374 (engr. p. 368)./ G.C. Mason, *Stuart*, New York, 1879, pp. 89, 90, 106, 115–119 (repr. opp. p. 103)./ E.B. Johnston, *Original Portraits of Washington*, Boston, 1881, pp. 84–85, 103 (pl. XIII)./ W.H. Downes, "Boston Painters and Paintings," *Atlantic Monthly*, 1888, LXII, no. 369, p. 97./ L.M. Bryant, *American Pictures and Their Painters*, New York, 1917, pp. 30–31 (fig. 6)./ W. Dunlap, *History of the Arts of Design*, Boston, 1918, I, pp. 231–232./ G.A. Eisen, "Stuart's Three Washingtons," *International Studio*, 1923, LXXVI, no. 309, pp. 386, 394 (repr. p. 394)./ M. Fielding, *Stuart's Portraits of Washington*, Philadelphia, 1923, pp. 100–105, no. 33 (repr. p. 152)./ L. Park, *Stuart*, New York, 1926, II, p. 863, no. 34 (repr. IV, p. 604)./ Mrs. Basil Hall, U. Pope-Hennessy ed., *The Aristocratic Journey 1827–28*, New York, 1931, p. 93./ J.H. Morgan and M. Fielding, *Life Portraits of Washington*, Philadelphia, 1931, pp. 223–224, 226, 228–229, 234, 240, no. 34 (repr. opp. p. 240)./ W.T. Whitley, *Stuart*, Cambridge, Mass., 1932, pp. 112–114, 215–219./ M.M. Swan, *The Athenaeum Gallery*, Boston, 1940, pp. 74, 78–84 (repr. opp. p. 74)./ J.T. Flexner, *Light of Distant Skies*, New York, 1954, p. 77 (fig. 37)./ —, *Stuart*, New York, 1955, pp. 122–131, 145–146./ C.M. Mount, *Stuart*, New York, 1964, pp. 201–203, 212, 249, 304, 313, 316 (repr. pp. 224–225).

Exhibitions: Boston Athenaeum, *Stuart*, 1828, no. 120./ Boston, MFA, *Contemporary Art*, 1879, no. 101./ —, *Stuart*, 1880, no. 201./ —, *Stuart*, 1928, no. 76 (repr. cover).

908.

fig. 117

Martha Washington (Martha Dandridge Custis)

The head of an elderly lady, turned three-quarters right; she wears a white cap and only the edge of her fichu shows. The unfinished background is sketched in brown.
Oil on canvas. 48 × 37 in. (121.9 × 94 cm.)
Painted in 1796.
Collections: Purchased from the artist's estate by the Washington Association, Boston, and twenty-two subscribers, and given to the Boston Athenaeum, 1831.
Deposited by the Boston Athenaeum, 1876. Ath. 2

Martha Dandridge (1731–1802), eldest child of Col. John and Frances Jones Dandridge of Kent County, Va., married in 1749 Daniel Parke Custis, and had two children by him. He died in 1757, and two years later she married George Washington. She accompanied her husband in campaigns during the Revolution, and afterwards, known for her complacent and unpretentious ways, managed his household at Mt. Vernon until her death. Her portrait, the only one painted by Stuart from life, has the same history as that of its pendant, Cat. no. 907.

References: T.S. Cary, *Thomas Handasyd Perkins Memoir*, Boston, 1856, p. 201./ H.T. Tuckerman, *Book of the Artists*, New York, 1870, p. 627./ G.C. Mason, *Stuart*, 1879, pp. 27, 116–117 (repr. opp. p. 115)./ E.B. Johnston, *Original Portraits of Washington*, Boston, 1881, pp. 84–85, 103./ W.H. Downes, "Boston Painters and Paintings," *Atlantic Monthly*, 1888, LXII, no. 369, p. 97./ W. Dunlap, *History of the Arts of*

Design, Boston, 1918, I, p. 232./ L. Park, *Stuart*, New York, 1926, II, no. 882 (repr. IV, p. 551)./ W.T. Whitley, *Stuart*, Cambridge, Mass., 1932, p. 216./ M.M. Swan, *The Athenaeum Gallery*, Boston, 1940, pp. 79–82 (repr. opp. p. 80)./ J.T. Flexner, *Stuart*, New York, 1955, pp. 142–143./ C.M. Mount, *Stuart*, New York, 1964, pp. 202, 212, 220 (repr. pp. 128–129).

Exhibitions: Boston Athenaeum, *Stuart*, 1828, no. 121./ Boston, MFA, *Contemporary Art*, 1879, no. 102./ —, *Stuart*, 1880, no. 202./ —, *Stuart*, 1928, no. 79.

909. **Counsellor John Dunn**

Half-length in left profile, his head turned front, he fingers the fur collar of his black and red coat. The background is brown.

Oil on canvas. 28½ × 23½ in. (72.3 × 59.7 cm.)

Painted about 1798.

Collections: Given by the sitter to Mrs. Perez Morton, Dorchester, Mass., about 1798; George Watson Brimmer, Boston, 1828; Martin Brimmer, his nephew, Boston, by 1855; Mrs. Martin Brimmer.

Bequest of Mrs. Martin Brimmer. 06.2427

John Dunn, a member of the Irish Parliament for the borough of Randalstown, County Antrim, from 1783 to 1787, came to America to study Indian languages and was in Philadelphia about 1798, when he sat to Stuart. The artist painted two other portraits of him. A sketch with which Stuart was unwilling to part, and which his daughter Jane sold to J. Montgomery Sears, Boston, belonged to Mrs. J.D. Cameron Bradley, Southboro, Mass. A third version was purchased from the Dunn family in Norfolk, England about 1923, for the Thomas B. Clarke Collection. What appears to be possibly an early copy after the MFA picture (oval, oil on canvas, 22¾ × 18¾ in.) was recently on the art market.

References: H.T. Tuckerman, *Book of the Artists*, New York, 1870, p. 110./ G.C. Mason, *Stuart*, New York, 1879, p. 176./ L. Park, *Stuart*, New York, 1926, I, no. 257./ P.S. Harris, "The Enigmatic Mr. Dunn," *Winterthur Portfolio*, 1964, I, p. 215 (fig. 6)./ C.M. Mount, *Stuart*, New York, 1964, p. 367.

Exhibitions: Boston Athenaeum, *Stuart*, 1828, no. 34./ —, *Exhibitions*, 1834, no. 135; 1837, no. 91; 1838, no. 68; 1855, no. 168./ Boston, MFA, *Stuart*, 1880, no. 215./ Chicago, *World's Columbian Exposition*, 1893, no. 2853c./ Boston, MFA, *Stuart*, 1928, no. 22./ University of Minnesota Gallery, *Survey of Colonial and Provincial Painting*, 1939, no. 35.

910. **Mrs. Perez Morton (Sarah Wentworth Apthorp)**

fig. 121

Half-length, seated and turned three-quarters left, her left hand rests upon books before her; she wears a black dress, trimmed in white, with a green and brown shawl. The chair is red; the background, brown.

Oil on canvas. 29¼ × 24 in. (74.3 × 61 cm.)

Painted about 1802.

Collections: Griselda Eastwick Cunningham Clinch, the sitter's granddaughter, Boston, 1846; the Rev. Joseph Hart Clinch, her husband, Boston, 1873; Sarah Apthorp Clinch Bond, their daughter, Boston, 1884; Mary Griselda Clinch Fogg, her sister, Boston, about 1890; Miss Una Gray, her niece, Boston, 1905; Hannah Marcy and Grace M. Edwards, Boston, 1916.

Juliana Cheney Edwards Collection. Bequest of Hannah Marcy Edwards in memory of her mother. 39.681

Sarah Wentworth Apthorp (1759–1846), daughter of James and Sarah Wentworth Apthorp of Braintree, Mass., married Perez Morton, a Boston lawyer, in 1781. She became famous for her writing and poetry, for her beauty and cultural accomplishment, and was called the "American Sappho." Her portrait was painted in Philadelphia. Both the Winterthur Museum and the Worcester Art Museum own versions of the portrait by Stuart; the latter is unfinished.

References: J. Wentworth, *The Wentworth Genealogy*, Boston, 1878, p. 520./ G.C. Mason, *Stuart*, New York, 1879, pp. 225–228./ C.H. Hart, "Stuart," *American Art*

Review, 1880, I, no. 2, pp. 2, 486./ L. Park, *Stuart*, New York, 1926, II, no. 562 (repr. IV, p. 341)./ "Juliana Cheney Edwards Collection," *MFA Bulletin*, 1939, XXXVII, no. 224, p. 112, no. 56./ J.T. Flexner, *Stuart*, New York, 1955, pp. 112–114./ P.S. Harris, "Stuart and a Portrait of Mrs. Sarah Morton," *Winterthur Portfolio*, 1964, I, pp. 202–206 (fig. 2)./ C.M. Mount, *Stuart*, New York, 1964, pp. 242–248, 257, 275–276.

Exhibitions: Boston Athenaeum, *Stuart*, 1828, no. 181?./ Boston, MFA, *Stuart*, 1880, no. 232./ Boston, Copley Society, *Portraits and Pictures of Fair Women*, 1902, no. 66./ Boston, MFA, *Stuart*, 1928, no. 47.

911.

fig. 113

Dr. Thomas Bartlett

A young man, but with white hair, stands half-length, turned three-quarters right, before a gray column and red drapery. He wears a black coat over a white stock and ruffled shirt.

Oil on panel. 29 × 23½ in. (73.6 × 59.7 cm.)

Painted about 1805.

Collections: Maria Bartlett Hall, the sitter's daughter, Springfield, Mass.; Thomas B. Hall, her son, Brookline, Mass.; Minna B. Hall, his daughter, Brookline.

Bequest of Minna Bartlett Hall. 51.2360

Thomas Bartlett (1767–1856), son of John and Tabitha Kidder Bartlett of Boston, began his career as a Boston apothecary, but retired early. He was married twice: in 1794 to Alice Fitzpatrick, widow of Edward Wyer; and in 1802 to Hannah Gray, widow of James Wilson. His portrait is pendant to the following one, *Mrs. Thomas Bartlett (Hannah Gray Wilson)* (Cat. no. 912).

References: G.C. Mason, *Stuart*, New York, 1879, p. 134./ L. Park, *Stuart*, New York, 1926, I, no. 65 (repr. III, p. 42)./ C.M. Mount, *Stuart*, New York, 1964, p. 364.

Exhibitions: Boston Athenaeum, *Stuart*, 1828, no. 21./ Boston, Copley Hall, *Portraits*, 1896, no. 262.

912.

fig. 114

Mrs. Thomas Bartlett (Hannah Gray Wilson)

Half-length and turned three-quarters left, she sits in a red upholstered chair, her arms folded about a yellow stole; her empire dress and turban are white. Behind, a red curtain is draped about a central gray column before cloudy blue sky.

Oil on panel. 28¾ × 23½ in. (73 × 59.7 cm.)

Painted about 1805.

Collections: Same as Cat. no. 911.

Bequest of Minna Bartlett Hall. 51.2361

Hannah Gray (1774–1808), daughter of Ellis and Sarah Dolbeare Gray of Boston, in 1793 married the Hon. James Wilson of Philadelphia, Justice of the U.S. Supreme Court and a signer of the Declaration of Independence. He died in 1798 and she was remarried in 1802 to Thomas Bartlett. In 1806 she and her husband left Boston for London, where she died. This portrait is pendant to the preceding portrait.

References: G.C. Mason, *Stuart*, New York, 1879, p. 134./ L. Park, *Stuart*, New York, 1926, I, no. 66 (repr. III, p. 43)./ C.M. Mount, *Stuart*, New York, 1964, pp. 255, 364.

Exhibitions: Boston Athenaeum, *Stuart*, 1828, no. 22./ Boston, Copley Hall, *Portraits*, 1896, no. 263./ Boston, MFA, *Stuart*, 1928, no. 8.

913.

fig. 119

General Henry Knox

Standing in three-quarter length, he turns three-quarters right and rests his left hand on the barrel of a gray cannon; his blue uniform coat, lined in yellow with gold epaulets, is worn over yellow breeches and waistcoat. The clouds behind are gray and brown.

Oil on panel. 47 × 38½ in. (119.4 × 97.8 cm.)

Painted about 1805.

Deposited by the City of Boston. 30.76b

Henry Knox (1750–1806) was born in Boston, the son of William and Mary Campbell Knox. He was active in military affairs at an early age and by the beginning of the Revolution had become a close friend and adviser of George Washington. His speciality was the artillery, and he participated in almost every important battle of the war. From 1785 to 1794 he served as Secretary of War, and he and his wife became known for their lavish hospitality and mode of life. He died in Thomaston, Me., where he had retired to manage his extensive farmlands. His portrait was probably painted soon after Stuart had settled in Boston. Copies are owned by Bowdoin College, Brunswick, Me., the State House of Augusta, Me., and Faneuil Hall, Boston; there are many others. A copy by Jane Stuart was owned by Mrs. John P. Hollingsworth, Philadelphia. The MFA owns a miniature copy of the head by Elkanah Tisdale.

References: "General Henry Knox," *The Port-Folio*, 1812, VII, no. 2 (engr. opp. p. 101)./ "Early American Art," *Harper's New Monthly Magazine*, 1879, LIX, no. 354 (repr. p. 823)./ G.C. Mason, *Stuart*, New York, 1879, p. 55 (repr. p. 211)./ W.H. Downes, "Boston Painters and Paintings," *Atlantic Monthly*, 1888, LXII, no. 369, pp. 97–98./ S. Isham, *American Painting*, New York, 1905 (fig. 19)./ L. Park, *Stuart*, New York, 1926, I, no. 468 (repr. III, p. 280)./ A. Burroughs, *Limners and Likenesses*, Cambridge, Mass., 1936, p. 104./ N. Callahan, *Knox*, New York, 1958, p. 26 (repr.)./ C.M. Mount, *Stuart*, New York, 1964, pp. 273–274, 284.

Exhibitions: Boston Athenaeum, *Exhibition*, 1828, no. 125./ —, *Stuart*, 1828, no. 70./ Boston, MFA, *Contemporary Art*, 1879, no. 104./ —, *Stuart*, 1880, no. 257./ —, *Stuart*, 1928, no. 40./ Paris, Musée du Jeu de Paume, *Trois Siècles d'Art aux Etats-Unis*, 1938, no. 166; Pittsburgh, Pa., Carnegie Institute, *Survey of American Painting*, 1940, no. 54 (pl. 13)./ Waterville, Me., Colby College and circulated in the U.S., *Maine and Its Artists*, 1963–1964, no. 112.

914.

fig. 122

George Washington

Bust-length and turned three-quarters left on a brown background, he wears a black coat with a white stock and ruffled shirt.

Oil on panel. 26¼ × 21¼ in. (66.7 × 54 cm.)

Painted probably after 1805.

Collections: Thomas Handasyd Perkins I, Boston; Elizabeth Perkins Cabot, his daughter, Boston; Arthur Tracy Cabot, her grandson, Boston, 1885.

Bequest of Arthur Tracy Cabot. 42.543

The portrait is a replica of Stuart's "Athenaeum Head" (Cat. no. 907) of Washington. In his memoirs, Thomas Handasyd Perkins documents his painting thus: "In the summer of 1796, I visited the city of Washington ... and was invited to visit Mt. Vernon. ... In the autumn of the year of my visit, Mr. Stuart painted a full length portrait of the General. ... The bust I have, also by Stuart, is a fac-simile of the original." Perkins undoubtedly acquired the painting years after his visit to Washington in 1796, the same year in which the "Athenaeum Head" prototype itself was painted; the replica was probably bought from Stuart in Boston after 1805.

References: T.G. Cary, *Thomas Handasyd Perkins Memoir*, Boston, 1856, pp. 197–201./ C.M. Mount, *Stuart*, New York, 1964, p. 379.

Exhibition: Colorado Springs Fine Arts Center, *Likeness of America 1680–1820*, 1949, no. 39.

915.

fig. 120

Washington at Dorchester Heights

He stands full-length, facing front, and holds the reins of his gray horse. His uniform coat is blue lined with buff; his breeches and waistcoat are white; his boots, black. Behind, smoke from burning ships in the harbor below fills the sky with brown and gray clouds, lighted with flashes of pink and orange.

Oil on panel. 107½ × 71¼ in. (273 × 181 cm.)

Painted in 1806.

Collection: Ordered for and presented to the City of Boston by Samuel Parkman, 1806.

Deposited by the City of Boston. 30.76a

Washington's strategic seizure of Dorchester Heights, overlooking Boston

Harbor, in the spring of 1776 forced the British fleet to abandon the harbor. Painted seven years after the death of Washington, Stuart used his full-length "Lansdowne" portrait (Pennsylvania Academy of the Fine Arts) as a model, which made Washington twenty years older than he would have been at Dorchester Heights, and exercised poetic license in giving him dress uniform. The picture was painted in nine days; before cradling, it was inscribed on the back: *Gilbert Stuart/ Painted this picture/ of/ Genl. Washington/ for/ The Honbl/ Saml. Parkman/ who/ Presented it to the Town/ of/ Boston/ July 4th/ 1806.* Jane Stuart painted copies which hang in Faneuil Hall and the Bostonian Society, Boston; many other copies exist, of which none are by Stuart.

References: G.C. Mason, *Stuart*, New York, 1879, pp. 103–105, 236./ E.B. Johnston, *Original Portraits of Washington*, Boston, 1881, pp. 80, 90, 91, 103 (pl. xiv)./ W.H. Downes, "Boston Painters and Paintings," *Atlantic Monthly*, 1888, lxii no. 369, p. 97./ W. Dunlap, *History of the Arts of Design*, Boston, 1918, i, p. 236./ M. Fielding, *Stuart's Portraits of Washington*, Philadelphia, 1923, no. 27 (repr. p. 64)./ L. Park, *Stuart*, New York, 1926, ii, p. 860, no. 28 (repr. iv, p. 602)./ J.H. Morgan and M. Fielding, *Life Portraits of Washington*, Philadelphia, 1931, p. 269, no. 28 (repr.)./ J.T. Flexner, *Stuart*, New York, 1955, p. 156./ C.M. Mount, *Stuart*, New York, 1964, pp. 272, 379.

Exhibitions: Boston Athenaeum, *Exhibition*, 1827, no. 97./ —, *Stuart*, 1828, no. 119.

916.

fig. 115

John Amory, Jr.

Bust-length, turned three-quarters right, on an olive-brown background, he wears a black coat over a white stock and high collar.

Oil on panel. 26 × 21¼ in. (66 × 54 cm.)

Painted about 1806.

Collections: Catherine Amory Codman, the sitter's daughter, Boston; Misses Catherine E. and Maria P. Codman, her daughters, Bristol, R.I.; Martha Codman Karolik, their niece, Newport, R.I., about 1902.

M. and M. Karolik Collection of Eighteenth Century American Arts. 37.40

John Amory, Jr. (1759–1832) was the son of John Amory and Katharine Greene Amory (portraits by Copley, Cat. nos. 278, 258) of Boston. He started a mercantile business with his brother Thomas and prospered enough to enable him to retire when forty years old. He lived in Boston and Roxbury, Mass. From his apparent age, the portrait was painted soon after Stuart arrived in Boston; it is pendant to that of his wife (Cat. no. 917). His daughter, Mrs. Henry Codman, was portrayed by Alvan Clark (Cat. no. 220).

References: G.C. Mason, *Stuart*, New York, 1879, p. 128./ L. Park, *Stuart*, New York, 1926, i, no. 16 (repr. iii, p. 8)./ E.J. Hipkiss, *M. and M. Karolik Collection of Eighteenth Century American Arts*, Boston, 1941, no. 9 (repr. p. 19)./ —, "American Tradition in Its First Maturity," *Art News*, 1941, xl, no. 16, p. 13./ C.M. Mount, *Stuart*, New York, 1964, p. 363.

917.

fig. 116

Mrs. John Amory, Jr. (Catherine Willard)

Bust-length and facing three-quarters left, she wears a red stole about a gray-pink dress tied with a white ribbon, a high white neck-ruffle, and a turban. The background is brown.

Oil on panel. 26 × 21¼ in. (66 × 54 cm.)

Painted about 1806.

Collections: Same as Cat. no. 916.

M. and M. Karolik Collection of Eighteenth Century American Arts. 37.39

Catherine Willard (1758–1831), daughter of Col. Levi and Catherine Chandler Willard (portraits by Winthrop Chandler, Cat. nos. 204, 205) married John Amory, Jr. in 1792. The portrait is a pendant to the preceding.

References: G.C. Mason, *Stuart*, New York, 1879, p. 128./ L. Park, *Stuart*, New York, 1926, i, no. 17 (repr. iii, p. 9)./ E.J. Hipkiss, *M. and M. Karolik Collection of Eighteenth*

Century American Arts, Boston, 1941, no. 10 (repr. p. 21)./ —, "American Tradition in Its First Maturity," *Art News*, 1941, XL, no. 16 (repr. p. 13)./ C.M. Mount, *Stuart*, New York, 1964, p. 363.

918.

fig. 123

Adam Babcock

An elderly man, seated half-length, turned three-quarters left, and holding a gold snuff box, wears a black coat and white stock. His gilt chair is upholstered in red, and the wall behind is dark gray.

Oil on panel. 32¼ × 26¼ in. (81.9 × 66.7 cm.)
Painted about 1806–1810.
Collections: William P. Babcock, grandson of the sitter, San Francisco; William Babcock, his son, San Francisco; Harry Babcock, his brother, San Francisco.
Bequest of Harry Babcock. 30.729
Adam Babcock (1740–1817), son of Dr. Joshua Babcock (portrait by Blackburn, Cat. no. 150) and Hannah Stanton Babcock, was born in Westerly, R.I. During the Revolution he lived in New Haven, Conn. and as merchant and shipowner carried supplies for the Colonial Army. He later moved to Boston and Brookline, Mass., where he lived the rest of his days. When questioned about the missing finger on Babcock's left hand, Stuart is said to have suggested that it might be in the snuff box. The portrait was painted soon after Stuart arrived in Boston.
References: G.C. Mason, *Stuart*, New York, 1879, p. 131./ L. Park, *Stuart*, New York, 1926, I, no. 41 (repr. III, p. 27)./ C.M. Mount, *Stuart*, New York, 1964, p. 364.

919.

William Orne

Turned three-quarters left, half-length, he wears a black coat with a high white collar and neckcloth. The background is brown.

Oil on panel. 26¼ × 21½ in. (66.7 × 54.6 cm.)
Painted about 1806–1810.
Collection: Eliza Orne White, great-granddaughter of the sitter, Brookline, Mass.
Bequest of Eliza Orne White. 47.210
William Orne (1751–1815) was a prominent shipowner and East India merchant of Salem, Mass. Park was apparently unaware of this painting in 1926 but does record a version (L. Park, *Stuart*, New York, 1926, I, no. 596) painted in Boston about 1806 (Mrs. W. Douglas Hopkins, Buffalo, N.Y.). A copy attributed variously to Charles Osgood or James Frothingham is in the Essex Institute, Salem. The underlying strength of the face in our picture indicates that the head and neckcloth are by Stuart; the remainder, possibly sketched out by Stuart, seems to be the work of another artist whose hand strayed occasionally into areas of the hair and cheeks.
Reference: C.M. Mount, *Stuart*, New York, 1964, p. 372 (as Stuart).

920.

fig. 124

Mrs. James Swan (Hepzibah Clark)

Seated half-length in a gilt chair upholstered in red and turned three-quarters left, her black dress is edged with white lace. Over her head and one shoulder she wears a white lace scarf. The background is olive brown.

Oil on panel. 32½ × 26½ in. (82.5 × 67.3 cm.)
Painted about 1806–1810.
Collections: Mrs. John Clarke Howard, the sitter's daughter, Boston; about 1830; Hepzibah Howard Wayland, her daughter, Providence, R.I., 1833; Howard Wayland, her son, Providence; Mrs. Charles Stafford, his widow, remarried, Providence; Miss Elizabeth Howard Bartol, the sitter's great-granddaughter, Boston.
Swan Collection. Bequest of Elizabeth Howard Bartol. 27.539
Hepzibah Clark (1756–1825), daughter of Barnabas Clark, was left a large fortune by her father's friend William Dennie and in 1776 married James Swan (Cat. no. 906). In 1796 they built a mansion in Dorchester, Mass.

which contained an exceptional collection of French furnishings and art objects. She lived there for the rest of her life in a glamorous and eccentric fashion. The portrait was painted in Boston. Park reproduces a different and unlocated portrait of Mrs. Swan.

References: H.T. Tuckerman, *Book of the Artists*, New York, 1870, p. 109./ G.C. Mason, *Stuart*, New York, 1879, p. 263./ "The 1895 Exhibition of Portraits of Women," *Harper's Weekly*, 1895, xxxix, no. 1996 (repr. p. 269)./ L. Park, *Stuart*, New York, 1926, ii, no. 814./ C.M. Mount, *Stuart*, New York, 1964, p. 375.

Exhibitions: Boston Athenaeum, *Stuart*, 1828, no. 190./ Boston, MFA, *Stuart*, 1880, no. 223./ Boston, Copley Hall, *Portraits of Women*, 1895, no. 328./ Boston, MFA, *Stuart*, 1928, no. 73.

921.

fig. 125

Mrs. John Clarke Howard (Hepzibah Swan)

A young woman, half-length, in a white empire dress and red stole, turns three-quarters left. Behind her is a red curtain before a brown wall.

Oil on panel. 29 × 23½ in. (73.6 × 59.7 cm.)
Painted about 1806–1810.
Collections: Mrs. Cyrus A. Bartol, the sitter's daughter, Boston, by 1880; Elizabeth H. Bartol, her daughter, Boston, by 1895.
Swan Collection. Bequest of Elizabeth Howard Bartol. 27.540

Hepzibah Swan (1777–1833), daughter of Colonel James Swan and Hepzibah Clark Swan (Cat. nos. 906, 920), married Dr. John Clarke Howard of Boston in 1800; they had six children. The portrait was probably painted at the same time as that of her mother.

References: G.C. Mason, *Stuart*, New York, 1879, p. 201./ L. Park, *Stuart*, New York, 1926, i, no. 416 (repr. iii, p. 251)./ C.M. Mount, *Stuart*, New York, 1964, p. 369.

Exhibitions: Boston, Athenaeum, *Stuart*, 1828, no. 192./ Boston, MFA, *Stuart*, 1880, no. 221./ Boston, Copley Hall, *Portraits of Women*, 1895, no. 303.

922.

fig. 126

Governor James Sullivan

Seated in half-length, turned three-quarters left, he wears a dark blue coat and white stock with a frilled shirt and holds a brown book upright. His chair is upholstered in red. The background is brown.

Oil on panel. 33 × 26½ in. (83.8 × 67.3 cm.)
Painted in 1807.
Collections: William Sullivan, Boston, 1808; Sarah Sullivan Oakey, his daughter, New York; Alexander Cochrane, Boston, 1883.
Bequest of Alexander Cochrane. 19.760

James Sullivan (1744–1808), born in Berwick, Me., was a lawyer, a member of the first Provincial Congress, for six years a Judge of the Superior Court, and from 1790 until shortly before his death Attorney General for Massachusetts. He was elected Governor of the state in 1807. First President of the Massachusetts Historical Society, he wrote on political subjects. He died in Boston, where his portrait had been painted in 1807 (from correspondence of his granddaughter, Mrs. Oakey). The Massachusetts Historical Society owns a replica of the same year.

References: G.C. Mason, *Stuart*, New York, 1879, p. 262./ L. Park, *Stuart*, New York, 1926, ii, no. 809./ C.M. Mount, *Stuart*, New York, 1964, p. 575.

Exhibitions: Boston Athenaeum, *Stuart*, 1828, no. 85./ —, *Exhibition*, 1831, no. 122./ New York, Metropolitan Museum, *Early American Artists*, 1895–1896, no. 208n.

923.

fig. 127

Theodore Sedgwick

Bust-length, he is turned three-quarters left before a brown background and wears a black coat with a white ruffled shirt and stock.

Oil on canvas. 29 × 23¾ in. (73.6 × 60.3 cm.)
Painted about 1808.
Collections: Mrs. Elizabeth Sedgwick Pomeroy, the sitter's daughter, Stockbridge, Mass.; Mrs. Catherine Pomeroy Parker, her daughter, Stockbridge; Miss Grace Parker, her daughter, Stockbridge; Charles Sedgwick Racke-

mann, her cousin, Milton, Mass., 1908.
Bequest of Charles Sedgwick Rackemann. 33.508

Theodore Sedgwick (1746–1813), born in Hartford, Conn., was the son of Benjamin and Ann Thompson Sedgwick. A lawyer, famous for his defense of an escaped Negro slave and Revolutionary soldier, he was a member both of the Massachusetts House of Representatives (for Sheffield) and of the Continental Congress. A right-wing Federalist, he was a member of Congress from 1789 to 1800 and a strong suppressor of Shays' Rebellion. From 1802 until his death he was Judge of the Superior Court of Massachusetts. The portrait hung in his Stockbridge home for nearly a century; several copies of it are extant.

References: G.C. Mason, *Stuart*, New York, 1879, p. 253./ L. Park, *Stuart*, New York, 1926, II, no. 743 (repr. LV, p. 456)./ C.M. Mount, *Stuart*, New York, 1964, p. 374.

924.

fig. 128

Dr. Samuel Danforth

Half-length and posed in left profile before a rose-colored drapery, his face turns forward. He wears a white stock and neckcloth and a high-collared black coat, and is seated in a red upholstered gilt armchair. His hands crossed before him hold a book and an open letter.

Oil on canvas: 36 × 30½ in. (91.5 × 77.5 cm.)
Painted about 1809.
Signed on letter: *G. Stuart*. Painted about 1809.
Collections: Daughters of the sitter; bequeathed by Elizabeth Shelburne Bowers Danforth, a daughter, to the Massachusetts Medical Society, 1885; the Boston Medical Library.
Lent by the Boston Medical Library. 256.48

Dr. Samuel Danforth (1740–1827), son of Samuel and Elizabeth Symmes Danforth of Cambridge, Mass., was a Boston physician whose popularity—despite an emotional temperament—dimmed only at the time of the American Revolution, when his Loyalist inclinations caused him to live in Newport, R.I. for two years. A Fellow of the American Academy of Arts and Sciences, he was also President of the Massachusetts Medical Society from 1794 to 1798. He married first in 1770, Hannah Watts, who died in 1780; Margaret Billings, who died only two years later; and Martha Gray Hall. Rembrandt Peale copied the bust in lithograph for Pendleton of Boston, who published *Thacher's American Medical Biography* in 1828 (vol. II).

References: L. Park, *Stuart*, New York, 1926, I, no. 207./ C.M. Mount, *Stuart*, New York, 1964, p. 366.
Exhibitions: Boston Athenaeum, *Stuart*, 1828, no. 208./ —, *Exhibition*, 1871.

925.

Mrs. Ebenezer Battelle (Anna Durant)

Seated half-length and turned three-quarters left before a green and black background, she holds an open letter. Her dress is gray with a white lace ruffled collar and cap; the chair is red.

Oil on panel. 33 × 26½ in. (83.8 × 67.3 cm.)
Painted in 1810.
Collection: Harriet Smith Tolman, great-granddaughter of the sitter, Boston.
Bequest of Harriet Smith Tolman. 23.546

Anna Durant (1756–1815), daughter of Thomas and Ann Hunt Durant of Boston, married Ebenezer Battelle of Dedham, Mass. in 1775. Although he left to work in Ohio in 1788, she remained in Boston and there ran a girls' boarding school. She died at sea while returning from the West Indies. Said to have been painted in 1810 in the home of her daughter, Mrs. Michael Smith, at the request of her son, Cornelius, who had settled in the West Indies. The letter she holds is addressed to *Mrs. Anna Battelle/ Boston*. The portrait was engraved by Charles B. Hall; three early copies of it are owned by descendants.

References: L. Park, *Stuart*, New York, 1926, I, no. 67 (repr. III, p. 44)./ C.M. Mount, *Stuart*, New York, 1964, p. 364.

926.

George Washington

Bust-length, turned three-quarters left before a brown background, he wears a black coat with a white stock and lace jabot.

Oil on panel. 25¼ × 21 in. (64.1 × 53.3 cm.)

Painted in 1810.

Collections: Hon. Josiah Quincy, Quincy, Mass., 1810; Josiah Quincy, his son, Boston; Josiah Phillips Quincy, his son, Boston; George Nixon Black, Boston, 1896.

Bequest of George Nixon Black. 29.788

One of the many replicas made by Stuart from his "Athenaeum Head" (Cat. no. 907) of George Washington, this portrait was painted in 1810 for the Hon. Josiah Quincy (letter from J.P. Quincy to George N. Black, Nov. 9, 1896). *See also* Cat. no. 914.

References: G.C. Mason, *Stuart*, New York, 1879, p. 106./ M. Fielding, *Stuart's Portraits of Washington*, Philadelphia, 1923, no. 102./ L. Park, *Stuart*, New York, 1926, II, no. 98./ J.H. Morgan and M. Fielding, *Life Portraits of Washington*, Philadelphia, 1931, p. 309, no. 102 (repr. opp. p. 308)./ C.M. Mount, *Stuart*, New York, 1964, p. 379.

Exhibition: Newport, R.I., Preservation Society of Newport County, *Washington-Rochambeau Celebration*, 1955, no. 15 (repr. cover).

927.

fig. 131

Sally Patten (Mrs. Francis Smith Eastman)

A child, wearing a low-cut white dress, sits half-length in left profile, her head turned front. The armchair is upholstered in red; the background is brown.

Oil on panel. 26¼ × 21¼ in. (66.7 × 54 cm.)

Painted about 1812–1814.

Collection: Mrs. George Hollingsworth, daughter of the sitter, Milton, Mass.

Bequest of Mrs. George Hollingsworth. 16.106

Sally Patten, daughter of William and Sally Williams Patten, was born in Roxbury, Mass. in 1807. In 1833 she married Francis Eastman, a Latin teacher in Boston. She died in Milton, Mass. in 1873. The portrait was probably painted in the Bartlett Mansion, West Roxbury when Stuart lived there from 1812 to 1814, at the same time that he painted her grandmother, Mrs. John Williams (Cat. no. 928).

References: H.T. Tuckerman, *Book of the Artists*, New York, 1870, p. 110./ G.C. Mason, *Stuart*, New York, 1879, p. 237./ L. Park, *Stuart*, New York, 1926, II, no. 616 (repr. IV, p. 376)./ C.M. Mount, *Stuart*, New York, 1964, p. 372.

Exhibitions: Boston, Copley Hall, *Portraits of Women*, 1895, no. 311./ Colorado Springs Fine Arts Center, *Likeness of America, 1680–1820*, 1949, no. 38./ New-York Historical Society, *Up from the Cradle*, 1949, no. 25.

928.

Mrs. John Williams (Mary Sumner)

Turned three-quarters left, bust-length, the elderly lady wears a black dress with a white ruffled collar and bonnet, tied with a black ribbon. The background is brown.

Oil on panel. 26½ × 24¼ in. (67.3 × 61.6 cm.)

Painted about 1812–1814.

Collections: Mrs. William Patten, daughter of the sitter, Boston; Sally Patten Eastman, her daughter; Mrs. George Hollingsworth, great-granddaughter of the sitter, Milton, Mass.

Bequest of Mrs. George Hollingsworth. 16.107

Mary Sumner (1744–1824), daughter of Samuel and Abigail Mather Sumner of Roxbury, Mass., in 1768 married John Williams, a local merchant, and bore him eight children. She died in Roxbury. She probably sat to Stuart in the Bartlett Mansion in West Roxbury, where he lived from 1812 to 1814 (see *Sally Patten [Mrs. Francis Smith Eastman]*, Cat. no. 927).

References, H.T. Tuckerman, *Book of the Artists*, New York, 1870, p. 110./ G.C. Mason, *Stuart*, New York, 1879, p. 279./ L. Park, *Stuart*, New York, 1926, II, no. 920 (repr. IV, p. 579)./ C.M. Mount, *Stuart*, New York, 1964, p. 377.

Exhibitions: Boston, Copley Hall, *Portraits of Women*, 1895, no. 330./ Colorado Springs Fine Arts Center, *Likeness of America, 1680–1820*, 1949, no. 36./ New York, American Federation of Arts, circulated in Germany and Italy, and Whitney Museum, *American Painting in the Nineteenth Century*, 1953–1954, no. 1./ New York, IBM Gallery of Arts and Sciences, *Realism in American Art*, 1963, no. 57.

929.

fig. 129

Paul Revere

Turned three-quarters right, bust-length, the elderly man wears a black coat over a white stock and waistcoat. The background is brown and black.

Oil on panel. 28½ × 23¾ in. (72.3 × 60.3 cm.)

Painted in 1813.

Collections: Commissioned by Joseph Warren Revere, the sitter's son, Boston, 1813; John Revere, his son, Boston, in 1879; Joseph W., William B. and Edward H.R. Revere, Boston.

Gift of Joseph W., William B., and Edward H.R. Revere. 30.782

Paul Revere (1735–1818), son of Paul and Deborah Hitchbourn Revere, was famous for his patriotic services during the Revolution and as a Boston silversmith. (For a more complete biography *see* Copley, *Paul Revere*, Cat. no. 279). Stuart's receipt for payment for the portrait and its pendant (Cat. no. 930), is dated June 3, 1813. Copies by Chester Harding of the two portraits were owned in 1926 by Mrs. Nathaniel Thayer of Boston; other copies are in the Bostonian Society, Boston, the Public Library, Lexington, Mass., and the Massachusetts Charitable Mechanics Association.

References: G.C. Mason, *Stuart*, New York, 1879, p. 248./ J. Winsor, *Memorial History of Boston*, Boston, 1881, III (engr. p. 69)./ L. Park, *Stuart*, New York, 1926, II, no. 699 (repr. IV, p. 427)./ E. Forbes, *Paul Revere and the World He Lived In*, Cambridge, Mass., 1942, pp. 442–443 (repr. opp. p. 338, erroneously dated 1815)./ C.M. Mount, *Stuart*, New York, 1964, p. 374.

Exhibitions: Boston Athenaeum, *Stuart*, 1828, no. 117./ Boston, MFA, *Stuart*, 1880, no. 216./ Boston, Copley Hall, *Portraits*, 1896, no. 238./ Chicago Art Institute, *From Colony to Nation*, 1949, no. 113.

930.

fig. 130

Mrs. Paul Revere (Rachel Walker)

The lady, half-length, seated and turned three-quarters left, wears a pale blue dress with white trim and a neck ruffle, and a white lace cap. The background is black and gray.

Oil on panel. 28½ × 23¾ in. (72.3 × 60.3 cm.)

Painted in 1813.

Collections: Same as Cat. no. 929.

Gift of Joseph W., William B., and Edward H.R. Revere. 30.783

Rachel Walker (1745–1813) was the daughter of Richard and Rachel Carlile Walker of Boston. She married Paul Revere in 1773, his second wife, and had eight children by him. Inscribed on the back of her portrait is: *Painted by G. Stuart Esqr./ For Joseph W. Revere/ In the Spring of 1813.*

References: G.C. Mason, *Stuart*, New York, 1879, p. 248./ L. Park, *Stuart*, New York, 1926, II, no. 700 (repr. IV, p. 428)./ E. Forbes, *Paul Revere and the World He Lived In*, Cambridge, Mass., 1942, pp. 442–443 (repr. opp. p. 338, erroneously dated 1815)./ C.M. Mount, *Stuart*, New York, 1964, p. 374.

Exhibitions: Boston Athenaeum, *Stuart*, 1828, no. 118./ Boston, MFA, *Stuart*, 1880, no. 217./ Boston, Copley Hall, *Portraits*, 1896, no. 239.

931.

Maria Bartlett (Mrs. Joseph Hall, Jr.)

Bust-length, a young lady, turned three-quarters right and wearing a white dress and red shawl, stands before a gray column and yellow curtain; the sky at the lower right is blue.

Oil on panel. 21¾ × 17 in. (55.2 × 43.2 cm.)

Painted in 1814.

Collections: Caroline Hall Eustis, daughter of the sitter, Brookline, Mass.; George D. Eustis, her son, Vineyard Haven, Mass.

Bequest of George D. Eustis. 39.513

Maria Bartlett (1796–1873), daughter of Thomas and Alice Wyer Bartlett of Boston, married Joseph Hall, Jr. of Springfield, Mass. in 1816. Painted in the Bartlett Mansion in Roxbury, Mass., in 1814; in about 1865 the portrait was cut down to match a portrait of Joseph Hall by Chester Harding. Portraits of her father, Dr. Thomas Bartlett, and stepmother, Hannah Gray Wilson Bartlett, are Cat. nos. 911 and 912.

References: G.C. Mason, *Stuart*, New York, 1879, p. 193./ L. Park, *Stuart*, New York, 1926, I, no. 64 (repr. III, p. 41)./ C.M. Mount, *Stuart*, New York, 1964, p. 364.

Exhibitions: Boston Athenaeum, *Stuart*, 1828, no. 81./ Boston, Copley Hall, *Portraits of Women*, 1895, no. 302./ Brookline, Mass., Town Hall, *Loan Exhibition*, 1897, no. 92.

932.

Nathan Bond

Bust-length and turned three-quarters left on a brown background, he wears a black coat over a white waistcoat and stock.

Oil on panel. 26 × 21¼ in. (66 × 54 cm.)

Painted in 1815.

Collections: Descended in the Bond family, Boston, to Mrs. E. Stuart Peck (Mary Louise Bond), great-great-great-granddaughter of the sitter, New York.

Gift of Mrs. E. Stuart Peck. 50.748

Nathan Bond (1752–1816), son of Abijah Bond of Concord, Mass., graduated from Harvard in 1772, and studied for the ministry. Because of poor health, however, he became a merchant. A label on the back of the portrait, signed by George W. Bond, the sitter's grandson, reads: *This portrait, painted by Stuart/ in the summer of 1815/ and is an excellent likeness./ Its only fault is being rather/ too youthful.*

References: L. Park, *Stuart*, New York, 1926, I, no. 92 (repr. III, p. 61)./ C.M. Mount, *Stuart*, New York, 1964, p. 365.

Exhibition: Boston Athenaeum, *Stuart*, 1828, no. 61.

933.

Mrs. Nathan Bond (Joanna Sigourney)

An elderly lady, bust-length and turned three-quarters right, wears a black dress with a white fichu and cap tied with a black ribbon. The background is brown.

Oil on panel. 26 × 20½ in. (66 × 52 cm.)

Painted in 1815.

Collections: Same as Cat. no. 932.

Gift of Mrs. E. Stuart Peck. 50.749

Joanna Sigourney (1750–1828), daughter of Daniel and Joanna Tileston Sigourney of Boston, married Nathan Bond in 1783 after her first husband, the mariner Herman Doane, was lost at sea in 1778. A label on the back of the picture, signed by the sitter's grandson, George Bond, reads: *Joanna Bond wife of Nathan/ Born—August 8, 1750/ Died—November 3, 1828/ This portrait painted by Stuart in 1815 is a perfect likeness.* It is pendant to the preceding portrait.

References: L. Park, *Stuart*, New York, 1926, I, no. 93 (repr. III, p. 62)./ C.M. Mount, *Stuart*, New York, 1964, p. 365.

Exhibitions: Boston Athenaeum, *Stuart*, 1828, no. 60./ Boston, Copley Hall, *Portraits of Women*, 1895, no. 288.

934.

fig. 132

Mrs. John Gore (Mary Babcock)

Half-length and seated in a yellow upholstered chair, she turns three-quarters right and wears a white satin empire dress with a red shawl. Behind her are a brown curtain and column before a blue sky with pink clouds.

Oil on canvas. 30 × 24¾ in. (76.2 × 62.8 cm.)

Painted about 1815.

Collections: Mrs. Horatio Greenough, daughter of the sitter, Boston, 1836; Mrs. Charlotte Hervoches du Quilliou, her daughter, La Tour de Peilz, Switzerland.

Bequest of Charlotte Gore Greenough Hervoches du Quilliou. 21.106

Mary Babcock (1782–1836), the beautiful daughter of Adam and Martha Hubbard Babcock, was born in Boston. She was married twice: in 1802 to John Gore of Boston and in 1827 to Joseph Russell. Her first husband was the nephew of the celebrated Christopher Gore, once Governor of Massachusetts and owner of the exceptional Federal mansion in Waltham, Gore Place. Her husband, John Gore, was one of the original stockholders and directors of the New England Bank. She died in Paris. An early copy of the unlocated portrait of her husband, John Gore, is Cat. no. 952.

References: G.C. Mason, *Stuart*, New York, 1879, p. 186./ L. Park, *Stuart*, New York, 1926, I, no. 336 (repr. III, p. 201)./ C.M. Mount, *Stuart*, New York, 1964, pp. 278–279, 368.

Exhibitions: Philadelphia Museum, *Fairmount Park Centennial*, 1876, no. 53b./ Boston, MFA, *Stuart*, 1880, no. 267./ —, *Stuart*, 1928, no. 31.

935.

Mrs. Samuel Smith

Seated in half-length in a red upholstered empire chair and turned three-quarters left, she wears a dark brown dress with a large white fichu and a lace shawl and cap. The background is brown.

Oil on panel. 32½ × 26½ in. (82.5 × 67.3 cm.)
Painted about 1815.

Collection: Dr. William Sturgis Bigelow, Boston, about 1890.

Gift of Dr. William Sturgis Bigelow. 21.1430

The date is Park's (*see below*); her contemporary Samuel Smiths are so many as to make identification impossible.

References: M. Fielding, "Portraits by Stuart Not in Mason," *Pennsylvania Magazine of the Historical Society*, 1923, no. 122./ L. Park, *Stuart*, New York, 1926, II, no. 777 (repr. IV, p. 477)./ C.M. Mount, *Stuart*, New York, 1964, p. 375.

Exhibitions: Boston Athenaeum, *Stuart*, 1828, no. 147./ Chicago, *World's Columbian Exposition*, 1893, no. 2853f.

936.

Aaron Davis

Half-length, turned three-quarters right, the balding gentleman wears a black coat over a white stock. The background is dark green-gray.

Oil on panel. 28¾ × 23 in. (73 × 58.4 cm.)
Painted about 1816.

Collections: Miss Davis, the sitter's niece, Roxbury, Mass.; Charles Davis, her brother, Boston; Charles Davis, Jr., his son, Boston, about 1885; Aaron Davis, his son, Boston, 1914.

Bequest of Aaron Davis. 55.12

Aaron Davis (1763–1817) was the son of Captain Aaron and Susannah Craft Davis of Roxbury, Mass. With his brother Charles he had a lucrative packing and shipping business and also ran a distillery and tannery. He married Theoda Williams in 1793. He died, without children, while returning from a trip to the West Indies. The painting is similar in style to that of Nathan Bond (Cat. no. 932).

References: M. Fielding, "Portraits by Stuart Not in Mason," *Pennsylvania Magazine of the Historical Society*, 1923, no. 37./ L. Park, *Stuart*, New York, 1926, I, no. 210 (repr. III, p. 125)./ C.M. Mount, *Stuart*, New York, 1964, p. 366.

Exhibition: Boston, Copley Hall, *Portraits*, 1896, no. 256.

937.

fig. 138

Mrs. James Smith Colburn (Sarah Dunn Prince)

Half-length, turned half left, the young lady wears an empire dress with a red India shawl. Behind, a brown column and wall are silhouetted against blue sky with gray clouds.

Oil on panel. 28¼ × 22¾ in. (71.7 × 57.8 cm.)

Painted about 1817.

Collections: James Smith Colburn, Charleston, S.C.; Sarah Jane Colburn, the sitter's granddaughter, Boston and Charleston.

Bequest of Sarah Jane Colburn. 10.232

Sarah Dunn Prince (1790–1836), daughter of Job Prince, a sea-captain, was born in Boston. She married James Smith Colburn in 1808, and although he moved his mercantile business to Charleston before 1831, she, frequently ill, remained in Boston until her death.

References: L. Park, *Stuart*, New York, 1926, I, no. 176 (repr. III, p. 111)./ C.M. Mount, *Stuart*, New York, 1964, p. 366.

Exhibition: Boston, MFA, *Stuart*, 1928, no. 17.

938.

fig. 135

Thomas Dennie

Dressed in a dark blue jacket with gold buttons and a white stock with ruffled shirt, he is shown half-length and turned three-quarters left before a brown background.

Oil on canvas. 30¼ × 25¼ in. (76.8 × 64.1 cm.)

Painted in 1818.

Collection: James Dennie, grandson of the sitter, Boston.

Bequest of James Dennie. 05.295

Thomas Dennie (1756–1842), born in Brighton, Mass., was the son of John and Sarah Wendell Dennie. As a merchant and shipmaster, he was highly respected for his honesty and dependability in all affairs; he lived in Boston until his death. An old label on the back reads: *Painted in 1818 aged 62.* The portrait of his wife (Cat. no. 939) is pendant to this one.

References: G.C. Mason, *Stuart*, New York, 1879, p. 173./ L. Park, *Stuart*, New York, 1926, I, no. 234 (repr. III, p. 142)./ C.M. Mount, *Stuart*, New York, 1964, p. 367.

Exhibition: Boston Athenaeum, *Stuart*, 1828, no. 143.

939.

fig. 134

Mrs. Thomas Dennie (Sarah Bryant)

Seated half-length in a chair upholstered in soft red, she turns half right before a brown background. Her dress is light blue; the shawl is dark blue; her ruffled collar and cap are white.

Oil on canvas. 30¼ × 25¼ in. (76.8 × 64.1 cm.)

Painted in 1818.

Collection: Same as Cat. no. 938.

Bequest of James Dennie. 05.296

Sarah Bryant (1760–1827), daughter of James and Esther Kidder Bryant, married Thomas Dennie in 1778. The Rev. John Lowell, Minister of West Church, Boston, said of her: "her good sense, and prudence and judicious economy contributed materially to the success of her husband." The portrait is pendant to the preceding.

References: G.C. Mason, *Stuart*, New York, 1879, p. 173./ L. Park, *Stuart*, New York, 1926, I, no. 235 (repr. III, p. 143)./ C.M. Mount, *Stuart*, New York, 1964, pl. 367.

Exhibitions: Boston, Copley Hall, *Portraits of Women*, 1895, no. 290./ San Francisco, M.H. de Young Memorial Museum and California Palace of the Legion of Honor, *American Painting*, 1935, no. 26.

940.

fig. 137

Nathaniel Pope Russell

Half-length and turned three-quarters right, he is seated in a red chair before a red-covered table with a silver and crystal inkwell and strewn with letters; his coat is black and his stock is white. The background is brown.

Painted about 1818.

Collections: Samuel H. Russell, the sitter's son, Boston, 1848; Edith, Lady Playfair and Mrs. J.R. FitzGerald, his daughters, London, 1894.

Gift of Edith, Lady Playfair and Mrs. J.R. FitzGerald. 30.231

Nathaniel Pope Russell (1779–1848) was born in Danvers, Mass., the son of Ezekiel and Sarah Hood Russell of Boston. He headed the underwriting firm of Peter Chardon Brooks from 1803 to 1820, was twice member of the city government, and served in both houses of the State Legislature. The MFA also owns portraits of his son Samuel H. Russell by Frederick Vinton (Cat. no. 997) and of his granddaughter Edith, Lady Playfair by John Singer Sargent (Cat. no. 859).

References: G.C. Mason, *Stuart*, New York, 1879, pp. 250–251./ L. Park, *Stuart*, New York, 1926, II, no. 720./ C.M. Mount, *Stuart*, New York, 1964, p. 374.

Exhibitions: Boston Athenaeum, *Stuart*, 1828, no. 6./ Boston, MFA, *Stuart*, 1880, no. 273.

941.

Mrs. William Hunt (Jane Bethune)

Seated in a red upholstered gilt armchair, bust-length, before a brown background, she turns three-quarters left and wears a white neck ruffle and a turban with a black dress.

Oil on panel. 27 × 21¾ in. (68.6 × 55.2 cm.)
Painted about 1819.

Collections: Marie Bethune Hunt (Mrs. H.K. Craig), daughter of the sitter; Mrs. John P. Hawkins, her daughter, Indianapolis.

Gift of Gen. John P. Hawkins, in the name of his wife, Jane Bethune Craig Hawkins. 13.2806

Jane Bethune (died 1844) was the daughter of George and Mary Faneuil Bethune of Boston. By her marriage in 1787 to William Hunt of Watertown, Mass., she had four children. Her husband, a lawyer, was several times Representative to the General Court. An old label on the back of the panel records that the picture was painted in Boston in 1819, a stylistically consistent date.

References: G.C. Mason, *Stuart*, New York, 1879, p. 202./ L. Park, *Stuart*, New York, 1926, I, no. 425 (repr. III, p. 257)./ C.M. Mount, *Stuart*, New York, 1964, p. 369.

942.
fig. 141

Mrs. George Williams (Lydia Pickering)

Half-length, seated, and turned three-quarters left, an elderly lady wears a white fichu and lace-edged bonnet with a black dress. Her chair and the drapery behind are dull red damask before a brown wall.

Oil on canvas. 36 × 28 in. (91.4 × 71.1 cm.)
Painted about 1819.

Collections: Stephen Williams, the sitter's son, Northboro, Mass.; George H. Williams, his son, Northboro; Ellen Williams, his daughter, Northboro; Mrs. Edward R. Fairbanks, Boston, 1917.

Gift of Mrs. Edward R. Fairbanks in memory of her friend, Ellen Williams. 17.3141

Lydia Pickering (1736–1824) was the daughter of Timothy and Mary Wingate Pickering of Salem, Mass., and sister of Col. Timothy Pickering, Secretary of State under Adams. She was the second wife of George Williams, a shipmaster and merchant of Baltimore and Salem, and after his death in 1797 moved to Boston, where her portrait was painted. There are three versions of the portrait: the probable original is owned by Miss Evelyn Sears of Boston, great-great-granddaughter of Mrs. Williams, and the third, unfinished, by Cyril B. Judge of Newport, R.I. In the MFA version, Stuart's brushstrokes may be seen in the face, but some later artist probably filled in the costume and the background. A copy by Jane Stuart was owned in 1926 by Mrs. A.O. Whitney, Cambridge, Mass.

References: M. Fielding, "Portraits by Stuart Not in Mason," *Pennsylvania Magazine of the Historical Society*, 1923, no. 143./ L. Park, *Stuart*, New York, 1926, II, no. 912./ C.M. Mount, *Stuart*, New York, 1964, p. 377 (Mrs. George Williams [Elizabeth Hawkins], Park, no. 916, is not in the MFA).

Exhibitions: Possibly Boston Athenaeum, *Stuart*, 1828, no. 152./ Vancouver Art Gallery, *Two Hundred Years of American Painting*, 1955, no. 9 (repr.).

943.
fig. 139

Bishop Jean-Louis Lefebvre de Cheverus

Half-length and turned three-quarters left, he is seated in a gold upholstered chair and with one hand holds a book. Over the white rochet, embroidered in gold, he wears

a dark gray mozzetta, *edged in red, which supports a gold cross. Behind, a gold curtain hangs before a blue sky with pink clouds.*
Oil on canvas. 36¼ × 28½ in. (92.1 × 72.3 cm.)
Painted in 1823.
Collections: Commissioned by Mrs. John Gore (Mrs. Joseph Russell), Boston, 1823; Mrs. Horatio Greenough, her daughter, Boston, 1836; Mrs. Charlotte Hervoches du Quilliou, her daughter, La Tour de Peilz, Switzerland.
Bequest of Mrs. Charlotte Gore Greenough Hervoches du Quilliou. 21.9

Jean-Louis Anne Magdeleine Lefebvre de Cheverus (1768–1836), born in Mayenne, France, was ordained to the priesthood in 1790. In 1792 he fled the Revolution to England, worked there until 1796, then came to Boston to assist Dr. François Matignon in his Roman Catholic parish. There he remained, consecrated first Bishop of Boston in 1810 and beloved by Catholics and Protestants alike. In 1823, he was recalled to the Bishopric of Montauban, France. Shortly before his death he was elevated to the College of Cardinals. His portrait was painted in Boston in 1823, on the commission of Mrs. John Gore (Cat. no. 934).

References: H.T. Tuckerman, *Book of the Artists*, New York, 1870, p. 109./ G.C. Mason, *Stuart*, New York, 1879, p. 158./ J. Winsor, *Memorial History of Boston*, Boston, 1881, III, p. 518./ L. Park, *Stuart*, New York, 1926, I, no. 155 (repr. III, p. 99)./ C.M. Mount, *Stuart*, New York, 1964, pp. 365–366.

Exhibitions: Boston Athenaeum, *Exhibition*, 1827, no. 118./ —, *Stuart*, 1828, no. 109./ Philadelphia Museum of Art, *Fairmount Park Centennial*, 1876, no. 53c./ Boston, MFA, *Stuart*, 1880, no. 251./ Boston Athenaeum, *Memorial to Bishop Cheverus*, 1951, pp. XII, XVIII (pl. 1).

944.

fig. 133

Josiah Quincy

Seated half-length in a red upholstered armchair, he turns three-quarters right and holds an architectural drawing on a green table. He wears a black coat and waistcoat with white shirt, collar, and stock. Behind are a gray column draped in red and the gray Faneuil Hall Market under blue and gray sky.
Oil on canvas. 36 × 28 in. (91.4 × 71.1 cm.)
Painted in 1824.
Collection: Commissioned by Miss Eliza Susan Quincy, daughter of the sitter, Boston, 1824.
Gift of Eliza Susan Quincy. 76.347

Josiah Quincy (1772–1864), son of Josiah and Abigail Phillips Quincy, was born in Braintree (later Quincy), Mass., graduated from Harvard in 1790, and was admitted to the bar three years later. He was in the national House of Representatives from 1804 to 1813, the Massachusetts Senate from 1813 to 1819, and Speaker of the Massachusetts House in 1820–1821. Judge of the Municipal Court of Boston in 1822, he was then an active reform Mayor of Boston from 1823 to 1828 and finally the distinguished President of Harvard from 1829 to 1845. His last years were devoted to extensive political and historical writing, and he died in Boston. The painting was done in Boston at the request of his daughter, who, in correspondence with the MFA and G.C. Mason (*see below*), gave the painting's date as both 1824 and 1826. He is represented as Mayor of Boston, with the Faneuil Hall Market, one of his achievements, visible behind him. Another portrait of Quincy by Stuart, in nearly left profile, was painted in 1806 (Park, no. 685).

References: G.C. Mason, *Stuart*, New York, 1879, pp. 242–247./ W.H. Downes, "Boston Painters and Paintings," *Atlantic Monthly*, 1888, LXII, no. 369, p. 98./ L. Park, *Stuart*, New York, 1926, II, no. 686 (repr. IV, p. 419)./ A. Burroughs, *Limners and Likenesses*, Cambridge, Mass., 1936, p. 104 (fig. 83)./ C.M. Mount, *Stuart*, New York, 1964, pp. 321–322, 327, 373.

Exhibitions: Boston Athenaeum, *Stuart*, 1828, no. 157./ Boston, MFA, *Contemporary Art*, 1879, no. 105./ —, *Stuart*, 1880, no. 256./ Boston, Copley Hall, *Portraits*, 1896, no. 237./ Boston, MFA, *Stuart*, 1928, no. 59./ Harvard University, *Tercentenary*, 1936, no. 29./ Indianapolis, Herron Museum of Art, *Stuart*, 1942, no. 27 (repr.)./ London, Tate Gallery, *American Painting*, 1946, p. 19, no. 202.

945.

Robert Waterston

Half-length and turned three-quarters left, he sits wearing a black coat and white stock and holds a brown book. A table beside him, his chair, and the drapery, right, are red; the background is brown.

Oil on canvas. 30 × 25 in. (76.2 × 63.5 cm.)

Painted in 1824.

Collections: Robert Cassie Waterston, son of the sitter, Boston, 1869; Mrs. Charles Deane, his sister, Cambridge, 1893; Mrs. George Greig, her sister, Toronto, 1897; Mrs. George Lord, her sister, Newton, Mass., 1901; Charles E. Lord, her son, Newton, 1910; grandchildren of the sitter.

Gift of Mr. and Mrs. Robert Waterston's grandchildren. 19.1367

Robert Waterston (1778–1869), son of Robert and Mary Cassie Waterston, was born in Edinburgh, Scotland and in 1803 emigrated to America to escape the so-called "tyrannical regime" in England and the Napoleonic War. He settled first in South Berwick, then Kennebunk, Me., and finally in Boston, where he was a prominent wholesale dry-goods merchant until his death. The date for the portrait is from family tradition. The portrait of his wife (Cat. no. 946) is pendant to this one.

References: G.C. Mason, *Stuart*, New York, 1879, p. 275./ C.L. Lord, *Ancestors and Descendants of Lt. Tobias Lord*, Boston, 1913 (repr. opp. p. 106)./ L. Park, *Stuart*, New York, 1926, II, no. 885 (repr. IV, p. 554)./ C.M. Mount, *Stuart*, New York, 1964, p. 377.

Exhibitions: Boston Athenaeum, *Stuart*, 1828, no. 175./ Boston, MFA, *Stuart*, 1880, no. 236.

946.

Mrs. Robert Waterston (Hephzibah Lord)

Half-length, she turns three-quarters right before a brown background, and wears a red India shawl, embroidered with black and yellow, over a black dress with a white lace cap.

Oil on canvas. 30 × 25 in. (76.2 × 63.5 cm.)

Painted in 1824.

Collections: Same as Cat. no. 945.

Gift of Mr. and Mrs. Robert Waterston's grandchildren. 19.1368

Hephzibah Lord, daughter of Tobias and Hepzea Conant Lord, was born in Kennebunk, Me. in 1788. She married Robert Waterston in 1810, then lived in Boston until her death in 1826. Her portrait was painted at the same time as its pendant (Cat. no. 945).

References: G.C. Mason, *Stuart*, New York, 1879, p. 275./ C.L. Lord, *Ancestors and Descendants of Lt. Tobias Lord*, Boston, 1913 (repr. opp. p. 106)./ L. Park, *Stuart*, New York, 1926, II, no. 886 (repr. IV, p. 555)./ C.M. Mount, *Stuart*, New York, 1964, p. 377.

Exhibitions: Boston Athenaeum, *Stuart*, 1828, no. 174./ Boston, MFA, *Stuart*, 1880, no. 237.

947.

fig. 136

Ward Nicholas Boylston (Unfinished Sketch)

The bust alone in full left profile, with light gray hair and ruddy complexion on an unpainted gray ground.

Oil on panel. 21 × 17 in. (55 × 45 cm.)

Painted in 1825.

Collections: Alicia Darrow Boylston, wife of the sitter, Princeton, Mass., 1828; Dr. Ward Nicholas Boylston, grandson of the sitter, Princeton, 1843; bequeathed to his brothers and sisters, 1870; Mrs. Louisa Boylston (Mrs. Edwin J.) Nightingale, the surviving sister, Providence, R.I., 1887; Estate of Mrs. Nightingale, 1895; Mrs. Paul Webster Bean, her niece, 1925.

Lent by Mrs. Paul Webster Bean. 307.25

An unfinished sketch painted to assist in the preparation of the Boylston medal, an award established by Ward N. Boylston in 1800, presented to the Harvard Medical School student who prepares the best medical dissertation (*see* Cat. no. 948).

948.
fig. 140

Ward Nicholas Boylston

Half-length, turned half left, he is seated in a green upholstered armchair at a green covered table on which are papers, a book, and a feather pen in an inkstand. He wears a dark brown coat with a fur collar over an embroidered yellow waistcoat, a high white collar, stock, and frilled shirt. The background is green-brown.

Oil on canvas. 36 × 28 in. (91.8 × 71.1 cm.)
Painted in 1825.
Collections: Alicia Darrow Boylston, wife of the sitter, Princeton, Mass., 1828; Dr. Ward Nicholas Boylston, grandson of the sitter, Princeton, 1843; bequeathed to his brothers and sisters, 1870; Mrs. Louisa Boylston (Mrs. Edwin J.) Nightingale, the surviving sister, Providence, R.I., 1887; Estate of Mrs. Nightingale, 1895; Ward Nicholas Boylston, Jr., her nephew, Brattleboro, Vt., 1925; Mrs. Paul Webster Bean, 1963.
Lent by Mrs. Paul Webster Bean. 59.63

Ward Nicholas Boylston (1749–1828) was named originally Ward Hallowell, the son of Benjamin and Mary Boylston Hallowell. He changed his name in 1770 to please his maternal uncle Nicholas Boylston, and became his principal heir. From 1773 to 1775, a "Grand Tour" of the Mediterranean and western Europe brought him to London, where, a Loyalist, he established himself as a merchant. He returned to Boston in 1800; after 1804 he summered at Princeton, Mass., where he built a large country estate in 1819–1820, and lived in Jamaica Plain in winter. Married twice, first to Mary (Ann) Molineaux (died 1779), his second wife and mother of his children was Alicia Darrow of Yarmouth, England (*see* Cat. no. 475, portrait by Harding). A version of this painting (Park, no. 108), owned by the Boston Medical Society, hangs in the Harvard Medical School, Boston. *See also* Cat. no. 947.

References: G.C. Mason, *Stuart*, New York, 1879, pp. 150–151./ E. Blake, *History of the Town of Princeton*, Princeton, 1915, I, p. 278./ L. Park, *Stuart*, New York, 1926, I, no. 106 (repr. III, no. 106)./ C.M. Mount, *Stuart*, New York, 1964, pp. 322, 365.
Exhibition: Boston, MFA, *Stuart*, 1928, no. 11.

949.

Zachariah Hicks

Seated, bust-length, in a red upholstered chair, the elderly gentleman faces slightly left. He wears a black coat with a white stock and frilled shirt. The background is dark brown.

Oil on canvas. 30 × 24¾ in. (76.2 × 62.8 cm.)
Painted about 1825.
Collection: Anna Gower Endicott, great-granddaughter of the sitter, Boston.
Gift of Anna Gower Endicott. 25.178

Zachariah Hicks (1755–1843) was the third son of John Hicks of Cambridge, Mass., a Revolutionary patriot, and Elizabeth Nutting Hicks. A saddler by trade, he had a long and respectable career in Boston; he was elected twice to the House of Representatives and, when eighty-two, Representative to the General Court of Massachusetts. A copy of this portrait, probably by Jane Stuart, is in the Massachusetts Charitable Mechanics Association. Fielding (*see below*) confuses this portrait with the copy.

References: M. Fielding, "Portraits by Stuart Not in Mason," *Pennsylvania Magazine of the Historical Society*, 1923, no. 68./ L. Park, *Stuart*, New York, 1926, I, no. 397./ C.M. Mount, *Stuart*, New York, 1964, p. 369.
Exhibition: Boston, MFA, *Stuart*, 1928, no. 35.

950.

Robert Gilmor

Bust-length, the young man turns three-quarters left and wears a black coat with a

white stock and a frilled shirt front. The background is brown.
Oil on panel. 25¼ × 21¼ in. (64.1 × 54 cm.)
Painted about 1826.
Collection: James Thomas Fields, Boston, 1874.
James T. Fields Collection. 24.20

Robert Gilmor (1808–1874), son of William and Marianne Smith Gilmor and nephew of the diarist and noted art collector Robert Gilmor, was born in Baltimore. His family was one of great wealth and prominence, and having graduated from Harvard in 1828, Robert served as Attaché to the American Legation in Paris. He later built an estate near Baltimore, modeled after Sir Walter Scott's "Abbotsford." From his apparent age, he was painted about 1826, while at Harvard.

References: L. Park, *Stuart*, New York, 1926, I, no. 334 (repr. III, p. 200)./ C.M. Mount, *Stuart*, New York, 1964, p. 368.
Exhibition: Boston, Copley Society, *A New Look at Gilbert Stuart*, 1965, no. 6.

951.   **Thomas Oliver Selfridge II**

The head of a young man with dark hair and sideburns faces slightly left. The high white collar and stock are sketched in, and the dark background is barely indicated.
Oil on canvas. 27¼ × 22¼ in. (69.2 × 56.5 cm.)
Painted about 1826.
Gift of Rear-Admiral Thomas Oliver Selfridge III, U.S.N., the sitter's son. 24.265

Thomas Selfridge (1804–1902), son of Thomas Oliver and Susan Conde Selfridge, was born in Boston. Entering the Navy in 1818 as a midshipman, he pursued a long and successful career until his promotion to Rear-Admiral in 1866. He died in Boston. His portrait is dated according to his apparent age. Park (*see below*), in tracing the painting's history, confuses the subject of the portrait with a nonexistent son, and gives him the erroneous death date of 1876.

References: G.C. Mason, *Stuart*, New York, 1879, p. 253./ L. Park, *Stuart*, New York, 1926, II, no. 744 (repr. IV, p. 457)./ C.M. Mount, *Stuart*, New York, 1964, p. 374.
Exhibition: Boston, MFA, *Stuart*, 1928, no. 61.

952.   **John Gore (after Stuart)**

Half-length, turned three-quarters left, he wears a dark green jacket with a black velvet collar over a white waistcoat and stock. Behind, right, is a red curtain and brown column before blue and pink sky.
Oil on canvas. 30 × 24¾ in. (76.2 × 62.8 cm.)
Bequest of Charlotte Gore Greenough Hervoches du Quilliou, granddaughter of the sitter. Res. 21.265

A label on the back of the painting reads: *Copy of Stuart's portrait of John Gore.* While the dry handling of paint and inadequate modeling are like the work of a copyist, no record exists of an original by Stuart. In composition, it is a pendant to his portrait of Mrs. John Gore (Cat. no. 934), painted about 1815. The copy dates probably from the mid-nineteenth century.

Reference: C.M. Mount, *Stuart*, New York, 1964, p. 368.

953.   **Mrs. Richard Yates (Catherine Brass) (after Stuart)**

Half-length, in left profile, her face turns forward as she sits in a red chair sewing; she wears a pale gray dress with a white shawl and bonnet. The background is brown.
Oil on canvas. 30¼ × 25¼ in. (76.2 × 64.1 cm.)
Collection: Mrs. Emma G. Lull, great-granddaughter of the sitter, Washington, D.C.
Henry Lillie Pierce Residuary Fund. 96.29

Catherine Brass (c.1736–1808), the second child of Adolph and Maria Carstang Brass of New York, in 1757 married Richard Yates, senior partner in the firm Yates and Pollack, New York merchants. This is an early copy, by an unknown hand, of Stuart's portrait of Mrs. Yates in the National

Gallery, Washington, D.C., which was painted in New York about 1793. L. Park (*see below*) published our painting as a replica by Stuart.

References: L. Park, *Stuart*, New York, 1926, II, no. 944./ W. Sawitzky, "Stuart," *Art in America*, 1933, XXI, no. 3, pp. 89, 91.

JAMES REEVE STUART (1834–1915)

954.

Sword, Pistols, and Teacup
Oil on canvas. 20 × 24 in. (50.8 × 61 cm.)
Signed lower right: *Jas. R. Stuart/ Madison Wisconsin.*
M. and M. Karolik Collection. 48.478
Reference: Karolik Catalogue, 1949, no. 214 (repr.).

JANE STUART

(1812–1888), born in Boston, was the youngest child of Gilbert Stuart, her tutor. After his death in 1828, she moved with her mother and three sisters to Newport, R.I., where she remained for the rest of her life, except for some work in Boston in the 1850's. Active as a miniature painter, she also painted portraits in oil and made numerous copies after her father's portraits of Washington.

955.

Alicia Boylston
Half-length, facing front, the young lady wears a white dress with a white lace bodice and a red shawl. The background is brown.
Oil on canvas. Painted oval. 30½ × 25¼ in. (77.5 × 64 cm.)
Painted about 1835–1840.
Collections: Mrs. Louisa Boylston (Mrs. Edwin J.) Nightingale, Providence, R.I., by 1903; Mrs. Paul Webster Bean, her niece, 1925.
Lent by Mrs. Paul Webster Bean. 310.25

THOMAS SULLY

(1783–1872), born in Horncastle, Lincolnshire, England, came with his family to Charleston, S.C. in 1792. His first studies in painting were with a schoolmate, Charles Fraser, then in Richmond, Va. with his brother-in-law, Jean Belzons, and his brother Lawrence, both miniaturists. In 1801 he began work in Norfolk, Va.; he moved in 1806 to New York City, and to Hartford, Conn. in 1807. From there he went to Boston, where he received advice from Gilbert Stuart. In 1808 he settled permanently in Philadelphia as the leading portrait and figure painter. He visited England twice, in 1809–1810 to study with West, and again in 1838.

956.

John Myers
Oil on canvas. 36 × 30 in. (91.4 × 76.2 cm.)
Signed with initials and dated lower left: *TS 1814* (initials in monogram).
M. and M. Karolik Collection. 45.894
Reference: Karolik Catalogue, 1949, no. 215 (repr.).

957.
fig. 168

The Passage of the Delaware
From a snow-covered hill, Washington, in a blue uniform with buff breeches and mounted on a white charger, watches boatloads of troops crossing the gray river far below him. With him are officers in gray and blue, with brown horses, and to the left men in gray and brown uniforms maneuver a cannon. The distant landscape is white with snow under a sky clouded in gray and yellow, touched with pink at the horizon.
Oil in canvas. 146½ × 207 in. (372.1 × 525.8 cm.)
Signed and dated lower center: *TS F—ect. 1819* (T and F in monogram).
Collections: John Doggett, Boston; Boston Museum and Gallery of Fine Arts (Old Boston Museum), about 1841.
Gift of the Owners of the Old Boston Museum. 03.1079
The crossing of the Delaware River by General Washington and his troops took place on Christmas night, 1776. The principal figures in the painting were said to be "faithful portraits of Washington, Knox, Green and Morgan" (*Catalogue of the Boston Museum, see below*). According to his Register, Sully completed this huge canvas between August 7 and Decem-

ber 15, 1819. It was intended for the Capitol building of the State of North Carolina. The commission was for $1,000, but the painting was too large for the intended space and was rejected. Biddle and Fielding list two studies for the painting, which are at present unlocated.

References: "Washington Crossing the Delaware," *New York Mirror*, 1842, xx, no. 39, pp. 305–306./ *Catalogue of Paintings . . . in the Collection of the Boston Museum and Gallery of Fine Arts*, Boston, 1844, no. 128./ W.H. Downes, "Boston Painters and Paintings," *Atlantic Monthly*, 1888, LXII, no. 371, p. 385./ "Small Talk and Palaver," *Collector*, 1892, III, no. 16, p. 244./ C.H. Hart, ed., *Thomas Sully's Register of Portraits*, Philadelphia, 1909./ W. Dunlap, *History of the Arts of Design*, Boston, 1918, I, p. 328, II, p. 272–273./ E. Biddle and M. Fielding, *Sully*, Philadelphia, 1921, p. 309, no. 2616./ E.P. Richardson, *American Romantic Painting*, New York, 1945, no. 33 (repr.).

958.
fig. 169

The Torn Hat

A young boy, bust-length, wears a torn yellow straw hat and a white shirt under a blue-gray coat. The background is brown.

Oil on panel. 19 × 14½ in. (48.2 × 36.8 cm.)

Signed and dated on hatband: *TS 1820* (initials in monogram).

Collections: J. Hubbard, Boston, by 1827; Miss Margaret Greene, Boston, in 1894.

Gift of Belle Greene and Henry Copley Greene, in memory of their mother, Mary Abby Greene. 16.104

Posed by the artist's son, Thomas Wilcocks Sully (1811–1847), who himself became a portrait painter in Philadelphia.

References: C.H. Hart, ed., *Register of Portraits by Thomas Sully*, Philadelphia, 1909, p. 161, no. 1645./ E. Biddle and M. Fielding, *Sully*, Philadelphia, 1921, p. 292, no. 1745.

Exhibitions: Boston Athenaeum, *Exhibitions*, 1827, no. 106; 1831, no. 44./ Philadelphia, Pennsylvania Academy of the Fine Arts, *Sully Memorial*, 1922, no. 86 (repr.)./ Andover, Mass., Addison Gallery, *American Paintings in New England Museums*, 1932, no. 7./ Hartford, Conn., Wadsworth Atheneum, *American Painting and Sculpture of the 18th, 19th and 20th Centuries*, 1935, p. 18, no. 9./ Baltimore Museum, *Romanticism in America*, 1940 (under "Paintings")./ Pittsburgh, Pa., Carnegie Institute, *Survey of American Painting*, 1940, no. 109./ Pennsylvania State University, Mineral Industries Gallery, *Centennial Exhibition—Pennsylvania Painters*, 1955, no. 12 (repr.)./ Los Angeles, Municipal Art Gallery, *Old Favorites Revisited*, 1959, no. 39 (repr. cover)./ Dallas Museum of Fine Arts, *Famous Families in Art*, 1960, no. 22 (repr. cover)./ Minneapolis Institute of Arts, *Four Centuries of American Art*, 1963–1964 (under "Nineteenth Century").

959.

Victor René Value and His Daughter Charlotte

Oil on canvas. 50 × 40 in. (127 × 101.6 cm.)

Signed with initials and dated on paper in Mr. Value's hand: *TS 1828* (initials in monogram).

M. and M. Karolik Collection. 48.479

Reference: *Karolik Catalogue*, 1949, no. 216 (repr.).

960.
fig. 170

Fanny Kemble

The head of a young woman, turned three-quarters right, who wears a dress with a brown collar. The unfinished background behind her head is gray.

Oil on canvas. 30 × 25 in. (76.2 × 63.5 cm.)

Signed and dated on back, upper center: *Miss F.A. Kemble/ March 10, 1832/ TS* (in monogram). Actually painted 1833.

Collections: Sarah Sully, the artist's wife, Philadelphia, 1833; Blanche Sully, her daughter, Philadelphia, 1872; Garrett C. Neagle, her nephew, Philadelphia, 1898.

Abbott Lawrence Fund. 03.737

Frances Ann Kemble (1809–1893), illustrious member of a famous English acting family, began in the autumn of 1832 a highly successful stage tour of the United States. She left the theater in 1834 to marry Pierce Butler, wealthy Philadelphia lawyer and Georgia landowner. The marriage terminated in a divorce in 1847, after which she made her headquarters in Lenox, Mass., for many years touring the country giving readings from Shakespeare. Poetess, author, and translator, she lived her last years, from 1877 until her death, in England. The painting was done in Philadelphia on March 10, 1833, as entered in Sully's account book. The year 1832 inscribed on the back of the painting was probably added years later. The portrait was given by Sully to his wife; Miss Kemble herself wrote of it to a friend: "He [Sully] pressed upon my acceptance for you, a little melancholy head of me, an admirable and not too much flattered likeness; but as he had given that to his wife, of whom I am very fond, of course I could not deprive her of it." (Fanny Kemble to Harriet St. Leger, May 27, 1835; F.A. Kemble, *Records of a Later Life*, London, 1882, I, p. 21.) Another portrait of Miss Kemble was painted by Sully in the same year (Pennsylvania Academy of the Fine Arts).

References: C.H. Hart, ed., *Register of Portraits by Thomas Sully*, Philadelphia, 1909, p. 95, no. 926./ E. Biddle and M. Fielding, *Sully*, Philadelphia, 1921, p. 196, no. 956.

Exhibition: Philadelphia, Pennsylvania Academy of the Fine Arts, *Sully Memorial*, 1922, no. 44.

961. **Rosebud**

A little girl in white sits on gray paving stones and holds a black bonnet filled with pink and white roses and their green leaves. Beside her lies a brown and white setter. A green wooded landscape behind is touched with yellow, brown, and gray, and a distant brown tower stands against a blue and pink sky.

Oil on canvas. 28¼ × 36¼ in. (71.7 × 92.1 cm.)

Signed and dated lower left: *TS 1839* (initials in monogram).

Collections: F.T.S. Darley, Philadelphia; Joseph T. Kinsley, New York; David P. Kimball, Boston.

Bequest of David P. Kimball in memory of his wife, Clara Bertram Kimball. 23.543

An unsigned replica of the painting, with slight variations, is owned by the Pennsylvania Academy of the Fine Arts, Philadelphia. The Boston picture was engraved by John Sartain.

Reference: E. Biddle and M. Fielding, *Sully*, Philadelphia, 1921, no. 2162.

AUGUSTUS VINCENT TACK (1870–1949) was born in Pittsburgh, Pa., and graduated from Yale University. He then studied painting with H. Siddons Mowbray and John La Farge in New York, and later under Merson in Paris. A portrait, figure, and landscape painter, he was known for his murals and church altarpieces. He worked primarily in New York and Washington, D.C. until his death in Greenfield, Mass.

962. **Mrs. Gustave Schirmer (Grace May Tilton)**

Three-quarter length, nearly in right profile, she wears a white lace blouse and brown skirt and sits writing at a mahogany table. A vase of red flowers stands on a table behind a red brocade curtain.

Oil on canvas. 36 × 31 in. (91.4 × 78.7 cm.)

Signed and dated upper left: *Augustus Vincent Tack 1907.*

Collection: Mrs. W.R. Fay, daughter of the sitter, Boston.

Gift of Mrs. William Rodman Fay. 54.597

Grace May Tilton was the wife of Gustave Schirmer, founder of the well-known Schirmer Music Store, Boston.

EDMUND CHARLES TARBELL (1862–1938) was born in West Groton, Mass., but the family soon moved to Boston. He was apprenticed to the Forbes Lithograph Company; then with Benson, Reid, and Stacy Tolman he entered the first class of the Boston Museum School of Drawing and Painting under Otto Grundmann. After further study at the Académie Julian in Paris, under Boulanger and Lefebvre, he returned to Boston to work actively as a portrait and genre painter. Like his close friend, Benson, he was a member of the "Ten American Painters," admirers of French Impressionism. He taught at the Boston Museum School until his death at his home in Newcastle, N.H.

963.
fig. 496

Mother and Child in a Boat

In a blue and green boat a woman, dressed in pink, sits with her infant, who wears a white dress and blue shoes. Green leaves are reflected in the blue water.

Oil on canvas. 30 × 35 in. (76.2 × 88.9 cm.)

Signed and dated lower right: *Edmund C. Tarbell/ 1892.*

Bequest of David P. Kimball in memory of his wife, Clara Bertram Kimball. 23.532

Exhibitions: Boston, Chase's Gallery, *Tarbell*, 1894, no. 4./ Boston, St. Botolph Club, *Tarbell*, 1898, no. 6./ Boston, Copley Society, *Tarbell*, 1912, no. 48.

964.
fig. 497

Charles Greely Loring

Three-quarter length, he sits in a brown armchair and wears a black suit, white shirt, and blue tie. He faces front on a brown background.

Oil on canvas. 40¼ × 30 in. (102.2 × 76.2 cm.)

Signed lower right: *Tarbell.* Painted in 1905.

Charles Henry Hayden Fund. 06.2455

Charles Greely Loring (1828–1902) was born in Boston, and in 1848 and 1851 received his B.A. and M.A. degrees from Harvard. He rose to Major-General in the Civil War. He undertook the installation of the Way Collection of Egyptian Antiquities in the MFA, Boston, at its founding. In 1873 he became a Trustee of the Museum and in 1876 its first Director, a position he held until his death. This memorial portrait was commissioned by the Trustees in 1905.

Reference: F.W. Coburn, "Tarbell," *International Studio*, 1909, XXXII, no. 127, p. LXXX (pl. 30).

Exhibition: Washington, D.C., Corcoran Gallery, *Contemporary American Oils*, 1907, no. 121.

965.
fig. 495

Edward Robinson

In a black coat, white shirt, and brown waistcoat and tie he sits in a brown armchair, turned three-quarters right. He is portrayed three-quarter length before a brown table and background.

Oil on canvas. 44 × 34 in. (117 × 86.3 cm.)

Signed and dated lower left: *Edmund C. Tarbell 1906.*

Charles Henry Hayden Fund. 06.1895

Edward Robinson (1858–1931) was born in Boston, graduated from Harvard in 1879, and was Curator of Classical Antiquities at the Museum of Fine Arts, Boston from 1885 until he was appointed Director in 1902 on the death of General Loring (Cat. no. 964). In 1905, he resigned to become Assistant Director of the Metropolitan Museum in New York and was Director there from 1910 until his death. The portrait was commissioned by the Trustees of the MFA.

Exhibitions: Chicago Art Institute, *20th Annual Exhibition*, 1907, no. 370./ New York, Montross Gallery, *Tarbell*, 1907, no. 3./ Indianapolis, Herron Museum of Art, *23rd Annual*, 1908, p. 10, no. 73./ Philadelphia, Pennsylvania Academy of the Fine Arts, *Paintings by Ten American Painters*, 1908, no. 79./ Washington, D.C., Corcoran Gallery, *Tarbell*, 1908, no. 28./ New York, National Academy of Design, 1909–1910./ Boston, Copley Society, *Tarbell*, 1912, no. 36./ New York, Montross Gallery, *Tarbell*, 1912, no. 13./ New York, M. Knoedler and Co., *Tarbell*, 1918, no. 26.

966.
fig. 494

My Children in the Woods

In the brown and green forest, two young women in white dresses stand to the left watching a girl, also in white, and her brother, in brown, mounted on gray and brown horses. The background shows blue sky and water.

Oil on canvas: 50½ × 40¼ in. (128.2 × 102.2 cm.)

Signed and dated lower right: *Tarbell—1911.*

Gift of Mrs. W. Scott Fitz. 11.2809
Painted on Boatswains Hill, Newcastle, New Hampshire.

The artist's children, Josephine, aged nineteen, and Mercie, sixteen, stand watching their sister Mary, fourteen, and Edmund, thirteen, on horseback. Josephine (Mrs. Robert W. Ferrall) was born in 1890 and now lives in Madison, Virginia. Mercie (Mrs. Henry S.M. Clay) was born in 1895 and died in 1961. Mary (Mrs. R. Schaffer) was born in 1890 and now lives in the Tarbell house in Newcastle, N.H. Edmund A. was born in 1898 and died in 1954. Edmund was born in Newcastle; all the daughters were born in Boston.

Exhibitions: Boston, Copley Society, *Tarbell*, 1912, no. 14./ New York, Montross Gallery, *Tarbell*, 1912, no. 15./ Washington, D.C., Corcoran Gallery, *Tarbell*, 1916, no. 3.

967.
fig. 498

Reverie (Katharine Finn)

Full-length, seated in a brown chair, she turns in full left profile and rests her elbows on a cushion on the chair's arm. She wears a white dress and is seated before a brown wall; an oriental screen with blue and orange figures is in the left background.
Oil on canvas. 50¼ × 34¼ in. (127.6 × 87 cm.)
Signed and dated lower left: *Tarbell—1913.*
Bequest of Georgina S. Cary. 33.400

Katharine Stafford Finn (1893–1918), daughter of Dr. James Anthony Finn and sister of William J. Finn, a Paulist father, was married in about 1914 to Ignace Panzer. She was a friend of the donor and a student of Tarbell.

Reference: R.H.I. Gammell, *Twilight in Painting*, New York, 1946 (pl. 60).

Exhibitions: San Francisco, *Panama-Pacific International Exposition*, 1915–1916, no. 3950./ Maryhill, Washington, Maryhill Museum, *American Painting, 1875–1925*, 1956, no. 22.

968.
fig. 499

Girl Reading

In the light brown interior, surrounded by brown furniture, a gold mirror, black drapery, and a blue vase, a young woman is seated reading a book. She is portrayed in right profile and wears a black skirt and brown blouse.
Oil on canvas. 32½ × 28¼ in. (82.5 × 71.7 cm.)
Signed lower right: *Tarbell.*
Charles Henry Hayden Fund. 09.209

References: J.deW. Addison, *Boston Museum*, Boston, 1910, p. 52 (repr. opp. p. 52)./ R.H.I. Gammell, *Twilight in Painting*, New York, 1946 (pl. 51).

Exhibitions: Berlin, Königliche Akademie der Künste, *Ausstellung Amerikanischer Kunst*, 1910, p. 74./ Boston, Copley Society, *Tarbell*, 1912, no. 11./ New York, Montross Gallery, *Tarbell*, 1912, no. 14./ San Francisco, *Panama-Pacific International Exposition*, 1915–1916, no. 3942./ Pittsburgh, Pa., Carnegie Institute, *Paintings by Boston Artists*, 1922, no. 19./ Cambridge, Mass., Fogg Art Museum, *New England Genre*, 1939, no. 32.

ABBOTT HANDERSON THAYER (1849–1921), born in Boston, Mass., was brought up near Keene, N.H. He first took lessons in painting from H.D. Morse in Boston about 1865, then studied at the Brooklyn Art School and the National Academy of Design. He opened a studio in Brooklyn by 1869 but left in 1875 for Paris, where he studied at the École des Beaux Arts, then in the atelier of Jean Léon Gérôme. At first he did animal pictures, but later he turned to portraits, figure paintings, and occasional landscapes. In 1879 he opened a studio in New York, spending summers along the Hudson River and in New Hampshire. About 1901 he moved to Dublin, N.H., where, except for several European trips, he worked until his death. His work is generally characterized by an almost mystical idealism, especially his paintings of women.

969.

fig. 428

Girl in White

Three-quarter length and dressed in white, a young woman sits in profile to the right arranging white flowers upon a brown table. The background is dark brown.

Oil on canvas. 37½ × 29½ in. (95.2 × 74.9 cm.)

Signed lower right: *Abbott H. Thayer*. Painted about 1888.

Collection: Miss Mary Amory Greene, by 1891.

Gift of the Estate of Mary Amory Greene. 40.19

The portrait of Miss Margaret Greene, sister of Mary Amory Greene, was painted about 1888.

References: H.M. Beatty, "Thayer," *American Magazine of Art*, 1921, XII, no. 9, p. 331 (repr. p. 332)./ R. Cortissoz, "Personal Memories," *The Arts*, 1921, I, no. 6, p. 16 (repr. p. 13)./ N. Pousette-Dart, *Thayer*, New York, 1923, (repr.)./ N.C. White, *Thayer*, Hartford, Conn., 1951, p. 209 (repr.).

Exhibitions: Pittsburgh, Pa., Carnegie Institute, *Thayer*, 1919, no. 17 (repr. opp. p. 28)./ New York, Metropolitan Museum, *Thayer Memorial*, 1922, no. 30 (repr.)./ Washington, D.C., Corcoran Gallery, *Thayer Memorial*, 1922, no. 12 (repr.)./ New London, Conn., Lyman Allyn Museum, *Thayer*, 1961, no. 14./ Toronto Art Gallery and circulated in Canada, and New York, Whitney Museum, *American Painting from 1865–1905*, 1961, no. 65 (pl. XXVIII).

970.

fig. 427

Caritas

A woman, full-length and robed in white, stands upon green grass with her hands outstretched. Pink flowers fall upon two nude children who stand before a green-leafed tree and blue sky.

Oil on canvas. 85 × 55 in. (215.9 × 139.7 cm.)

Signed lower right: *Abbott H. Thayer*. Painted in 1894–1895.

The Warren Collection and contributions through the Paint and Clay Club. 97.199

"It has so far been called 'Caritas' . . . however since I never paint an idea, but rather try to harmonise human expressions till the looks of the canvas pleases me, trusting the certainty that when it looks beautiful the story may be found in it, and since I never have felt much satisfaction in 'Caritas' as its name, I should like to consider it open for further discussion, what to call it. . . . 'Spring' and 'Morning' are either of them pretty fair ones." (Letter from the artist, Dec. 15, 1897.) The model for the woman was Elise Pumpelly (Mrs. T. Handasyd Cabot), daughter of Raphael Pumpelly, geologist and explorer. The picture was painted in 1894–1895 for an exhibition at the Pennsylvania Academy of the Fine Arts.

References: *Art Amateur*, 1897, XXXVII, no. 4, p. 66./ N.A. Bell, "Thayer," *International Studio*, 1899, VI, no. 24, p. 252./ W.H. Downes, "American Paintings in the Boston Art Museum," *Brush and Pencil*, 1900, VI, no. 5, p. 207./ H.M. Beatty, "Thayer," *American Magazine of Art*, 1921, XII, no. 9, p. 331./ R. Cortissoz, "Personal Memories," *The Arts*, 1921, I, no. 6, p. 10./ N. Pousette-Dart, *Thayer*, New York, 1923, p. x (repr.)./ N.C. White, *Thayer*, Hartford, Conn., 1951, pp. 66, 70–72, 210, 213 (repr. opp. p. 72).

Exhibitions: Philadelphia, Pennsylvania Academy of the Fine Arts, *65th Annual*, 1895–1896, no. 322./ New York, American Fine Arts Society, *Native and Foreign Art*, 1904, no. 152./ Pittsburgh, Pa., Carnegie Institute, *Thayer*, 1919, no. 1 (repr. opp. p. 25)./ New York, Metropolitan Museum, *Thayer Memorial*, 1922, no. 45 (repr.)./ New York, National Academy of Design, Washington, D.C., Corcoran Gallery, and New York, Grand Central Art Galleries, *National Academy of Design Centennial*, 1925–1926, no. 159 (repr. p. 42)./ New London, Conn., Lyman Allyn Museum, *Thayer*, 1961, no. 16.

JEREMIAH THEÜS (about 1719–1774), born in Felsberg, Canton Grison, Switzerland, emigrated with his family to Orangeburg Township, S.C. about 1735. In 1740 he advertised himself as a "limner" in a Charleston newspaper, offering in addition to portraits, landscapes and coach decoration. By 1744 he offered art lessons. A prolific artist, he did portraits of many of the leading citizens of South Carolina.

971.

fig. 17

Dr. Lionel Chalmers

Half-length, facing three-quarters left, his left hand is placed in his black waistcoat, which he wears with a gray coat and white shirt. The black spandrels are before a gray background.

Oil on canvas. Painted oval. 16½ × 14¼ in. (41.9 × 36.2 cm.)

Signed and dated lower left: *J. Theüs 1756.*

Abraham Shuman Fund. 47.1544

Dr. Lionel Chalmers (about 1715–1777) was born in Cambleton, Scotland and probably was educated at the University of Edinburgh before going to Charleston. The author of *An Account of the Weather and Diseases of South Carolina,* he practiced medicine for about forty years. The portrait of his wife (Cat. no. 972) is pendant to this one.

References: J.H. Morgan, "Notes of Jeremiah Theüs," *Brooklyn Museum Quarterly,* 1924, XI, no. 2, p. 51./ M.S. Middleton, *Theüs,* Columbia, S.C., 1953, pp. 122, 174 (repr. p. 63).

Exhibition: Colorado Springs Fine Arts Center, *Likeness of America, 1680–1820,* 1949, no. 40.

972.

fig. 16

Mrs. Lionel Chalmers (Martha Logan)

Half-length, facing three-quarters right, but looking front, she wears a white dress trimmed with lace. The black spandrels are before a brown background.

Oil on canvas. Painted oval. 16½ × 14¼ in. (41.9 × 36.2 cm.)

Painted in 1756.

Abraham Shuman Fund. 47.1545

Martha Logan (1721–1765), daughter of George and Martha Daniell Logan of South Carolina, married Dr. Lionel Chalmers in 1738 or 1739. At her death she was survived by six of her eleven children. While some question has existed that the portrait might represent Elizabeth Warden, Dr. Chalmer's second wife, whom he married in 1766, the style so closely resembles his portrait (Cat. no. 971) that this must be a pendant of the same date.

References: J.H. Morgan, "Notes of Jeremiah Theüs," *Brooklyn Museum Quarterly,* 1924, XI, no. 2, p. 51./ M.S. Middleton, *Theüs,* Columbia, S.C., 1953, pp. 122–123 (repr. p. 64).

Exhibition: Colorado Springs Fine Arts Center, *Likeness of America, 1680–1820,* 1949, no. 41.

A. E. (?) THOMPSON

973.

fig. 272

Wetumpka Bridge, Alabama

Oil on canvas. 42¾ × 58¼ in. (108.6 × 147.9 cm.)

Signed and dated lower left: *Wetumpka/ From/ West Side River,/ Opposite/ Low-water rock/ A.E. (?) Thompson/ pt./ 1847.*

M. and M. Karolik Collection. 48.482

Reference: Karolik Catalogue, 1949, no. 219 (repr.).

JEROME B. THOMPSON (1814–1886)

974.

fig. 224

A "Pic Nick," Camden, Maine (formerly attributed to Jeremiah P. Hardy)

Oil on canvas. 41 × 62 in. (104.1 × 157.5 cm.)

Painted about 1850.

M. and M. Karolik Collection. 46.852

The present attribution is based on stylistic comparisons with *The "Pick Nick" near Mount Mansfield, Vermont* (San Francisco, M.H. de Young Memorial Museum), traditionally ascribed to Thompson, and with *The Peep Show* (Cat. no. 975), signed and dated *J. Thompson 1851.*

References: Karolik Catalogue, 1949, no. 128 (repr.)./ B.N. Parker, " A 'Pic Nick,' " Camden, Maine, by Jerome B. Thompson," *MFA Bulletin,* 1952, L, no. 282, pp. 79–82 (figs. 1, 3, and 4).

975. **The Peep Show**
Oil on canvas. 25 × 30 in. (63.5 × 76.2 cm.)
Signed and dated lower left: *J. Thompson 1851.*
M. and M. Karolik Collection. 48.481
Reference: *Karolik Catalogue*, 1949, no. 218 (repr.).

GEORGE TIRRELL is known only as a painter of views of California and the artist of "the longest panorama ever painted," which was exhibited for the first time in San Francisco in April, 1860. The panorama, a vista of California from Monterey to the Yosemite Valley, was completed in three years with the help of his partner, Hageman.

976. **View of Sacramento, California, from Across the Sacramento River**
fig. 289

Various boats of white, green, brown, and blue lie moored to the foreground bank. Beyond the gray river are gray and white boats before trees and pink buildings. Pink clouds streak the blue sky.
Oil on canvas. 27 × 47¾ in. (68.6 × 121.2 cm.)
Signed lower left: *G. Tirrell.* Painted about 1855–1860.
Collections: Richard Loeb, S. America; Maxim Karolik, Newport, R.I.
M. and M. Karolik Collection. 62.279

The view was painted from the town of Washington (now Broderick), where unused boats were docked. On the extreme left stands the Sacramento City Hall and the waterworks, a large two-story building, reputed to be "the first edifice and machinery in California for supplying her citizens and the fire department with water." (S. Colville, *City Directory of Sacramento*, 1854–1855, p. 5.) *Antelope*, the large white sidewheeler, was a veteran of the New York-New Brunswick and San Francisco-Panama runs. (Letter from M.R. Gillis, California State Library, to Dorothy Miller, Museum of Modern Art, New York, Dec. 26, 1950.)

References: J.I.H. Baur, *American Painting of the Nineteenth Century*, New York, 1953 (repr. p. 9)./ —, "American Luminism," *Perspective USA*, 1954, no. 9, pp. 94–95 (repr.).

Exhibitions: Worcester, Mass., Art Museum, *The Private Collection of Maxim Karolik*, 1952, no. 37./ New York, American Federation of Arts, circulated in Germany and Italy, and Whitney Museum, *American Painting in the Nineteenth Century*, 1953–1954, no. 25./ Washington, D.C., Smithsonian Institution, circulated in the U.S., *19th Century American Paintings*, 1954–1956, no. 47./ Boston, MFA, and circulated in the U.S., *The M. and M. Karolik Collection*, 1957–1959, no. 164.

JOHN TRUMBULL (1756–1843) was born in Lebanon, Conn., the youngest son of Governor Jonathan Trumbull. After graduating from Harvard in 1773 at seventeen, he was a Colonel in the Continental Army from 1775 to 1777, and aide-de-camp to General Washington. Already experienced as a surveyor, he taught himself to paint and in 1780 went to study in London under West. Imprisoned in retaliation for the Major André affair, he soon returned to America but was again with West from 1784 to 1789, painting portraits and commencing his life's work on a series of Revolutionary War murals. In 1789, before returning to America, he came under the influence of David and of Mme. Vigée-LeBrun in Paris. From 1794 to 1804 he was in London and Paris as a Commissioner under the Jay Treaty, then he spent four years in New York before returning to London from 1808 to 1816. From 1816 to 1837 he worked in New York, painting portraits and working on the commission for the Revolutionary War murals for the Capitol, Washington. He was also President of the American Academy of Fine Arts from 1816 to 1835. From 1837 to 1841 he lived in New Haven, Conn., where the Trumbull Gallery, a collection of his works, was established. He died in New York. In addition to the following paintings, the MFA owns one miniature, a portrait of Joel Barlow (1754–1812).

977.

fig. 142

Self-Portrait

Half-length, he faces nearly front while resting an elbow upon the brown table, which supports his brown palette and a book. He wears a red-brown suit over a white shirt and stock. The background is black.

Oil on canvas. 29¾ × 23¾ in. (75.5 × 60.3 cm.)

Painted in 1777.

Collections: Percy Webb McClellan, grandnephew of the artist, Haverhill, Mass.; George Nixon Black, Boston, about 1914.

Bequest of George Nixon Black. 29.791

Before the painting was relined in 1908, its stretcher bore the inscription: *John Trumbull Ipse pinxit aestat 21.* In his records the picture is referred to as "portrait of myself, head size, July, 1777. Given to Miss Tyler." The volume on the table is Hogarth's *The Analysis of Beauty.*

References: J. Trumbull, "Record of Paintings of before 1789" (MS, Yale University Library, New Haven), no. 28./ J. Trumbull, *Reminiscences of His own Time,* New York, 1841, no. 29, p. 59./ W.H. Downes, "Boston Painters and Paintings," *Atlantic Monthly,* 1888, LXII, no. 369, p. 96./ W. Dunlap, *History of the Arts of Design,* Boston, 1918, II, p. 13 (repr. opp. p. 12)./ T. Bolton and H.L. Binsse, "Trumbull," *The Antiquarian,* 1931, XVII, no. 1, p. 56./ A. Burroughs, *Limners and Likenesses,* Cambridge, Mass., 1936, p. 106./ T. Sizer, "An Early Check List of the Paintings of John Trumbull," *Yale University Library Gazette,* 1948, vol. 22, no. 4, p. 119./ —, "Trumbull," *Art in America,* 1949, XXXVII, no. 4, p. 197, no. 29 (repr. p. 190)./ —, "Checklist of Trumbull's Works," *Art Bulletin,* 1949, XXXI, no. 1, Part III, p. 28 (fig. 3)./ —, *Trumbull,* New Haven, 1950, p. 55 (fig. 3)./ — (ed.), *Autobiography of Trumbull,* New Haven, 1953, p. 53, no. 29.

Exhibitions: Boston, Copley Society, *Portraits by American Painters Before the Revolution,* 1922, no. 64./ Yale University Art Gallery, *Connecticut Tercentenary,* 1935, no. 42./ Harvard University, *Tercentenary,* 1936, no. 33./ New London, Conn., Lyman Allyn Museum, *Trumbull and His Contemporaries,* 1944, no. 2./ Yale University Art Gallery, *Trumbull,* 1949./ Washington, D.C., National Gallery, *Makers of History in Washington, 1800–1950,* 1950, no. 131 (repr. p. 157)./ Hartford, Conn., Wadsworth Atheneum, *Trumbull, Bicentennial of His Birth,* 1956, no. 7.

978.

fig. 144

Priam Returning with the Body of Hector

Hector, draped in white, is carried by a soldier in bronze armor and a man in a green robe. Priam, in red and gray, and the two women in green, red, and white robes lament with the group of mourners. Beyond the brown architecture can be seen blue sky with white clouds.

Oil on canvas. 24¾ × 36¾ in. (62.8 × 93.3 cm.)

Painted in 1785.

Collections: Given by the artist to Governor Christopher Gore, Waltham, Mass.; Mrs. Christopher Gore; bequeathed to the Boston Athenaeum by Mrs. Christopher Gore, 1834.

Deposited by the Boston Athenaeum, 1879. Ath. 412

The scene was taken from the twenty-fourth book of Homer's *Iliad.* Priam, King of Troy, went to Achilles in the Greek camp beyond the Trojan walls to beg for the body of his son, Hector, who had been slain by Achilles. Here, Priam presents the body to Hector's mother and wife, Hecuba and Andromache. An ink drawing for this work, signed and dated 1784 in London, is owned by Col. Ralph H. Isham, New York. An ink study for the painting (signed and dated on the back: *London 20 December 1784*) is in the Fordham University Collection, New York. A third ink study, signed and dated 1785 in London (Philadelphia, Stan V. Henkels Auction Gallery, *1st Silliman Sale,* 1896, no. 128) is in the collection of Mrs. Percy Chubb, Chester, N.J. An entry in Trumbull's notebook (T. Sizer, *Yale University Library Gazette,* 1948, *see below*) reads: "NO. 26. Priam returning to his Family with the dead body of Hector—composition of many figures—2 feet high by 3 feet long.—this little picture employed me about 3 Months, and in Models & frame cost me Ten Guineas—it was finished in August

1785. nineteen months after my arrival in England.—it was given to & is still in possession of one of my earliest & best friends, Cristo. Gore Esqr. —at Waltham. (1818)."

References: "Miscellanies Relating to the Arts," *The Artist's Repository and Drawing Magazine*, London, 1786, v, Part II, p. 25, no. 132./ J. Trumbull, "Record of Paintings of before 1789" (MS, Yale University Library, New Haven), no. 26./ J. Trumbull, *Reminiscences of His own Time*, New York, 1841, p. 92./ H.T. Tuckerman, *Book of the Artists*, New York, 1870, p. 627./ J. Durand, *Trumbull*, Boston, 1881, p. 7./ W.H. Downes, "Boston Painters and Painting," *Atlantic Monthly*, 1888, LXII, no. 369, p. 96./ J. Weir, *John Trumbull and His Works*, New York, 1901, p. 79./ W. Dunlap, *History of the Arts of Design*, Boston, 1918, II, p. 32./ T. Sizer, "An Early Check List of the Paintings of John Trumbull," *Yale University Library Gazette*, 1948, vol. 22, no. 4, p. 122./ —, "A Tentative 'Short-Title' Check List of the Works of Col. John Trumbull," *Art Bulletin*, 1948, vol. XXX, no. 3, p. 218./ —, *Trumbull*, New Haven, 1950, p. 78./ Y. Bizardel, "Trumbull," *Gazette des Beaux-Arts*, 1962, LX, p. 430.

Exhibitions: London, Royal Academy, 1786, no. 132./ Boston Athenaeum, *9th Exhibition*, 1835, no. 42./ Hartford, Conn., Wadsworth Atheneum, *Trumbull, Bicentennial of His Birth*, 1956, no. 29 (pl. II).

979. **Sortie from Gibraltar**

fig. 147

Don José Barboza, in a Spanish officer's uniform of red breeches and a dark blue coat, lies wounded before British and German officers, right, in red, white, black, and green uniforms. Soldiers fighting among brown fortifications on the left wear white, red, and blue. The sky is red and yellow.

Oil on canvas. 71 × 107 in. (180.3 × 271.8 cm.)
Signed and dated lower left: *John Trumbull 1789.*
Collection: Purchased from the artist by the Boston Athenaeum, 1828.
Deposited by the Boston Athenaeum, 1876. Ath. 10

On November 26, 1781, during the three-year siege of the English fortress at Gibraltar by French and Spanish troops, the British, under General Elliot, marched out by night and successfully destroyed an entire line of counterworks. Don José Barboza (posed by Sir Thomas Lawrence), though mortally wounded during the encounter, refused British help, as it would have meant complete surrender to the enemy. His "gallant conduct and death" inspired Trumbull to paint the scene. The British officers depicted as they offer their aid to the Spaniard are, from left to right: Capt. Alexander MacKenzie, 71st Regt. (Highland) Foot; Gen. George Elliot, Lord Heathfield, Governor of Gibraltar; Maj. Charles Vallotton, 56th Regt., aide-de-camp to Elliot; 2nd Lieut. George Koehler, Royal Artillery, aide-de-camp to Elliot; Lieut. Col. Hardy, 56th Regt., Quarter-Master General of the Garrison; Maj. Gen. Ross; Capt. Whitman, Royal Artillery; Comm. Sir Roger Curtis, Volunteer; Lieut. Col. Trigge, 12th Regt.; Lieut. Col. Maxwell, 71st Regt. (Highland) Foot; and Lieut. Col. Ernst von Hugo, 6th Hanoverian Infantry. The drawing key to the painting is in the Yale University Art Gallery, New Haven. The Boston Athenaeum owns the sketch book for the picture. Other studies are at the Connecticut Historical Society, Hartford, and with Col. Ralph H. Isham, New York. Studies and versions are owned by the Cincinnati Art Museum, Yale University, and Lieut. Comdr. Robinson of Newport, R.I. There are several others unlocated. The picture was engraved by William Sharpe, London, 1799.

References: J. Trumbull, "Record of Paintings of before 1789" (MS, Yale University Library, New Haven), no. 33./ J. Trumbull, *Reminiscences of His own Time*, New York, 1841, p. 149./ J. Durand, *Trumbull*, Boston, 1881, p. 10 (repr. opp. p. 18)./ W.H. Downes, "Boston Painters and Paintings," *Atlantic Monthly*, 1888, LXII, no. 369, p. 96./ J. Weir, *John Trumbull and His Works*, New York, 1901, p. 74 (repr. opp. p. 53)./ W. Dunlap, *History of the Arts of Design*, Boston, 1918, II, pp. 37–38, 49./ J. Brockway, "Trumbull's Sortie," *Art Bulletin*, 1934, XVI, no. 1, pp. 5–13 (fig. 9.) M.M. Swan, *The Athenaeum Gallery*, Boston, 1940, pp. 111–116 (repr.)./ T. Sizer, "An Early Check List of the Paintings of John Trumbull," *Yale University Library Gazette*, 1948, vol. 22, no. 4, p. 122./ —, "Checklist of Trumbull's Works," *Art*

Bulletin, 1948, XXX, no. 3, Part I, p. 218./ —, *Trumbull*, New Haven, 1950, pp. 2, 76./ — (ed.), *Autobiography of Trumbull*, New Haven, 1953, pp. 148, 295.

Exhibitions: London, Spring Garden, 1789./ New York, Park Theatre, 1804./ New York, Academy of Fine Arts, 1828./ Boston Athenaeum, *3rd Exhibition*, 1829, no. 86./ New York, Apollo Association, 1841./ Boston, MFA, *Contemporary Art*, 1879, no. 209./ Andover, Mass., Addison Gallery, *Reflections on American Paintings of a Century Ago*, 1939./ New York, World's Fair, *Masterpieces of Art*, 1939–1940, no. 178 (repr. p. 121).

980.
fig. 143

Alexander Hamilton

Three-quarters left and nearly half-length, he wears a black coat and white neckcloth. The background is brown.

Oil on canvas. 30½ × 24½ in. (77.5 × 62.2 cm.)
Painted in 1806.
Collections: S.S. Perkins, Boston, 1806; Robert C. Winthrop, Boston.
Bequest of Robert C. Winthrop. 94.167

Alexander Hamilton (1757–1804), born on the Island of Nevis, West Indies, a major figure in the Revolution, was first Secretary of the Treasury. He was shot to death while fighting a duel with his great political rival, Aaron Burr. The portrait, done in New York in 1806, is a replica of Trumbull's full-length portrait (City Hall, New York) which in turn was done posthumously from the marble bust of him by Giuseppi Ceracchi. The New-York Historical Society owns a replica by Trumbull of the MFA's portrait. In his account book, he noted: "May 6, 1806 . . . To cash red'd for a/c of S.S. Perkins of Boston for a portrait (head) of Gen'l Hamilton—100.00."

References: W.H. Downes, "Boston Painters and Paintings," *Atlantic Monthly*, 1888, LXII, no. 369, p. 96./ C.H. Hart, "Life Portraits of Alexander Hamilton," *McClure's Magazine*, March, 1897./ J. Weir, *John Trumbull and His Works*, New York, 1901, p. 75./ T. Bolton and H.L. Binsse, "Trumbull," *The Antiquarian*, 1931, XVII, no. 1, p. 54./ T. Sizer, "Checklist of Trumbull's Works," *Art Bulletin*, 1948, XXX, no. 4, Part II, p. 266./ —, *Trumbull*, New Haven, 1950, p. 29 (fig. 9).

Exhibitions: Yale University Art Gallery, *Trumbull*, 1901./ Hartford, Conn., Wadsworth Atheneum, *Trumbull, Bicentennial of His Birth*, 1956, no. 96.

981.
fig. 145

Stephen Minot

Nearly half-length, he turns three-quarters left in a black coat with a white stock. The background is brown.

Oil on canvas. 30 × 24 in. (76.2 × 61 cm.)
Painted in 1806.
Gift of Susan I. Minot, daughter of the sitter. 79.333

Stephen Minot (about 1772/3–?), the son of John Minot, a shipmaster, and Mary DeRue Minot, was a Boston merchant. After his marriage to Sally Minot in 1805, they went to Calcutta, where their daughter was born. In his account book (owned by Yale University), the artist recorded: "1806 Nov. 19 Cash rec'd from Capt. Minot for 2 portraits 200." The portrait of his wife (Cat. no. 982) is pendant to this one.

References: W.H. Downes, "Boston Painters and Paintings," *Atlantic Monthly*, 1888, LXII, no. 369, p. 96./ J. Weir, *John Trumbull and His Works*, New York, 1901, p. 75./ T. Bolton and H.L. Binsse, "Trumbull," *The Antiquarian*, 1931, XVII, no. 1, p. 54./ T. Sizer, "Checklist of Trumbull's Works," *Art Bulletin*, 1949, XXXI, no. 1, Part III, p. 23./ —, *Trumbull*, New Haven, 1950, p. 41.

Exhibitions: Yale University Art Gallery, *Trumbull*, 1901./ Vancouver Art Gallery, *Two Hundred Years of American Painting*, 1955, no. 10./ Hartford, Conn., Wadsworth Atheneum, *Trumbull, Bicentennial of His Birth*, 1956, no. 97.

982.
fig. 146

Mrs. Stephen Minot (Sally Minot)

Turned three-quarters right and half-length, she wears a white dress and a topaz brooch. The background is brown.

Oil on canvas. 30 × 24 in. (76.2 × 61 cm.)
Painted in 1806.

Gift of Susan I. Minot. 79.334

Sally Minot's dates and the names of her parents are not known. Her portrait was painted with that of her husband in New York in 1806. A replica of the portrait, now on loan to the Brandegee Charitable Foundation, Boston, is owned by Mrs. Marion S. Boit. Pendant to the preceding.

References: W.H. Downes, "Boston Painters and Paintings," *Atlantic Monthly*, 1888, LXII, no. 369, p. 96./ J. Weir, *John Trumbull and His Works*, New York, 1901, p. 75./ T. Bolton and H.L. Binsse, "Trumbull," *The Antiquarian*, 1931, XVII, no. 1, p. 54./ T. Sizer, "Checklist of Trumbull's Work," *Art Bulletin*, 1949, XXXI, no. 1, part II, p. 23./ —, *Trumbull*, New Haven, 1950, p. 41.

Exhibitions: Yale University Art Gallery, *Trumbull*, 1901./ Hartford, Conn., Wadsworth Atheneum, *Trumbull, Bicentennial of His Birth*, 1956, no. 98 (pl. IV).

DWIGHT WILLIAM TRYON (1849–1925) was born in Hartford, Conn. and studied painting with Daubigny and Harpignies in Paris from 1876 to 1881. Upon his return to America, he taught art at Smith College, Northampton, Mass. until 1923. He worked as a landscape painter in New York and in South Dartmouth, Mass. until his death in South Dartmouth.

983.
fig. 523

Early Morning—September

Beyond a meadow covered with green and brown shrubs, a row of brown poplars stands before gray hills. The morning sky is pale blue and white.
Oil on panel. 19¾ × 30 in. (50.1 × 76.2 cm.)
Signed lower right: *D.W. Tryon.* Dated lower left: *1904.*
Bequest of Ernest Wadsworth Longfellow. 23.500

References: F.F. Sherman, "Tryon," *Art in America*, 1919, VII, no. 1, p. 38 (fig. 3)./ —, *American Painters*, New York, 1919, pp. 17–18 (repr. opp. p. 16).

Exhibition: Philadelphia, Pennsylvania Academy of the Fine Arts, *100th Anniversary Exhibition*, 1905, no. 453.

JOHN HENRY TWACHTMAN (1853–1902) was born in Cincinnati, O. of German parents. He helped his father make decorated windowshades, then took night classes in drawing at the Ohio Mechanics Institute and later studied under Frank Duveneck at the Cincinnati School of Design. In 1875 he went with Duveneck to Munich, where he studied under Löfftz until 1877, when he joined Duveneck and William Merritt Chase in Venice for a year. He returned to New York, but made frequent trips to Europe. In 1883 he studied in Paris at the Académie Julian under Boulanger and Lefebvre, but he also came under the influence of Impressionism. He settled in Greenwich, Conn. in 1889 and taught at the Art Students League in New York. In 1898 he helped to found the "Ten American Painters" group, oriented toward Impressionism, which included Benson, Tarbell, De Camp, and Hassam. He died at his summer home in Gloucester, Mass.

984.
fig. 514

Venice Landscape

Brown and gray trees line a gray path through a dull green meadow before a row of brown houses, right, and distant white ones. The sky is dull blue.
Oil on canvas mounted on chipboard. 12 × 20½ in. (30.5 × 52 cm.)
Signed and dated lower right: *J.H. Twachtman/ Venice '78.*
Bequest of Sarah Wyman Whitman. 04.1715

The muted coloration reflects the teaching of Duveneck and the Munich school before the influence of French Impressionism.

Reference: A. Tucker, *Twachtman* (American Artist Series), New York, 1931 (repr. p. 52).

Exhibitions: Brooklyn Museum, *Leaders of American Impressionism*, 1937, p. 37, no. 56./ Utica, N.Y., Munson-Williams-Proctor Institute, *Twachtman*, 1939, no. 12.

985.

Canal Scene

Between green meadows and woods, black barges, right, float on calm gray water beside a wharf. The sky is pale blue-gray.

Oil on canvas. 15 × 18 in. (38.1 × 45.7 cm.)
Signed lower left: *J.H. Twachtman.*
Painted about 1880–1890.
Gift of the Estate of Sarah Wyman Whitman. 09.214
The subject is European, and the lightened palette indicates a date in the 1880's.

986.

fig. 515

February

The sky is gray over a snow-covered slope with a blue brook at its foot, and a few scattered trees.
Oil on canvas. 36¼ × 48 in. (92.1 × 121.9 cm.)
Signed lower right: *J.H. Twachtman.* Painted about 1890–1900.
Charles Henry Hayden Fund. 07.7
Probably painted at Greenwich, Conn.

References: E. Clark, "Twachtman," *Art in America*, 1919, VII, no. 3, p. 132 (repr. p. 133)./ —, *Twachtman*, New York, 1924, p. 47./ A. Tucker, *Twachtman* (American Artist Series), New York, 1931, p. 9 (repr. p. 42).

Exhibition: Utica, N.Y., Munson-Williams-Proctor Institute, *Twachtman*, 1939, no. 13.

987.

fig. 513

Winter Landscape

A blue stream flows between snowy hillsides touched with gray and purple. Gray trees are on a distant hill before a blue sky.
Oil on canvas. 12 × 18 in. (30.5 × 45.7 cm.)
Painted about 1890–1900.
The John Pickering Lyman Collection. Gift of Theodora Lyman. 19.1331

ELIHU VEDDER

(1836–1923), born in New York City, grew up in Schenectady, N.Y. At twelve he began to paint and studied briefly under T.H. Matteson in Sherburne, N.Y. In 1856 he studied under Picot in Paris before moving to Florence. He painted and did illustrations in New York from 1861 to 1865, but returned to Paris, then settled permanently in Rome in 1867, with occasional visits to America. Well known for imaginative paintings of Romantic fantasy, he also was a muralist. A portrait of Vedder by John F. Weir (Cat. no. 1013) is in the MFA collection.

988.

fig. 402

Italian Landscape

A gray sheep and her lamb stand on a red-brown and grassy slope before a brown well and trees. The distant brown buildings and green mountains, right, are under a clouded sky.
Oil on canvas. 14 × 28 in. (35.5 × 71.1 cm.)
Inscribed on back: *E. Vedder No.1.* Painted about 1857.
Bequest of Charles Sumner. 74.15
Probably referred to in Vedder's autobiography as: "sold in Florence between August 1857 and December 1860: Landscape with Sheep and Old Well."

Reference: E. Vedder, *Digressions of Vedder*, Boston, 1910, p. 459.

Exhibitions: Boston, MFA, *Contemporary Art*, 1879, no. 71./ New London, Conn., Lyman Allyn Museum, *Men of the Tile Club*, 1945, no. 161./ Detroit Institute of Arts and Toledo Museum, *Travelers in Arcadia*, 1951, no. 92 (repr. p. 61)./ New York, Grolier Club, *The Italian Influence on American Literature*, 1961, no. 280.

989.

Fisherman and the Genie (Sketch)

Description same as for the following (Cat. no. 990).
Oil on panel. 6¾ × 11½ in. (17.1 × 29.1 cm.)
Signed lower right: *Elihu Vedder.* Painted about 1861.
Collections: Estate of Francis E. Parker, Boston; William S. Bigelow, Boston.
Bequest of William Sturgis Bigelow. 26.770
Probably a sketch for, or a version of, the following painting.

990.
fig. 404

Fisherman and the Genie

A bearded man wearing a blue tunic and a red cap sits on a sandy shore before a bronze jug, which emits brown smoke forming a genie's head. Trees stand before blue sea and a clouded sky.

Oil on panel. 7½ × 13¾ in. (19 × 34.9 cm.)
Signed lower right: *Vedder.* Painted in 1861.
Collections: Purchased from the artist by Martin Brimmer, Boston, 1861; Mrs. M. Brimmer, 1896.
Bequest of Mrs. Martin Brimmer. 06.2431

Taken from "The Story of the Fisherman," from the *Arabian Nights.*

References: E. Radford, "Vedder," *Art Journal*, 1899, LI (repr. p. 98)./ E. Vedder, *Digressions of Vedder*, Boston, 1910, p. 460.

Exhibitions: Chicago, *World's Columbian Exposition*, 1893, no. 1044./ Providence, R.I., Art Club, *Spring Exhibition*, 1894, no. 38./ New York, American Academy of Arts and Letters, *Vedder*, 1937–1938, no. 154./ New London, Conn., Lyman Allyn Museum, *Men of the Tile Club*, 1945, no. 163.

991.
fig. 403

The Questioner of the Sphinx

A silvery moonlit scene: a dark-skinned man in blue robes kneels in the sand among brown ruins to listen to the gray stone sphinx. The night sky is blue.

Oil on canvas. 36 × 41¾ in. (91.5 × 106 cm.)
Signed and dated lower right: *Elihu Vedder/ 1863.*
Collections: Purchased from the artist by Martin Brimmer, Boston, between 1863 and 1865; Mrs. M. Brimmer, 1896.
Bequest of Mrs. Martin Brimmer. 06.2430

In the artist's autobiography, this painting is referred to as "a large sketch, more carefully studied later." Three other versions of a later date (unlocated) are mentioned.

References: H.T. Tuckerman, *Book of the Artists*, New York, 1870, p. 451./ E. Radford, "Vedder," *Art Journal*, 1899, LI, p. 102./ E. Vedder, *Digressions of Vedder*, Boston, 1910, p. 460 (repr. p. 229)./ L.M. Bryant, *American Pictures and Their Painters*, New York, 1917, pp. 74–76 (fig. 42)./ J.T. Soby and D. Miller, *Romantic Painting in America*, Museum of Modern Art, New York, 1943, p. 29./ E.P. Richardson, *Painting in America*, New York, 1956, p. 352./ R. Soria, "Vedder," *Art Quarterly*, 1960, XXVI, no. 2, p. 187 (fig. 3).

Exhibitions: Pittsburgh, Pa., Carnegie Institute, *Vedder*, 1901, no. 13./ Hartford, Conn., Wadsworth Atheneum, *Literature and Poetry in Painting Since 1850*, 1933, no. 75.

992.
fig. 401

Lair of the Sea Serpent

A gray sea serpent on a brown sand and grassy coast lies before the blue ocean and pink-clouded sky.

Oil on canvas. 21 × 36 in. (53.3 × 91.4 cm.)
Signed and dated lower left: *Elihu Vedder/ 1864.*
Collection: Purchased from the artist by Thomas G. Appleton, Boston, 1864–1865.
Bequest of Thomas G. Appleton. 84.283

In his autobiography, Vedder writes: "My two friends . . . had invited me . . . to Manchester-by-the-Sea to show me, they said, the place where I must have painted my Lair of the Sea Serpent. As a matter of fact I did not paint it there, but, like the talented boy, 'drew it all out of my own head with a common lead pencil.'" The sketch, bought from Vedder by Mrs. Agnes E. Tracy in 1899, was owned in 1938 by Mrs. Harold G. Henderson.

References: H.T. Tuckerman, *Book of the Artists*, New York, 1870, pp. 451–452./ L.G. Straham, *Art Treasures in America*, New York, 1879, III, p. 88./ *Art Amateur*, 1880, II, no. 5, p. 89./ "Vedder," *Scribner's Magazine*, 1880, p. 114 (repr. p. 111)./ W.H. Downes, "Boston Painters and Paintings," *Atlantic Monthly*, 1888, LXII, no. 373, p. 654./ E. Radford, "Vedder," *Art Journal*, 1899, LI, p. 102 (repr. p. 99)./

W.H. Downes, "American Paintings in the Boston Art Museum," *Brush and Pencil*, 1900, VI, no. 5, p. 210./ E. Vedder, *Digressions of Vedder*, Boston, 1910, p. 463 (repr. p. 247)./ R. Cortissoz, *American Artists*, New York, 1923, p. 94./ E.P. Richardson, *American Romantic Painting*, New York, 1945, p. 48, no. 208./ —, *Painting in America*, New York, 1956, p. 352 (fig. 144)./ R. Soria, "Vedder," *Art Quarterly*, 1960, XXVI, no. 2, p. 187 (fig. 2).

Exhibitions: Boston, MFA, *Contemporary Art*, 1879, no. 226./ Munich, *International Art*, 1883, no. 2090./ Chicago, *World's Columbian Exposition*, 1893, no. 1042./ Hartford, Conn., Wadsworth Atheneum, *American Painting and Sculpture of the 18th, 19th and 20th Centuries*, 1935, no. 36./ Baltimore Museum, *Souvenir of Romanticism in America*, 1940./ New York, Museum of Modern Art, *Romantic Painting in America*, 1943, p. 29, no. 199 (repr. p. 69)./ New London, Conn., Lyman Allyn Museum, *Men of the Tile Club*, 1945, no. 159./ Brooklyn Museum, *The Coast and The Sea*, 1948–1949, no. 120./ Detroit Institute of Arts and San Francisco, M.H. de Young Memorial Museum, *Painting in America, the Story of 450 Years*, 1957, no. 148./ Cambridge, Mass., Busch-Reisinger Museum, *Rivers and Seas—Changing Attitudes Toward Landscape 1700–1962*, 1962, no. 38.

993.

Head of a Girl

Bust-length and facing front, she wears a brown, green, and yellow brocade dress and has long black hair.
Oil on panel. 11¾ × 9¾ in. (29.7 × 24.7 cm.)
Signed and dated upper right: *Elihu Vedder/ 1879.*
Collections: Sold by Williams and Everett, Boston, *Vedder*, April, 1880, no. 8 (as *Eugenia, Head of a Roman Girl*) to Thomas G. Appleton, Boston, 1880; Ernest Wadsworth Longfellow, Boston.
Bequest of Ernest Wadsworth Longfellow. 23.488
Reference: E. Vedder, *Digressions of Vedder*, Boston, 1910, p. 478 (as *Head of Eugenia*).
Exhibitions: Munich, *International Art*, 1883, no. 2534./ Detroit Institute of Arts and Toledo Museum, *Travelers in Arcadia*, 1951, no. 91.

994.
fig. 400

Lazarus Rising from the Tomb

The head and shoulders of a man with dark skin, wearing a white turban and white robe, appear from within a cavelike tomb. The head is outlined against a bright blue sky and yellow cliffs.
Oil on canvas. 20 × 31½ in. (50.8 × 80 cm.)
Inscribed lower left: *V. Roma/ Copyright 1899 by E. Vedder.*
Collection: Purchased from the artist by Edwin Atkins Grozier, Boston, 1900.
Gift of Edwin Atkins Grozier. 01.1

Taken from the New Testament, *St. John*, 11. An earlier version was purchased by Melville E. Stone in 1892. Two drawings for the painting are owned by the Rhode Island School of Design Museum and by Edward Kemper, Jr. of Arlington, Va.

References: E. Vedder, *Digressions of Vedder*, Boston, 1910, p. 497./ L.M. Bryant, *American Pictures and Their Painters*, New York, 1917, p. 76.

995.

The Morning Glory

A nude, sitting upon a large gray and purple morning glory, turns to look at the blue sky and gray clouds behind her.
Oil on paper. Painted round. 14½ × 13¾ in. (36.8 × 34.9 cm.)
Signed and dated lower left: *Copyright 1899 by E. Vedder.*
Collection: Purchased from the artist by Dr. William Sturgis Bigelow, Boston, 1900.
Bequest of William Sturgis Bigelow. 26.781
Reference: E. Vedder, *Digressions of Vedder*, Boston, 1910, p. 496.
Exhibitions: Boston, Williams and Everett Galleries, *Vedder*, 1900, no. 27./ Pittsburgh, Pa., Carnegie Institute, *Vedder*, 1901, no. 32.

996.

Nude

Standing upon a pedestal set in a pool of blue water, a nude maiden hangs white

drapery upon the leaves above her. A gray and white marble column and clouded sky are behind her.
Oil on canvas. 20 × 7½ in. (50.8 × 19 cm.)
Signed lower right: *Elihu Vedder.*
Bequest of William Sturgis Bigelow. 26.773
Exhibition: New York, American Academy of Arts and Letters, *Vedder*, 1937, no. 137 (as *Young Woman Hanging a Curtain in a Pergola*).

FREDERIC PORTER VINTON (1846–1911) was born in Bangor, Me. About 1861 his family moved to Boston, and in 1864 he studied painting with Rimmer at the Lowell Institute. In 1875 he studied with Bonnat in Paris, then went with Duveneck to study in Munich. Once again in Paris, he worked with J.P. Laurens until 1878, when he returned to Boston to become a well-known portrait painter. In 1882 he visited Spain, with William Merritt Chase, to copy Velazquez.

997.   **Samuel H. Russell**

In a dark green overcoat trimmed with brown fur over a brown suit, he stands three-quarter length, turned three-quarters left, holding a cane and brown gloves. The background is dark red.
Oil on canvas. 54 × 34 in. (137.2 × 86.3 cm.)
Signed and dated lower left: *Fredᶜ P. Vinton/ 1880.*
Bequest of Edith, Lady Playfair. 33.531
Samuel Hammond Russell, a prominent Bostonian of the nineteenth century, was father of Edith, Lady Playfair (portrait by John Singer Sargent, Cat. no. 859), donor of the painting.

998.   **Wendell Phillips**
fig. 417

Three-quarter length, he stands turned half left while resting one hand upon a red-covered table. He wears a black coat, white shirt, and brown tie. The background is brown.
Oil on canvas. 54¼ × 40¼ in. (137.8 × 102.2 cm.)
Signed and dated lower right: *F.P. Vinton/ 1881* (initials in monogram).
Collections: Mr. J.C. Phillips, Boston, 1896; William Phillips, North Beverly, Mass.
Gift of William Phillips. 48.1290
Wendell Phillips (1811–1884), the son of John and Sally Walley Phillips, was born and died in Boston. The famous orator was a determined abolitionist and was active in prohibition, penal reform, women's suffrage, and the labor movement. Copies of the portrait are in Faneuil Hall and the Harvard Club of Boston.
Exhibition: Boston, Copley Hall, *Loan Collection of Portraits*, 1896, no. 313.

999.   **William Warren**
fig. 416

Standing full-length and facing front, he has one hand in the pocket of his black overcoat and holds brown gloves with his other. The background is brown.
Oil on canvas. 88¼ × 52¼ in. (224.1 × 132.7 cm.)
Signed and dated lower right: *Frederic P. Vinton. 1882.*
Gift of a Committee of Citizens. 22.54
William Warren, born in Philadelphia in 1812, came to Boston as an actor in 1846 and became one of the city's leading citizens. At the old Boston Museum, a theater, he performed as a comedian. In 1882, the date of the portrait, he celebrated his fiftieth anniversary in the acting profession. He died in Boston in 1888.
References: A. Burroughs, *Limners and Likenesses*, Cambridge, Mass., 1936, p. 187 (fig. 165)./ R.H.I. Gammell, *Twilight in Painting*, New York, 1946 (pl. 52).
Exhibition: Boston, MFA, *Vinton Memorial*, 1911, p. 18, no. 10.

1000.   **La Blanchisseuse**

A woman in a blue skirt and white blouse washes her clothes in a sunlit river which

reflects the bright green of the overhanging trees.
Oil on canvas. 18¼ × 24 in. (46.3 × 61 cm.)
Inscribed on the back: *Painted in Gréz, sur le Loing—France, 1890*; and, *F.P. Vinton APV. Executrix.*
Collections: Mrs. Frederic Vinton, Boston, 1911; Alexander Cochrane, Boston.
Gift of Alexander Cochrane. 13.554
Exhibition: Boston, MFA, *Vinton Memorial*, 1911, no. 91.

1001.   **The River Loing at Gréz, France**
The blue and gray river flows between green banks, beyond which are distant red, blue, and gray houses. The sky is pale blue.
Oil on canvas. 25¼ × 31¾ in. (64.1 × 80.6 cm.)
Signed and dated lower right: *Frederic P. Vinton. Gréz. '90.*
Collection: Estate of the artist, Boston.
Joseph Beale Glover Fund. 11.1388
Exhibitions: Boston, Copley Society, 1905, no. 66./ Boston, MFA, *Vinton Memorial*, 1911, no. 76 (repr. opp. p. 14).

1002.   **Alexander Moseley**
Three-quarter length, turned half-left, he is seated in an armchair before a brown background. Holding an ivory-handled cane, he wears a brown overcoat, gray trousers, and a black jacket.
Oil on canvas. 52¼ × 42 in. (132.7 × 106.7 cm.)
Bequest of Alexander Moseley. 00.373

Alexander Moseley (1822–1899), of Boston and Bar Harbor, Me., owned a tannery, later owned by Beggs and Cobb, on the road between Woburn and Winchester, Mass.

1003.   **Sketch of a Doorway**
The house is gray, shadowed in purple with a brown interior. Sparse green plants grow in the brown foreground.
Oil on canvas. 16 × 12 in. (40.6 × 30.5 cm.)
Inscribed on back: *D.W.R. from F.P. Vinton.*
Anonymous gift. Res. 12.356

JOHN VON WICHT was born in Malente, Holstein, Germany in 1888. About 1900 his family moved to Oldenburg, where in 1905 he was apprenticed to a firm of house painters. In 1906 he studied at the Privatschule of Hesse-Darmstadt, and in 1913 at the Royal School of Fine and Applied Arts, Berlin. He served in World War I and in 1923 came to Brooklyn, N.Y., where his association with Robert Laurent, Stephen Hirsch, and the Symbolist Jules Pascin led him to paint abstractly. For ten years he supported himself as a designer in stained glass. While his early work was Cubist in origin, his later painting drew inspiration from both the German Expressionists Klee and Kandinsky and the American Abstract Expressionists. He still lives in Brooklyn.

1004.   **Reveries**
fig. 591
A composition of a broad area of bright red relieved by areas of gray, white, and yellow, accented with lines and planes of black. The background is orange-red toning to pink and gray, right.
Oil on canvas. 48 × 60 in. (122 × 152 cm.)
Signed lower left: *V. Wicht.* Painted in 1957.
Collection: Institute of Contemporary Art, Boston, Provisional Collection, 1958.
Arthur Gordon Tompkins Residuary Fund. 61.200
Reference: D.G. Seckler, "John von Wicht," *Arts*, 1957, vol. 32, no. 2, p. 37 (repr.).
Exhibitions: Boston, Institute of Contemporary Art, *The Image Lost and Found*, 1960, no. 28 (repr.)./ —, *Provisional Collection*, 1961, no. 52./ Colorado Springs Fine Arts Center, *New Accessions, U.S.A.*, 1962, no. 6 (repr.).

ANDREW L. VON WITTKAMP

1005. **Black Cat on a Chair**
fig. 273
Oil on canvas. 36 × 29¼ in. (91.4 × 74.3 cm.)
Signed lower right: *Andrew L. von Wittkamp M.D.* Painted between 1850 and 1860.
M. and M. Karolik Collection. 48.494
Reference: Karolik Catalogue, 1949, no. 232 (repr.).

SAMUEL LOVETT WALDO (1783–1861), born in Windham, Conn., studied painting with Joseph Steward in Hartford about 1799. In 1803 he opened his own studio there but soon moved to Litchfield, Conn., then Charleston, S.C. From 1806 to 1808 he studied at the Royal Academy, London, and on his return in 1809 settled permanently in New York as a portrait painter. From 1818 to 1854 he and his former pupil William Jewett collaborated in the successful portrait painting firm of Waldo & Jewett. Waldo was a founder of the National Academy of Design in 1826. He died in New York.

1006. **Man with a Watch Fob**
Oil on canvas. 30 × 25 in. (76.2 × 63.5 cm.)
Painted in the 1820's.
M. and M. Karolik Collection. 48.483
Reference: Karolik Catalogue, 1949, no. 220 (repr.).

1007. **Deliverance Mapes Waldo and Her Son**
fig. 196
Oil on canvas. 30 × 25 in. (76.2 × 63.5 cm.)
Painted about 1830–1831.
M. and M. Karolik Collection. 45.891
Reference: Karolik Catalogue, 1949, no. 221 (repr.).

1008. **Charles Addoms**
fig. 194
Half-length, he sits upon a red upholstered chair facing three-quarters right before a brown wall. He wears a black suit with a white shirt and stock, and rests his left hand upon a letter and book on a green tablecloth.
Oil on panel. 33 × 25½ in. (83.8 × 64.8 cm.)
Painted in 1831.
Bequest of Maxim Karolik. 64.443

A label on the back reads: *Charles Addoms.| Born. Oct. 11 1802. D. Dec 5. 1881.| M. Sarah Steenback Gale. Dec. 19. 1827| Buried in New Rochelle. N.Y. in the| Churchyard of Trinity Church.* Inscribed in pencil on back of panel: *1831| 28 years.*
Exhibition: Minneapolis Institute of Arts and circulated in the U.S., *19th Century American Paintings from the Collection of Maxim Karolik*, 1953–1954.

SAMUEL L. WALDO and WILLIAM JEWETT (1789/90–1874)

1009. **Lady in a Dark Blue Dress**
fig. 195
Oil on panel. 37¼ × 28¼ in. (94.6 × 71.7 cm.)
Stenciled on the back of the panel: *Waldo & Jewett| 1855| New York.*
M. and M. Karolik Collection. 48.484
Reference: Karolik Catalogue, 1949, no. 222 (repr.).

WILLIAM AIKEN WALKER (about 1838–1921)

1010. **Dollarfish and Sheepshead**
Oil on canvas. 24 × 20 in. (61 × 50.8 cm.)
Signed and dated lower left: *WAW 1860* (initials in monogram).
M. and M. Karolik Collection. 48.485
Reference: Karolik Catalogue, 1949, no. 223 (repr.).

LAURENCE WARSHAW was born in New York in 1939 and first studied at the Art Students League from 1950 to 1954. He then attended New York University and at the same time studied with Philip Guston, from 1956 to 1958. In 1957–1958 he studied at the Skowhegan School of Painting and Sculpture, Maine. He has always lived in New York and has taught painting and drawing at various high schools there. In 1960 he studied at the Brooklyn Museum School and the following year spent three months working in China, Me.

1011.   **Cross**
An abstract composition of blue, brown, and green on a black background.
Oil on canvas. 52¾ × 50½ in. (134 × 128.2 cm.)
Signed and dated lower left: *Larry/ Warshaw/ 62.*
Gift of the Ford Foundation. 64.731
"The title *Cross* has no literal meaning. It is purely the curve rhythms of the letters C R O S S that are a linear delight in place." (Letter from the artist, May 20, 1964.)
Exhibition: Washington, D.C., Corcoran Gallery, *28th Biennial*, 1963, no. 139.

EDWIN AMBROSE WEBSTER (1869–1935) was born in Boston. He studied at the Boston Museum School under Tarbell and Benson from 1893 to 1898; with Benjamin Constant and J.P. Laurens at the Académie Julian, Paris; and with Albert Gleizes in France in 1918 and 1919. From 1900 until his death he was Director and teacher at a summer art school in Provincetown, Mass. The work of Claude Monet was a strong influence on his painting.

1012.   **Bermuda Roof, St. George's**
The red adobe house, with its blue and white striped roof, casts a purple shadow on the yellow ground, as do the purple trees. The foliage, touched with pink and yellow, and the adobe's shutters and door frame are green.
Oil on canvas. 16 × 20 in. (40.6 × 50.8 cm.)
Signed lower left: *E.A. Webster.* Painted in 1917.
Gift of Karl F. Rodgers, the artist's nephew. 63.2410

JOHN FERGUSON WEIR (1841–1926) was born in West Point, N.Y. and studied painting with his father, Robert W. Weir. In 1861 he began work in New York as a portrait, landscape, and genre painter, and in 1866 was elected to the National Academy. In 1868–1869 he traveled in France, Italy, Holland, and England. On his return to America, he became Director of the Yale University School of Fine Arts, a position he held until 1913, and was known as a lecturer and author. He died in Providence, R.I.

1013.   **Elihu Vedder**
fig. 414
Half-length, seated and turned three-quarters left, he holds a brown palette in his left hand and a brush in his right; his suit is gray, his tie green, and cap brown. A canvas, left, stands before a brown background.
Oil on canvas. 28½ × 23½ in. (72.3 × 59.7 cm.)
Signed and dated lower right: *John F. Weir/ Pinxit/ Rome 1902.*
Gift of the artist. 23.162
Exhibitions: Rhode Island School of Design Museum, *Weir Memorial*, 1927./ Dallas Museum of Fine Arts, *Famous Families in American Art*, 1960, no. 37.

JULIAN ALDEN WEIR (1852–1919), born in West Point, N.Y., was the younger brother of John Ferguson Weir and the son of Robert Weir, with whom he first studied. In 1873 he studied with Gérôme in Paris; he visited Europe again in 1874, 1876, and 1880. A founder of the Society of American Artists, New York, in 1877 and the "Ten American Painters" in 1898, he lived in New York City from 1883 until his death. He was elected to the National Academy in 1886, and was the Academy's President from 1915 to 1917.

1014.   **The Delft Plate**
fig. 477
Peaches in a blue and white plate beside a pewter tankard. A small bell and knife are set upon a white tablecloth before a branch of honeysuckle. The wall is brown.
Oil on panel, 22 × 13¾ in. (55.9 × 34.9 cm.)

Signed and dated lower left: *J. Alden Weir/ 1888.*
Collection: Smith College Museum, Northampton, Mass., probably before
1911.
Abraham Shuman Fund. 47.1289
References: J.B. Millet (ed.), *Weir*, New York, 1921, p. 129./ Smith College Museum,
Catalogue, 1937, p. 12 (repr. p. 66)./ D.W. Young, *Life and Letters of J. Alden Weir*,
New Haven, 1960 (fig. 9).
Exhibition: New York, American Academy of Arts and Letters, *Impressionist Mood
in American Painting*, 1959, no. 11.

ROBERT WALTER WEIR (1803–1889)

1015. **Bianca**
Oil on canvas. 32½ × 25¼ in. (82.5 × 64.1 cm.)
Signed and dated lower left: *Robt. W. Weir/ West Point/ 1836.*
M. and M. Karolik Collection. 48.486
Reference: *Karolik Catalogue*, 1949, no. 224 (repr.).

BENJAMIN WEST (1738–1820) was born in Springfield (now Swarthmore), Pa., the son of
an innkeeper. Self-taught, he began to draw and paint at eight, and was a
sign and portrait painter in Philadelphia by 1756. Like Copley after him,
he had a desire to see the work of the great masters. In 1760 benefactors
made possible a trip to Italy; he was the first American painter to study
there. Until 1763 he worked in Rome, Florence, Bologna, and Venice; he
was profoundly moved by the art and monuments of Greek and Roman
antiquity, by the High Renaissance masters, but also by the idealist Neo-
Classical teachings of Anton-Raphael Mengs. In 1763, after visiting Paris,
he reached London and settled there permanently. His allegorical and historical paintings won immediate success. By 1773 he was appointed
historical painter to George III, and was President of the Royal Academy
from 1792 until his death. Through his position he helped establish the
Neo-Classical style as the leading movement of his time; his daring compositions of contemporary history painted in contemporary dress were a
revolutionary step toward the nineteenth-century Romantic movement.
Dean of the American painters flocking to Europe, he was an influential
teacher; among the many outstanding American painters who studied
under him were Peale, Stuart, Allston, Trumbull, and Copley.

1016. **Reception to the Ambassador from Tunis**
fig. 97
*Three Arabs and a Negro stand grouped about the elderly Ambassador, who wears
fur-trimmed blue robes and a yellow shawl draped about his white turban; they all
wear robes and turbans of gray, brown, white, and red. Left, beyond green water, a
gray castle and a boat are under a cloudy blue sky.*
Oil on canvas. 28¼ × 36¼ in. (71.7 × 92.1 cm.)
Signed and dated lower right: *B. West 1781.*
Collections: *Pictures by West sold by George Robins*, London, May 22, 23, and
25, lot 115; Colonel D'Arcy, 1829; René Brimo, Paris, by 1940.
Abraham Shuman Fund. 55.932
The Robins Sale Catalogue records that in the early part of the reign of
George III, "these natives of Barbary" visited England on an embassy from
the Bey of Algiers.
References: "Catalogue of the Works of West," *La Belle Assemblée*, London, 1808, IV,
supplement, p. 17./ J. Galt, *West*, London, 1820, p. 226./ R. Brimo, *L'Evolution du
Goût aux Etats-Unis*, Paris, 1940 (pl. III).

1017. **St. Peter Released from Prison**
fig. 96
*A lighted cell is seen through the open prison door set in a dark brown stone arch. The
angel, in white with gray wings, raises the blue-robed Peter. Through a barred window
are seen white clouds and the moon in a blue sky. In the dark foreground, guards sleep
in dress of red, gray, green, and white.*

Oil on paper, mounted on panel. 14¼ × 10¾ in. (36.2 × 27.3 cm.)

Signed and dated lower left, on a stone block: *B. West/ Windsor (?)/ 1800.*

Collections: *Pictures by West sold by George Robins*, London, May 22, 23 and 25, 1829, lot 36 (as *Angel Delivering St. Peter*); Henry Pierce Bone, London, 1829; Joseph Neeld, London, by 1833; *L.W. Neeld Collection Sale*, Christie's, London, July 13, 1945, no. 176; sold Christie's, London, July 23, 1954, no. 139. *Ellen Kelleran Gardner Fund. 58.974*

Taken from the *Acts of the Apostles*, 12: "... the same night Peter was sleeping between two soldiers, bound with two chains: and the keepers before the door kept the prison. And, behold, the angel of the Lord came upon him, and a light shined in the prison: and he smote Peter ... and raised him up ... and his chains fell off from his hands." The central group is similar to that painted for the Royal Naval College, Greenwich, England, inspired by a Guercino painting of which West had an example in his collection.

References: J. Barlow, "Catalogue of West's Pictures," *The Columbiad*, Philadelphia, 1807, p. 435, note no. 45 (as *The Angel unchaining Peter in Prison*)./ "Catalogue of the Works of West," *La Belle Assemblée*, London, 1808, IV, supplement, p. 18./ J. Galt, *West*, London, 1820, p. 231.

Exhibition: London, Royal Academy, 1800, no. 63.

1018.
fig. 98

The Hope Family of Sydenham, Kent

A family of nine, three-quarter length, are seated or stand about a table. Three men to the left wear black coats over yellow and gray waistcoats; on the right are a man in a brown coat with a yellow waistcoat and a small boy in green. Three of the ladies wear white; an elderly woman has a brown dress with a white neck ruffle. The red table supports books and papers of red, green, and white, a gray urn, and a gilt-framed painting. Behind, left, the pedestal holding a red-figured lekythos and the support of a gray model mansion are red and brown. Blue, gold, and red drapery frames a background seascape of ships with white and gray sails on a blue sea; the blue sky is partly cloudy.

Oil on canvas. 70 × 100¾ in. (177.8 × 255.9 cm.)

Signed and dated lower left: *B. West/ 1802.*

Collections: Henry Phillips Hope, nephew of Henry Hope (*see* biography); Adrian John Hope, his nephew; V.H. Crosby; estate of Mrs. H. Hallahan, until 1894. *Abbott Lawrence Fund. 06.2362*

The elderly gentleman to the left is Henry Hope (1730–1812), son of Henry and Sarah Willard Hope and born in Quincy, Mass. A member of the famous Dutch-English Hope family, in 1762 he became head of Hope and Co., their banking firm in Amsterdam. The painting, vases, books, and ships in this picture are tokens of his great wealth and of his taste as a collector. He died a bachelor, but he had adopted John Williams (1757–1813), son of a clergyman, the young man standing on the right. Williams married Hope's favorite niece, Ann Goddard (1763–1820), the young lady seated before him, in 1782, and having become assistant in Hope and Co., adopted that family name in 1811. His wife, a willful and high-spirited woman, managed the company in Amsterdam alone from 1794 to 1797, and after her husband's death in 1813 married Jean François Pierre von Dopff, a dragoon officer she had known in Amsterdam. The elderly lady represented is Harriet Hope Goddard (about 1740–1790), wife of John Goddard of Essex, England, and Ann Williams' mother.

The children of John and Ann Williams are depicted, from left to right: Henry (b. 1785), who died unmarried; Adrian (b. 1788), who died childless; Elizabeth (1794–1860), born in Amsterdam, in 1816 married Hendrik, Baron van Heeckeren van Enghuizen; Henrietta Dorothea Maria (1790–1830), married first Reynaud, Graaf van Reede and second William Gambier; Francis (1798–after 1864) remained a bachelor and inherited the family fortune. The red-figured lekythos on the pedestal (unlocated) was published by H. Moses, *Vases from the Collection of Sir Henry Englefield*, London, 1848, p. 5 (pl. 35). In J.D. Beazley's *Attic Red-Figure Vase Painters* (Oxford, England, 1942, p. 473, no. 92), it is attributed to the "Bowdoin Painter." The model house is after the mansion built by Henry Hope in 1769 near Haarlem, Holland. It still stands as the seat of the North Holland Provincial Government.

A copy of the *Hope Family* by an unknown English artist (watercolor and tempera on ivory, 9 × 12¼ in.) is owned by Charles J. Duveen, New Hope, Pa. The copy differs by having an open window in the center background, the table in the foreground is covered with a cloth, and the gilt-framed picture is missing. A drawing which probably relates to our painting (MFA, 66.14, recto, black chalk and white on paper, 10⅛ × 14¾ in.) displays the same essential composition but contains fewer figures. It may have been made in preparation for a painting of the Hope family some years prior to this painting since the boys seem younger and other family members are entirely missing. The possibility exists too that it was related to a totally different group portrait, now lost.

References: J. Farington, *The Farington Diary*, London, 1802, I, p. 341 (March 7)./ —, 1804, II, pp. 196–197 (March 1)./ J. Galt, *West*, London, 1820, p. 221./ "Painting by West," *MFA Bulletin*, 1906, IV, no. 20, p. 21 (repr. with erroneous identification)./ A. Burroughs, *Limners and Likenesses*, Cambridge, Mass., 1936, p. 73 (fig. 58)./ R. Graham, "West—American Romantic," *Art News*, 1938, XXXVI, no. 25, p. 13./ W.J.J.C. Bijleveld, "De Hope-groep in Boston," *Historie in Woord en Beeld*, Assen, 1939, pp. 19–23 (repr. p. 21)./ David Watkin, " 'The Hope Family,' by Benjamin West," *Burlington Magazine*, 1964, CVI, no. 741, pp. 571–572 (repr.).

Exhibitions: Philadelphia Museum of Art, *West*, 1938, no. 54 (repr.)./ Pittsburgh, Pa., Carnegie Institute, *Survey of American Painting*, 1940, no. 81.

1019.

fig. 100

King Lear

The King, supported by Kent, stands rending his brown and white robes and red cloak; Edgar, half-naked as the madman, and the Fool, in brown, crouch at his feet. Gloucester, left, wears armor and a red cloak; his torch and lightning illuminate the brown and stormy scene.

Oil on canvas. 107 × 144 in. (271.8 × 365.7 cm.)

Signed, dated, and inscribed lower left center: *B. West 1788/ Retouched 1806.*

Collections: Boydell's Shakespeare Gallery, London; sold Christie's, London, May 20, 1805, no. 55; Robert Fulton, New York, 1805; purchased at auction, New York, by the Boston Athenaeum, 1828.

Deposited by the Boston Athenaeum, 1876. Ath. 9

From William Shakespeare's *King Lear*, Act III, Scene IV. Another version (17½ × 25½) is owned by the Rhode Island School of Design Museum and is the one painted for the engraver W. Sharpe for the catalogue of paintings in the J.J. Boydell Shakespeare Gallery, London (1786–1804). The MFA's version is said to have hung in the Shakespeare Gallery (H. von Erffa, *see below*).

References: J. Farington, *The Farington Diary*, London, May 5, 1807, IV, p. 132./ J. Galt, *West*, London, 1820, Part II, p. 229./ H.T. Tuckerman, *Book of the Artists*, New York, 1870, p. 627./ H.E. Jackson, *West*, Philadelphia, 1900 (pl. VII)./ M.M. Swan, *The Athenaeum Gallery*, Boston, 1940, pp. 117–118./ J.T. Flexner, "West's American Neo-Classicism," *New-York Historical Society Quarterly*, 1952, XXXVI, no. 50, p. 33./ H. von Erffa, "King Lear by West," *Rhode Island School of Design Bulletin*, 1956, XLIII, no. 2, pp. 6–7 (repr. p. 8)./ G. Evans, *West and the Tastes of His Times*, Carbondale, Ill., 1959, p. 76 (pl. 57).

Exhibitions: Boston Athenaeum, *Exhibition*, 1829, no. 138./ Boston, MFA, *Contemporary Art*, 1879, no. 206.

1020.

fig. 99

The Stolen Kiss

During a game played by four shepherdesses, Murtillo the shepherd, left, steals a kiss

from Amaryllis, one of them. All wear red, green, and brown robes, and Amaryllis holds a crook festooned with red, white, and yellow flowers. A similar wreath is behind her. A green mountainous landscape is in the background, under a gray and pink cloudy sky.
Oil on canvas. 48¾ × 62¾ in. (123.8 × 159.4 cm.)
Signed and dated lower left: *Benjamin West 1819.*
Collections: Pictures by West sold by George Robins, London, May 22, 23, and 25, 1829, lot 155; G. Walker, London(?), 1829; George R. White, Boston; Harriet White (Mrs. Frederick J. Bradbury), his sister, Boston.
Bequest of Harriet J. Bradbury. 30.494

Taken from Giovanni Battista Guarini's pastoral play, *Il Pastor Fido*, Act II, scene 1. *The Stolen Kiss* listed in Galt (J. Galt, *West*, London, 1820, Part II, p. 224) and in the *Belle Assemblée* ("Catalogue of the Works of West," *La Belle Assemblée*, 1808, IV, supplement, p. 16) was the original version of the subject, painted for a General Lawrence, but now unlocated. A drawing for that version was owned by Lord Buckinghamshire (Galt, p. 225). From an old label on the back of the painting, our replica is said to have been West's last work.

Exhibitions: London, Royal Academy, 1819, no. 157./ London, British Institution, 1820, no. 214.

JAMES ABBOTT McNEILL WHISTLER (1834–1903), born in Lowell, Mass., studied from 1851 to 1854 at West Point, then in 1854–1855 was trained as a draftsman at the Coast and Geodetic Survey, Washington. In 1856 he studied in the studio of Charles Gleyre, Paris, and in 1858 he published his first set of etchings. He frequently visited London from Paris, until in 1863 he settled there. At this time he developed a taste for the arts of Japan. He toured the Rhine in 1865 and the next year visited Valparaiso, Chile. In 1878 he attempted lithography, and from 1879 to 1880 he lived in Venice. He moved to Paris in 1892 but returned to London in 1898, and died there. First influenced by Courbet and the Impressionists through the 1860's, his later work developed independently with inspiration from oriental art, especially the Japanese woodcut, and from Velazquez. He was among the first to exploit technique at the expense of subject matter.

1021.
fig. 469

The Last of Old Westminster

The scaffolding over the new bridge across the Thames and the piles of the old below it are brown, touched with gray and yellow; men in white and brown work everywhere. Small craft are anchored in the yellow and brown water, left, and the distant city is gray against gray clouds in the blue sky.
Oil on canvas. 24 × 30½ in. (61 × 77.5 cm.)
Signed and dated lower left: *Whistler 1862.*
Collections: Bought from the artist by John Cavafy, London; Dr. John Cavafy, his son; Alfred Attmore Pope, Farmington, Conn., by 1898; Mrs. John W. Riddle, his daughter, Farmington, by 1928.
Abraham Shuman Fund. 39.44

References: S. Isham, *American Painting*, New York, 1905, p. 329./ J. La Farge and A.F. Jaccaci, eds., *Noteworthy Paintings in American Private Collections*, New York, 1907, pp. 265, 269, 278 (repr. p. 279)./ B. Sickert, *Whistler*, London, 1907, no. 11./ J. Meier-Graefe, *Modern Art*, London, 1908, II, pp. 206–207 (repr. p. 206)./ E.R. and J. Pennell, *Whistler*, Philadelphia, 1908, I, pp. 100–101 (repr. II, opp. p. 126)/. E.L. Cary, *Whistler*, New York, 1913, p. 160, no. 34./ "Impressionist Paintings," Hartford, Conn., *Wadsworth Atheneum Bulletin*, 1928, V, no. 1 (repr. p. 7)./ E. Abbot, "Exhibition of Whistleriana," *Chicago Art Institute Bulletin*, 1934, XXVIII, no. 4 (repr. p. 55)./ B.N. Parker, "Whistler," *MFA Bulletin*, 1939, XXXVII, no. 220, pp. 28–29 (repr. p. 28)./ "Whistler's *Last of Old Westminster*," *Connoisseur*, 1946, CXVII, pp. 45–46 (repr. p. 45).

Exhibitions: London, Royal Academy, 1863, no. 352./ New York, Society of American Artists, *20th Annual*, 1898, no. 282 (as *Westminster Bridge*)./ Boston, Copley Society, *Whistler*, 1904, no. 34./ London, New Gallery, *Whistler*, 1905, p. 88, no. 35

(repr. opp. p. 86)./ Paris, Palais de l'École des Beaux Arts, *Whistler*, 1905, no. 56./ Hartford, Conn., Wadsworth Atheneum, *Impressionism*, 1928./ Boston, MFA, *Whistler*, 1934, no. 6./ Chicago Art Institute, *Century of Progress*, 1934, no. 426./ Hartford, Conn., Wadsworth Atheneum, *American Painting and Sculpture of the 18th, 19th and 20th Centuries*, 1935, no. 37./ New York, Macbeth Gallery, *Whistler*, 1947, no. 7 (repr.)./ London, Arts Council Gallery and New York, M. Knoedler and Co , *Whistler*, 1960, no. 7.

1022.
fig. 465

Symphony in Red

Three young ladies in red and white dresses are seated on a bench or stand before a pink wall decorated with fans and white flowers. A gray and purple striped carpet is in the foreground.

Oil on canvas. 15¼ × 14 in. (38.7 × 35.5 cm.)

Inscribed center left with butterfly (later addition). Painted about 1867–1870.

Collections: Arthur Morrison, Chalfont St. Peter, Bucks.; sold Sotheby's, March 20, 1946, lot 241; John Bryson, Oxford.

Emily L. Ainsley Fund. 60.1158

The painting is similar to a number of studies from about 1867 to 1870, among them the series *Six Projects* (Freer Gallery, Washington, D.C.). At this point, Whistler was breaking away from the somber influence of Courbet, seeking harmonies in color, a prelude to his nocturnes.

References: "The Lyrical Trend in English Painting," *Burlington Magazine*, 1946, LXXXVIII, no. 518, p. 128 (repr. p. 126)./ E.P. Richardson, "Sophisticates and Innocents Abroad," *Art News*, 1954, LIII, no. 2, p. 21./ A.S. Weller, "Expatriates Return," *Art Digest*, 1954, XXVIII, no. 8, p. 24.

Exhibitions: London, Roland, Browse, and Delbanco, *The Lyrical Trend in English Painting*, 1946, no. 35./ Chicago Art Institute and New York, Metropolitan Museum, *Sargent, Whistler and Mary Cassatt*, 1954, no. 191./ London, Arts Council Gallery and New York, M. Knoedler and Co., *Whistler*, 1960, no. 19./ Ottawa, The National Gallery, *Victorian Artists in England*, 1965, no. 164 (repr.).

1023.
fig. 466

The Lagoon, Venice: Nocturne in Blue and Silver

In the foreground four gondolas are thinly painted in gray; points of light on the distant shore are reflected in the green lagoon water. A schooner is moored left, and to the right, San Giorgio Maggiore is silhouetted in gray against misty gray-green sky.

Oil on canvas. 20 × 25¾ in. (50.8 × 65.4 cm.)

Signed lower right with butterfly. Painted in 1879–1880.

Collections: Sold, Hôtel Drouot, Paris, Nov. 25, 1903, no. 1; Richard A. Canfield, Providence, R.I., in 1904; Mrs. William H. Bliss, New York, 1914; Mrs. Robert Woods Bliss, her daughter, Washington, D.C.

Emily L. Ainsley Fund. 42.302

A letter from Harper Pennington, New York, to Richard Canfield, March 20, 1914 reads: "So, dear Dick, you have let the Whistlers go! You will miss the great Nocturne—possibly the most peace-bringing of all Jimmy's pictures; certainly his finest night scene. I was with him when he painted it, and many a time he and I would stand for as much as twenty minutes looking at St. Mark's while he memorized the tints and tones. Long before it was finished I left for Florence; and when, two years later, when I joined him in London, it had disappeared—that is, he would not show it. When I asked what had become of it, he merely cocked his head and laughed 'ha-ha!—ha-ha!' with a wise wink. It was, probably, in his studio all the time. . . ." Whistler lived in Venice from 1879 to 1880.

References: E.R. and J. Pennell, *Whistler*, Philadelphia, 1908, I, pp. 266–267./ B. Sickert, *Whistler*, London, 1908, p. 90./ E.L. Cary, *Whistler*, New York, 1913, p. 167, no. 67 (repr. opp. p. 28)./ H. Haydon, "Chicago's Annual Plays Safe," *Art News*, 1945, XLIV, no. 14 (repr. p. 21).

Exhibitions: Boston, Copley Society, *Whistler*, 1904, no. 67./ Berlin, Königliche Akademie der Künste, *Ausstellung Amerikanischer Kunst*, 1910, p. 80 (repr.)./ Buffalo,

Albright Art Gallery, *Oils . . . by Whistler, lent by Richard Canfield*, 1911, no. 5 (repr p. 12)./ Hartford, Conn., Wadsworth Atheneum, *Night Scenes*, 1940, no. 57 (repr.)./ Pittsburgh, Pa., Carnegie Institute, *Survey of American Painting*, 1940, no. 137 (pl. 51)./ New York, M. Knoedler and Co., *Cortissoz—Fifty Years*, 1941, p. 23, no. 25./ Santa Barbara Museum, *Painting Today and Yesterday in the U.S.*, 1941, no. 134./ New York, Museum of Modern Art, *Romantic Painting in America*, 1943, p. 31, no. 208 (repr. p. 73)./ Brooklyn Museum, *Landscape*, 1945, no. 51./ Dayton Art Institute and Columbus, O., Columbus Gallery, *America and Impressionism*, 1951./ New York, American Federation of Arts, circulated in Germany and Italy, and Whitney Museum, *American Painting in the Nineteenth Century*, 1953–1954, no. 77./ Boston, MFA, *American Marine Paintings*, 1955, no. 22 (repr.)./ Milwaukee, Marquette University, Brooks Memorial Union Building, *American Painting of the Past Seventy-five Years*, 1956, no. 74./ London, Arts Council Gallery and New York, M. Knoedler and Co., *Whistler*, 1960, no. 43./ Utica, N.Y., Munson-Williams-Proctor Institute, *19th Century American Painting*, 1960, no. 25.

1024.

Study of a Girl

Full-length, a girl in a dimly lit brown room stands facing front but looking three-quarters left. She wears a black dress and shoes, brown shawl, blue apron, and gray stockings.

Oil on chipboard. 13 × 6¾ in. (33 × 17.1 cm.)

Painted about 1880.

Collection: Mr. Ritter, Venice, about 1880.

Gift of Robert D. Andrews. 19.6

Painted in Venice about 1880. Given to a Mr. Ritter, who worked with Whistler in Venice.

Exhibition: Boston, MFA, *Whistler*, 1934, no. 27.

1025.

fig. 468

A Street in Old Chelsea

Gray figures in the foreground stroll along the gray-brown street before brown and green buildings with black windows.

Oil on panel. 5½ × 9 in. (14 × 22.9 cm.)

Painted about 1890.

Collection: Denman Waldo Ross, Cambridge, Mass., 1904.

Gift of Denman Waldo Ross. 09.297

Several tiny panels of this district of London were done after Whistler first moved there in 1863.

Reference: E.L. Cary, *Whistler*, New York, 1913, p. 168, no. 72.

Exhibitions: Boston, Copley Society, *Whistler*, 1904, no. 72./ Philadelphia, Pennsylvania Academy of the Fine Arts, *Whistler*, 1905, no. 427./ Boston, MFA, *Whistler*, 1934, no. 26.

1026.

Alma Stanley in "The Street Walker"

Full-length, she stands facing front before a gray wall. The black of her costume is interrupted only by a white trim and a purple flower at her shoulder.

Pastel on paper. 99¼ × 38¼ in. (252 × 97.1 cm.)

Drawn about 1893.

Collection: Alfred R. Hakoumoff, Richmond, Surrey, England.

Charles Henry Hayden Fund. 31.505

Alma Stanley (Mrs. Alice Porter, 1853–1931), a famous English actress, was trained as a dancer in Milan. She played leading roles in London theaters until about 1902. The pastel was drawn about 1893, when she was playing in *The Street Walker* at the Strand Theatre, London. (Letter from Alma Stanley to Alfred Hakoumoff, July 22, 1930.)

Reference: "Museum Accessions," *Magazine of Art*, 1931, XXIII, no. 6 (repr. p. 500).

Exhibition: Boston, MFA, *Whistler*, 1934, no. 3.

1027.

fig. 467

The Blacksmith of Lyme Regis

Half-length on a brown background, turned three-quarters right with his arms folded, the bearded man wears a brown coat over a white shirt.

Oil on canvas. 20 × 12¼ in. (50.8 × 31.1 cm.)

Signed center right with a butterfly. Painted in 1895.

William Wilkins Warren Fund. 96.951

An unidentified English newspaper clipping names one Sam Govier as the blacksmith model. The painting, also known as the *Master Smith of Lyme Regis*, was done in 1895 during Whistler's stay at Lyme Regis.

References: W.H. Downes, "American Paintings in the Boston Art Museum," *Brush and Pencil*, 1900, VI, no. 5, pp. 204–205./ S. Isham, *American Painting*, New York, 1905, p. 330./ E.R. and J. Pennell, *Whistler*, Philadelphia, 1908, II, pp. 78, 166, 170, 207, 293, 298 (repr. opp. p. 170)./ E.L. Cary, *Whistler*, New York, 1913, pp. 141, 161, no. 36./ T. Duret, *Whistler*, Paris, 1914, p. 89./ L.M. Bryant, *American Pictures and Their Painters*, New York, 1917, pp. 92–93 (fig. 52)./ H. Pearson, *Whistler*, New York, 1952, p. 227.

Exhibitions: Buffalo, *Pan American Exposition*, 1901, no. 99./ Boston, Copley Society, *Whistler*, 1904, no. 36./ London, New Gallery, *Whistler*, 1905, no. 24./ Paris, Palais de l'École des Beaux Arts, *Whistler*, 1905, no. 27./ New York, Metropolitan Museum, *Whistler*, 1910, no. 37./ Boston, MFA, *Whistler*, 1934, no. 24./ New York, Macbeth Gallery, *Whistler*, 1947, no. 10./ New London, Conn., Lyman Allyn Museum, *Whistler*, 1949, no. 5.

1028.

fig. 470

The Little Rose of Lyme Regis

A young girl, half-length, faces front, with her hands folded in the lap of her red pinafore, under which she wears a black blouse. The background is brown.

Oil on canvas. 20 × 12¼ in. (50.8 × 31.1 cm.)

Painted in 1895.

William Wilkins Warren Fund. 96.950

Two women have been proposed as the subject: first, Mrs. Irene Rose Feilden of Beaconsfield, Buckinghamshire, and second, Rosie Rendall Herridge of Exeter, Devon. Of the two, the latter was more probably Whistler's model. Rosie Rendall (1887–1958) was the daughter of G.J. Rendall, Mayor and Alderman of Lyme Regis in Dorset. She married Ernest Aubrey Herridge of Bath, Somerset, in 1914, had one son, and lived in Exeter until her death. Whistler portrayed her in 1895 on a visit to Lyme Regis.

References: W.H. Downes, "American Paintings in the Boston Art Museum," *Brush and Pencil*, 1900, VI, no. 5, pp. 204–205 (repr. p. 204)./ S. Isham, *American Painting*, New York, 1905, p. 330 (pl. 71)./ E.R. and J. Pennell, *Whistler*, Philadelphia, 1908, II, pp. 78, 166, 205, 207, 298 (repr. opp. p. 166)./ J.deW. Addison, *The Boston Museum*, Boston, 1910, p. 39 (repr. opp. p. 38)./ E.L. Cary, *Whistler*, New York, 1913, pp. 79, 162, no. 43./ T. Duret, *Whistler*, Paris, 1914, p. 89./ H. Pearson, *Whistler*, New York, 1952, p. 227.

Exhibitions: Boston, Copley Society, *Whistler*, 1904, no. 43./ London, New Gallery, *Whistler*, 1905, no. 26 (repr. p. 48)./ Paris, Palais de l'École des Beaux Arts, *Whistler*, 1905, no. 42./ New York, Metropolitan Museum, *Whistler*, 1910, no. 38./ Boston, MFA, *Whistler*, 1934, no. 25./ New York, Museum of Modern Art, *Art in Progress*, *15th Anniversary*, 1944, no. 4 (repr. p. 18)./ New York, Wildenstein and Co., *The Child Through Four Centuries*, 1945, no. 33 (repr.)./ New London, Conn., Lyman Allyn Museum, *Whistler*, 1949, no. 4./ New Orleans, Isaac Delgado Museum, *World of Art in 1910*, 1960 (repr.).

EDWIN WHITE

(1817–1877) was born in South Hadley, Mass. and began to paint in 1829. He lived in Bridgeport, Conn. before 1840, when he moved to New York, and from 1850 to 1858 he studied in Düsseldorf, Paris, Rome, and Florence. On his return he settled in New York, again visiting Europe in 1869. Elected to the National Academy in 1849, he died in Saratoga Springs, N.Y.

1029.

A Room in the Bargello, Florence

An arched corridor of the brown interior is pervaded by a yellow light from the windows. The furniture is brown and the urn and Florentine flag are red.

Oil on canvas. 30 × 20 in. (76.2 × 50.8 cm.)

Signed and dated lower right: *Edwin White/ 1872.*

Gift of Mrs. Edwin White. 78.26

Exhibition: Boston, MFA, *Contemporary Art*, 1879, no. 73.

1030.   **Studio Interior**

fig. 399

A woman in a long brown dress sits facing her easel before a window draped with green curtains. On the walls of the green studio hang various artist's models of red, gold, and gray. A white dog sits by a red stool draped with yellow cloth.
Oil on canvas. 17¼ × 22 in. (43.8 × 55.9 cm.)
Signed and dated lower left: *Edwin White/ 1872.*
Collection: Maxim Karolik, Newport, R.I., 1962.
Bequest of Maxim Karolik. 64.464

THOMAS WORTHINGTON WHITTREDGE (1820–1910)

1031.   **View of West Point on the Hudson**
Oil on canvas. 13¼ × 11¼ in. (33.6 × 28.5 cm.)
Signed and dated lower right: *W. Whittredge 1861.*
M. and M. Karolik Collection. 48.487
Reference: Karolik Catalogue, 1949, no. 225 (repr.).

1032.   **On the Platte River**
Oil on canvas. 6¼ × 20 in. (15.9 × 50.8 cm.)
Signed lower left: *W. Whittredge.* Inscribed on stretcher: *On the Platte— Genl Pope's Expedition 1865.*
M. and M. Karolik Collection. 48.489
Reference: Karolik Catalogue, 1949, no. 227 (repr.).

1033.   **Long's Peak, Colorado**
Oil on canvas. 14½ × 22 in. (36.8 × 55.9 cm.)
Signed lower right: *W. Whittredge.* Painted about 1865.
M. and M. Karolik Collection. 48.488
Reference: Karolik Catalogue, 1949, no. 226 (repr.).

1034.   **Apples**
Oil on canvas. 15¼ × 11¾ in. (38.7 × 29.7 cm.)
Signed and dated lower right: *W. Whittredge/ 1867.*
M. and M. Karolik Collection. 48.490
Reference: Karolik Catalogue, 1949, no. 228 (repr.).

1035.   **Old Homestead by the Sea**

fig. 303

Oil on canvas. 22 × 32 in. (55.9 × 81.2 cm.)
Signed and dated lower left: *W. Whittredge 1883.*
M. and M. Karolik Collection. 48.492
Reference: Karolik Catalogue, 1949, no. 230 (repr.).

1036.   **Outskirts of the Forest**
Oil on canvas. 25½ × 35½ in. (64.8 × 90.2 cm.)
Signed lower left: *W. Whittredge.*
M. and M. Karolik Collection. 48.491
Reference: Karolik Catalogue, 1949, no. 229 (repr.).

JOHN WHORF   (1903–1959) was born in Winthrop, Mass. and studied at the Boston Museum School, in Paris at the Grande Chaumière and at the École des Beaux Arts, and last with Charles Hawthorne in Provincetown, Mass. After travel in the West Indies, Canada, North Africa, and France, he worked in New York City. In 1940 he moved to Provincetown, where he spent the remainder of his life.

1037.   **Italian Fishing Village**
In the blue harbor, right, brown boats with red sails are docked before white houses, which stand against blue sky and white clouds. The foreground is yellow.
Oil on canvas. 19 × 26 in. (48.2 × 66 cm.)
Signed and dated lower left: *John Whorf 23.*
Bequest of John T. Spaulding. 48.613
Exhibition: Boston, MFA, The Spaulding Collections, 1948, no. 89.

MOSES WIGHT (1827–1895) was born in Boston, where he began painting in 1845. In Paris he studied with Hébert and Bonnat from 1851 to 1854, then returned to the U.S. via Rome. He remained in Boston, taking a brief trip to France in 1860, and then settled permanently in Paris in 1865. Shortly before his death, he came once again to Boston.

1038. **Baron Alexander von Humboldt**
Half-length, turned three-quarters right, he wears a black coat and white stock. The background is brown.
Oil on canvas. 28 × 24¾ in. (71.1 × 62.8 cm.)
Signed and dated lower right: *M. Wight pt Berlin 1852.* Inscribed on back, center: *Portrait of Baron von Humboldt/ Painted in his 82nd year.* And below, right: *M.Wight/ Berlin Feb. 1852.*
Bequest of the Artist. 96.47
Baron Alexander von Humboldt (1769–1859), a scientist, was born in Berlin and traveled throughout South America and Mexico from 1799 to 1804. Among other scientific treatises, he published *Voyages aux Equinoxiales du Nouveau Continent.* An unlocated replica of the picture was included in a sale at S.T. Freeman and Co., Philadelphia, from the collections of Elizabeth Hepp and Margaretta F.G. Purves (Jan. 25–26, 1932, no. 43, repr.); a copy of the portrait is in the Fogg Art Museum, Cambridge, Mass.
Exhibitions: Boston Athenaeum, *Exhibitions*, 1853, no. 24; 1865, no. 240; 1866, no. 256; 1867, no. 236.

ROBERT D. WILKIE (1828–1903) **(Formerly Anonymous)**

1039. **Christmas Party**
Oil on canvas. 17¼ × 30¼ in. (43.8 × 76.8 cm.)
M. and M. Karolik Collection. 47.1214
The attribution to Robert Wilkie was determined by B.N. Parker and Miss Ruth K. Wilkie, the artist's granddaughter, on the basis of style.
Reference: Karolik Catalogue, 1949, no. 13 (repr.).

HENRY WILLIAMS (1787–1830), the author of *Elements of Drawing* (1814), was born and remained in Boston, working as a portrait and miniature painter, wax modeler, engraver, and Professor of Electricity.

1040. **Sally Bass (Mrs. Enoch Bartlett)**
fig. 150
Bust-length, turned slightly right before a brown background, she wears a pale blue dress trimmed with white lace and a white lace ruffle.
Pastel on paper. 23½ × 18 in. (59.7 × 45.7 cm.)
Drawn about 1804.
Collection: Mrs. Edwin A. Brigham, a descendant of the sitter.
Julia Henrietta Copeland Fund. 20.188
Sally Bass, the daughter of Samuel and Sarah Lawrence Bass, was born about 1784, probably in Braintree, Vt. In 1804 she married Enoch Bartlett, a dry goods merchant of Boston; she died in 1809, shortly after the birth of her two children. Her husband, an amateur horticulturist, gave his name to the Bartlett pear. The portrait was at one time attributed to John Johnston.
References: Proceedings in Observance of the One Hundred and Fiftieth Anniversary of the Organization of the First Church in Lincoln (Cambridge, Mass.), 1899, p. 68./ M. Vaughan, "Pastels in Colonial America," *International Studio*, 1928, xc, no. 372, p. 20 (repr. p. 20).

C. WINTER

1041. **Minstrel Show**
Oil on canvas. 25¼ × 50 in. (64.1 × 127 cm.)
Signed lower right: *C. Winter/ Phila.*
M. and M. Karolik Collection. 48.493
Reference: Karolik Catalogue, 1949, no. 231 (repr.).

CHARLES HERBERT WOODBURY (1864–1940) was born in Lynn, Mass. and graduated from the Massachusetts Institute of Technology in 1886 as a mechanical engineer. After attending life classes at the Boston Art Club, he studied at the Académie Julian in Paris in 1890–1891. He traveled in Holland and worked as a marine painter in oil and watercolor in Boston and Ogunquit, Me. until his death in Jamaica Plain, Mass.

1042.   **The North Atlantic**
Waves of blue and green are touched with yellow and gray before a lavender blue sky.
Oil on canvas. 54¼ × 72 in. (137.8 × 182.9 cm.)
Signed lower right: *Charles H. Woodbury.* Painted about 1902.
The Abraham Shuman Fund and by gift of subscribers. 26.116
The Boston Public Library owns a sketch (12 × 16 in.) for this larger painting of about 1902.
Reference: MFA *Bulletin*, 1926, XXIV, no. 144 (repr. p. 60).

1043.   **Ocean Waves**
Blue and green waves break in yellow and lavender tinted foam and spray over purple, brown, and gray rocks; yellow and white foam flies before a mottled light blue-gray sky.
Oil on canvas. 48¼ × 72 in. (122.5 × 182.9 cm.)
Signed lower right: *Charles H. Woodbury.* Painted about 1922.
Gift of Frederick L. Jack. 35.1242
Exhibition: Boston, MFA, *Woodbury*, 1945, no. 35.

1044.   **Off the Florida Coast**
Green, white, and blue swells rise against a blue, pink, and gray sky.
Oil on canvas. 29 × 36¼ in. (73.6 × 92.1 cm.)
Signed lower left: *Woodbury.*
Gift of subscribers, through Miss Martha Silsbee. 05.47

JAMES HENRY WRIGHT (1813–1883)

1045.   **U.S. Ship "Constellation"**
fig. 254   Oil on canvas. 20 × 30 in. (50.8 × 76.2 cm.)
Inscribed on black border below, at right: *Painted by J. H. Wright;* at center: *U.S. Ship Constellation Capt. Reed* [sic]. *16 Dec. 1833.*
M. and M. Karolik Collection. 48.495
Reference: Karolik Catalogue, 1949, no. 233 (repr.).

ALEXANDER HELWIG WYANT (1836–1892), born in Evans Creek, O., was brought up in Defiance, O., where he was apprenticed to a harness maker. In 1857, in New York, he visited George Inness, who gave him encouragement. He returned to work in Cincinnati, where the patronage of Nicholas Longworth made possible a year of study in New York at the National Academy, and a year in Karlsruhe, Germany under Hans Gude. On his return journey to America he visited Ireland and England, then settled permanently in New York with summers spent in the Adirondacks and Catskills.

1046.   **Road in Ireland**
fig. 368   *Brown figures, center, travel a brown path which cuts through a green field before distant brown hills. The rocks in the left foreground are gray, and the sky is blue.*
Oil on canvas. 12½ × 20¼ in. (31.7 × 51.4 cm.)
Signed lower right: *A.H. Wyant.* Painted in 1866.
Gift of Hiram Hyde Logan. 22.816
Painted along Kenmore Road, County Kerry, Ireland, in 1866, when Wyant visited Ireland on his journey back to America.

1047.   **A Gray Day**
Under gray sky, a rock clearing is surrounded by oaks.
Oil on canvas. 16¼ × 22 in. (41.2 × 55.9 cm.)
Signed lower left: *A.H. Wyant.* Painted in 1891.
Bequest of George H. Webster. 34.130
Inscribed on the back: *1891.*

ADDENDA

E. L. GEORGE Nothing is known of the artist.

1048. **Child in a Rocking Chair**
fig. 324 *In a brown interior with a green floor, a child, dressed in red, sits on a brown chair beside an outsize basket of strawberries.*
Oil on canvas. 15 × 13 in. (38.1 × 33 cm.)
Signed and dated lower left: *E.L. George/ 1870.*
Collection: Maxim Karolik, Newport, R.I., 1958.
M. and M. Karolik Collection. 62.272
A primitive painting with remarkable Surrealist qualities by an artist of whom no other works are yet known.
Exhibition: Boston, MFA, *New Paintings in the M. and M. Karolik Collection*, 1962–1963.

MARSDEN HARTLEY (See Biography, p. 134)

1049. **Carnival of Autumn**
fig. 545 Rolling high hills of yellow-gold, dark blue and red rise up against big white clouds in a blue sky. Blue water and trees in the foreground.
Oil on canvas. 30¼ × 30⅛ in. (76.2 × 76 cm.)
Painted in 1908.
Collection: Hudson D. Walker.
Charles Henry Hayden Fund. 68.296
References: E. McCausland, Marsden Hartley, Minnesota, 1952. pp. 13–14, (repr. p. 10).

PAINTINGS IN THE COLLECTION
not included in the Catalogue

Anonymous
Mrs. Samuel Adams. 94.133
Head of a Child. Res. 27.103
Portrait of a Man. Res. 10.11

Francis Alexander
George Washington. 66.183

Joseph Alexander Ames
A Gypsy Girl. 85.518

Karl Anderson
The Apple Gatherers. 36.81

Alexis Arapoff
Flowers with Picture of the Resurrection. 52.473

Edmund Archer
Colored Clairvoyant. 42.557

Darrel Austin
The Vixen. 41.66

Will Barnet
Movement Within Orange. 54.928

Abraham Baylinson
My Daughters. 40.17

Ture Bengtz
Noon Nap. 48.283

John Prentiss Benson
The Trawlers. 33.369

Jacob Binder
The Talmudist. 26.201

Julien Binford
The Harmonica Player. 41.563

Harriet Blackstone
Man of Sorrows. 42.177

Edwin Howland Blashfield
Lady in a Satin Gown. 37.488

Robert Bliss
Spring on Brimmer Street. 64.589
Left No Address. 50.521

George Hirst Bogert
Venice. 12.328

Frank Myer Boggs
A Rough Day, Harbour of Honfleur. 86.56

Aaron Bohrod
Oak Street Platform. 41.801

Frederick Andrew Bosley
The Dreamer. 16.43

Henry Botkin
The Ceremony. 55.254

George Henry Boughton
Sea Breeze. 16.67

Emile Pierre Branchard
Winter Night. 48.522

Frederick Bridgman
A Circassian. 37.591
Scene on the Nile. 34.185

William Gedney Bunce
Venetian Boats. 23.473

David Burliuk
Asters. 41.476

Richard Burnier
Landscape with Cattle. 22.586

Moshe Castel
Sacrifice. 53.218

Francis Brooks Chadwick
Landscape. 36.268

Adelaide Cole Chase
The Violinist (John Murray) .16.97

William Abbott Cheever
Easter, 1948. 48.288

Russell Cheney
Kittery Point. 36.157

William Worcester Churchill
Leisure. 12.325

Nicolai Cikovsky
Flowers and Fruit with a Trumpet. 47.96

William Baxter Closson
Mrs. David P. Kimball. 29.40
Preparing for the Pageant. 38.1841
Tree-Day Guests at Wellesley College. 29.948

King Moncrieff Coffin
January Cove, Maine. 48.289

Calvert Coggeshall
Near Stockbridge, Massachusetts. 49.1791

Joseph Greenleaf Cole
Dr. Isaac Green. 56.1195
Mrs. Isaac Green (Ann Barrett). 56.1196

Thomas Cole
Adoration of the Shepherds. 179.48

Alfred Quinton Collins
Thomas B. Clarke. 05.84

Charles Conder
Dance by the Fountains. 42.570

Jay Hall Connaway
White Mountains, Manchester, Vermont. 55.47

**John Singleton Copley, 19th century copy
  after**
Samuel Cooper. 64.2086

John Edward Costigan
Spring. 48.529

Christopher Pearse Cranch
San Pietro in Castell, Venice. 13.552

Lucius Crowell
Barge Canal and Bridge over Schuylkill. 50.859

Howard Gardiner Cushing
Mrs. Cushing. (Ethel Cochrane). 17.3170

William Turner Dannat
Eva Haviland. 13.2803

Sophia Towne Darrah
Glass Head, Manchester, Massachusetts. 82.45

Mauritz de Haas
Marine. 15.884

Joseph de Martini
Billiards at Julian's. 41.260

Jan Dennis
The Green Bottle. 47.95

Sarah Paxton Ball Dodson
Psyche Carried Away by the Sephyrs. 12.48
The Wych, Malvern. 23.602
Le Berceau. Res. 37.59
In Ashdown Forest, Sussex. 23.603

Paul Dougherty
Rocks and Sea. 61.956

Wyatt Eaton
Mother and Child. 04.102

Carnig Ekserzian
Mrs. Julia Ward Howe. Res. 11.12

Maurice Fromkes
The Little White Bonnet (Carol Westmorland). 48.544

John Orne Johnson Frost
Fishermen Leaving for the Grand Banks. 64.445

Richard Henry Fuller
Poplar Trees. 87.412
View-Malden. Res. 29.28
Edgeworth Near Medford. Res. 27.54
Near Chelsea. 19.92

Henry Hammond Gallison
The Golden Haze. 11.2801
The Morning Shadow. 20.8

Robert David Gauley
Fountain, Rome, 1896. 28.76

Winckworth Allan Gay
The Alps. 13.463
The Waggoner. 20.439
At the Shore. 10.251
Farm House at Rye Beach, N.H. 13.468
By the Sea. 13.469
A Farmhouse. 13.453
Rocks at Cohasset, Massachusetts. 23.495
Presidential Range in Early Autumn. 23.496
Child in a Rocking Chair. 62.272

Samuel Lancaster Gerry
John Oscar Kent and his Sister Sarah Kent. 43.29

Howard Gibbs
Marriage Party. 46.395

Anne Goldthwaite
Flowers in a Green Bottle. 46.47
On the Road, Alabama. 46.46

William Graham
*Snowing in Campo SS Giovanni e Paolo, Venice.
  Res. 27.100*
A Rainy Day in Venice. 96.656

Elizabeth Greene
Magnolia Blossoms. Res. 27.101
A Rose. 37.596

Walter Parsons Shaw Griffin
Old Houses, Stroudwater, Maine. 57.713

William Davenport Griffin
Town School, St. Thomas, Virgin Islands. 48.559

Albert Lorey Groll
Landscape Near Hopi Village. 19.7

Adelaide Milton de Groot
Outdoor Sculpture Exhibition. 42.114

Lillian Westcott Hale
L'Edition de Luxe. 35. 1487

Philip Leslie Hale
Girls in Sunlight. 53.2209

Carl Hall
Interlochen, Michigan. 41.569

George Hawley Hallowell
Notre Dame, Paris. 45.733
Two Foxes. 35.1240

Samuel Halpert
The Chinese God. 48.561

Melbourne Havelock Hardwick
Midsummer. 17.1078

Channing Hare
Peggy Thomas, Mode. 49.554

Laura Coombs Hill
Bowl of Zinnias. 22.650
Larkspur, Peonies and Canterbury Bells. 26.240
Yellow Dahlias. 27.575

John E. Hollen
Bowl with Fruit and Wine Glass. 64.459

Paul Merrick Hollister
Freighters, East River. 62.39

Felicie Waldo Howell
Assembly House, Salem, Massachusetts. 48.565

Buffie Johnson
Reflections. 56.1317

John Bernard Johnston
Cow at Ease. 14.1
Cow Grazing. 99.307
Cow in Landscape. Res. 08.11
Cow Reclining. 99.308
Landscape with Cattle. 87.49
The Newborn Calf. 87.48
Study of Cows. 37.592

Hugh Bolton Jones
Autumn Landscape. 27.1325
Early Autumn. 37.593

Leon Foster Jones
Suncook, New Hampshire. 19.1326
Winter Landscape. 19.1325

Mervin Jules
Banquet. 41.480

Jules David Katzieff
Dr. Arthur Fairbanks. 40.220

William Jurian Kaula
Midsummer Storm. 51.695

William Sargent Kendall
The Critics. 45.661

Yeffe Kimball
Accretion. 61.390

Helen Mary Knowlton
Haystacks. 18.403

John Koch
At the Museum. 41.565

Emil Jean Kosa, Jr.
Murietta's Retreat. 42.687

Louis Kronberg
Algerian Girl. 37.622
Ballet Girl Against the Light. 35.43
The Lady of Clan-Care. 12.130
Preparing for the Dance. 39.652
Seated Nude. 37.624
Seated Nude with Vase of Flowers. 37.623

Aimée Lamb
The Snow Storm. 63.661
Waiting. 41.473

Harry Lane
The Tide Pool. 53.2005

Susan Minot Lane
Moon Street, Boston. 12.172

Philip Little
January Thaw. 19.1328

William Horace Littlefield
Stable Yard and Paddock. 36.251

Ernest Wadsworth Longfellow
Marine. 13.549
The Seine. 22.695
Esneh on the Nile. 22.693

Francis William Loring
Great Bridge at Chioggia. 01.7253
The Army of Peace. 12.2

Eric Lundgren
Trick Rider. 51.696

Mary Lizzie Macomber
Isabella. 22.645
My Mother. 17.1687
Saint Catherine. 98.622

Edward Harrison May
The Falconer (after Couture). 24.220

Paul Meltsner
Life with Father. 42.393

Francis Davis Millet
Seacoast. Res. 16.76

Charles Eliot Mills
Atrani, Italy. 21.1066

John Ames Mitchell
Chateau de Chillon. Res. 30.9
Moses in the Bulrushes. Res. 20.9

John Austin Sands Monks
Sheep. 13.476

George Frederick Munn
Still Life with Violin. 36.78

Hermann Dudley Murphy
The Adriatic Sea. 45.777
Fishing Boats on the Adriatic. 45.778
Zinnias and Marigolds. 43.30

Kanji Nakamura
Hiroshige and the Goldfish. 29.977
The Jolly God. 29.976
Denman Waldo Ross. 32.77

Gertrude Nason
Mrs. George Field Lawton (Ida A. Hill) 55.506

Elias Newman
Procession of the Torah. 50.3415

Henry Roderick Newman
Gulf of Spezia. 25.155

William Edward Norton
View of the John Hancock House. Res. 33.217
Day Dreams. 23.472

George Loftus Noyes
Gloucester Wharves. 15.1233

Ivan Gregorevitch Olinsky
Before the Mirror. 23.469

Walter Launt Palmer
The Upland Stream. 28.822

Charles Robert Patterson
Marine. 35.1231

Margaret Jordan Patterson
Aunt Polly's Back Door. 48.585

Lilla Cabot Perry
Open Air Concert. 64.2055
A Young Violincellist. 13.2905

Marjorie Phillips
Bohemian Glass Vase. 41.255

Carl Emile Pickhardt
The Cook. 41.475
The Crossing. 50.251

William Lamb Picknell
Morning on the Loing at Moret. 06.2398
Sand Dunes of Essex. 85.486

Charles Franklin Pierce
Landscape with Cattle. 25.177

Charles Adams Platt
Landscape Near Cornish. 37.1173

Dana Ripley Pond
Self Portrait. 63.192
Self Portrait in his Studio. 63.191

Arthur Pope
Lemons. 50.3412

Benjamin Curtis Porter
Mrs. John Elliot (Maud Howe). 26.245

Edward Henry Pottast
At the Seaside. 23.497

Zarh Pritchard
Sunset in Granite Crags. 13.1381

Hovsep Pushman
The End of the Trail. 33.681

Harry Newton Redman
The Ridge. 33.24

James Rogers Rich
The Sphinx. 10.546

William Trost Richards
Twilight. 11.1277

Thomas Romney Robinson
Arab and Horse, Algiers. 19.100
Hillside in Summer. 08.12
Oxen Ploughing. 88.343
Study of Cows. 20.859
Woods and Equestrienne. 18.400

James Naumberg Rosenberg
Cloudburst. 46.709
Green April. 46.708
Maytime Storm. 47.94

Denman Waldo Ross
Head of Young Man. 19.767
The Musician. 19.770
Portrait of a Young Man. 19.768
Scene in Mexico City. 34.184
A Study of Cross-Lights. 19.810
A Translation into Chinese. 19.769

William Rothenstein
The Exposition of the Talmud. 50.3435

John Singer Sargent
(Decorations in the Dome of the Rotunda)
Ganymede and the Eagle. 21.10508
Music. 21.10509
Astronomy. 21.10510
Prometheus. 21.10511
Apollo and the Muses. 21.10512
Architecture, Painting, and Sculpture Protected by Athena
   from the Ravages of Time. 21.10513
Classic and Romantic Art. 21.10514
The Sphinx and the Chimaera. 21.10515

(Decorations over the Main Stairway and Library)
The Danaides 25.636
Philosophy. 25.637
The Unveiling of Truth. 25.638
Science. 25.639
Apollo and his Chariot with the Hours. 25.640
The Winds. 25.641
Perseus on Pegasus Slaying Medusa. 25.642

Atlas and the Hesperides. 25.643
Chiron and Achilles. 25.644
Orestes. 25.645
Phaethon. 25.646
Hercules and the Hydra. 25.647

(Studies for the Decorations over the Stairway)
Perseus on Pegasus Slaying Medusa. 29.137
Atlas and the Hesperides. 29.138
Chiron and Achilles. 29.139
Phaethon. 29.140

The Road. 19.759

Albert Felix Schmitt
On the River Bank. 17.3148

Jean Paul Selinger
Mrs. Virginia H. Salisbury. 13.8
The Water Seller. 10.101

Charles Green Shaw
Birth of Day. 57.393

Frank Hill Smith
Chapel of the Crucifix, St. Mark's Venice. 18.402

Francis Speight
When the Wind Blows. 36.80

Richard Morell Staigg
The Misses Case. 20.1862

Albert Edward Sterner
Olivia in Riding Habit. 50.3331

Harold Sterner
Beach Scene with a Newspaper. 42.115

Will Henry Stevens
Pinnacles. 41.256

Fritz Bradley Talbot
Washing Day at Mastigouche Club, P.Q. 51.1392

Polly Thayer
Spring Morning on the River. 50.860
Trees. 40.212

Anthony Thieme
Mount Pleasant Street, Rockport, Massachusetts. 48.604
Rockport Wharf. 31.147

Caroline Thurber
Serenity. 50.747

John Rollins Tilton
Campagna. Res. 10.18

Frank Hector Tompkins
Self Portrait. Res. 24.39
The Young Mother. 19.1381

Giovanni Battista Troccoli
Mrs. Edwin Champney. 42.562
Dr. Denman Waldo Ross. 34.132

Mrs. S. J. Tryon
Summer Landscape. 28.871

Stephen Salisbury Tuckerman
Marine. 19.93
Marine View: A Breezy Day Off Shore. 99.311
The Stranding of Fishing Boats. Res. 10.14

Pieter Van Veen
Sunflowers. 48.609

Harry Aiken Vincent
Old Time Fishing Village. 48.610

Robert Vonnoh
Mrs. Lucy Kilham. 61.40

Harry Oliver Walker
Narcissus. 17.164

Abraham Walkowitz
Head of a Girl. 40.621
Still Life: Flowers. 40.622

Lawrence Warshaw
Cross. 65.731

Marcus Waterman
Hillside in Autumn. 18.401
Interior of a Wood. 42.192
Spring. Res. 10.16
Washing the Horses. 24.335
Wood Interior. 24.267

Theodore Wendel
Snow Scene. 23.556

Sarah Wyman Whitman
Autumn Marshes. 21.2175
Martin Brimmer. 19.143
Draped Female Figure. 04.1723
Edge of Evening at Annisquam. 04.1716
Gloucester Harbor. 04.1717
Rhododendrons. 04.1720
Roses. 04.1719
Sunset. 04.1721
A Warm Night. 04.1722
Winter Daffodils. 04.1724

Esther Williams
The Path. 36.627

Frederick Dickinson Williams
Moonlit Mountainside. 64.603

Robert Woodward
The Window: Still Life. 48.614

INDEXES

Bliss, Mrs. Robert Woods:
  Whistler, No. 1023
Bliss, Mrs. William H.:
  Whistler, No. 1023
Bloom, Lew:
  Blakelock, No. 153
Boit, Edward Darley:
  John Singer Sargent, No. 858
Boit, Mrs. Julia Overing:
  John Singer Sargent, No. 860
Bond, Mary Louise, *see* Peck,
  Mrs. E. Stuart
Bond, Sarah Apthorp Clinch:
  Gilbert Stuart, No. 910
Bond Family:
  Gilbert Stuart, No. 932, 933
Borland, W. Woolsey:
  Hunt, No. 595
Boston Athenaeum:
  Allston, No. 60, 61
  Bierstadt, No. 105
  Rembrandt Peale, No. 807
  Gilbert Stuart, No. 908
  Trumbull, No. 979
  West, No. 1019
Boston Museum and Gallery of Fine
  Arts:
  Rembrandt Peale, No. 806
  Sully, No. 957
Bowditch, Mrs. Ernest W.:
  Blackburn, No. 150
Bowen, Dr. John T.:
  Copley, No. 287
Boydell's Shakespeare Gallery:
  West, No. 1019
Boylston, Alice Darrow:
  Gilbert Stuart, No. 947, 948
Boylston, Mrs. Louisa:
  Gilbert Stuart, No. 947, 948
  Jane Stuart, No. 955
Boylston, Dr. Ward Nicholas:
  Gilbert Stuart, No. 947, 948
  Harding, No. 475
Boylston, Ward Nicholas, Jr.:
  Copley, No. 263
  Harding, No. 475
  Gilbert Stuart, No. 948
Bradbury, Mrs. Frederick J., *see*
  White, Harriet
Bradlee, Mr.:
  Hunt, No. 577
Bradlee, Mrs. Josiah:
  Hamilton, No. 467
Bradlee, Josiah Putnam:
  Fisher, No. 405
  Salmon, No. 840, 841
Bradlee, Sarah:
  Hunt, No. 577, 578
Bradley, Mrs. J. D. Cameron:
  John Singer Sargent, No. 865
Bradley, William:
  Earl, No. 381
Brady, Thelma:
  Hope, No. 567

Braun, John F.:
  Bellows, No. 89
Brenner, Mrs. Marcella Louis:
  Louis, No. 730
Brewster, William:
  Anonymous, No. 9
  Johnston, No. 674
Brigham, Mrs. Edwin A.:
  Williams, No. 1040
Brimmer, George Watson:
  Gilbert Stuart, No. 909
Brimmer, Martin:
  Hunt, No. 587
  Gilbert Stuart, No. 909
  Vedder, No. 990, 991
Brimmer, Mrs. Martin:
  Gilbert Stuart, No. 909
  Vedder, No. 990, 991
Brimo, René:
  West, No. 1016
Brooks, Elizabeth, *see* Wheelwright,
  Mrs. Edmund
Brooks, Francis:
  Charles W. Peale, No. 797
Brooks, Frank B.:
  Hunt, No. 584
Brooks, Peter Chardon:
  Charles W. Peale, No. 797
Brooks, Peter Chardon, Jr.:
  Hunt, No. 636
Brown, Annie Kimball:
  Frothingham, No. 414
Brown, Dr. Buckminster:
  Copley, No. 292
  Harding, No. 473, 474
Brown, D. L.:
  Henry Sargent, No. 851, 852
Brown, Rebecca Warren:
  Copley, No. 292, 293
Browning, Elizabeth:
  Jonathan Eastman Johnson,
  No. 672
Browning, Pearl:
  Jonathan Eastman Johnson,
  No. 672
Bryson, John:
  Whistler, No. 1022
Buckham, George:
  Inman, No. 643
Bullard, Ellen T.:
  Allston, No. 64
Bunting, J. D., family:
  Bunting, No. 190
Burr, Mrs. I. Tucker:
  Keith, No. 675

C

Cabot, Dr. Arthur C.:
  Benson, No. 94
  Benson, No. 100
Cabot, Arthur Tracy:
  John Appleton Brown, No. 176
  Bunker, No. 187
  La Farge, No. 695

Gilbert Stuart, No. 914
Cabot, Elizabeth Perkins:
  Gilbert Stuart, No. 914
Calahan, Mrs.:
  Charles W. Peale, No. 798
Canfield, Richard A.:
  Whistler, No. 1023
Cappell, George Devereux de Vere:
  John Singer Sargent, No. 871
Carr, Mrs. Lucien:
  Page, No. 792
Carroll, John:
  Bellows, No. 90
Carter, Nellie P.:
  Charles Harold Davis, No. 331
  Enneking, No. 389
Cary, Mrs. F. E.:
  Copley, No. 295
Cary, Georgina S.:
  Tarbell, No. 967
Case, James Brown:
  William Hart, No. 491
  Hinckley, No. 554
  Inness, No. 656, 658
  La Farge, No. 698
Case, Louisa, W.:
  Joseph Foxcroft Cole, No. 236
  Gaugengigl, No. 432
  William Hart, No. 491
  Inness, No. 656, 658
  La Farge, No. 698
Case, Marian R.:
  Joseph Foxcroft Cole, No. 236
  Gaugengigl, No. 432
  William Hart, No. 491
  Inness, No. 656, 658
  La Farge, No. 698
Cassatt, J. Gardner:
  Cassatt, No. 196
Castano, Giovanni:
  Meneghelli, No. 754
Cavafy, John:
  Whistler, No. 1021
Cavafy, Dr. John:
  Whistler, No. 1021
Cazeaux, Elizabeth Warner:
  Blackburn, No. 149
Cazeaux, Lendall Pitts:
  Blackburn, No. 149
Champlin, George H.:
  Charles Harold Davis, No. 325
Champlin, Mrs. G. H.:
  John Appleton Brown, No. 177
Channing, William Ellery:
  Feke, No. 397
Channing, William Francis:
  Allston, No. 55
Chase, Frederick:
  Morse, No. 762
Chase, Mrs. Mary Fuller (Mrs.
  Maxey N. Morrison):
  Morse, No. 762
Christie's, London:
  Copley, No. 304, 306, 307, 308

* Paintings already published in *Karolik Catalogue*, 1949, do not appear in this index.

Fuller, Mary, *see* Wilson, Mrs.
   Andrew Chalmers
Fuller, Dr. and Mrs. Thomas:
   Morse, No. 762

G

Galerie Manzi-Joyant, Paris:
   Cassatt, No. 197
Gardner, George Peabody:
   Hunt, No. 161
Gardner, John L.:
   Hunt, No. 628
Gardner, Mrs. John L.:
   Hunt, No. 628
Gatch, Lee (estate of):
   Gatch, No. 428
Gay, Walter:
   Cassatt, No. 195
   Gay, No. 439
Gay, Mrs. Walter:
   Gay, No. 437, 439
Gervais, Mrs. Katherine Mary:
   Gilbert Stuart, No. 904
Gifford, Sanford Robinson (estate of):
   Gifford, No. 441
Gilbert, Dr. David:
   Rembrandt Peale, No. 805
Gilbert, W. Kent:
   Rembrandt Peale, No. 805
Gillet, Louis:
   Gay, No. 439
Gilman, Bradley:
   Murphy, No. 772
Gilman, Low:
   Clark, No. 218
Glackens, Ira:
   Glackens, No. 447
Goodyear, Miss:
   Goodwin, No. 458
Gore, Governor Christopher:
   Trumbull, No. 978
Gore, Mrs. Christopher:
   Trumbull, No. 978
Gore, Mrs. John (Mrs. Joseph Russell):
   Gilbert Stuart, No. 943
Gray, Una:
   Gilbert Stuart, No. 910
Green, Dr. Joshua:
   Copley, No. 265
Green, Dr. Samuel Abbott:
   Copley, No. 265
Greene, Mrs. Charlotte Nichols:
   Henri, No. 548
Greene, Henry Copley:
   Allston, No. 59
Greene, J. S. Copley:
   Allston, No. 59
Greene, Margaret:
   Sully, No. 958
Greene, Mary Amory:
   Allston, No. 59
   Thayer, No. 969

Greenough, Mrs. Horatio:
   Gilbert Stuart, No. 934, 943
Gregerson, Elizabeth S.:
   Hunt, No. 595, 603, 604, 607
Gregerson, James R.:
   Hunt, No. 584, 595, 603, 604, 607
Greig, Mrs. George:
   Gilbert Stuart, No. 945, 946
Grey, Anna G.:
   Newton, No. 780
Grist, M.:
   Copley, No. 297, 308
Grozier, Edwin Atkins:
   Vedder, No. 994
Guggenheim, Mrs. Peggy:
   Hennessy, No. 541, 542

H

Hakoumoff, Alfred R.:
   Whistler, No. 1026
Hale, Mrs. Edward:
   Bierstadt, No. 111
Hall, John Richardson:
   Babcock, No. 71
   Inness, No. 651
Hall, Maria Bartlett:
   Gilbert Stuart, No. 911, 912
Hall, Minna Bartlett:
   Gilbert Stuart, No. 911
Hall, Thomas B.:
   Gilbert Stuart, No. 911, 912
Hallahan, Mrs. H. (estate of):
   West, No. 1018
Hamilton, Carl:
   Sterne, No. 896
Hamilton, Constance Mary:
   Copley, No. 294
Hancock, Charles Lowell:
   Copley, No. 64
Hancock, Dorothy Quincy:
   Smibert, No. 887
Hancock, John:
   Copley, No. 264, 286
   Smibert, No. 887
Hancock, Lydia:
   Smibert, No. 887
Hancock, Washington:
   Copley, No. 264
Harding, Russell:
   Harding, No. 481, 483
Hardy, Anna E.:
   Hardy, No. 486
Harlow, Mrs. H. S.:
   Copley, No. 277
Harlow, Mabel:
   Copley, No. 277
Haskell, Mrs. Margaret Riker:
   Frothingham, No. 416, 417
Hassam, Childe (estate of):
   Hassam, No. 499, 500
Haven, Mary:
   Healy, No. 538
Hawkins, Mrs. Frances Alice:
   Copley, No. 302

Hawkins, George Frederick:
   Copley, No. 302
Hawkins, John:
   Copley, No. 302
Hawkins, Mrs. John P.:
   Stuart, No. 941
Hayden, Harold Buckminster:
   Copley, No. 261
Hayden, Mrs. Harold B.:
   Copley, No. 261
Hayden, Horace John:
   Copley, No. 261
Hayden, Susanna Ann Williams:
   Copley, No. 261
Healy, Mrs. G. P. A.:
   Healy, No. 540
Henri, Robert (estate of):
   Henri, No. 544, 549
Henshaw, Joseph P. B.:
   Salmon, No. 840
Henshaw, Samuel:
   Salmon, No. 841
Hervoches du Quilliou, Mrs. Charlotte:
   Gilbert Stuart, No. 934, 943, 952
Hewitt, Edwin:
   MacIver, No. 742
Hicks, Emma E.:
   Babcock, No. 69
Higginson, Francis L.:
   Hunt, No. 613
Higginson, Henry Lee, Sr.:
   La Farge, No. 693, 694, 700
Higginson, Ida Agassiz:
   Fuller, No. 421
Hilles, Susan Morse (Mrs. Frederick H.):
   Kline, No. 687
Hilliard, Elizabeth Heddle:
   Copley, No. 253
Hilliard, Mrs. Timothy:
   Copley, No. 277
Hilliard, William Tyng:
   Copley, No. 277
Hilliker, Mr. and Mrs.:
   Field, No. 401
Hinckley, Mary Hewes:
   Hinckley, No. 555
Hines, Mrs. Louis:
   Melchers, No. 751
Hirschl, Norman:
   Bierstadt, No. 126
Holland, Miss E. F. P.:
   Salmon, No. 838
Holland, Mrs. James W.:
   Eakins, No. 378
Holland, Leicester Bodine:
   Eakins, No. 378
Holland, Rupert Sargent:
   Eakins, No. 378
Hollingsworth, Mrs. George:
   Frothingham, No. 415
   Gilbert Stuart, No. 927, 928
Hollingsworth, Polly Robbins:

* Paintings already published in *Karolik Catalogue*, 1949, do not appear in this index.

Tarbell, No. 963
Kimball, Mrs. David P.:
  Benson, No. 93
Kimball, Moses:
  Copley, No. 275
King's Chapel, Boston:
  Luks, No. 735
Kinsley, Joseph T.:
  Sully, No. 961
Kinsley, Lyman:
  Hidley, No. 551
Kitchel, Mr. and Mrs. W. Ray:
  Kepes, No. 684
Knoedler, M. and Company:
  Jonathan Eastman Johnson, No.
    673
  Meneghelli, No. 752

L

Labey, Herbert C.:
  Gilbert Stuart, No. 905
Labouchere, Henry:
  Anonymous, No. 63
Lamb, Aimée:
  Harding, No. 478, 479, 482
  Henry Sargent, No. 848, 849
Lamb, Mrs. Horatio A.:
  Harding, No. 478, 479, 482
  Henry Sargent, No. 848, 849, 850,
    851, 852
  Smibert, No. 890
Lamb, Rosamond:
  Harding, No. 478, 479, 482
Lane, Harriot Eleanor:
  Copley, No. 302
Lane, Jonathan:
  Lane, No. 710
Lawrence, Abbott:
  Harding, No. 482
Lawton, Herbert:
  Copley, No. 252, 277
Lee, Henry:
  John Greenwood, No. 462
Levinson, E. D.:
  Cassatt, No. 194
Levyne, Sydney A.:
  Blakelock, No. 152
Lintott, Marie Sterner:
  Lintott, No. 727
Little, Mrs. Nina Fletcher:
  Prior, No. 821
Littlehale, Mary Frances:
  Page, No. 790, 791
Loeb, Richard:
  Tirrell, No. 976
Logan, Mrs. H. H., *see* Davis, Miss
  A. A.
Logan, Hiram Hyde:
  Inness, No. 648
  Murphy, No. 774
  Wyant, No. 1046
Long, Mrs. G. W.:
  Hunt, No. 591
Longfellow, Ernest Wadsworth:

John White Alexander, No. 51
John Appleton Brown, No. 174
Chase, No. 208
Gay, No. 436
Metcalf, No. 756
Story, No. 901
Tryon, No. 983
Vedder, No. 993
Longyear, John M.:
  Cassatt, No. 200
Longyear, Mrs. John M.:
  Cassatt, No. 200
Lord, Charles E.:
  Gilbert Stuart, No. 945, 946
Lord, Mrs. George:
  Gilbert Stuart, No. 945, 946
Lord, Newton:
  Gilbert Stuart, No. 945
Lorie, Douglas:
  Goodwin, No. 458
Lougee, Mrs. Willis:
  Lane, No. 712
Lowell, Abbott Lawrence:
  Harding, No. 478, 479
Lowell, Mrs. Augustus:
  Harding, No. 478, 479
Lowell, Elizabeth, *see* Dutton, Mrs.
  Warren
Lowell, Mrs. John:
  Copley, No. 285
Luks, Mrs. George (Mrs. Werner
  Frankenberg):
  Luks, No. 731
Lull, Mrs. Emma G.:
  Gilbert Stuart, No. 953
Lyman, John Pickering:
  Hassam, No. 503
  Lie, No. 724
Lyman, Theodora:
  Hassam, No. 503
  Lie, No. 724
Lyman, Theodore:
  Allston, No. 64
Lyndhurst, Lord:
  Copley, No. 297, 299, 304, 306,
    307, 308

M

McAndrew, Mr. and Mrs. John:
  MacIver, No. 743
McClellan, Percy Webb:
  Trumbull, No. 977
McKean, Mr. and Mrs. Q. A.
  Shaw:
  Luks, No. 734, 736
McKelvey, Susan A. D.:
  Doughty, No. 359
McMahon, Mrs. Edward W.:
  Jonathan Eastman Johnson, No.
    669
Manigault, Dr. Gabriel:
  Copley, No. 298
Manigault, Joseph:
  Copley, No. 298

March, Hannah:
  Copley, No. 253
  Gilbert Stuart, No. 910
Marrs, Mrs. Laura Norcross:
  Homer, No. 561
Marston, Professor A. R.:
  Babcock, No. 74
Martin and Camentron, Paris:
  Cassatt, No. 196
Mason, Abigail Hall:
  Beard, No. 86
Mason, J.:
  Allston, No. 53
Mason, Maud:
  Beard, No. 86
Mason, Timothy Batelle:
  Beard, No. 86
Mather, Mrs. M. W.:
  Healy, No. 539
Matthews, Rev. Samuel S.:
  Blackburn, No. 150
Metcalf, Frederick H.:
  Copley, No. 250
Metcalf, John George:
  Copley, No. 249, 250
Metcalf, Susannah Torrey:
  Copley, No. 249, 250
Meyer, Mrs. George von Lengerke:
  Copley, No. 299
Milliken, Mrs. E. T.:
  Bierstadt, No. 111
Milliken, Elias T.:
  Bierstadt, No. 111
Minot, Mrs. George, *see* Dawes,
  Elizabeth
Minot, Susan I.:
  Trumbull, No. 981, 982
Monks, John P.:
  Bunker, No. 185, 186
Moore, Joseph:
  Field, No. 399
Morehouse, Mrs. E. B.:
  Earl, No. 381
Morehouse, Louise E.:
  Earl, No. 381
Morrill, Miss A. W.:
  Hunt, No. 617
Morrill, Charles J.:
  Hunt, No. 617
Morrill, Ellen A. W.:
  Copley, No. 86
Morrison, Arthur:
  Whistler, No. 1022
Morrison, Mrs. Maxey N., *see*
  Chase, Mary Fuller
Morse, Charlotte G. S.:
  Harding, No. 472
Morse, Edward L.:
  Morse, No. 764
Morse, Jessie Gwendolen:
  Bunker, No. 185
Morse, John Torrey, Jr.:
  Harding, No. 472
Morton, Mrs. Perez:

Raymond, Mrs. C. B.:
  Copley, No. 251
Rehn, Frank K. M., Inc.:
  Bellows, No. 89, 91
  Hopper, No. 573
  Luks, No. 732
Revere, Edward H. R.:
  Gilbert Stuart, No. 929, 930
Revere, John:
  Copley, No. 279
  Gilbert Stuart, No. 929, 930
Revere, Mrs. John:
  Copley, No. 279
Revere, Joseph W.:
  Gilbert Stuart, No. 929, 930
Revere, Joseph Warren:
  Gilbert Stuart, No. 929, 930
Revere, William B.:
  Gilbert Stuart, No. 929, 930
Richards, Elise Bordman:
  Ball, No. 83
Richards, William B.:
  Ball, No. 83
Richardson, William K.:
  Gilbert Stuart, No. 904
Riddle, Mrs. John W.:
  Whistler, No. 1021
Ridgeley, Mrs.:
  Charles W. Peale, No. 798
Rimmer, Mrs. Caroline H.:
  Rimmer, No. 832
Rindge, Frederick H.:
  Copley, No. 262
Rindge, Mrs. Frederick H.:
  Copley, No. 262
Rindge, Samuel B.:
  Copley, No. 262
Ritter, Mr.:
  Whistler, No. 1024
Robbins, Elizabeth Murray:
  Copley, No. 281
Robbins, James Murray:
  Copley, No. 281
Robeson, Mrs. Andrew:
  Rembrandt Peale, No. 802
Robins, George:
  West, No. 1016, 1020
Robinson, Mrs. Newton:
  Copley, No. 311
Robinson, Sumner:
  Heade, No. 514
Rogers, Anna Perkins:
  Fuller, No. 424
  Hunt, No. 630
Rogers, Mrs. Daniel:
  Inness, No. 647
Rogers, Mrs. Fanny:
  Copley, No. 267
Rogers, H. B.:
  Copley, No. 268
Rogers, Joseph W. R.:
  Copley, No. 281
Rogers, Mary C.:
  Copley, No. 281

Rogers, Mrs. N. Martin:
  Copley, No. 267
Rogers, Mrs. Robert P.:
  Copley, No. 281
Roome, Mrs. J. G.:
  Blakelock, No. 152
Roome, Col. William P.:
  Blakelock, No. 152
Rose, Mrs. George S.:
  Copley, No. 291
Rosenberg, James N.:
  Eilshemius, No. 387
Rosenberg, Mr. and Mrs. James N.:
  Soyer, No. 892
Rosenthal, Albert:
  Frothingham, No. 419
Ross, Denman Waldo:
  Whistler, No. 1025
Ross, Mrs. Waldo O.:
  Healy, No. 538
Rotch, Mrs. Benjamin:
  Harding, No. 482
Rouart, Henri:
  Cassatt, No. 197
Russell, Chambers, the Younger:
  Copley, No. 269
Russell, Dr. Charles:
  Copley, No. 269
Russell, Elizabeth Dutton, *see*
  Dalton, Mrs. Henry Rogers
Russell, James Dalton:
  Copley, No. 285
Russell, Mrs. Joseph, *see* Gore, Mrs.
  John
Russell, Mrs. Robert S.:
  Badger, No. 81
Russell, Samuel H.:
  Gilbert Stuart, No. 940
Ryder, Murray:
  Homer, No. 559
Ryder, Murray P.:
  Homer, No. 559

S

Saltonstall, Mrs. Richard:
  Hunt, No. 636
Sargeant, Mrs. Grace H.:
  Lane, No. 712
Sargent, Charles Sprague:
  Allston, No. 56
Sargent, Ignatius:
  Allston, No. 56
Sargent, J. D.:
  Anonymous, No. 2
  Blackburn, No. 151
Sargent, Winthrop:
  Smibert, No. 890
Sargent, Mrs. Winthrop:
  Henry Sargent, No. 851
Sargent, Winthrop Henry:
  Henry Sargent, No. 847, 848, 849,
    850, 851, 852
Sawyer, M. P.:
  Copley, No. 251

Sedgwick, Theodore:
  Gilbert Stuart, No. 923
Selfridge, Rear Adm. Thomas Oling
  III:
  Copley, No. 266
  Gilbert Stuart, No. 951
Sewall, Rev. Joseph:
  Smibert, No. 885
Sewall, Samuel:
  Smibert, No. 885
Sewall, Judge Samuel:
  Smibert, No. 885
Sewall, Rev. Samuel:
  Smibert, No. 885
Shapiro, Mr. and Mrs. Irving R.:
  Christopher, No. 213
Shattuck, Henry Lee:
  Bingham, No. 131
  John Greenwood, No. 462
Shaw, Francis G.:
  Page, No. 789
Shaw, Mrs. Henry S.:
  Gaugengigl, No. 430
Sherman, Mr. and Mrs. Henry
  Hall:
  John Singer Sargent, No. 854
Sherman, Zoe O.:
  Paxton, No. 794
Silsbee, Mrs. Martha:
  Woodbury, No. 1044
Silversweig, Stanley:
  Prior, No. 823
Simkins, Mabel, *see* Agassiz, Mrs.
  George
Simpson, Miss:
  Blackburn, No. 147, 148
Simpson, Mrs. E. P.:
  Frothingham, No. 420
Skinner, Francis:
  Hunt, No. 608
Slade, Mrs. Margaret Bromfield:
  John Greenwood, No. 463
Slater, Mrs. H. N.:
  Hunt, No. 590, 596, 628, 631
Smibert, John (estate):
  Smibert, No. 883
Smith, C. B.:
  Ryder, No. 835
Smith, Mrs. Charles Gaston:
  Alexander James, No. 662
Smith, Charles P.:
  Healy, No. 539
Smith, Sir Donald Alexander:
  Gifford, No. 441
Smith, Elizabeth Storer (Mrs.
  Edward Cruft):
  Badger, No. 77
Smiley, Mrs. George:
  Peto, No. 809, 811
Smith, Lillie C.:
  Ethan Allen Greenwood, No. 459
Smith, Robert L.:
  Healy, No. 539
Smith, Thomas Carter: